Solar System Data

Body	Mass (kg)	Mean Radius (m)	Period (s)	Distance from Sun (m)
Mercury	3.18×10^{23}	2.43×10^6	7.60×10^6	5.79×10^{10}
Venus	4.88×10^{24}	6.06×10^6	1.94×10^7	1.08×10^{11}
Earth	5.98×10^{24}	6.37×10^6	3.156×10^7	1.496×10^{11}
Mars	6.42×10^{23}	3.37×10^6	5.94×10^7	2.28×10^{11}
Jupiter	1.90×10^{27}	6.99×10^7	3.74×10^8	7.78×10^{11}
Saturn	5.68×10^{26}	5.85×10^7	9.35×10^8	1.43×10^{12}
Uranus	8.68×10^{25}	2.33×10^7	2.64×10^9	2.87×10^{12}
Neptune	1.03×10^{26}	2.21×10^7	5.22×10^9	4.50×10^{12}
Pluto	$\approx 1.4 \times 10^{22}$	$\approx 1.5 \times 10^6$	7.82×10^9	5.91×10^{12}
Moon	7.36×10^{22}	1.74×10^6	—	—
Sun	1.991×10^{30}	6.96×10^8	—	—

Physical Data Often Used[a]

Average Earth-Moon distance	3.84×10^8 m
Average Earth-Sun distance	1.496×10^{11} m
Average radius of the Earth	6.37×10^6 m
Density of air (20°C and 1 atm)	1.20 kg/m^3
Density of water (20°C and 1 atm)	1.00×10^3 kg/m^3
Free-fall acceleration	9.80 m/s^2
Mass of the Earth	5.98×10^{24} kg
Mass of the Moon	7.36×10^{22} kg
Mass of the Sun	1.99×10^{30} kg
Standard atmospheric pressure	1.013×10^5 Pa

[a] These are the values of the constants as used in the text.

Some Prefixes for Powers of Ten

Power	Prefix	Abbreviation	Power	Prefix	Abbreviation
10^{-18}	atto	a	10^1	deka	da
10^{-15}	femto	f	10^2	hecto	h
10^{-12}	pico	p	10^3	kilo	k
10^{-9}	nano	n	10^6	mega	M
10^{-6}	micro	μ	10^9	giga	G
10^{-3}	milli	m	10^{12}	tera	T
10^{-2}	centi	c	10^{15}	peta	P
10^{-1}	deci	d	10^{18}	exa	E

Standard Abbreviations and Symbols of Units

Abbreviation	Unit	Abbreviation	Unit
A	ampere	in.	inch
Å	angstrom	J	joule
u	atomic mass unit	K	kelvin
atm	atmosphere	kcal	kilocalorie
Btu	British thermal unit	kg	kilogram
C	coulomb	kmol	kilomole
°C	degree Celsius	lb	pound
cal	calorie	m	meter
deg	degree (angle)	min	minute
eV	electron volt	N	newton
°F	degree Fahrenheit	Pa	pascal
F	farad	rev	revolution
ft	foot	s	second
G	gauss	T	tesla
g	gram	V	volt
H	henry	W	watt
h	hour	Wb	weber
hp	horsepower	μm	micrometer
Hz	hertz	Ω	ohm

Mathematical Symbols Used in the Text and Their Meaning

Symbol	Meaning
$=$	is equal to
$\equiv$	is defined as
$\neq$	is not equal to
$\propto$	is proportional to
$>$	is greater than
$<$	is less than
$\gg (\ll)$	is much greater (less) than
$\approx$	is approximately equal to
Δx	the change in x
$\sum_{i=1}^{N} x_i$	the sum of all quantities x_i from $i = 1$ to $i = N$
$\|x\|$	the magnitude of x (always a nonnegative quantity)
$\Delta x \rightarrow 0$	Δx approaches zero
$\dfrac{dx}{dt}$	the derivative of x with respect to t
$\dfrac{\partial x}{\partial t}$	the partial derivative of x with respect to t
$\int$	integral

PHYSICS

For Scientists & Engineers

Fourth Edition

This dramatic photograph captures multiple
lightning bolts near some rural homes.
The most intense bolt strikes a tree
adjacent to one of the homes.

(© Johnny Autery)

PART IV

Electricity and Magnetism

For the sake of persons of . . . different types, scientific truth should be presented in different forms, and should be regarded as equally scientific, whether it appears in the robust form and the vivid coloring of a physical illustration, or in the tenuity and paleness of a symbolic expression.

JAMES CLERK MAXWELL

We now begin the study of that branch of physics that is concerned with electric and magnetic phenomena. The laws of electricity and magnetism play a central role in the operation of various devices such as radios, televisions, electric motors, computers, high-energy accelerators, and a host of electronic devices used in medicine. However, more fundamentally, we now know that the interatomic and intermolecular forces that are responsible for the formation of solids and liquids are electric in origin. Furthermore, such forces as the pushes and pulls between objects and the elastic force in a spring arise from electric forces at the atomic level.

Evidence in Chinese documents suggests that magnetism was known as early as around 2000 B.C. The ancient Greeks observed electric and magnetic phenomena possibly as early as 700 B.C. They found that a piece of amber, when rubbed, becomes electrified and attracts pieces of straw or feathers. The existence of magnetic forces was known from observations that pieces of a naturally occurring stone called *magnetite* (Fe_3O_4) are attracted to iron. (The word *electric* comes from the Greek word for amber, *elecktron*. The word *magnetic* comes from the name of *Magnesia,* on the coast of Turkey, where magnetite was found.

In 1600, William Gilbert discovered that electrification was not limited to amber but is a general phenomenon. Scientists went on to electrify a variety of objects, including chickens and people! Experiments by Charles Coulomb in 1785 confirmed the inverse-square law for electric forces.

It was not until the early part of the 19th century that scientists established that electricity and magnetism are, in fact, related phenomena. In 1820, Hans Oersted discovered that a compass needle is deflected when placed near a circuit carrying an electric current. In 1831, Joseph Henry in America, and almost simultaneously Michael Faraday in Britain, showed that when a wire is moved near a magnet (or, equivalently, when a magnet is moved near a wire), an electric current is established in the wire. In 1873, James Clerk Maxwell used these observations and other experimental facts as a basis for formulating the laws of electromagnetism as we know them today. (*Electromagnetism* is a name given to the combined fields of electricity and magnetism.) Shortly thereafter (around 1888), Heinrich Hertz verified Maxwell's predictions by producing electromagnetic waves in the laboratory. This led to such practical developments as radio and television.

Maxwell's contributions to the field of electromagnetism were especially significant because the laws he formulated are basic to *all* forms of electromagnetic phenomena. His work is as important as Newton's work on the laws of motion and the theory of gravitation.

CHAPTER 23

Electric Fields

This metallic sphere is charged by a generator to a very high voltage. The high concentration of charge formed on the sphere creates a strong electric field around the sphere. The charges then leak through the gas, producing the pink glow. *(E. R. Degginger/ H. Armstrong Roberts)*

The electromagnetic force between charged particles is one of the fundamental forces of nature. In this chapter, we begin by describing some of the basic properties of electric forces. We then discuss Coulomb's law, which is the fundamental law of force between any two charged particles. The concept of an electric field associated with a charge distribution is then introduced, and its effect on other charged particles is described. The method of using Coulomb's law to calculate electric fields of a given charge distribution is discussed, and several examples are given. Then the motion of a charged particle in a uniform electric field is discussed. We conclude the chapter with a brief discussion of the oscilloscope.

23.1 PROPERTIES OF ELECTRIC CHARGES

A number of simple experiments demonstrate the existence of electric forces and charges. For example, after running a comb through your hair on a dry day, you will find that the comb attracts bits of paper. The attractive force is often strong enough to suspend the pieces of paper. The same effect occurs when materials such as glass or rubber are rubbed with silk or fur.

Another simple experiment is to rub an inflated balloon with wool. The balloon then adheres to the wall or the ceiling of a room, often for hours. When materials behave in this way, they are said to be *electrified,* or to have become **electrically charged.** You can easily electrify your body by vigorously rubbing your shoes on a wool rug. The charge on your body can be sensed and removed by lightly touching (and startling) a friend. Under the right conditions, a visible spark is seen when you touch one another, and a slight tingle will be felt by both parties. (Experiments such as these work best on a dry day, since an excessive amount of moisture can lead to a leakage of charge from the electrified body to the Earth by various conducting paths.)

In a systematic series of simple experiments, it is found that there are two kinds of electric charges, which were given the names **positive** and **negative** by Benjamin Franklin (1706–1790). To demonstrate this fact, consider a hard rubber rod that has been rubbed with fur and then suspended by a nonmetallic thread as in Figure 23.1. When a glass rod that has been rubbed with silk is brought near the rubber rod, the rubber rod is attracted toward the glass rod. On the other hand, if two charged rubber rods (or two charged glass rods) are brought near each other, as in Figure 23.1b, the force between them is repulsive. This observation shows that the rubber and glass are in two different states of electrification. On the basis of these observations, we conclude that *like charges repel one another and unlike charges attract one another.* Using the convention suggested by Franklin, the electric charge on the glass rod is called *positive* and that on the rubber rod is called *negative.* Therefore, any charged body that is attracted to a charged rubber rod (or repelled by a charged glass rod) must have a positive charge. Conversely, any charged body that is repelled by a charged rubber rod (or attracted to a charged glass rod) has a negative charge on it.

| Charge is conserved |

Another important aspect of Franklin's model of electricity is the implication that *electric charge is always conserved.* That is, when one body is rubbed against another, charge is not created in the process. The electrified state is due to a *transfer* of charge from one body to the other. Therefore, one body gains some

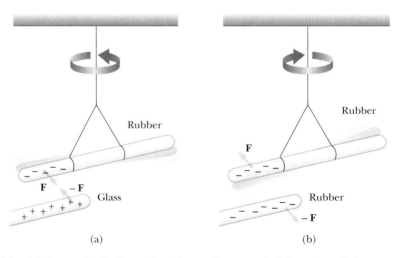

(a)   (b)

FIGURE 23.1   (a) A negatively charged rubber rod, suspended by a thread, is attracted to a positively charged glass rod. (b) A negatively charged rubber rod is repelled by another negatively charged rubber rod.

amount of negative charge while the other gains an equal amount of positive charge. For example, when a glass rod is rubbed with silk, the silk obtains a negative charge that is equal in magnitude to the positive charge on the glass rod. We now know from our understanding of atomic structure that *it is the negatively charged electrons that are transferred* from the glass to the silk in the rubbing process. Likewise, when rubber is rubbed with fur, electrons are transferred from the fur to the rubber, giving the rubber a net negative charge and the fur a net positive charge. This is consistent with the fact that neutral, uncharged matter contains as many positive charges (protons within atomic nuclei) as negative charges (electrons).

In 1909, Robert Millikan (1868–1953) confirmed that electric charge always occurs as some integral multiple of some fundamental unit of charge, *e*. In modern terms, the charge *q* is said to be **quantized,** where *q* is the standard symbol used for charge. That is, electric charge exists as discrete "packets." Thus, we can write $q = Ne$, where N is some integer. Other experiments in the same period showed that the electron has a charge $-e$ and the proton has an equal and opposite charge, $+e$. Some elementary particles, such as the neutron, have no charge. A neutral atom must contain as many protons as electrons.

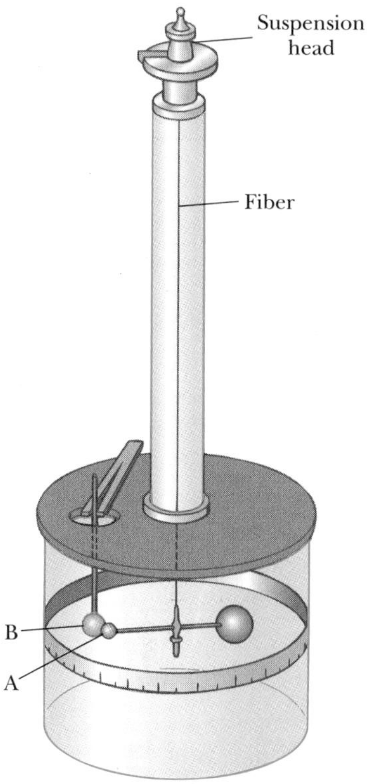

Electric forces between charged objects were measured quantitatively by Coulomb using the torsion balance, which he invented (Fig. 23.2). Using this apparatus, Coulomb confirmed that the electric force between two small charged spheres is proportional to the inverse square of their separation, that is, $F \propto 1/r^2$. The operating principle of the torsion balance is the same as that of the apparatus used by Cavendish to measure the gravitational constant (Section 14.2), with masses replaced by charged spheres. The electric force between the charged spheres produces a twist in the suspended fiber. Since the restoring torque of the twisted fiber is proportional to the angle through which it rotates, a measurement of this angle provides a quantitative measure of the electric force of attraction or repulsion. If the spheres are charged by rubbing, the electrical force between the spheres is very large compared with the gravitational attraction; hence, the gravitational force can be neglected.

From our discussion thus far, we conclude that electric charge has the following important properties:

FIGURE 23.2 Coulomb's torsion balance, which was used to establish the inverse-square law for the electrostatic force between two charges.

- There are two kinds of charges in nature, with the property that unlike charges attract one another and like charges repel one another.
- The force between charges varies as the inverse square of their separation.
- Charge is conserved.
- Charge is quantized.

Properties of electric charge

23.2 INSULATORS AND CONDUCTORS

It is convenient to classify substances in terms of their ability to conduct electrical charge.

Conductors are materials in which electric charges move quite freely, whereas **insulators** are materials that do not readily transport charge.

Materials such as glass, rubber, and lucite fall into the category of insulators. When such materials are charged by rubbing, only the area that is rubbed becomes charged and the charge is unable to move to other regions of the material.

In contrast, materials such as copper, aluminum, and silver are good conductors. When such materials are charged in some small region, the charge readily distributes itself over the entire surface of the conductor. If you hold a copper rod in your hand and rub it with wool or fur, it will not attract a small piece of paper. This might suggest that a metal cannot be charged. On the other hand, if you hold the copper rod by a lucite handle and then rub, the rod will remain charged and attract the piece of paper. This is explained by noting that in the first case, the electric charges produced by rubbing will readily move from copper through your body and finally to Earth. In the second case, the insulating lucite handle prevents the flow of charge to Earth.

Semiconductors are a third class of materials, and their electrical properties are somewhere between those of insulators and those of conductors. Silicon and germanium are well-known examples of semiconductors commonly used in the fabrication of a variety of electronic devices. The electrical properties of semiconductors can be changed over many orders of magnitude by adding controlled amounts of certain foreign atoms to the materials.

When a conductor is connected to Earth by means of a conducting wire or pipe, it is said to be **grounded**. The Earth can then be considered an infinite "sink" to which electrons can easily migrate. With this in mind, we can understand how to charge a conductor by a process known as **induction**.

To understand induction, consider a negatively charged rubber rod brought near a neutral (uncharged) conducting sphere insulated from ground. That is, there is no conducting path to ground (Fig. 23.3a). The region of the sphere nearest the rod obtains an excess of positive charge, while the region of the sphere farthest from the rod obtains an equal excess of negative charge. (That is, electrons in the part of the sphere nearest the rod migrate to the opposite side of the sphere.) If the same experiment is performed with a conducting wire connected from the sphere to ground (Fig. 23.3b), some of the electrons in the conductor are so strongly repelled by the presence of the negative charge that they move out of the sphere through the ground wire and into the Earth. If the wire to ground is then removed (Fig. 23.3c), the conducting sphere contains an excess of *induced* positive charge. Finally, when the rubber rod is removed from the vicinity of the sphere (Fig. 23.3d), the induced positive charge remains on the ungrounded sphere. Note that the charge remaining on the sphere is uniformly distributed over its surface because of the repulsive forces among the like charges. In the process, the electrified rubber rod loses none of its negative charge.

Thus, we see that charging an object by induction requires no contact with the body inducing the charge. This is in contrast to charging an object by rubbing (that is, charging by *conduction*), which does require contact between the two objects.

A process very similar to charging by induction in conductors also takes place in insulators. In most neutral atoms and molecules, the center of positive charge coincides with the center of negative charge. However, in the presence of a charged object, these centers may shift slightly, resulting in more positive charge on one side of the molecule than on the other. This effect, known as polarization, is discussed more completely in Chapter 26. This realignment of charge within individual molecules produces an induced charge on the surface of the insulator, as shown in Figure 23.4. With these ideas, you should be able to explain why a comb that has been rubbed through hair attracts bits of neutral paper, or why a balloon that has been rubbed against your clothing is able to stick to a neutral wall.

Metals are good conductors

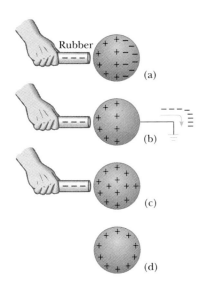

FIGURE 23.3 Charging a metallic object by induction. (a) The charge on a neutral metallic sphere is redistributed when a charged rubber rod is placed near the sphere. (b) The sphere is grounded, and some of the electrons leave. (c) The ground connection is removed, and the sphere has a net nonuniform positive charge. (d) When the rubber rod is removed, the excess positive charge becomes uniformly distributed over the surface of the sphere.

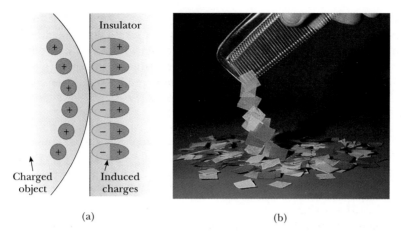

(a) (b)

FIGURE 23.4 (a) The charged object induces charges on the surface of an insulator. (b) A charged comb attracts bits of paper because charges are displaced in the paper. The paper is neutral but polarized. *(© 1968 Fundamental Photographs)*

CONCEPTUAL EXAMPLE 23.1

If a suspended object A is attracted to object B, which is charged, can we conclude that object A is charged?

Reasoning No. Object A might have a charge opposite in sign to that of B, but it also might be neutral. In the latter case, object B causes A to be polarized, pulling charge of one sign to the near face of A and pushing an equal amount of charge of the opposite sign to the far face, as in Figure 23.5. Then the force of attraction exerted on B by the induced charge on the near side of A is slightly larger than the force of repulsion exerted on B by the induced charge on the far side of A. Therefore, the net force on A is toward B.

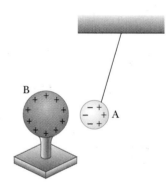

FIGURE 23.5 (Conceptual Example 23.1) Electrostatic attraction between a charged sphere B and a neutral conductor A.

23.3 COULOMB'S LAW

In 1785, Coulomb established the fundamental law of electric force between two stationary, charged particles. Experiments show that an **electric force** has the following properties:

- The force is inversely proportional to the square of the separation, r, between the two particles and directed along the line joining the particles.
- The force is proportional to the product of the charges q_1 and q_2 on the two particles.
- The force is attractive if the charges are of opposite sign and repulsive if the charges have the same sign.

From these observations, we can express the magnitude of the electric force between the two charges as

$$F = k_e \frac{|q_1||q_2|}{r^2}$$

(23.1) Coulomb's law

Charles Coulomb

| 1 7 3 6 – 1 8 0 6 |

Charles Coulomb, the great French physicist after whom the unit of electric charge called the *coulomb* was named, was born in Angoulême in 1736. He was educated at the École du Génie in Mézieres, graduating in 1761 as a military engineer with a rank of First Lieutenant. Coulomb served in the West Indies for nine years, where he supervised the building of fortifications in Martinique.

In 1774, Coulomb became a correspondent to the Paris Academy of Science. There he shared the Academy's first prize for his paper on magnetic compasses and also received first prize for his classic work on friction, a study that was unsurpassed for 150 years. During the next 25 years, he presented 25 papers to the Academy on electricity, magnetism, torsion, and applications to the torsion balance, as well as several hundred committee reports on engineering and civil projects.

Coulomb took full advantage of the various positions he held during his lifetime. For example, his experience as an engineer led him to investigate the strengths of materials and determine the forces that affect objects on beams, thereby contributing to the field of structural mechanics. He also contributed to the field of ergonom-

ics. His research provided a fundamental understanding of the ways in which people and animals can best do work and greatly influenced the subsequent research of Gaspard Coriolis (1792–1843).

Coulomb's major contribution to science was in the field of electrostatics and magnetism, in which he made use of the torsion balance he developed (see Fig. 23.2). The paper describing this invention also contained a design for a compass using the principle of torsion suspension. His next paper gave proof of the inverse square law for the electrostatic force between two charges.

Coulomb died in 1806, five years after becoming president of the Institut de France (formerly the Paris Academy of Science). His research on electricity and magnetism brought this area of physics out of traditional natural philosophy and made it an exact science.

(Photograph courtesy of AIP Niels Bohr Library, E. Scott Barr Collection)

where k_e is a constant called the **Coulomb constant.** In his experiments, Coulomb was able to show that the value of the exponent of r was 2 to within an uncertainty of a few percent. Modern experiments have shown that the exponent is 2 to a precision of a few parts in 10^9.

The Coulomb constant has a value that depends on the choice of units. The unit of charge in SI units is the coulomb (C). The coulomb is defined in terms of a unit current called the *ampere* (A), where current equals the rate of flow of charge. (The ampere is defined in Chapter 27.) When the current in a wire is 1 A, the amount of charge that flows past a given point in the wire in 1 s is 1 C. The Coulomb constant k_e in SI units has the value

Coulomb constant

$$k_e = 8.9875 \times 10^9 \ \mathrm{N \cdot m^2/C^2}$$

To simplify our calculations, we shall use the approximate value

$$k_e \cong 8.99 \times 10^9 \ \mathrm{N \cdot m^2/C^2}$$

The constant k_e is also written

$$k_e = \frac{1}{4\pi\epsilon_0}$$

where the constant ϵ_0 is known as the *permittivity of free space* and has the value

$$\epsilon_0 = 8.8542 \times 10^{-12} \; \text{C}^2/\text{N} \cdot \text{m}^2$$

The smallest unit of charge known in nature is the charge on an electron or proton.[1] The charge of an electron or proton has a magnitude

$$|e| = 1.60219 \times 10^{-19} \; \text{C}$$

Charge on an electron or proton

Therefore, 1 C of charge is equal to the charge of 6.3×10^{18} electrons. This number can be compared with the number of free electrons[2] in 1 cm^3 of copper, which is of the order of 10^{23}. Note that 1 C is a substantial amount of charge. In typical electrostatic experiments, where a rubber or glass rod is charged by friction, a net charge of the order of 10^{-6} C is obtained. In other words, only a very small fraction of the total available charge is transferred between the rod and the rubbing material.

The charges and masses of the electron, proton, and neutron are given in Table 23.1.

When dealing with Coulomb's force law, you must remember that force is a vector quantity and must be treated accordingly. Furthermore, note that *Coulomb's law applies exactly only to point charges or particles*. The electric force exerted on q_2 due to a charge q_1, written $\mathbf{F}_{21}$, can be expressed in vector form as

$$\mathbf{F}_{21} = k_e \frac{q_1 q_2}{r^2} \hat{\mathbf{r}} \qquad (23.2)$$

where $\hat{\mathbf{r}}$ is a unit vector directed from q_1 to q_2 as in Figure 23.6a. Since Coulomb's law obeys Newton's third law, the electric force exerted on q_1 by q_2 is equal in magnitude to the force exerted on q_2 by q_1 and in the opposite direction, that is, $\mathbf{F}_{12} = -\mathbf{F}_{21}$. Finally, from Equation 23.2 we see that if q_1 and q_2 have the same sign, the product $q_1 q_2$ is positive and the force is repulsive, as in Figure 23.6a. If q_1 and q_2 are of opposite sign, as in Figure 23.6b, the product $q_1 q_2$ is negative and the force is attractive.

When more than two charges are present, the force between any pair of them is given by Equation 23.2. Therefore, the resultant force on any one of them equals the vector sum of the forces exerted by the various individual charges. For exam-

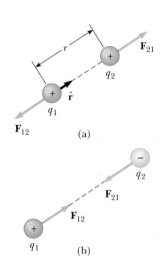

FIGURE 23.6 Two point charges separated by a distance r exert a force on each other given by Coulomb's law. Note that the force on q_1 is equal to and opposite the force on q_2. (a) When the charges are of the same sign, the force is repulsive. (b) When the charges are of the opposite sign, the force is attractive.

TABLE 23.1 Charge and Mass of the Electron, Proton, and Neutron

Particle	Charge (C)	Mass (kg)
Electron (e)	$-1.6021917 \times 10^{-19}$	9.1095×10^{-31}
Proton (p)	$+1.6021917 \times 10^{-19}$	1.67261×10^{-27}
Neutron (n)	0	1.67492×10^{-27}

[1] No unit of charge smaller than e has been detected as a free charge; however, some recent theories have proposed the existence of particles called *quarks* having charges $e/3$ and $2e/3$. Although there is experimental evidence for such particles inside nuclear matter, *free* quarks have never been detected. We discuss other properties of quarks in Chapter 47 of the extended version of this text.

[2] A metal atom, such as copper, contains one or more outer electrons, which are weakly bound to the nucleus. When many atoms combine to form a metal, the so-called free electrons are these outer electrons, which are not bound to any one atom. These electrons move about the metal in a manner similar to gas molecules moving in a container.

ple, if there are four charges, then the resultant force on particle 1 due to particles 2, 3, and 4 is

$$\mathbf{F}_1 = \mathbf{F}_{12} + \mathbf{F}_{13} + \mathbf{F}_{14}$$

This principle of superposition as applied to electrostatic forces is an experimentally observed fact.

EXAMPLE 23.2   Find the Resultant Force

Consider three point charges located at the corners of a triangle, as in Figure 23.7, where $q_1 = q_3 = 5.0\ \mu C$, $q_2 = -2.0\ \mu C$, and $a = 0.10$ m. Find the resultant force on q_3.

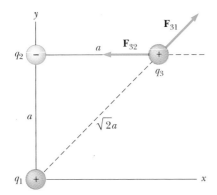

FIGURE 23.7   (Example 23.2) The force exerted on q_3 by q_1 is $\mathbf{F}_{31}$. The force exerted on q_3 by q_2 is $\mathbf{F}_{32}$. The resultant force $\mathbf{F}_3$ exerted on q_3 is the vector sum $\mathbf{F}_{31} + \mathbf{F}_{32}$.

Solution   First, note the direction of the individual forces exerted on q_3 by q_1 and q_2. The force exerted on q_3 by q_2 is attractive because q_2 and q_3 have opposite signs. The force exerted on q_3 by q_1 is repulsive because they are both positive.

Now let us calculate the magnitude of the forces on q_3. The magnitude of $\mathbf{F}_{32}$ is

$$F_{32} = k_e \frac{|q_3||q_2|}{a^2}$$

$$= \left(8.99 \times 10^9\ \frac{\mathrm{N \cdot m^2}}{\mathrm{C^2}}\right) \frac{(5.0 \times 10^{-6}\ \mathrm{C})(2.0 \times 10^{-6}\ \mathrm{C})}{(0.10\ \mathrm{m})^2}$$

$$= 9.0\ \mathrm{N}$$

Note that since q_3 and q_2 have opposite signs, $\mathbf{F}_{32}$ is to the left, as shown in Figure 23.7.

The magnitude of the force exerted on q_3 by q_1 is

$$F_{31} = k_e \frac{|q_3||q_1|}{(\sqrt{2}a)^2}$$

$$= \left(8.99 \times 10^9\ \frac{\mathrm{N \cdot m^2}}{\mathrm{C^2}}\right) \frac{(5.0 \times 10^{-6}\ \mathrm{C})(5.0 \times 10^{-6}\ \mathrm{C})}{2(0.10\ \mathrm{m})^2}$$

$$= 11\ \mathrm{N}$$

The force $\mathbf{F}_{31}$ is repulsive and makes an angle of $45°$ with the x axis. Therefore, the x and y components of $\mathbf{F}_{31}$ are equal, with magnitude given by $F_{31} \cos 45° = 7.9$ N. The force $\mathbf{F}_{32}$ is in the negative x direction. Hence, the x and y components of the resultant force on q_3 are

$$F_x = F_{31x} + F_{32} = 7.9\ \mathrm{N} - 9.0\ \mathrm{N} = -1.1\ \mathrm{N}$$

$$F_y = F_{31y} = 7.9\ \mathrm{N}$$

We can also express the resultant force on q_3 in unit-vector form as $\mathbf{F}_3 = (-1.1\mathbf{i} + 7.9\mathbf{j})$ N.

Exercise   Find the magnitude and direction of the resultant force on q_3.

Answer   8.0 N at an angle of $98°$ with the x axis.

EXAMPLE 23.3   Where is the Resultant Force Zero?

Three charges lie along the x axis as in Figure 23.8. The positive charge $q_1 = 15.0\ \mu C$ is at $x = 2.00$ m, and the positive charge $q_2 = 6.00\ \mu C$ is at the origin. Where must a negative charge q_3 be placed on the x axis such that the resultant force on it is zero?

Solution   Since q_3 is negative and both q_1 and q_2 are positive, the forces $\mathbf{F}_{31}$ and $\mathbf{F}_{32}$ are both attractive, as indicated in Figure 23.8. If we let x be the coordinate of q_3, then the forces $\mathbf{F}_{31}$ and $\mathbf{F}_{32}$ have magnitudes

$$F_{31} = k_e \frac{|q_3||q_1|}{(2.00 - x)^2} \quad \text{and} \quad F_{32} = k_e \frac{|q_3||q_2|}{x^2}$$

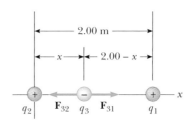

FIGURE 23.8   (Example 23.3) Three point charges are placed along the x axis. The charge q_3 is negative, whereas q_1 and q_2 are positive. If the net force on q_3 is zero, then the force on q_3 due to q_1 must be equal and opposite to the force on q_3 due to q_2.

In order for the resultant force on q_3 to be zero, $\mathbf{F}_{32}$ must be equal to and opposite $\mathbf{F}_{31}$, or

$$k_e \frac{|q_3||q_2|}{x^2} = k_e \frac{|q_3||q_1|}{(2.00 - x)^2}$$

Since k_e and q_3 are common to both sides, we solve for x and

find that

$$(2.00 - x)^2|q_2| = x^2|q_1|$$

$$(4.00 - 4.00x + x^2)(6.00 \times 10^{-6} \text{ C}) = x^2(15.0 \times 10^{-6} \text{ C})$$

Solving this quadratic equation for x, we find that $x = 0.775$ m. Why is the negative root not acceptable?

EXAMPLE 23.4   The Hydrogen Atom

The electron and proton of a hydrogen atom are separated (on the average) by a distance of approximately 5.3×10^{-11} m. Find the magnitude of the electric force and the gravitational force between the two particles.

Solution   From Coulomb's law, we find that the attractive electric force has the magnitude

$$F_e = k_e \frac{|e|^2}{r^2} = 8.99 \times 10^9 \frac{\text{N} \cdot \text{m}^2}{\text{C}^2} \frac{(1.60 \times 10^{-19} \text{ C})^2}{(5.3 \times 10^{-11} \text{ m})^2}$$

$$= 8.2 \times 10^{-8} \text{ N}$$

Using Newton's law of gravity and Table 23.1 for the parti-

cle masses, we find that the gravitational force has the magnitude

$$F_g = G \frac{m_e m_p}{r^2} = \left(6.7 \times 10^{-11} \frac{\text{N} \cdot \text{m}^2}{\text{kg}^2} \right)$$

$$\times \frac{(9.11 \times 10^{-31} \text{ kg})(1.67 \times 10^{-27} \text{ kg})}{(5.3 \times 10^{-11} \text{ m})^2}$$

$$= 3.6 \times 10^{-47} \text{ N}$$

The ratio $F_e/F_g \approx 2 \times 10^{39}$. Thus the gravitational force between charged atomic particles is negligible compared with the electric force.

EXAMPLE 23.5   Find the Charge on the Spheres

Two identical small charged spheres, each having a mass of 3.0×10^{-2} kg, hang in equilibrium as shown in Figure 23.9a. If the length of each string is 0.15 m and the angle $\theta = 5.0°$, find the magnitude of the charge on each sphere.

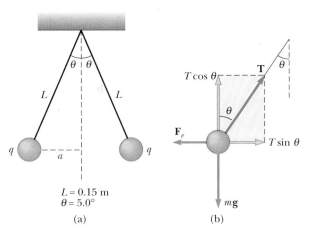

$L = 0.15$ m
$\theta = 5.0°$

(a)   (b)

FIGURE 23.9   (Example 23.5) (a) Two identical spheres, each with the same charge q, suspended in equilibrium by strings. (b) The free-body diagram for the charged spheres on the left side.

Solution   From the right triangle in Figure 23.9a, we see that $\sin \theta = a/L$. Therefore,

$$a = L \sin \theta = (0.15 \text{ m}) \sin 5.0° = 0.013 \text{ m}$$

The separation of the spheres is $2a = 0.026$ m.

The forces acting on one of the spheres are shown in Figure 23.9b. Because the sphere is in equilibrium, the resultants of the forces in the horizontal and vertical directions must separately add up to zero:

$$(1) \qquad \sum F_x = T \sin \theta - F_e = 0$$

$$(2) \qquad \sum F_y = T \cos \theta - mg = 0$$

From (2), we see that $T = mg/\cos \theta$, and so T can be eliminated from (1) if we make this substitution. This gives a value for the electric force, F_e:

$$(3) \qquad F_e = mg \tan \theta$$

$$= (3.0 \times 10^{-2} \text{ kg})(9.80 \text{ m/s}^2) \tan(5.0°)$$

$$= 2.6 \times 10^{-2} \text{ N}$$

From Coulomb's law (Eq. 23.1), the electric force between the charges has magnitude

$$F_e = k_e \frac{|q|^2}{r^2}$$

where $r = 2a = 0.026$ m and $|q|$ is the magnitude of the charge on each sphere. (Note that the term $|q|^2$ arises here because the charge is the same on both spheres.) This equation can be solved for $|q|^2$ to give

$$|q|^2 = \frac{F_e r^2}{k_e} = \frac{(2.6 \times 10^{-2}\ \text{N})(0.026\ \text{m})^2}{8.99 \times 10^9\ \text{N} \cdot \text{m}^2/\text{C}^2}$$

$$|q| = 4.4 \times 10^{-8}\ \text{C}$$

Exercise   If the charge on the spheres is negative, how many electrons had to be added to them to give a net charge of -4.4×10^{-8} C?

Answer 2.7×10^{11} electrons.

23.4   THE ELECTRIC FIELD

The gravitational field **g** at a point in space was defined in Chapter 14 to be equal to the gravitational force **F** acting on a test mass m_0 divided by the test mass: $\mathbf{g} \equiv \mathbf{F}/m_0$. In a similar manner, an electric field at a point in space can be defined in terms of the electric force acting on a test charge q_0 placed at that point. To be more precise,

Definition of electric field

> the electric field vector **E** at a point in space is defined as the electric force **F** acting on a positive test charge placed at that point divided by the magnitude of the test charge q_0:

$$\mathbf{E} \equiv \frac{\mathbf{F}}{q_0} \tag{23.3}$$

Note that **E** is the field produced by some charge *external* to the test charge — not the field produced by the test charge. This is analogous to the gravitational field set up by some body such as the Earth. The vector **E** has the SI units of newtons per coulomb (N/C). The direction of **E** is in the direction of **F** because we have assumed that **F** acts on a positive test charge. Thus, we can say that *an electric field exists at a point if a test charge at rest placed at that point experiences an electric force.* Once the electric field is known at some point, the force on *any* charged particle placed at that point can be calculated from Equation 23.3. Furthermore, the electric field is said to exist at some point (even empty space) regardless of whether or not a test charge is located at that point.

When Equation 23.3 is applied, we must assume that the test charge q_0 is small enough that it does not disturb the charge distribution responsible for the electric field. For instance, if a vanishingly small test charge q_0 is placed near a uniformly charged metallic sphere as in Figure 23.10a, the charge on the metallic sphere,

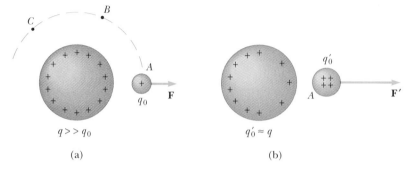

FIGURE 23.10   (a) When a small test charge q_0 is placed near a conducting sphere of charge q (where $q \gg q_0$), the charge on the conducting sphere remains uniform. (b) If the test charge q_0' is of the order of the charge on the sphere, the charge on the sphere is nonuniform.

which produces the electric field, remains uniformly distributed. Furthermore, the force **F** on the test charge has the same magnitude at *A*, *B*, and *C*, which are equidistant from the sphere. If the test charge is large enough ($q_0' \gg q_0$) as in Figure 23.10b, the charge on the metallic sphere is redistributed and the ratio of the force to the test charge at *A* is different: ($F'/q_0' \neq F/q_0$). That is, because of this redistribution of charge on the metallic sphere, the electric field at *A* set up by the sphere in Figure 23.10b must be different from that of the field at *A* in Figure 23.10a. Furthermore, the distribution of charge on the sphere changes as q_0' is moved from *A* to *B* or *C*.

Consider a point charge *q* located a distance *r* from a test charge q_0. According to Coulomb's law, the force exerted on the test charge by *q* is

$$\mathbf{F} = k_e \frac{qq_0}{r^2}\,\hat{\mathbf{r}}$$

Since the electric field at the position of the test charge is defined by $\mathbf{E} = \mathbf{F}/q_0$, we find that, at the position of q_0, the electric field created by *q* is

$$\mathbf{E} = k_e \frac{q}{r^2}\,\hat{\mathbf{r}} \qquad (23.4)$$

where $\hat{\mathbf{r}}$ is a unit vector directed from *q* toward q_0 (Fig. 23.11). If *q* is positive, as in Figure 23.11a, the electric field is directed radially outward from it. If *q* is negative, as in Figure 23.11b, the field is directed toward it.

In order to calculate the electric field at a point *P* due to a group of point charges, we first calculate the electric field vectors at *P* individually using Equation 23.4 and then add them vectorially. In other words,

> the total electric field due to a group of charges equals the vector sum of the electric fields of all the charges.

This superposition principle applied to fields follows directly from the superposition property of electric forces. Thus, the electric field of a group of charges (excluding the test charge q_0) can be expressed as

$$\mathbf{E} = k_e \sum_i \frac{q_i}{r_i^2}\,\hat{\mathbf{r}}_i \qquad (23.5)$$

where r_i is the distance from the *i*th charge, q_i, to the point *P* (the location of the test charge) and $\hat{\mathbf{r}}_i$ is a unit vector directed from q_i toward *P*.

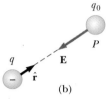

FIGURE 23.11 A test charge q_0 at point *P* is a distance *r* from a point charge *q*. (a) If *q* is positive, the electric field at *P* points radially outward from *q*. (b) If *q* is negative, the electric field at *P* points radially inward toward *q*.

CONCEPTUAL EXAMPLE 23.6

An uncharged, metallic coated Styrofoam ball is suspended in the region between two vertical metal plates as in Figure 23.12. If the two plates are charged, one positive and one negative, describe the motion of the ball after it is brought into contact with one of the plates.

Reasoning The two charged plates create a region of uniform electric field between them, directed from the positive toward the negative plate. Once the ball is disturbed so as to touch one plate, say the negative one, some negative charge will be transferred to the ball and it experiences an electric force that accelerates it to the positive plate. Once the charge touches the positive plate, it releases its negative charge, acquires a positive charge, and accelerates back to the negative plate. The ball continues to move back and forth between the plates until it has transferred all its net charge, thereby making both plates neutral.

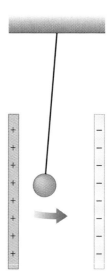

FIGURE 23.12   (Conceptual Example 23.6) An edge view of a sphere suspended between two oppositely charged plates.

EXAMPLE 23.7   Electric Force on a Proton

Find the electric force on a proton placed in an electric field of 2.0×10^4 N/C directed along the positive x axis.

Solution   Since the charge on a proton is $+e = 1.6 \times 10^{-19}$ C, the electric force on it is

$$\mathbf{F} = e\mathbf{E} = (1.6 \times 10^{-19} \text{ C})(2.0 \times 10^4 \mathbf{i} \text{ N/C})$$

$$= 3.2 \times 10^{-15} \mathbf{i} \text{ N}$$

where $\mathbf{i}$ is a unit vector in the positive x direction.

The weight of the proton is $mg = (1.67 \times 10^{-27}$ kg$)$ $(9.8 \text{ m/s}^2) = 1.6 \times 10^{-26}$ N. Hence, we see that the magnitude of the gravitational force in this case is negligible compared with the electric force.

EXAMPLE 23.8   Electric Field Due to Two Charges

A charge $q_1 = 7.0 \ \mu\text{C}$ is located at the origin, and a second charge $q_2 = -5.0 \ \mu\text{C}$ is located on the x axis 0.30 m from the origin (Figure 23.13). Find the electric field at the point P, which has coordinates (0, 0.40) m.

Solution   First, let us find the magnitude of the electric field due to each charge. The fields $\mathbf{E}_1$ due to the 7.0-μC charge and $\mathbf{E}_2$ due to the -5.0-μC charge are shown in Figure 23.13. Their magnitudes are

$$E_1 = k_e \frac{|q_1|}{r_1{}^2} = \left(8.99 \times 10^9 \ \frac{\text{N} \cdot \text{m}^2}{\text{C}^2} \right) \frac{(7.0 \times 10^{-6} \text{ C})}{(0.40 \text{ m})^2}$$

$$= 3.9 \times 10^5 \text{ N/C}$$

$$E_2 = k_e \frac{|q_2|}{r_2{}^2} = \left(8.99 \times 10^9 \ \frac{\text{N} \cdot \text{m}^2}{\text{C}^2} \right) \frac{(5.0 \times 10^{-6} \text{ C}}{(0.50 \text{ m})^2}$$

$$= 1.8 \times 10^5 \text{ N/C}$$

The vector $\mathbf{E}_1$ has only a y component. The vector $\mathbf{E}_2$ has an x component given by $E_2 \cos \theta = \frac{3}{5} E_2$ and a negative y component given by $-E_2 \sin \theta = -\frac{4}{5} E_2$. Hence, we can express the

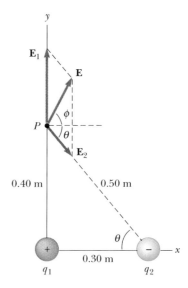

FIGURE 23.13   (Example 23.8) The total electric field $\mathbf{E}$ at P equals the vector sum $\mathbf{E}_1 + \mathbf{E}_2$, where $\mathbf{E}_1$ is the field due to the positive charge q_1 and $\mathbf{E}_2$ is the field due to the negative charge q_2.

vectors as

$$E_1 = 3.9 \times 10^5 \mathbf{j} \text{ N/C}$$

$$E_2 = (1.1 \times 10^5 \mathbf{i} - 1.4 \times 10^5 \mathbf{j}) \text{ N/C}$$

The resultant field E at P is the superposition of E_1 and E_2:

$$E = E_1 + E_2 = \boxed{(1.1 \times 10^5 \mathbf{i} + 2.5 \times 10^5 \mathbf{j}) \text{ N/C}}$$

From this result, we find that E has a magnitude of 2.7×10^5 N/C and makes an angle ϕ of 66° with the positive x axis.

Exercise Find the electric force on a positive test charge of 2×10^{-8} C placed at P.

Answer 5.4×10^{-3} N in the same direction as E.

EXAMPLE 23.9 Electric Field of a Dipole

An **electric dipole** consists of a positive charge q and a negative charge $-q$ separated by a distance $2a$, as in Figure 23.14. Find the electric field E due to these charges along the y axis at the point P, which is a distance y from the origin. Assume that $y \gg a$.

Solution At P, the fields E_1 and E_2 due to the two charges are equal in magnitude, since P is equidistant from the two equal and opposite charges. The total field $E = E_1 + E_2$, where

$$E_1 = E_2 = k_e \frac{q}{r^2} = k_e \frac{q}{y^2 + a^2}$$

The y components of E_1 and E_2 cancel each other. The x components are equal since they are both along the x axis. Therefore, E is parallel to the x axis and has a magnitude equal to $2E_1 \cos \theta$. From Figure 23.14 we see that $\cos \theta = a/r = a/(y^2 + a^2)^{1/2}$. Therefore,

$$E = 2E_1 \cos \theta = 2k_e \frac{q}{(y^2 + a^2)} \frac{a}{(y^2 + a^2)^{1/2}}$$

$$= k_e \frac{2qa}{(y^2 + a^2)^{3/2}}$$

Using the approximation $y \gg a$, we can neglect a^2 in the denominator and write

$$E \approx k_e \frac{2qa}{y^3}$$

Thus we see that along the y axis the field of a dipole at a distant point varies as $1/r^3$, whereas the more slowly varying field of a point charge goes as $1/r^2$. This is because at distant points, the fields of the two equal and opposite charges almost cancel each other. The $1/r^3$ variation in E for the dipole is also obtained for a distant point along the x axis (Problem

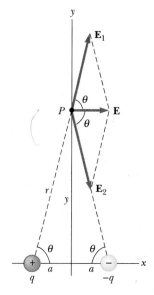

FIGURE 23.14 (Example 23.9) The total electric field E at P due to two equal and opposite charges (an electric dipole) equals the vector sum $E_1 + E_2$. The field E_1 is due to the positive charge q, and E_2 is the field due to the negative charge $-q$.

61) and for a general distant point. The dipole is a good model of many molecules, such as HCl.

As we shall see in later chapters, neutral atoms and molecules behave as dipoles when placed in an external electric field. Furthermore, many molecules, such as HCl, are permanent dipoles. (HCl is partially described as an H^+ ion combined with a Cl^- ion.) The effect of such dipoles on the behavior of materials subjected to electric fields is discussed in Chapter 26.

23.5 ELECTRIC FIELD OF A CONTINUOUS CHARGE DISTRIBUTION

Very often a group of charges are located very close together compared with their distances to points of interest (for example, a point where the electric field is to be calculated). In such situations, the system of charges can be considered to be *continuous*. That is, we imagine that the system of closely spaced charges is equiva-

A continuous charge distribution

FIGURE 23.15   The electric field at *P* due to a continuous charge distribution is the vector sum of the fields due to all the elements Δq of the charge distribution.

lent to a total charge that is continuously distributed along a line, over some surface, or throughout a volume.

To evaluate the electric field of a continuous charge distribution, the following procedure is used. First, we divide the charge distribution into small elements each of which contains a small charge Δq, as in Figure 23.15. Next, we use Coulomb's law to calculate the electric field due to one of these elements at a point *P*. Finally, we evaluate the total field at *P* due to the charge distribution by summing the contributions of all the charge elements (that is, by applying the superposition principle).

The electric field at *P* due to one element of charge Δq is

$$\Delta \mathbf{E} = k_e \frac{\Delta q}{r^2} \hat{\mathbf{r}}$$

where *r* is the distance from the element to point *P* and $\hat{\mathbf{r}}$ is a unit vector directed from the charge element toward *P*. The total electric field at *P* due to all elements in the charge distribution is approximately

$$\mathbf{E} \approx k_e \sum_i \frac{\Delta q_i}{r_i^2} \hat{\mathbf{r}}_i$$

where the index *i* refers to the *i*th element in the distribution. If the separation between elements in the charge distribution is small compared with the distance to *P*, the charge distribution can be approximated to be continuous. Therefore, the total field at *P* in the limit $\Delta q_i \rightarrow 0$ becomes

Electric field of a continuous charge distribution

$$\mathbf{E} = k_e \lim_{\Delta q_1 \rightarrow 0} \sum_i \frac{\Delta q_i}{r_i^2} \hat{\mathbf{r}}_i = k_e \int \frac{dq}{r^2} \hat{\mathbf{r}} \qquad (23.6)$$

where the integration is a vector operation and must be treated with caution. We illustrate this type of calculation with several examples. In these examples, we assume that the charge is uniformly distributed on a line or a surface or throughout some volume. When performing such calculations, it is convenient to use the concept of a charge density along with the following notations:

- If a charge *Q* is uniformly distributed throughout a volume *V*, the *charge per unit volume*, ρ, is defined by

Volume charge density

$$\rho \equiv \frac{Q}{V}$$

where ρ has units of C/m^3.
- If a charge *Q* is uniformly distributed on a surface of area *A*, the *surface charge density*, σ, is defined by

Surface charge density

$$\sigma \equiv \frac{Q}{A}$$

where σ has units of C/m^2.
- Finally, if a charge *Q* is uniformly distributed along a line of length ℓ, the *linear charge density*, λ, is defined by

Linear charge density

$$\lambda \equiv \frac{Q}{\ell}$$

where λ has units of C/m.

If the charge is nonuniformly distributed over a volume, surface, or line, we have to express the charge densities as

$$\rho = \frac{dQ}{dV} \qquad \sigma = \frac{dQ}{dA} \qquad \lambda = \frac{dQ}{d\ell}$$

where dQ is the amount of charge in a small volume, surface, or length element.

EXAMPLE 23.10   The Electric Field Due to a Charged Rod

A rod of length ℓ has a uniform positive charge per unit length λ and a total charge Q. Calculate the electric field at a point P along the axis of the rod, a distance d from one end (Fig. 23.16).

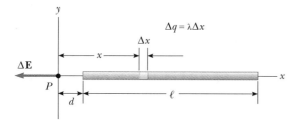

FIGURE 23.16   (Example 23.10) The electric field at P due to a uniformly charged rod lying along the x axis. The field at P due to the segment of charge Δq is $k_e \Delta q / x^2$. The total field at P is the vector sum over all segments of the rod.

Reasoning and Solution   For this calculation, the rod is taken to be along the x axis. Let us use Δx to represent the length of one small segment of the rod and let Δq be the charge on the segment. The ratio of Δq to Δx is equal to the ratio of the total charge to the total length of the rod. That is, $\Delta q / \Delta x = Q/\ell = \lambda$. Therefore, the charge Δq on the small segment is $\Delta q = \lambda\,\Delta x$.

The field $\Delta \mathbf{E}$ due to this segment at the point P is in the negative x direction, and its magnitude is[3]

$$\Delta E = k_e \frac{\Delta q}{x^2} = k_e \frac{\lambda\,\Delta x}{x^2}$$

Note that each element produces a field in the negative x direction, and so the problem of summing their contributions is particularly simple in this case. The total field at P due to all segments of the rod, which are at different dis-

tances from P, is given by Equation 23.6, which in this case becomes

$$E = \int_d^{\ell + d} k_e \lambda \frac{dx}{x^2}$$

where the limits on the integral extend from one end of the rod ($x = d$) to the other ($x = \ell + d$). Since k_e and λ are constants, they can be removed from the integral. Thus, we find that

$$E = k_e \lambda \int_d^{\ell + d} \frac{dx}{x^2} = k_e \lambda \left[-\frac{1}{x} \right]_d^{\ell + d}$$

$$= k_e \lambda \left(\frac{1}{d} - \frac{1}{\ell + d} \right) = \frac{k_e Q}{d(\ell + d)}$$

where we have used the fact that the total charge $Q = \lambda \ell$.

From this result we see that if the point P is far from the rod ($d \gg \ell$), then ℓ in the denominator can be neglected, and $E \approx k_e Q/d^2$. This is just the form you would expect for a point charge. Therefore, at large values of d/ℓ the charge distribution appears to be a point charge of magnitude Q. The use of the limiting technique ($d/\ell \to \infty$) is often a good method for checking a theoretical formula.

[3] It is important that you understand the procedure being used to carry out integrations such as this. First, choose an element whose parts are all equidistant from the point at which the field is being calculated. Next, express the charge element Δq in terms of the other variables within the integral (in this example, there is one variable, x). The integral must be over scalar quantities, and therefore must be expressed in terms of components. Then reduce the form to an integral over a single variable (or multiple integrals, each over a single variable). In examples that have spherical or cylindrical symmetry, the variables will be radial coordinates.

EXAMPLE 23.11   The Electric Field of a Uniform Ring of Charge

A ring of radius a has a uniform positive charge per unit length, with a total charge Q. Calculate the electric field along the axis of the ring at a point P lying a distance x from the center of the ring (Fig. 23.17a).

Reasoning and Solution   The magnitude of the electric field at P due to the segment of charge dq is

$$dE = k_e \frac{dq}{r^2}$$

This field has an x component $dE_x = dE \cos \theta$ along the axis of the ring and a component $dE_\perp$ perpendicular to the axis. But as we see in Figure 23.17b, the resultant field at P must lie along the x axis because the perpendicular components sum to zero. That is, the perpendicular component of any element is canceled by the perpendicular component of an element on the opposite side of the ring. Since $r = (x^2 + a^2)^{1/2}$ and $\cos \theta = x/r$, we find that

$$dE_x = dE \cos \theta = \left(k_e \frac{dq}{r^2} \right) \frac{x}{r} = \frac{k_e x}{(x^2 + a^2)^{3/2}} \, dq$$

In this case, all segments of the ring give the same contribution to the field at P since they are all equidistant from this point. Thus, we can integrate the expression above to get the total field at P:

$$E_x = \int \frac{k_e x}{(x^2 + a^2)^{3/2}} \, dq = \frac{k_e x}{(x^2 + a^2)^{3/2}} \int dq$$

$$= \frac{k_e x}{(x^2 + a^2)^{3/2}} \, Q$$

This result shows that the field is zero at $x = 0$. Does this surprise you?

Exercise   Show that at large distances from the ring ($x \gg a$) the electric field along the axis approaches that of a point charge of magnitude Q.

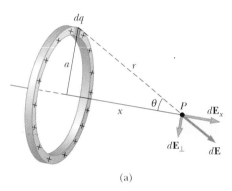
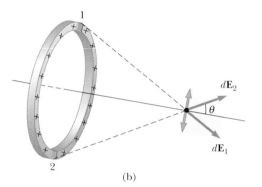

FIGURE 23.17   (Example 23.11) A uniformly charged ring of radius a. (a) The field at P on the x axis due to an element of charge dq. (b) The total electric field at P is along the x axis. Note that the perpendicular component of the electric field at P due to segment 1 is canceled by the perpendicular component due to segment 2, which is located on the ring opposite segment 1.

EXAMPLE 23.12   The Electric Field of a Uniformly Charged Disk

A disk of radius R has a uniform charge per unit area σ. Calculate the electric field at a point P that lies along the central axis of the disk and a distance x from its center (Fig. 23.18).

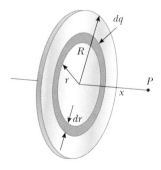

FIGURE 23.18   (Example 23.12) A uniformly charged disk of radius R. The electric field at an axial point P is directed along this axis, perpendicular to the plane of the disk.

Reasoning   The solution to this problem is straightforward if we consider the disk as a set of concentric rings. We can then make use of Example 23.11, which gives the field of a ring of radius r, and sum up contributions of all rings making up the disk. By symmetry, the field on an axial point must be parallel to this axis.

Solution   The ring of radius r and width dr has an area equal to $2\pi r \, dr$ (Fig. 23.18). The charge dq on this ring is equal to the area of the ring multiplied by the charge per unit area, or $dq = 2\pi \sigma r \, dr$. Using this result in the equation given for E_x in Example 23.11 (with a replaced by r) gives for the field due to the ring the expression

$$dE = \frac{k_e x}{(x^2 + r^2)^{3/2}} (2\pi \sigma r \, dr)$$

To get the total field at P, we integrate this expression over the limits $r = 0$ to $r = R$, noting that x is a constant. This gives

$$E = k_e x\pi\sigma \int_0^R \frac{2r\, dr}{(x^2 + r^2)^{3/2}}$$

$$= k_e x\pi\sigma \left[\frac{(x^2 + r^2)^{-1/2}}{-1/2} \right]_0^R$$

$$= 2\pi k_e \sigma \left(\frac{x}{|x|} - \frac{x}{(x^2 + R^2)^{1/2}} \right) \quad (1)$$

The result is valid for all values of x. The field close to the disk along an axial point can also be obtained from (1) by assuming $R \gg x$:

$$E = 2\pi k_e \sigma = \frac{\sigma}{2\epsilon_0} \quad (2)$$

where ϵ_0 is the permittivity of free space. As we shall find in the next chapter, the same result is obtained for the field of a uniformly charged infinite sheet.

23.6 ELECTRIC FIELD LINES

A convenient aid for visualizing electric field patterns is to draw lines pointing in the same direction as the electric field vector at any point. These lines, called **electric field lines,** are related to the electric field in any region of space in the following manner:

- The electric field vector **E** is tangent to the electric field line at each point.
- The number of lines per unit area through a surface perpendicular to the lines is proportional to the strength of the electric field in that region. Thus E is large when the field lines are close together and small when they are far apart.

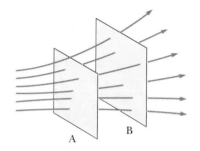

FIGURE 23.19 Electric field lines penetrating two surfaces. The magnitude of the field is greater on surface A than on surface B.

These properties are illustrated in Figure 23.19. The density of lines through surface A is greater than the density of lines through surface B. Therefore, the electric field is more intense on surface A than on surface B. Furthermore, the fact that the lines at different locations point in different directions tells us that the field is nonuniform.

Some representative electric field lines for a single positive point charge are shown in Figure 23.20a. Note that in this two-dimensional drawing we show only the field lines that lie in the plane containing the point charge. The lines are actually directed radially outward from the charge in all directions, somewhat like the needles protruding from a curled-up porcupine. Since a positive test charge placed in this field would be repelled by the positive point charge, the lines are directed radially away from the positive point charge. Similarly, the electric field lines for a single negative point charge are directed toward the charge (Fig.

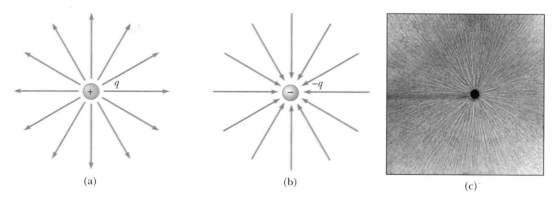

(a) (b) (c)

FIGURE 23.20 The electric field lines for a point charge. (a) For a positive point charge, the lines are radially outward. (b) For a negative point charge, the lines are radially inward. Note that the figures show only those field lines that lie in the plane containing the charge. (c) The dark areas are small pieces of thread suspended in oil, which align with the electric field produced by a small charged conductor at the center. *(Photo courtesy of Harold M. Waage, Princeton University)*

23.20b). In either case, the lines are along the radial direction and extend all the way to infinity. Note that the lines are closer together as they get near the charge, indicating that the strength of the field is increasing.

The rules for drawing electric field lines for any charge distribution are as follows:

Rules for drawing electric field lines

- The lines must begin on positive charges and terminate on negative charges, although if the net charge is not zero, lines may begin or terminate at infinity.
- The number of lines drawn leaving a positive charge or approaching a negative charge is proportional to the magnitude of the charge.
- No two field lines can cross or touch.

Is this visualization of the electric field in terms of field lines consistent with Coulomb's law? To answer this question, consider an imaginary spherical surface of radius r concentric with the charge. From symmetry, we see that the magnitude of the electric field is the same everywhere on the surface of the sphere. The number of lines, N, that emerge from the charge is equal to the number that penetrate the spherical surface. Hence, the number of lines per unit area on the sphere is $N/4\pi r^2$ (where the surface area of the sphere is $4\pi r^2$). Since E is proportional to the number of lines per unit area, we see that E varies as $1/r^2$. This is consistent with the result obtained from Coulomb's law, that is, $E = k_e q / r^2$.

It is important to note that electric field lines are not material objects. They are used only to provide us with a qualitative description of the electric field. One problem with this model is the fact that we always draw a finite number of lines from each charge, which makes it appear as if the field were quantized and acted only along certain lines. The field, in fact, is continuous—existing at every point. Another problem with this model is the danger of getting the wrong impression from a two-dimensional drawing of field lines being used to describe a three-dimensional situation.

Since charge is quantized, the number of lines leaving any material object must be 0, $\pm C'e$, $\pm 2C'e$, . . . , where C' is an arbitrary (but fixed) proportionality constant. Once C' is chosen, the number of lines is fixed. For example, if object 1 has charge Q_1 and object 2 has charge Q_2, then the ratio of number of lines is $N_2/N_1 = Q_2/Q_1$.

The electric field lines for two point charges of equal magnitude but opposite signs (the electric dipole) are shown in Figure 23.21. In this case, the number of lines that begin at the positive charge must equal the number that terminate at the negative charge. At points very near the charges, the lines are nearly radial. The high density of lines between the charges indicates a region of strong electric field.

Figure 23.22 shows the electric field lines in the vicinity of two equal positive point charges. Again, the lines are nearly radial at points close to either charge. The same number of lines emerge from each charge since the charges are equal in magnitude. At large distances from the charges, the field is approximately equal to that of a single point charge of magnitude $2q$.

Finally, in Figure 23.23 we sketch the electric field lines associated with a positive charge $+2q$ and a negative charge $-q$. In this case, the number of lines leaving $+2q$ is twice the number entering $-q$. Hence only half of the lines that leave the positive charge enter the negative charge. The remaining half terminate on a negative charge we assume to be at infinity. At distances that are large compared

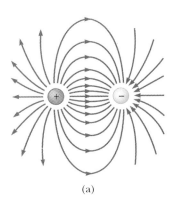

(a)

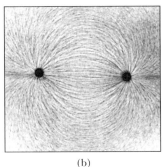

(b)

FIGURE 23.21   (a) The electric field lines for two equal and opposite point charges (an electric dipole). Note that the number of lines leaving the positive charge equals the number terminating at the negative charge. (b) The photograph was taken using small pieces of thread suspended in oil, which align with the electric field.   *(Photo courtesy of Harold M. Waage, Princeton University)*

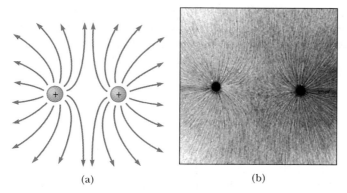
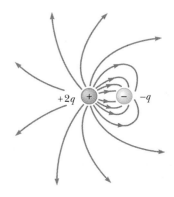

FIGURE 23.22   (a) The electric field lines for two positive point charges. (b) The photograph was taken using small pieces of thread suspended in oil, which align with the electric field.   *(Photo courtesy of Harold M. Waage, Princeton University)*

FIGURE 23.23   The electric field lines for a point charge $+2q$ and a second point charge $-q$. Note that two lines leave the charge $+2q$ for every one that terminates on $-q$.

with the charge separation, the electric field lines are equivalent to those of a single charge $+q$.

23.7   MOTION OF CHARGED PARTICLES IN A UNIFORM ELECTRIC FIELD

In this section we describe the motion of a charged particle in a uniform electric field. As we shall see, the motion is equivalent to that of a projectile moving in a uniform gravitational field. When a particle of charge q and mass m is placed in an electric field $\mathbf{E}$, the electric force on the charge is $q\mathbf{E}$. If this is the only force exerted on the charge, then Newton's second law applied to the charge gives

$$\mathbf{F} = q\mathbf{E} = m\mathbf{a}$$

The acceleration of the particle is therefore

$$\mathbf{a} = \frac{q\mathbf{E}}{m} \qquad (23.7)$$

This simulator enables you to investigate the influence of electric fields on the motion of charged particles. You will be able to specify the charge on the particle and its velocity and and also have control over the magnitude and direction of an applied electric field. By varying these parameters, you can observe the motion of such particles as electrons and protons in the presence (or absence) of an electric field as well as the behavior of a system of charged particles.

Motion in an Electric Field

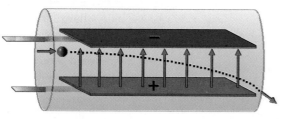
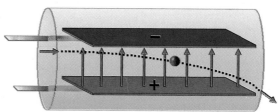

If **E** is uniform (that is, constant in magnitude and direction), we see that the acceleration is a constant of the motion. If the charge is positive, the acceleration is in the direction of the electric field. If the charge is negative, the acceleration is in the direction opposite the electric field.

EXAMPLE 23.13   An Accelerating Positive Charge

A positive point charge q of mass m is released from rest in a uniform electric field **E** directed along the x axis as in Figure 23.24. Describe its motion.

Reasoning and Solution   The acceleration of the charge is constant and given by $q\mathbf{E}/m$. The motion is simple linear motion along the x axis. Therefore, we can apply the equations of kinematics in one dimension (from Chapter 2):

$$x - x_0 = v_0 t + \tfrac{1}{2}at^2 \qquad v = v_0 + at$$

$$v^2 = v_0{}^2 + 2a(x - x_0)$$

Taking $x_0 = 0$ and $v_0 = 0$ gives

$$x = \tfrac{1}{2}at^2 = \frac{qE}{2m}\,t^2$$

$$v = at = \frac{qE}{m}\,t$$

$$v^2 = 2ax = \left(\frac{2qE}{m}\right)x$$

The kinetic energy of the charge after it has moved a distance x is

$$K = \tfrac{1}{2}mv^2 = \tfrac{1}{2}m\left(\frac{2qE}{m}\right)x = qEx$$

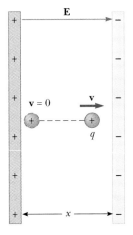

FIGURE 23.24   (Example 23.13) A positive point charge q in a uniform electric field E undergoes constant acceleration in the direction of the field.

This result can also be obtained from the work-energy theorem, since the work done by the electric force is $F_e x = qEx$ and $W = \Delta K$.

The electric field in the region between two oppositely charged flat metal plates is approximately uniform (Fig. 23.25). Suppose an electron of charge $-e$ is projected horizontally into this field with an initial velocity $v_0\mathbf{i}$. Since the electric field **E** is in the positive y direction, the acceleration of the electron is in the negative y direction. That is,

$$\mathbf{a} = -\frac{eE}{m}\mathbf{j} \qquad\qquad (23.8)$$

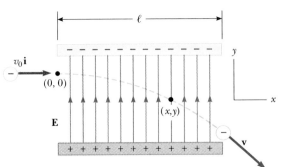

FIGURE 23.25   An electron is projected horizontally into a uniform electric field produced by two charged plates. The electron undergoes a downward acceleration (opposite E), and its motion is parabolic.

Because the acceleration is constant, we can apply the equations of kinematics in two dimensions (from Chapter 4) with $v_{x0} = v_0$ and $v_{y0} = 0$. After it has been in the electric field for a time t, the components of velocity of the electron are

$$v_x = v_0 = \text{constant} \qquad (23.9)$$

$$v_y = at = -\frac{eE}{m}t \qquad (23.10)$$

Likewise, the coordinates of the electron after a time t in the electric field are

$$x = v_0 t \qquad (23.11)$$

$$y = \tfrac{1}{2}at^2 = -\tfrac{1}{2}\frac{eE}{m}t^2 \qquad (23.12)$$

Substituting the value $t = x/v_0$ from Equation 23.11 into Equation 23.12, we see that y is proportional to x^2. Hence, the trajectory is a parabola. After the electron leaves the region of uniform electric field, it continues to move in a straight line with a speed $v > v_0$.

Note that we have neglected the gravitational force on the electron. This is a good approximation when dealing with atomic particles. For an electric field of 10^4 N/C, the ratio of the electric force, eE, to the gravitational force, mg, for the electron is of the order of 10^{14}. The corresponding ratio for a proton is of the order of 10^{11}.

EXAMPLE 23.14 An Accelerated Electron

An electron enters the region of a uniform electric field as in Figure 23.25, with $v_0 = 3.00 \times 10^6$ m/s and $E = 200$ N/C. The width of the plates is $\ell = 0.100$ m. (a) Find the acceleration of the electron while in the electric field.

Solution Since the charge on the electron has a magnitude of 1.60×10^{-19} C and $m = 9.11 \times 10^{-31}$ kg, Equation 23.8 gives

$$\mathbf{a} = -\frac{eE}{m}\mathbf{j} = -\frac{(1.60 \times 10^{-19}\text{ C})(200\text{ N/C})}{9.11 \times 10^{-31}\text{ kg}}\mathbf{j}$$

$$= -3.51 \times 10^{13}\,\mathbf{j}\text{ m/s}^2$$

(b) Find the time it takes the electron to travel through the region of the electric field.

Solution The horizontal distance traveled by the electron while in the electric field is $\ell = 0.100$ m. Using Equation 23.11 with $x = \ell$, we find that the time spent in the electric field is

$$t = \frac{\ell}{v_0} = \frac{0.100\text{ m}}{3.00 \times 10^6\text{ m/s}} = \boxed{3.33 \times 10^{-8}\text{ s}}$$

(c) What is the vertical displacement y of the electron while it is in the electric field?

Solution Using Equation 23.12 and the results from (a) and (b), we find that

$$y = \tfrac{1}{2}at^2 = -\tfrac{1}{2}(3.51 \times 10^{13}\text{ m/s}^2)(3.33 \times 10^{-8}\text{ s})^2$$

$$= -0.0195\text{ m} = -1.95\text{ cm}$$

If the separation between the plates is smaller than this, the electron will strike the positive plate.

Exercise Find the speed of the electron as it emerges from the electric field.

Answer 3.22×10^6 m/s.

*23.8 THE OSCILLOSCOPE

The oscilloscope is an electronic instrument widely used in making electrical measurements. Its main component is the cathode ray tube (CRT), shown in Figure 23.26. This tube is commonly used to obtain a visual display of electronic information for other applications, including radar systems, television receivers, and computers. The CRT is a vacuum tube in which electrons are accelerated and deflected under the influence of electric fields.

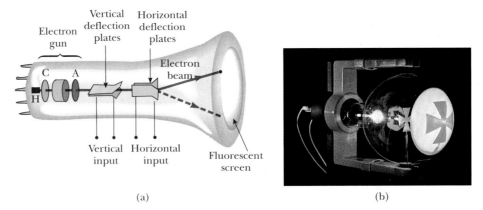

FIGURE 23.26   (a) Schematic diagram of a cathode ray tube. Electrons leaving the hot cathode C are accelerated to the anode A. The electron gun is also used to focus the beam, and the plates deflect the beam. (b) Photograph of a ''Maltese Cross'' tube showing the shadow of a beam of cathode rays falling on the tube's screen. The hot filament also produces a beam of light and a second shadow of the cross.   *(Courtesy of Central Scientific Co.)*

The electron beam is produced by an assembly called an *electron gun,* located in the neck of the tube. The assembly shown in Figure 23.26 consists of a heater (H), a negatively charged cathode (C), and a positively charged anode (A). An electric current maintained in the heater causes its temperature to rise, which in turn heats the cathode. The cathode reaches temperatures high enough to cause electrons to be ''boiled off.'' Although they are not shown in the figure, the electron gun also includes an element that focuses the electron beam and one that controls the number of electrons reaching the anode (that is, a brightness control). The anode has a hole in its center that allows the electrons to pass through without striking the anode. These electrons, if left undisturbed, travel in a straight-line path until they strike the front of the CRT, ''the screen,'' which is coated with a material that emits visible light when bombarded with electrons. This emission results in a visible spot of light on the screen.

The electrons are deflected in various directions by two sets of plates placed at right angles to each other in the neck of the tube. In order to understand how the deflection plates operate, first consider the horizontal deflection plates in Figure 23.26a. An external electric circuit is used to control and change the amount of charge present on these plates, with positive charge being placed on one plate and negative on the other. (In Chapter 25 we shall see that this can be accomplished by applying a voltage across the plates.) This increasing charge creates an increasing electric field between the plates, which causes the electron beam to be deflected from its straight-line path. The screen is slightly phosphorescent and therefore glows briefly after the electron beam moves from one point to another on it. Slowly increasing the charge on the horizontal plates causes the electron beam to move gradually from the center toward the side of the screen. Because of the phosphorescence, however, one sees a horizontal line extending across the screen instead of the simple movement of the dot. The horizontal line can be maintained on the screen by rapid, repetitive tracing.

The vertical deflection plates act in exactly the same way as the horizontal plates, except that changing the charge on them causes a vertical line on the screen. In practice, the horizontal and vertical deflection plates are used simultaneously.

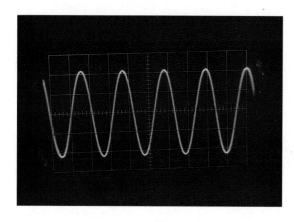

FIGURE 23.27 A sinusoidal wave produced by a vibrating tuning fork and displayed on an oscilloscope screen. *(Henry Leap and Jim Lehman)*

To see how the oscilloscope can display visual information, let us examine how we could observe the sound wave from a tuning fork on the screen. For this purpose, the charge on the horizontal plates changes in such a manner that the beam sweeps across the face of the tube at a constant rate. The tuning fork is then sounded into a microphone, which changes the sound signal to an electric signal that is applied to the vertical plates. The combined effect of the horizontal and vertical plates causes the beam to sweep the tube horizontally and up and down at the same time, with the vertical motion corresponding to the tuning fork signal. A pattern such as that shown in Figure 23.27 is seen on the screen.

SUMMARY

Electric charges have the following important properties:

- Unlike charges attract one another and like charges repel one another.
- Electric charge is always conserved.
- Charge is quantized, that is, it exists in discrete packets that are some integral multiple of the electronic charge.
- The force between charged particles varies as the inverse square of their separation.

Conductors are materials in which charges move freely. **Insulators** are materials that do not readily transport charge.

Coulomb's law states that the electrostatic force between two stationary, charged particles separated by a distance r has magnitude

$$F = k_e \frac{|q_1||q_2|}{r^2} \tag{23.1}$$

where the constant k_e, called the Coulomb constant, has the value

$$k_e = 8.9875 \times 10^9 \ \text{N} \cdot \text{m}^2/\text{C}^2$$

The smallest unit of charge known to exist in nature is the charge on an electron or proton:

$$|e| = 1.60219 \times 10^{-19} \ \text{C}$$

The electric field **E** at some point in space is defined as the electric force **F** that acts on a small positive test charge placed at that point divided by the magnitude of the test charge q_0:

$$\mathbf{E} \equiv \frac{\mathbf{F}}{q_0} \qquad (23.3)$$

The electric field due to a point charge q at a distance r from the charge is

$$\mathbf{E} = k_e \frac{q}{r^2} \hat{\mathbf{r}} \qquad (23.4)$$

where $\hat{\mathbf{r}}$ is a unit vector directed from the charge to the point in question. The electric field is directed radially outward from a positive charge and directed toward a negative charge.

The electric field due to a group of charges can be obtained using the superposition principle. That is, the total electric field equals the vector sum of the electric fields of all the charges at some point:

$$\mathbf{E} = k_e \sum_i \frac{q_i}{r_i^2} \hat{\mathbf{r}}_i \qquad (23.5)$$

The electric field of a continuous charge distribution at some point is

$$\mathbf{E} = k_e \int \frac{dq}{r^2} \hat{\mathbf{r}} \qquad (23.6)$$

where dq is the charge on one element of the charge distribution and r is the distance from the element to the point in question.

Electric field lines are useful for describing the electric field in any region of space. The electric field vector $\mathbf{E}$ is always tangent to the electric field lines at every point. The number of lines per unit area through a surface perpendicular to the lines is proportional to the magnitude of $\mathbf{E}$ in that region.

A charged particle of mass m and charge q moving in an electric field $\mathbf{E}$ has an acceleration

$$\mathbf{a} = \frac{q\mathbf{E}}{m} \qquad (23.7)$$

If the electric field is uniform, the acceleration is constant and the motion of the charge is similar to that of a projectile moving in a uniform gravitational field.

Problem-Solving Strategy and Hints
Finding the Electric Field

- Units: When performing calculations that involve the Coulomb constant k_e ($= 1/4\pi\epsilon_0$), charges must be in coulombs and distances in meters. If they appear in other units, you must convert them.
- Applying Coulomb's law to point charges: Use the superposition principle properly when dealing with a collection of interacting charges. When several charges are present, the resultant force on any one of them is the vector sum of the forces exerted by the individual charges. You must be very careful in the algebraic manipulation of vector quantities. It may be useful to review the material on vector addition in Chapter 3.
- Calculating the electric field of point charges: The superposition principle can be applied to electric fields. To find the total electric field at a given point, first calculate the electric field at the point due to each individual

charge. The resultant field at the point is the vector sum of the fields due to the individual charges.

- Continuous charge distributions: When you are confronted with problems that involve a continuous distribution of charge, the vector sums for evaluating the total electric field at some point must be replaced by vector integrals. The charge distribution is divided into infinitesimal pieces, and the vector sum is carried out by integrating over the entire charge distribution. You should review Examples 23.10–23.12, which demonstrate such procedures.
- Symmetry: Whenever dealing with either a distribution of point charges or a continuous charge distribution, you should take advantage of any symmetry in the system to simplify your calculations.

QUESTIONS

1. Sparks are often observed (or heard) on a dry day when clothes are removed in the dark. Explain.
2. Explain from an atomic viewpoint why charge is usually transferred by electrons.
3. A balloon is negatively charged by rubbing and then clings to a wall. Does this mean that the wall is positively charged? Why does the balloon eventually fall?
4. A light, uncharged metal sphere suspended from a thread is attracted to a charged rubber rod. After touching the rod, the sphere is repelled by the rod. Explain.
5. Explain what we mean by a neutral atom.
6. Why do some clothes cling together and to your body after being removed from a dryer?
7. A large metal sphere insulated from ground is charged with an electrostatic generator while a person standing on an insulating stool holds the sphere. Why is it safe to do this? Why wouldn't it be safe for another person to touch the sphere after it has been charged?
8. What is the difference between charging an object by induction and charging by conduction?
9. What are the similarities and differences between Newton's law of gravity, $F = Gm_1 m_2/r^2$, and Coulomb's law, $F = k_e q_1 q_2/r^2$?
10. Assume that someone proposes a theory that says people are bound to the Earth by electric forces rather than by gravity. How could you prove this theory wrong?
11. Would life be different if the electron were positively charged and the proton were negatively charged? Does the choice of signs have any bearing on physical and chemical interactions? Explain.
12. When defining the electric field, why is it necessary to specify that the magnitude of the test charge be very small (that is, take the limit of F/q as $q \rightarrow 0$)?
13. Two charged conducting spheres, each of radius a, are separated by a distance $r > 2a$. Is the force on either sphere given by Coulomb's law? Explain. (*Hint:* Refer to Chapter 14 on gravitation and Fig. 23.10.)
14. When is it valid to approximate a charge distribution by a point charge?
15. Is it possible for an electric field to exist in empty space? Explain.
16. Explain why electric field lines do not form closed loops.
17. Explain why electric field lines never cross. (*Hint:* E must have a unique direction at all points.)
18. A free electron and free proton are placed in an identical electric field. Compare the electric forces on each particle. Compare their accelerations.
19. Explain what happens to the magnitude of the electric field of a point charge as r approaches zero.
20. A negative charge is placed in a region of space where the electric field is directed vertically upward. What is the direction of the electric force experienced by this charge?
21. A charge $4q$ is a distance r from a charge $-q$. Compare the number of electric field lines leaving the charge $4q$ with the number entering the charge $-q$.
22. In Figure 23.23, where do the extra lines leaving the charge $+2q$ end?
23. Consider two equal point charges separated by some distance d. At what point (other than ∞) would a third test charge experience no net force?
24. A negative point charge $-q$ is placed at the point P near the positively charged ring shown in Figure 23.17. If $x \ll a$, describe the motion of the point charge if it is released from rest.
25. Explain the differences between linear, surface, and volume charge densities, and give examples of when each would be used.
26. If the electron in Figure 23.25 is projected into the electric field with an arbitrary velocity v_0 (at an angle to **E**), will its trajectory still be parabolic? Explain.

27. If a metal object receives a positive charge, does the mass of the object increase, decrease, or stay the same? What happens to its mass if the object is given a negative charge?

28. It has been reported that in some instances people near where a lightning bolt strikes the Earth have had their clothes thrown off. Explain why this might happen.

29. Why should a ground wire be connected to the metal support rod for a television antenna?

30. A light piece of aluminum foil is draped over a wooden rod. When a rod carrying a positive charge is brought close to the foil, the two parts of the foil stand apart. Why? What kind of charge is on the foil?

31. Why is it more difficult to charge an object by friction on a humid day than on a dry day?

32. How would you experimentally distinguish an electric field from a gravitational field?

PROBLEMS

Section 23.3   Coulomb's Law

1. Suppose that 1.00 g of hydrogen is separated into electrons and protons. Suppose also that the protons are placed at the Earth's North Pole and the electrons are placed at the South Pole. What is the resulting compressional force on the Earth?

2. (a) Calculate the number of electrons in a small silver pin, electrically neutral, that has a mass of 10.0 g. Silver has 47 electrons per atom, and its atomic mass is 107.87. (b) Electrons are added to the pin until the net charge is 1.00 mC. How many electrons are added for every 10^9 electrons already present?

3. Two protons in a molecule are separated by 3.80×10^{-10} m. (a) Find the electrostatic force exerted by one proton on the other. (b) How does the magnitude of this force compare with the magnitude of the gravitational force between the two protons? (c) What must be the charge-to-mass ratio of a particle if the magnitude of the gravitational force between it and a particle equals the magnitude of electrostatic force between them?

4. Can an electron remain suspended between a neutral insulating horizontal surface and a fixed positive charge, *q*, 7.62 m from the electron? Is this observation possible? Explain.

5. (a) What magnitude of charge must be placed equally on the Earth and Moon to make the magnitude of the electrical force between these two bodies equal the gravitational force between them? (b) What would be the electric field on the Moon due to the Earth's charge?

6. In fission, a nucleus of uranium-238, which contains 92 protons, divides into two smaller spheres, each having 46 protons and a radius of 5.9×10^{-15} m. What is the magnitude of the repulsive electric force pushing the two spheres apart?

7. Three point charges are located at the corners of an equilateral triangle as in Figure P23.7. Calculate the net electric force on the 7.0-μC charge.

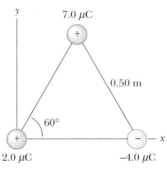

FIGURE P23.7

8. Two identical point charges $+q$ are fixed in space and separated by a distance d. A third point charge $-Q$ is free to move and lies initially at rest on a perpendicular bisector of line connecting the two fixed charges a distance x from the line (Fig. P23.8). (a) Show that if x is small relative with d, the motion of $-Q$ is simple harmonic along the bisector, and determine the period of that motion. (b) How fast is

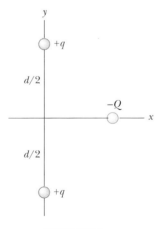

FIGURE P23.8

□ indicates problems that have full solutions available in the Student Solutions Manual and Study Guide.

−Q moving when it is at the midpoint between the two fixed charges?

9. Four identical point charges ($q = + 10.0 \mu$C) are located on the corners of a rectangle as shown in Figure P23.9. The dimensions of the rectangle are $L = 60.0$ cm and $W = 15.0$ cm. Calculate the magnitude and direction of the net electric force exerted on the charge at the lower left corner by the other three charges.

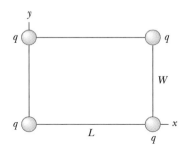

FIGURE P23.9

10. Three identical point charges, each of mass $m = 0.100$ kg and charge q, hang from three strings, as in Figure P23.10. If the lengths of the left and right strings are $L = 30.0$ cm and angle $\theta = 45.0°$, determine the value of q.

10A. Three identical point charges, each of mass m and charge q, hang from three strings, as in Figure P23.10. Determine the value of q in terms of m, L, and θ.

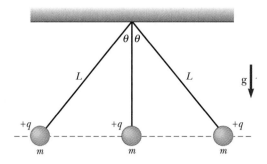

FIGURE P23.10

11. Two small silver spheres, each with a mass of 100 g, are separated by 1.0 m. Calculate the fraction of the electrons in one sphere that must be transferred to the other in order to produce an attractive force of 1.0×10^4 N (about a ton) between the spheres. (The number of electrons per atom of silver is 47, and the number of atoms per gram is Avogadro's number divided by the molar mass of silver, 107.87.)

12. Richard Feynman once said that if two persons stood at arm's length from each other and each person had 1% more electrons than protons, the force of repulsion between them would be enough to lift a

"weight" equal to that of the entire Earth. Carry out an order-of-magnitude calculation to substantiate this assertion.

13. In a thundercloud there may be an electric charge of $+ 40$ C near the top and $- 40$ C near the bottom. These charges are separated by approximately 2.0 km. What is the electric force between them?

Section 23.4 The Electric Field

14. An airplane is flying through a thundercloud at a height of 2000 m. (This is a very dangerous thing to do because of updrafts, turbulence, and the possibility of electric discharge.) If there is a charge concentration of $+ 40$ C at height 3000 m within the cloud and $- 40$ C at height 1000 m, what is the electric field E at the aircraft?

15. What are the magnitude and direction of the electric field that will balance the weight of (a) an electron and (b) a proton? (Use the data in Table 23.1.)

16. An object having a net charge of 24 μC is placed in a uniform electric field of 610 N/C directed vertically. What is the mass of this object if it "floats" in the field?

16A. An object having a net charge Q is placed in a uniform electric field of magnitude E directed vertically. What is the mass of this object if it "floats" in the field?

17. On a dry winter day, if you scuff your feet across a carpet, you build up a charge and get a shock when you touch a metal doorknob. In a dark room you can actually see a spark about 2.0 cm long. Air breaks down at a field strength of 3.0×10^6 N/C. Assume that just before the spark occurs, all the charge is in your finger, drawn there by induction due to the proximity of the doorknob. Approximate your fingertip as a sphere of diameter 1.5 cm, and assume that there is an equal amount of charge on the doorknob 2.0 cm away. (a) How much charge have you built up? (b) How many electrons does this correspond to?

18. A point having charge q is located at (x_0, y_0) in the xy plane. Show that the x and y components of the electric field at (x, y) due to this charge are

$$E_x = \frac{k_e q(x - x_0)}{[(x - x_0)^2 + (y - y_0)^2]^{3/2}}$$

$$E_y = \frac{k_e q(y - y_0)}{[(x - x_0)^2 + (y - y_0)^2]^{3/2}}$$

19. Two 2.0-μC point charges are located on the x axis. One is at $x = 1.0$ m, and the other is at $x = - 1.0$ m. (a) Determine the electric field on the y axis at $y = 0.50$ m. (b) Calculate the electric force on a $- 3.0$-μC charge placed on the y axis at $y = 0.50$ m.

20. Determine the magnitude of the electric field at the surface of a lead-208 nucleus, which contains 82 pro-

tons and 126 neutrons. Assume the lead nucleus has a volume 208 times that of one proton, and consider a proton to be a hard sphere of radius 1.2×10^{-15} m.

21. Consider n equal positive point charges each of magnitude q/n placed symmetrically around a circle of radius R. (a) Calculate the magnitude of the electric field at a point a distance x from the plane on the line passing through the center of the circle and perpendicular to the plane of the circle. (b) Explain why this result is identical to the calculation done in Example 23.11.

22. Three point charges, q, $2q$, and $3q$, are arranged on the vertices of an equilateral triangle. Determine the magnitude of electric field at the geometric center of the triangle.

23. Three equal positive charges q are at the corners of an equilateral triangle of sides a as in Figure P23.23. (a) At what point in the plane of the charges (other than ∞) is the electric field zero? (b) What are the magnitude and direction of the electric field at P due to the two charges at the base?

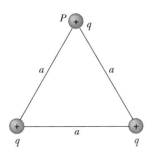

FIGURE P23.23

24. Three charges are at the corners of an equilateral triangle as in Figure P23.7. Calculate the electric field intensity at the position of the 2.0-μC charge due to the 7.0-μC and -4.0-μC charges.

25. Four point charges are at the corners of a square of side a as in Figure P23.25. (a) Determine the magnitude and direction of the electric field at the location of charge q. (b) What is the resultant force on q?

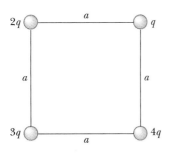

FIGURE P23.25

26. A charge of -4.0 μC is located at the origin, and a charge of -5.0 μC is located along the y axis at $y = 2.0$ m. At what point along the y axis is the electric field zero?

26A. A charge $-q_1$ is located at the origin, and a charge $-q_2$ is located along the y axis at $y = d$. At what point along the y axis is the electric field zero?

27. Consider an infinite number of identical charges (each of charge q) placed along the x axis at distances, a, $2a$, $3a$, $4a$, . . . , from the origin. What is the electric field at the origin due to this distribution? *Hint:* Use the fact that

$$1 + \frac{1}{2^2} + \frac{1}{3^2} + \frac{1}{4^2} + \cdots = \frac{\pi^2}{6}$$

Section 23.5   Electric Field of a Continuous Charge Distribution

28. A rod 14 cm long is uniformly charged and has a total charge of -22 μC. Determine the magnitude and direction of the electric field along the axis of the rod at a point 36 cm from its center.

29. A continuous line of charge lies along the x axis, extending from $x = +x_0$ to positive infinity. The line carries a uniform linear charge density λ_0. What are the magnitude and direction of the electric field at the origin?

30. A line of charge starts at $x = +x_0$ and extends to positive infinity. If the linear charge density is $\lambda = \lambda_0 x_0 / x$, determine the electric field at the origin.

31. A uniformly charged ring of radius 10 cm has a total charge of 75 μC. Find the electric field on the axis of the ring at (a) 1.0 cm, (b) 5.0 cm, (c) 30 cm, and (d) 100 cm from the center of the ring.

32. Show that the maximum field strength E_{max} along the axis of a uniformly charged ring occurs at $x = a/\sqrt{2}$ (see Fig. 23.17) and has the value $Q/(6\sqrt{3}\pi\epsilon_0 a^2)$.

33. (a) Consider a uniformly charged right circular cylindrical shell having total charge Q, radius R, and height h. Determine the electric field at a point a distance d from the right side of the cylinder as in Figure P23.33. (*Hint:* Use the result of Example 23.11 and treat the cylinder as a collection of ring charges.) (b) Use the result of Example 23.12 to

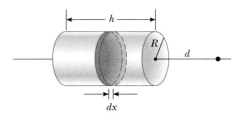

FIGURE P23.33

solve the same problem, but this time assume the cylinder is solid.

34. A uniformly charged disk of radius 35 cm carries a charge density of 7.9×10^{-3} C/m^2. Calculate the electric field on the axis of the disk at (a) 5.0 cm, (b) 10 cm, (c) 50 cm, and (d) 200 cm from the center of the disk.

35. Example 23.12 derives the exact expression for the electric field at a point on the axis of a uniformly charged disk. Consider a disk of radius $R = 3.0$ cm, having a uniformly distributed charge of $+5.2$ μC. (a) Using the result of Example 23.12, compute the electric field at a point on the axis and 3.0 mm from the center. Compare this answer with the field computed from the near-field approximation. (b) Using the result of Example 23.12, compute the electric field at a point on the axis and 30 cm from the center of the disk. Compare this with the electric field obtained by treating the disk as a $+5.2$-μC point charge at a distance of 30 cm.

36. The electric field along the axis of a uniformly charged disk of radius R and total charge Q was calculated in Example 23.12. Show that the electric field at distances x that are large compared with R approaches that of a point charge $Q = \sigma \pi R^2$. (*Hint:* First show that $x/(x^2 + R^2)^{1/2} = (1 + R^2/x^2)^{-1/2}$ and use the binomial expansion $(1 + \delta)^n \approx 1 + n\delta$ when $\delta \ll 1$.)

37. A uniformly charged ring and a uniformly charged disk each have a charge of $+25$ μC and a radius of 3.0 cm. For each of these charged objects, determine the electric field at a point along the axis 4.0 cm from the center of the object.

38. A 10.0-g piece of Styrofoam carries a net charge of -0.700 μC and floats above the center of a very large horizontal sheet of plastic that has a uniform charge density on its surface. What is the charge per unit area on the plastic sheet?

38A. A piece of Styrofoam having a mass m carries a net charge of $-q$ and floats above the center of a very large horizontal sheet of plastic that has a uniform charge density on its surface. What is the charge per unit area on the plastic sheet?

39. A uniformly charged insulating rod of length 14 cm is bent into the shape of a semicircle as in Figure P23.39. If the rod has a total charge of -7.5 μC, find the magnitude and direction of the electric field at O, the center of the semicircle.

Section 23.6 Electric Field Lines

40. A positively charged disk has a uniform charge per unit area as described in Example 23.12. Sketch the electric field lines in a plane perpendicular to the plane of the disk passing through its center.

41. A negatively charged rod of finite length has a uni-

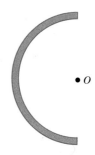

FIGURE P23.39

form charge per unit length. Sketch the electric field lines in a plane containing the rod.

42. A positive point charge is at a distance $R/2$ from the center of an uncharged thin conducting spherical shell of radius R. Sketch the electric field lines both inside and outside the shell.

43. Figure P23.43 shows the electric field lines for two point charges separated by a small distance. (a) Determine the ratio q_1/q_2. (b) What are the signs of q_1 and q_2?

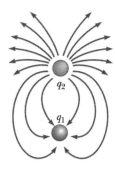

FIGURE P23.43

Section 23.7 Motion of Charged Particles in a Uniform Electric Field

44. An electron and a proton are each placed at rest in an electric field of 520 N/C. Calculate the speed of each particle 48 ns after being released.

45. A proton accelerates from rest in a uniform electric field of 640 N/C. At some later time, its speed is 1.20×10^6 m/s (nonrelativistic since v is much less than the speed of light). (a) Find the acceleration of the proton. (b) How long does it take the proton to reach this speed? (c) How far has it moved in this time? (d) What is its kinetic energy at this time?

46. An electron moves at 3×10^6 m/s into a uniform electric field of magnitude 1000 N/C. The field is parallel to the electron's velocity and acts to decelerate the electron. How far does the electron travel before it is brought to rest?

47. The electrons in a particle beam each have a kinetic energy of 1.60×10^{-17} J. What are the magnitude and direction of the electric field that will stop these electrons in a distance of 10.0 cm?

47A. The electrons in a particle beam each have a kinetic energy K. What are the magnitude and direction of the electric field that will stop these electrons in a distance d?

48. An electron traveling with an initial velocity equal to $8.6 \times 10^5 \mathbf{i}$ m/s enters a region of a uniform electric field given by $\mathbf{E} = 4.1 \times 10^3 \mathbf{i}$ N/C. (a) Find the acceleration of the electron. (b) Determine the time it takes for the electron to come to rest after it enters the field. (c) How far does the electron move in the electric field before coming to rest?

49. A proton is projected in the positive x direction into a region of a uniform electric field $\mathbf{E} = -6.00 \times 10^5 \mathbf{i}$ N/C. The proton travels 7.00 cm before coming to rest. Determine (a) the acceleration of the proton, (b) its initial speed, and (c) the time it takes the proton to come to rest.

50. A positively charged 1.00-g bead initially at rest in a vacuum falls 5.00 m through a uniform vertical electric field of magnitude 1.00×10^4 N/C. The bead hits the ground at 21.0 m/s. Determine (a) the direction of the electric field (up or down) and (b) the charge on the bead.

50A. A positively charged bead having a mass m falls from rest in a vacuum at a height h in a uniform vertical electric field of magnitude E. The bead hits the ground at a speed $v > \sqrt{2gh}$. Determine (a) the direction of the electric field (up or down) and (b) the charge on the bead.

51. A proton moves at 4.50×10^5 m/s in the horizontal direction. It enters a uniform electric field of 9.60×10^3 N/C directed vertically downward. Ignore any gravitational effects and find (a) the time it takes the proton to travel 5.00 cm horizontally, (b) its vertical displacement after it has traveled 5.00 cm horizontally, and (c) the horizontal and vertical components of its velocity after it has traveled 5.00 cm horizontally.

52. An electron is projected at an angle of 30° above the horizontal at a speed of 8.2×10^5 m/s, in a region where the electric field is $\mathbf{E} = 390\mathbf{j}$ N/C. Neglect gravity and find (a) the time it takes the electron to return to its initial height, (b) the maximum height it reaches, and (c) its horizontal displacement when it reaches its maximum height.

52A. An electron is projected at an angle θ above the horizontal at a speed v, in a region where the electric field is $\mathbf{E} = E_0\mathbf{j}$ N/C. Neglect gravity and find (a) the time it takes the electron to return to its initial

height, (b) the maximum height it reaches, and (c) its horizontal displacement when it reaches its maximum height.

53. Protons are projected with an initial speed $v_0 = 9.55 \times 10^3$ m/s into a region where a uniform electric field $\mathbf{E} = (-720\,\mathbf{j})$ N/C is present, as in Figure P23.53. The protons are to hit a target that lies at a horizontal distance of 1.27 mm from the point where the protons are launched. Find (a) the two projection angles θ that will result in a hit and (b) the total time of flight for each trajectory.

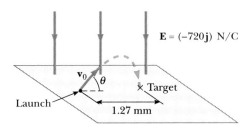

FIGURE P23.53

ADDITIONAL PROBLEMS

54. A small 2.00-g plastic ball is suspended by a 20.0-cm-long string in a uniform electric field as in Figure P23.54. If the ball is in equilibrium when the string makes a 15.0° angle with the vertical, what is the net charge on the ball?

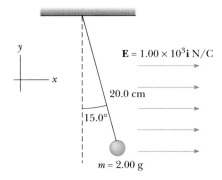

FIGURE P23.54

55. A charged cork ball of mass 1.00 g is suspended on a light string in the presence of a uniform electric field as in Figure P23.55. When $\mathbf{E} = (3.00\mathbf{i} + 5.00\mathbf{j}) \times$

10^5 N/C, the ball is in equilibrium at $\theta = 37.0°$. Find (a) the charge on the ball and (b) the tension in the string.

55A. A charged cork ball of mass m is suspended on a light string in the presence of a uniform electric field as in Figure P23.55. When $\mathbf{E} = (E_x \mathbf{i} + E_y \mathbf{j})$ N/C, the ball is in equilibrium at the angle θ. Find (a) the charge on the ball and (b) the tension in the string.

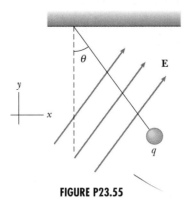

FIGURE P23.55

56. Two small spheres each of mass 2.00 g are suspended by light strings 10.0 cm in length (Fig. P23.56). A uniform electric field is applied in the x direction. If the spheres have charges equal to -5.00×10^{-8} C and $+5.00 \times 10^{-8}$ C, determine the electric field that enables the spheres to be in equilibrium at an angle of $\theta = 10.0°$.

56A. Two small spheres each of mass m are suspended by light strings of length L (Fig. P23.56). A uniform electric field is applied in the x direction. If the spheres have charges equal to $-q$ and $+q$, determine the electric field that enables the spheres to be in equilibrium at an angle θ.

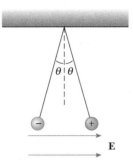

FIGURE P23.56

57. Two small spheres of mass m are suspended from strings of length ℓ that are connected at a common point. One sphere has charge Q; the other has charge $2Q$. Assume the angles θ_1 and θ_2 that the

strings make with the vertical are small. (a) How are θ_1 and θ_2 related? (b) Show that the distance r between the spheres is

$$r \cong \left(\frac{4k_e Q^2 \ell}{mg} \right)^{1/3}$$

58. Three charges of equal magnitude q are fixed in position at the vertices of an equilateral triangle (Fig. P23.58). A fourth charge Q is free to move along the positive x axis under the influence of the forces exerted by the three fixed charges. Find a value for s for which Q is in equilibrium.

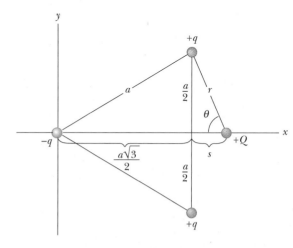

FIGURE P23.58

59. Three identical small Styrofoam balls ($m = 2.00$ g) are suspended from a fixed point by three nonconducting threads, each with a length of 50.0 cm and with negligible mass. At equilibrium the three balls form an equilateral triangle with sides of 30.0 cm. What is the common charge q carried by each ball?

60. A uniform electric field of magnitude 640 N/C exists between two parallel plates that are 4.00 cm apart. A proton is released from the positive plate at the same instant that an electron is released from the negative plate. (a) Determine the distance from the positive plate that the two pass each other. (Ignore the electrostatic attraction between the proton and electron.) (b) Repeat part (a) for a sodium ion (Na$^+$) and a chlorine ion (Cl$^-$).

61. Consider the electric dipole shown in Figure P23.61. Show that the electric field at a *distant* point along the x axis is $E_x \cong 4k_e qa/x^3$.

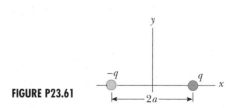

FIGURE P23.61

62. Four identical point charges each having charge $+q$ are fixed at the corners of a square of side d. A fifth point charge $-Q$ lies a distance z from the square, along the line that is perpendicular to the plane of the square and passes through its center (Fig. P23.62). (a) Show that the force exerted on $-Q$ by the other four charges is

$$\mathbf{F} = -\frac{4k_e qQz}{\left(z^2 + \dfrac{d^2}{2}\right)^{3/2}}\,\mathbf{k}$$

Note that this force is directed toward the center of the square whether z is positive ($-Q$ above the square) or negative ($-Q$ below the square). (b) If $z \ll d$, the above expression reduces to $\mathbf{F} \approx -(\text{const})z\,\mathbf{k}$. Why does this result imply that the motion of $-Q$ is simple harmonic, and what would be the period of this motion if the mass of $-Q$ is m?

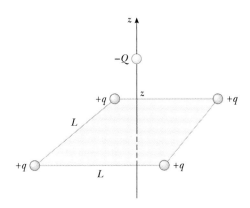

FIGURE P23.62

63. Three charges of equal magnitude q reside at the corners of an equilateral triangle of side length a (Fig. P23.63). (a) Find the magnitude and direction of the electric field at point P, midway between the negative charges, in terms of k_e, q, and a. (b) Where must a $-4q$ charge be placed so that any charge located at P will experience no net electric force? In part (b) let the distance between the $+q$ charge and P be 1.00 m.

64. Two identical beads each have a mass $m = 0.300$ kg and charge q. When placed in a spherical bowl with frictionless, nonconducting walls, the beads move until at equilibrium they are $R = 0.750$ m apart (Fig. P23.64). If the radius of the bowl is also $R = 0.750$ m, determine the charge on each bead.

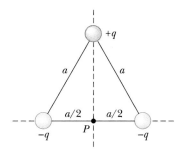

FIGURE P23.63

64A. Two identical beads each have a mass m and charge q. When placed in a hemispherical bowl of radius R with frictionless, nonconducting walls, the beads move until at equilibrium they are a distance R apart (Fig. P23.64). Determine the charge on each bead.

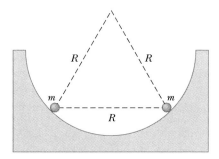

FIGURE P23.64

65. A 1.00-g cork ball carrying a charge of 2.00 μC is suspended vertically on a light string in a uniform, downward-directed electric field of magnitude $E = 1.00 \times 10^5$ N/C. If the ball is displaced slightly from the vertical, it oscillates like a simple pendulum. (a) Determine the period of this oscillation if the string is 0.500 m long. (b) Should gravity be included in the calculation for part (a)? Explain.

65A. A cork ball having mass m and charge q is suspended vertically on a light string of length L in a uniform, downward-directed electric field of magnitude E. If the ball is displaced slightly from the vertical, it oscillates like a simple pendulum. (a) Determine the period of this oscillation. (b) Should gravity be included in the calculation for part (a)? Explain.

66. A line of positive charge is formed into a semicircle of radius $R = 60.0$ cm as shown in Figure P23.66. The charge per unit length along the semicircle is described by the expression $\lambda = \lambda_0 \cos\theta$. The total charge on the semicircle is 12.0 μC. Calculate the total force on a charge of 3.00 μC placed at the center of curvature.

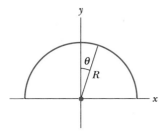

FIGURE P23.66

67. Air breaks down (loses its insulating quality) and sparking results if the electric field strength gets above 3.0×10^6 N/C. What acceleration does an electron experience in such a field? If the electron starts from rest, in what distance does it acquire a speed equal to 10% of the speed of light?

68. A line charge of length ℓ and oriented along the x axis as in Figure 23.16 has a charge per unit length λ, which varies with x as $\lambda = \lambda_0 (x - d)/d$, where d is the distance of the line from the origin (point P in the figure) and λ_0 is a constant. Find the electric field at the origin. (*Hint:* An infinitesimal element has a charge $dq = \lambda\, dx$, but note that λ is not constant.)

69. A thin rod of length ℓ and uniform charge per unit length λ lies along the x axis as shown in Figure P23.69. (a) Show that the electric field at P, a distance y from the rod, along the perpendicular bisector has no x component and is given by $E = 2k_e\lambda \sin \theta_0 / y$. (b) Using your result to part (a), show that the field of a rod of infinite length is $E = 2k_e\lambda/y$. (*Hint:* First calculate the field at P due to an element of length dx, which has a charge $\lambda\, dx$. Then change variables from x to θ using the facts that $x = y \tan \theta$ and $dx = y \sec^2 \theta\, d\theta$ and integrate over θ.)

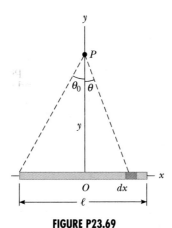

FIGURE P23.69

70. A charge q of mass M is free to move along the x axis. It is in equilibrium at the origin, midway between a pair of identical point charges, q, located on the x

axis at $x = +a$ and $x = -a$. The charge at the origin is displaced a small distance $x \ll a$ and released. Show that it can undergo simple harmonic motion with an angular frequency

$$\omega = \left(\frac{4k_e q^2}{Ma^3} \right)^{1/2}$$

71. Eight point charges, each of magnitude q, are located on the corners of a cube of side s, as in Figure P23.71. (a) Determine the x, y, and z components of the resultant force exerted on the charge located at point A by the other charges. (b) What are the magnitude and direction of this resultant force?

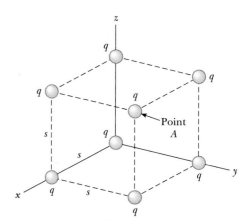

FIGURE P23.71

72. Consider the charge distribution shown in Figure P23.71. (a) Show that the magnitude of the electric field at the center of any face of the cube has a value of $2.18k_e q/s^2$. (b) What is the direction of the electric field at the center of the top face of the cube?

73. Three point charges q, $-2q$, and q are located along the x axis as in Figure P23.73. Show that the electric field at P ($y \gg a$) along the y axis is

$$\mathbf{E} = -k_e\,\frac{3qa^2}{y^4}\,\mathbf{j}$$

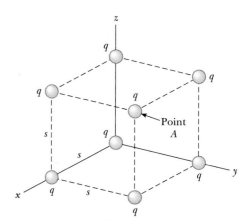

FIGURE P23.73

This charge distribution, which is essentially that of two electric dipoles, is called an *electric quadrupole*. Note that E varies as r^{-4} for the quadrupole, compared with variations of r^{-3} for the dipole and r^{-2} for the monopole (a single charge).

74. An electric dipole in a uniform electric field is displaced slightly from its equilibrium position, as in Figure P23.74, where θ is small. The moment of inertia of the dipole is I. If the dipole is released from this position, show that it exhibits simple harmonic motion with a frequency

$$ f = \frac{1}{2\pi} \sqrt{\frac{2qaE}{I}} $$

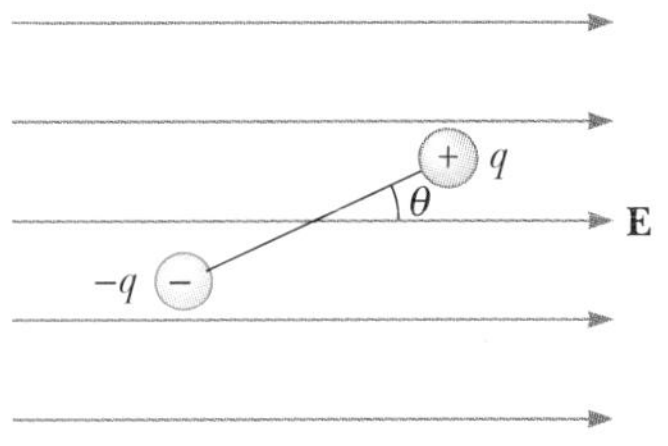

FIGURE P23.74

75. A negatively charged particle $-q$ is placed at the center of a uniformly charged ring, where the ring has a total positive charge Q as in Example 23.11. The particle, confined to move along the x axis, is displaced a *small* distance x along the axis (where $x \ll a$) and released. Show that the particle oscillates with simple harmonic motion along the x axis with a frequency given by

$$ f = \frac{1}{2\pi} \left(\frac{k_e qQ}{ma^3} \right)^{1/2} $$

SPREADSHEET PROBLEMS

S1. Spreadsheet 23.1 calculates the x and y components of the electric field E along the x axis due to any two point charges Q_1 and Q_2. Enter the values of the charges and their x and y coordinates. Choose $Q_1 = 4\ \mu$C at the origin, and set $Q_2 = 0$. Plot the electric field along the x axis. *Note:* You will have to choose a step size and adjust the scaling for the graph because the electric field at the position of the point charge is infinite.

S2. (a) Using Spreadsheet 23.1, place $Q_1 = 4\ \mu$C at the origin and $Q_2 = 4\ \mu$C at $x = 0.08$ m, $y = 0$. Plot the components of the electric field E as a function of x. (b) Change Q_2 to $-4\ \mu$C, and plot the components of the electric field as a function of x. (This is a dipole.) You will need to adjust the scales of your graphs.

S3. Using Spreadsheet 23.1, take $Q_1 = 6$ nC at $x = 0$, $y = 0.03$ m and $Q_2 = 6$ nC at $x = 0$, $y = -0.03$ m. Plot the components of the electric field as a function of x. (b) Change Q_2 to -6 nC and repeat part (a).

S4. The electric field on the perpendicular bisector of a uniformly charged wire of length L is

$$ E_y = \frac{2\,k_e\lambda}{y} \sin\theta_0 $$

(Problem 69), where

$$ \sin\theta_0 = \frac{L/2}{\sqrt{(L/2)^2 + x^2}}, $$

y is the distance from the wire, and λ is the charge per unit length. At sufficiently large distances from the wire, the field looks like that of a point charge. At very close distances, the field approaches that of an infinite line charge. Spreadsheet 23.2 calculates the fields at a distance y from (1) a point charge Q, (2) a finite wire of length L and total charge Q, and (3) an infinite charged wire with a linear charge density the same as that of the finite wire. Plot the three fields as a function of y. Choose $Q = 3\ \mu$C and $L = 0.05$ m. (a) At what distance from the finite wire is its electric field within 2 percent of that due to an infinite wire? (b) At what distance from the finite wire is its electric field within 2 percent of that due to a point charge? (c) Change Q to $10\ \mu$C and repeat parts (a) and (b). Do your answers to the questions change? Why? (d) Change L to 0.10 m, keeping $Q = 3\ \mu$C. Repeat parts (a) and (b). Do your answers change? (e) Spreadsheet 23.2 also includes a column giving the values of y/L. Answer the questions in parts (a) and (b) in terms of y/L for each case considered. Do your answers change? Why?

S5. Consider an electric dipole in which a charge $+q$ is on the x axis at $x = a$ and a charge $-q$ is on the x axis at $x = -a$. Take $q = 6$ nC and $a = 0.02$ m. Use Spreadsheet 23.1 to plot the components of the electric field along the x axis for values of x greater than 4 cm. Modify Spreadsheet 23.1 to add a plot of $2k_e p/x^3$ (the E field in the dipole approximation $x \gg a$), where $p = 2aq$ is the dipole moment of the charge distribution. For what range of values of x is the dipole approximation within 20 percent of the actual value? Within 5 percent?

S6. A quadrupole consists of two dipoles placed next to each other as in Figure PS23.6. The effective charge at the origin is $-2q$, and the other charges on the y axis at $y = a$ and $y = -a$ are each $+q$. Modify Spreadsheet 23.1 to calculate and plot the components of the electric field along the x axis, taking $q = 1\ \mu$C and $a = 1.5$ cm.

S7. The electric field on the symmetry axis of a uniformly charged disk with surface charge density σ and radius

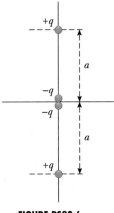

FIGURE PS23.6

R at a distance x from the disk is derived in Example 23.12:

$$E_{\text{disk}} = 2\pi k_e\sigma \left(1 - \frac{x}{\sqrt{x^2 + R^2}} \right)$$

For points sufficiently close to the disk, the field approaches that of an infinite sheet of charge; $E_{\text{sheet}} = 2\pi k_e\sigma$. For points sufficiently far away, the field approaches that of a point charge $Q = \sigma\pi R^2$. To examine these limits, note that the equation for E_{disk} can be written in the dimensionless form

$$\frac{E_{\text{disk}}}{E_{\text{sheet}}} = 1 - \frac{x/R}{\sqrt{1 + (x/R)^2}}$$

The ratio $E_{\text{disk}}/E_{\text{sheet}}$ approaches 1 as x/R approaches 0. The field of the point charge Q defined above can be written as

$$E_{\text{point}} = \frac{k_e Q}{x^2} = \frac{E_{\text{sheet}}}{2(x/R)^2}$$

So,

$$\frac{E_{\text{disk}}}{E_{\text{point}}} = 2(x/R)^2 \frac{E_{\text{disk}}}{E_{\text{sheet}}}$$

$$= 2(x/R)^2 \left(1 - \frac{x/R}{\sqrt{1 + (x/R)^2}} \right)$$

This ratio $E_{\text{disk}}/E_{\text{point}}$ approaches 1 as x/R gets large. (a) Using a spreadsheet, plot the quantity $E_{\text{disk}}/E_{\text{sheet}}$ as a function of x/R. From your graph, for what values of x/R can you approximate the field of a disk by that of a sheet of charge to within 99%? (That is, $E_{\text{disk}}/E_{\text{sheet}} \leq 0.99$.) 90%? 50%? (b) Plot $E_{\text{disk}}/E_{\text{point}}$ as a function of x/R. From your graph, for what values of x/R is the field of a disk approximated by that of a point charge to within 99%? 90%? 50%? (*Hint:* Choose the scales for each graph in such a way as to express your results clearly.)

CHAPTER 24

Gauss's Law

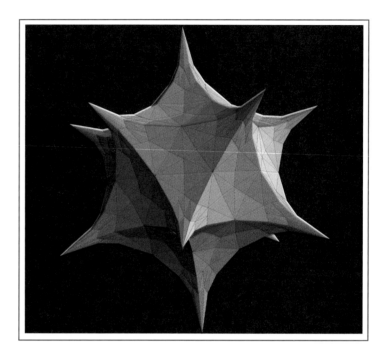

This beautiful closed surface generated by a computer is one example of a mathematical construct in hyperbolic space. In this chapter, we use simpler mathematical constructs to calculate the electric fields due to charge distributions that have spherical, cylindrical, or planar symmetry. *(Courtesy of Wolfram Research, Inc.)*

I n the preceding chapter we showed how to calculate the electric field generated by a given charge distribution from Coulomb's law. In this chapter we describe an alternative procedure for calculating electric fields. This procedure is known as *Gauss's law.* This formulation is based on the fact that the fundamental electrostatic force between point charges is an inverse-square law. Although Gauss's law is a consequence of Coulomb's law, Gauss's law is much more convenient for calculating the electric field of highly symmetric charge distributions. Furthermore, Gauss's law serves as a guide for understanding more complicated problems.

24.1 ELECTRIC FLUX

The concept of electric field lines is described qualitatively in the previous chapter. We now use the concept of electric flux to put this idea on a quantitative basis. *Electric flux is represented by the number of electric field lines penetrating some surface.* When the surface being penetrated encloses some net charge, the net number of lines that go through the surface is proportional to the net charge within the surface. The number of lines counted is independent of the shape of the surface enclosing the charge. This is essentially a statement of Gauss's law, which we describe in the next section.

First consider an electric field that is uniform in both magnitude and direction, as in Figure 24.1. The electric field lines penetrate a rectangular surface of area A, which is perpendicular to the field. Recall that the number of lines per unit area is proportional to the magnitude of the electric field. Therefore, the number of lines penetrating the surface is proportional to the product EA. The product of the electric field strength E and a surface area A perpendicular to the field is called the **electric flux, Φ**:

$$\Phi = EA \qquad (24.1)$$

From the SI units of E and A, we see that electric flux has the units of $N \cdot m^2/C$.

If the surface under consideration is not perpendicular to the field, the number of lines (in other words, the flux) through it must be less than that given by Equation 24.1. This can be understood by considering Figure 24.2, where the normal to the surface of area A is at an angle θ to the uniform electric field. Note that the number of lines that cross this area is equal to the number that cross the projected area A', which is perpendicular to the field. From Figure 24.2 we see that the two areas are related by $A' = A \cos \theta$. Since the flux through the area A equals the flux through A', we conclude that the flux through A is

$$\Phi = EA \cos \theta \qquad (24.2)$$

From this result, we see that the flux through a surface of fixed area has the maximum value, EA, when the surface is perpendicular to the field (in other words, when the normal to the surface is parallel to the field, that is, $\theta = 0°$); the flux is zero when the surface is parallel to the field (when the normal to the surface is perpendicular to the field, that is, $\theta = 90°$).

In more general situations, the electric field may vary over the surface in question. Therefore, our definition of flux given by Equation 24.2 has meaning only over a small element of area. Consider a general surface divided up into a large number of small elements, each of area ΔA. The variation in the electric field over the element can be neglected if the element is small enough. It is convenient to define a vector $\Delta \mathbf{A}_i$ whose magnitude represents the area of the ith element and whose direction is *defined to be perpendicular* to the surface, as in Figure 24.3. The electric flux $\Delta \Phi_i$ through this small element is

$$\Delta \Phi_i = E_i \, \Delta A_i \cos \theta = \mathbf{E}_i \cdot \Delta \mathbf{A}_i$$

where we have used the definition of the scalar product of two vectors ($\mathbf{A} \cdot \mathbf{B} = AB \cos \theta$). By summing the contributions of all elements, we obtain the total flux

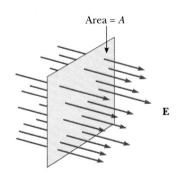

FIGURE 24.1   Field lines of a uniform electric field penetrating a plane of area A perpendicular to the field. The electric flux, Φ, through this area is equal to EA.

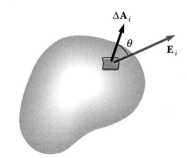

FIGURE 24.3   A small element of a surface of area ΔA_i. The electric field makes an angle θ with the normal to the surface (the direction of ΔA_i), and the flux through the element is equal to $E_i \, \Delta A_i \cos \theta$.

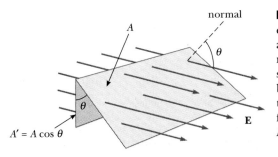

FIGURE 24.2   Field lines for a uniform electric field through an area A that is at an angle θ to the field. Since the number of lines that go through the shaded area A' is the same as the number that go through A, we conclude that the flux through A' is equal to the flux through A and is given by $\Phi = EA \cos \theta$.

through the surface.[1] If we let the area of each element approach zero, then the number of elements approaches infinity and the sum is replaced by an integral. Therefore *the general definition of electric flux is*

$$\Phi \equiv \lim_{\Delta A_i \to 0} \sum \mathbf{E}_i \cdot \Delta \mathbf{A}_i = \int_{\text{surface}} \mathbf{E} \cdot d\mathbf{A} \qquad (24.3)$$

Equation 24.3 is a surface integral, which must be evaluated over the hypothetical surface in question. In general, the value of Φ depends both on the field pattern and on the specified surface.

We are usually interested in evaluating the flux through a *closed surface*. (A **closed surface** is defined as one that divides space into an inside and an outside region, so that one cannot move from one region to the other without crossing the surface. The surface of a sphere, for example, is a closed surface.) Consider the closed surface in Figure 24.4. Note that the vectors $\Delta \mathbf{A}_i$ point in different directions for the various surface elements. At each point, these vectors are normal to the surface and, by convention, always point outward. At the elements labeled ① and ②, $\mathbf{E}$ is outward and $\theta < 90°$; hence, the flux $\Delta \Phi = \mathbf{E} \cdot \Delta \mathbf{A}$ through these elements is positive. For elements such as ③, where the field lines are directed into the surface, $\theta > 90°$ and the flux becomes negative because $\cos \theta$ is negative. The net flux through the surface is proportional to the net number of lines leaving the surface (where the net number means *the number leaving the surface minus the number entering the surface*). If there are more lines leaving than entering, the net flux is positive. If more lines enter than leave, the net flux is negative. Using the symbol $\oint$ to represent an *integral over a closed surface*, we can write the net flux, Φ_c, through a closed surface

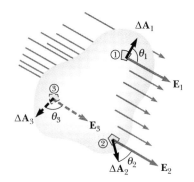

FIGURE 24.4   A closed surface in an electric field. The area vectors $\Delta \mathbf{A}_i$ are, by convention, normal to the surface and point outward. The flux through an area element can be positive (elements ① and ②) or negative (element ③).

$$\Phi_c = \oint \mathbf{E} \cdot d\mathbf{A} = \oint E_n \, dA \qquad (24.4)$$

where E_n represents the component of the electric field normal to the surface and the subscript c denotes a closed surface. Evaluating the net flux through a closed surface could be very cumbersome. However, if the field is normal to the surface at each point and constant in magnitude, the calculation is straightforward. The following example illustrates this point.

EXAMPLE 24.1   Flux Through a Cube

Consider a uniform electric field $\mathbf{E}$ oriented in the x direction. Find the net electric flux through the surface of a cube of edges ℓ oriented as shown in Figure 24.5.

Solution   The net flux can be evaluated by summing up the fluxes through each face of the cube. First, note that the flux through four of the faces is zero, because $\mathbf{E}$ is perpendicular to $d\mathbf{A}$ on these faces. In particular, the orientation of $d\mathbf{A}$ is

perpendicular to $\mathbf{E}$ for the faces labeled ③ and ④ in Figure 24.5. Therefore, $\theta = 90°$, so that $\mathbf{E} \cdot d\mathbf{A} = E \, dA \cos 90° = 0$. The flux through each of the planes parallel to the yx plane is also zero for the same reason.

Now consider the faces labeled ① and ②. The net flux through these faces is

$$\Phi_c = \int_1 \mathbf{E} \cdot d\mathbf{A} + \int_2 \mathbf{E} \cdot d\mathbf{A}$$

---

[1] It is important to note that drawings with field lines have their inaccuracies, since a small area (depending on its location) may happen to have too many or too few penetrating lines, and the density of lines in three-dimensional space is not well represented in a two-dimensional cross-section. At any rate, it is stressed that the basic definition of electric flux is $\int \mathbf{E} \cdot d\mathbf{A}$. The use of lines is only an aid for visualizing the concept.

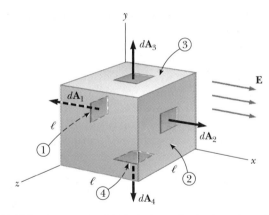

FIGURE 24.5 (Example 24.1) A hypothetical surface in the shape of a cube in a uniform electric field parallel to the x axis. The net flux through the surface is zero.

For face ①, $\mathbf{E}$ is constant and inward while $d\mathbf{A}$ is outward ($\theta = 180°$), so that we find that the flux through this face is

$$\int_1 \mathbf{E} \cdot d\mathbf{A} = \int_1 E \cdot dA \cos 180° = -E \int_1 dA = -EA = -E\ell^2$$

since the area of each face is $A = \ell^2$.

Likewise, for ②, $\mathbf{E}$ is constant and outward and in the same direction as $d\mathbf{A}$ ($\theta = 0°$), so that the flux through this face is

$$\int_2 \mathbf{E} \cdot d\mathbf{A} = \int_2 E \cdot dA \cos 0° = E \int_2 dA = +EA = E\ell^2$$

Hence, the net flux over all faces is zero, because

$$\Phi_c = -E\ell^2 + E\ell^2 = 0$$

24.2 GAUSS'S LAW

In this section we describe a general relationship between the net electric flux through a closed surface (often called a *gaussian surface*) and the charge enclosed by the surface. This relationship, known as *Gauss's law,* is of fundamental importance in the study of electric fields.

First, let us consider a positive point charge q located at the center of a sphere of radius r as in Figure 24.6. From Coulomb's law we know that the magnitude of the electric field everywhere on the surface of the sphere is $E = k_e q/r^2$. Furthermore, the field lines are radial outward and hence are perpendicular to the surface at each point. That is, at each point, $\mathbf{E}$ is parallel to the vector $\Delta\mathbf{A}_i$ representing the local element of area ΔA_i. Therefore,

$$\mathbf{E} \cdot \Delta\mathbf{A}_i = E_n \, \Delta A_i = E \, \Delta A_i$$

and from Equation 24.4 we find that the net flux through the gaussian surface is

$$\Phi_c = \oint E_n \, dA = \oint E \, dA = E \oint dA$$

since by symmetry E is constant over the surface and given by $E = k_e q/r^2$. Furthermore, for a spherical gaussian surface, $\oint dA = A = 4\pi r^2$ (the surface area of a sphere). Hence, the net flux through the gaussian surface is

$$\Phi_c = \frac{k_e q}{r^2} (4\pi r^2) = 4\pi k_e q$$

Recalling from Section 23.3 that $k_e = 1/4\pi\epsilon_0$, we can write the above expression in the form

$$\Phi_c = \frac{q}{\epsilon_0} \tag{24.5}$$

Note that this result, which is independent of r, says that the net flux through a spherical gaussian surface is proportional to the charge q *inside* the surface. The fact that the flux is independent of the radius is a consequence of the inverse-square dependence of the electric field given by Coulomb's law. That is, E varies as

Karl Friedrich Gauss (1777–1855).

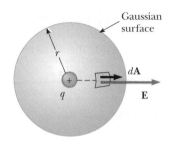

FIGURE 24.6 A spherical gaussian surface of radius r surrounding a point charge q. When the charge is at the center of the sphere, the electric field is normal to the surface and constant in magnitude everywhere on the surface.

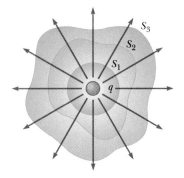

FIGURE 24.7 Closed surfaces of various shapes surrounding a charge *q*. Note that the net electric flux through each surface is the same.

The net flux through a closed surface is zero if there is no charge inside

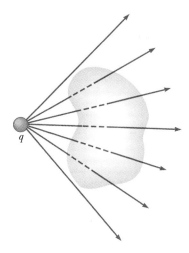

FIGURE 24.8 A point charge located *outside* a closed surface. In this case, note that the number of lines entering the surface equals the number leaving the surface.

$1/r^2$, but the area of the sphere varies as r^2. Their combined effect produces a flux that is independent of r.

Now consider several closed surfaces surrounding a charge q as in Figure 24.7. Surface S_1 is spherical, whereas surfaces S_2 and S_3 are nonspherical. The flux that passes through surface S_1 has the value q/ϵ_0. As we discussed in the previous section, the flux is proportional to the number of electric field lines passing through that surface. The construction in Figure 24.7 shows that the number of electric field lines through the spherical surface S_1 is equal to the number of electric field lines through the nonspherical surfaces S_2 and S_3. Therefore, it is reasonable to conclude that the net flux through any closed surface is independent of the shape of that surface. (One can prove that this is the case if $E \propto 1/r^2$.) In fact, *the net flux through any closed surface surrounding a point charge q is given by* q/ϵ_0.

Now consider a point charge located *outside* a closed surface of arbitrary shape, as in Figure 24.8. As you can see from this construction, some electric field lines enter the surface, and others leave the surface. However, *the number of electric field lines entering the surface equals the number leaving the surface*. Therefore, we conclude that *the net electric flux through a closed surface that surrounds no charge is zero*. If we apply this result to Example 24.1, we can easily see that the net flux through the cube is zero, since there is no charge inside the cube.

Let us extend these arguments to the generalized case of either many point charges or a continuous distribution of charge. We once again use the superposition principle, which says that *the electric field due to many charges is the vector sum of the electric fields produced by the individual charges.* That is, we can express the flux through any closed surface as

$$\oint \mathbf{E} \cdot d\mathbf{A} = \oint (\mathbf{E}_1 + \mathbf{E}_2 + \mathbf{E}_3) \cdot d\mathbf{A}$$

where $\mathbf{E}$ is the total electric field at any point on the surface and $\mathbf{E}_1$, $\mathbf{E}_2$, and $\mathbf{E}_3$ are the fields produced by the individual charges at that point. Consider the system of charges shown in Figure 24.9. The surface S surrounds only one charge, q_1; hence, the net flux through S is q_1/ϵ_0. The flux through S due to the charges outside it is zero because each electric field line that enters S at one point leaves it at another. The surface S' surrounds charges q_2 and q_3; hence, the net flux through S' is $(q_2 + q_3)/\epsilon_0$. Finally, the net flux through surface S'' is zero because there is no charge inside this surface. That is, *all* the electric field lines that enter S'' at one point leave S'' at another.

Gauss's law, which is a generalization of the above discussion, states that the net flux through *any* closed surface is

$$\Phi_c = \oint \mathbf{E} \cdot d\mathbf{A} = \frac{q_{in}}{\epsilon_0} \qquad (24.6)$$

where q_{in} represents the *net charge inside* the surface and $\mathbf{E}$ represents the electric field at any point on the surface. In words, **Gauss's law** states that

Gauss's law

the net electric flux through any closed surface is equal to the net charge inside the surface divided by ϵ_0.

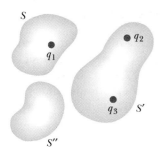

FIGURE 24.9 The net electric flux through any closed surface depends only on the charge *inside* that surface. The net flux through surface S is q_1/ϵ_0, the net flux through surface S' is $(q_2 + q_3)/\epsilon_0$, and the net flux through surface S'' is zero.

A formal proof of Gauss's law is presented in Section 24.6. When using Equation 24.6, you should note that although the charge q_{in} is the net charge inside the gaussian surface, the **E** that appears in Gauss's law represents the *total electric field,* which includes contributions from charges both inside and outside the gaussian surface.

In principle, Gauss's law can always be used to calculate the electric field of a system of charges or a continuous distribution of charge. However, in practice, *the technique is useful only in a limited number of situations where there is a high degree of symmetry.* As we see in the next section, *Gauss's law can be used to evaluate the electric field for charge distributions that have spherical, cylindrical, or planar symmetry.* If one carefully chooses the gaussian surface surrounding the charge distribution, the integral in Equation 24.6 is easy to evaluate. You should also note that a gaussian surface is a mathematical surface and need not coincide with any real physical surface.

Gauss's law is useful for evaluating *E* when the charge distribution has symmetry

---

CONCEPTUAL EXAMPLE 24.2

If the net flux through a gaussian surface is zero, which of the following statements are true? (a) There are no charges inside the surface. (b) The net charge inside the surface is zero. (c) The electric field is zero everywhere on the surface. (d) The number of electric field lines entering the surface equals the number leaving the surface.

Reasoning Statements (b) and (d) are true and follow from Gauss's law. Statement (a) is not necessarily true be-

cause Gauss's law says that the net flux through any closed surface equals the net charge inside the surface divided by ϵ_0. For example, an electric dipole (whose net charge is zero) might be inside the surface. Statement (c) is not necessarily true. Although the net flux through the surface is zero, the electric field in that region may not be zero (Fig. 24.8).

CONCEPTUAL EXAMPLE 24.3

A spherical gaussian surface surrounds a point charge q. Describe what happens to the total flux through the surface if (a) the charge is tripled, (b) the volume of the sphere is doubled, (c) the surface is changed to a cube, and (d) the charge is moved to another location *inside* the surface.

Reasoning (a) If the charge is tripled, the flux through the surface is also tripled, because the net flux is proportional to

the charge inside the surface. (b) The flux remains constant when the volume changes, because the surface surrounds the same amount of charge, regardless of its volume. (c) The total flux does not change when the shape of the closed surface changes. (d) The total flux through the closed surface remains unchanged as the charge inside the surface is moved to another location inside that surface. All of these conclusions are arrived at through an understanding of Gauss's law.

24.3   APPLICATION OF GAUSS'S LAW TO CHARGED INSULATORS

Gauss's law is useful when there is a high degree of symmetry in the charge distribution, as in the case of uniformly charged spheres, long cylinders, and flat sheets. In such cases, it is possible to find a simple gaussian surface over which the surface integral given by Equation 24.6 is easily evaluated. The surface should always be chosen to take advantage of the symmetry of the charge distribution.

EXAMPLE 24.4   The Electric Field Due to a Point Charge

Starting with Gauss's law, calculate the electric field due to an isolated point charge q and show that Coulomb's law follows from this result.

Solution   For this situation we choose a spherical gaussian surface of radius r and centered on the point charge, as in Figure 24.10. The electric field of a positive point charge is radial outward by symmetry and is therefore normal to the surface at every point. That is, **E** is parallel to $d\mathbf{A}$ at each

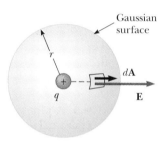

FIGURE 24.10   (Example 24.4) The point charge q is at the center of the spherical gaussian surface, and **E** is parallel to $d\mathbf{A}$ at every point on the surface.

point, and so $\mathbf{E} \cdot d\mathbf{A} = E\,dA$ and Gauss's law gives

$$\Phi_c = \oint \mathbf{E} \cdot d\mathbf{A} = \oint E\,dA = \frac{q}{\epsilon_0}$$

By symmetry, E is constant everywhere on the surface, and so it can be removed from the integral. Therefore,

$$\oint E\,dA = E \oint dA = E(4\pi r^2) = \frac{q}{\epsilon_0}$$

where we have used the fact that the surface area of a sphere is $4\pi r^2$. Hence, the magnitude of the field a distance r from q is

$$E = \frac{q}{4\pi\epsilon_0 r^2} = k_e \frac{q}{r^2}$$

If a second point charge q_0 is placed at a point where the field is E, the electric force on this charge has a magnitude

$$F = q_0 E = k_e \frac{qq_0}{r^2}$$

Previously we obtained Gauss's law from Coulomb's law. Here we show that Coulomb's law follows from Gauss's law. They are equivalent.

EXAMPLE 24.5   A Spherically Symmetric Charge Distribution

An insulating sphere of radius a has a uniform charge density ρ and a total positive charge Q (Fig. 24.11). (a) Calculate the magnitude of the electric field at a point outside the sphere.

Solution   Since the charge distribution is spherically symmetric, we again select a spherical gaussian surface of radius r, concentric with the sphere, as in Figure 24.11a. Following the line of reasoning given in Example 24.4, we find that

$$E = k_e \frac{Q}{r^2} \qquad \text{(for } r > a)$$

Note that this result is identical to that obtained for a point charge. Therefore, we conclude that, for a uniformly charged sphere, the field in the region external to the sphere

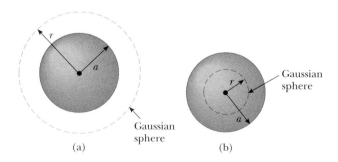

FIGURE 24.11   (Example 24.5) A uniformly charged insulating sphere of radius a and total charge Q. (a) The field at a point exterior to the sphere is $k_e Q/r^2$. (b) The field inside the sphere is due only to the charge *within* the gaussian surface and is given by $(k_e Q/a^3)r$.

is *equivalent* to that of a point charge located at the center of the sphere.

   (b) Find the magnitude of the electric field at a point inside the sphere.

Reasoning and Solution   In this case we select a spherical gaussian surface with radius $r < a$, concentric with the charge distribution (Fig. 24.11b). Let us denote the volume of this smaller sphere by V'. To apply Gauss's law in this situation, it is important to recognize that the charge q_{in} within the gaussian surface of volume V' is a quantity less than the total charge Q. To calculate the charge q_{in}, we use the fact that $q_{in} = \rho V'$, where ρ is the charge per unit volume and V' is the volume enclosed by the gaussian surface, given by $V' = \frac{4}{3}\pi r^3$ for a sphere. Therefore,

$$q_{in} = \rho V' = \rho\left(\tfrac{4}{3}\pi r^3\right)$$

As in Example 24.4, the magnitude of the electric field is constant everywhere on the spherical gaussian surface and is normal to the surface at each point. Therefore, Gauss's law in the region $r < a$ gives

$$\oint E\,dA = E \oint dA = E(4\pi r^2) = \frac{q_{in}}{\epsilon_0}$$

Solving for E gives

$$E = \frac{q_{in}}{4\pi\epsilon_0 r^2} = \frac{\rho\frac{4}{3}\pi r^3}{4\pi\epsilon_0 r^2} = \frac{\rho}{3\epsilon_0}\,r$$

Since by definition $\rho = Q/\frac{4}{3}\pi a^3$, this can be written

$$E = \frac{Qr}{4\pi\epsilon_0 a^3} = \frac{k_e Q}{a^3}\,r \qquad \text{(for } r < a\text{)}$$

   Note that this result for E differs from that obtained in part (a). It shows that $E \to 0$ as $r \to 0$, as you might have guessed based on the spherical symmetry of the charge distribution. Therefore, the result fortunately eliminates the singularity that would exist at $r = 0$ if E varied as $1/r^2$ inside the sphere. That is, if $E \propto 1/r^2$, the field would be infinite at $r = 0$, which is clearly a physically impossible situation. A plot of E versus r is shown in Figure 24.12.

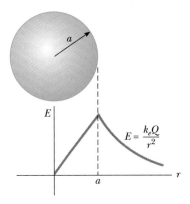

FIGURE 24.12   (Example 24.5) A plot of E versus r for a uniformly charged insulating sphere. The field inside the sphere ($r < a$) varies linearly with r. The field outside the sphere ($r > a$) is the same as that of a point charge Q located at the origin.

EXAMPLE 24.6   The Electric Field Due to a Thin Spherical Shell

A thin spherical shell of radius a has a total charge Q distributed uniformly over its surface (Fig. 24.13). Find the electric field at points inside and outside the shell.

Reasoning and Solution   The calculation of the field outside the shell is identical to that already carried out for the solid sphere in Example 24.5a. If we construct a spherical gaussian surface of radius $r > a$, concentric with the shell, then the charge inside this surface is Q. Therefore, the field at a point outside the shell is equivalent to that of a point charge Q at the center:

$$E = k_e\frac{Q}{r^2} \qquad \text{(for } r > a\text{)}$$

   The electric field inside the spherical shell is zero. This also follows from Gauss's law applied to a spherical surface of

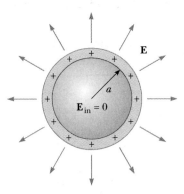

FIGURE 24.13   (Example 24.6) The electric field inside a uniformly charged spherical shell is *zero*. The field outside is the same as that of a point charge having a total charge Q located at the center of the shell.

radius $r < a$. Since the net charge inside the surface is zero, and because of the spherical symmetry of the charge distribution, application of Gauss's law shows that $E = 0$ in the region $r < a$.

The same results can be obtained using Coulomb's law and integrating over the charge distribution. This calculation is rather complicated and will be omitted.

EXAMPLE 24.7   A Cylindrically Symmetric Charge Distribution

Find the electric field a distance r from a uniform positive line charge of infinite length whose charge per unit length is λ = constant (Fig. 24.14).

Reasoning   The symmetry of the charge distribution shows that E must be perpendicular to the line charge and directed outward as in Figure 24.14a. The end view of the line charge shown in Figure 24.14b should help visualize the directions of the electric field lines. In this situation, we select a cylindrical gaussian surface of radius r and length ℓ that is coaxial with the line charge. For the curved part of this surface, **E** is constant in magnitude and perpendicular to the surface at each point. Furthermore, the flux through the ends of the gaussian cylinder is zero because **E** is parallel to these surfaces.

Solution   The total charge inside our gaussian surface is $\lambda\ell$. Applying Gauss's law and noting that **E** is parallel to $d\mathbf{A}$ everywhere on the cylindrical surface, we find that

$$\Phi_c = \oint \mathbf{E} \cdot d\mathbf{A} = E \oint dA = \frac{q_{\text{in}}}{\epsilon_0} = \frac{\lambda\ell}{\epsilon_0}$$

But the area of the curved surface is $A = 2\pi r\ell$; therefore,

$$E(2\pi r\ell) = \frac{\lambda\ell}{\epsilon_0}$$

$$E = \frac{\lambda}{2\pi\epsilon_0 r} = 2k_e \frac{\lambda}{r} \qquad (24.7)$$

Thus, we see that the field of a cylindrically symmetric charge distribution varies as $1/r$, whereas the field external to a spherically symmetric charge distribution varies as $1/r^2$. Equation 24.7 can also be obtained using Coulomb's law and integration; however, the mathematical techniques necessary for this calculation are more cumbersome.

If the line charge has a finite length, the result for E is not that given by Equation 24.7. For points close to the line charge and far from the ends, Equation 24.7 gives a good approximation of the value of the field. It turns out that Gauss's law is not useful for calculating E for a finite line charge. This is because the magnitude of the electric field is no longer constant over the surface of the gaussian cylinder. Furthermore, **E** is not perpendicular to the cylindrical sur-

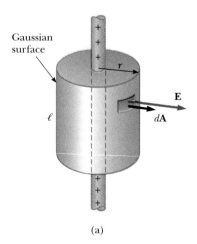

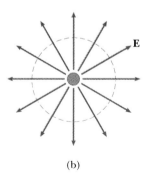

(b)

FIGURE 24.14   (Example 24.7) (a) An infinite line of charge surrounded by a cylindrical gaussian surface concentric with the line charge. (b) An end view shows that the field on the cylindrical surface is constant in magnitude and perpendicular to the surface.

face at all points. When there is little symmetry in the charge distribution, as in this situation, it is necessary to calculate **E** using Coulomb's law.

It is left as a problem (Problem 35) to show that the **E** field inside a uniformly charged rod of finite thickness is proportional to r.

EXAMPLE 24.8   A Nonconducting Plane Sheet of Charge

Find the electric field due to a nonconducting, infinite plane with uniform charge per unit area σ.

Reasoning and Solution   The symmetry of the situation shows that **E** must be perpendicular to the plane and that the direction of **E** on one side of the plane must be opposite its direction on the other side, as in Figure 24.15. It is conve-

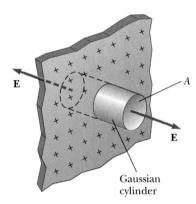

FIGURE 24.15   (Example 24.8) A cylindrical gaussian surface penetrating an infinite sheet of charge. The flux through each end of the gaussian surface is EA. There is no flux through the cylinder's curved surface.

nient to choose for our gaussian surface a small cylinder whose axis is perpendicular to the plane and whose ends each have an area A and are equidistant from the plane. Here we see that since **E** is parallel to the cylindrical surface, there is no flux through this surface. The flux out of each end of the cylinder is EA (since **E** is perpendicular to the ends); hence, the total flux through our gaussian surface is $2EA$.

Solution   Noting that the total charge inside the surface is σA, we use Gauss's law to get

$$\Phi_c = 2EA = \frac{q_{\text{in}}}{\epsilon_0} = \frac{\sigma A}{\epsilon_0}$$

$$E = \frac{\sigma}{2\epsilon_0} \qquad (24.8)$$

Since the distance of the surfaces from the plane does not appear in Equation 24.8, we conclude that $E = \sigma/2\epsilon_0$ at any distance from the plane. That is, the field is uniform everywhere.

An important configuration related to this example is the case of two parallel planes of charge, with charge densities σ and $-\sigma$, respectively (Problem 58). In this situation, the electric field is σ/ϵ_0 between the planes and approximately zero elsewhere.

CONCEPTUAL EXAMPLE 24.9

Explain why Gauss's law cannot be used to calculate the electric field of (a) an electric dipole, (b) a charged disk, and (c) three point charges at the corners of a triangle.

Reasoning   The electric field patterns of each of these three configurations do not have sufficient symmetry to make the calculations practical. (Gauss's law is only useful for

calculating the electric field of highly symmetric charge distributions, such as uniformly charged spheres, cylinders, and sheets.) In order to apply Gauss's law, you must be able to find a closed surface surrounding the charge distribution, which can be subdivided so that the field over the separate regions of the surface is constant. Such a surface cannot be found for these cases.

24.4   CONDUCTORS IN ELECTROSTATIC EQUILIBRIUM

As we learned in Section 23.2, a good electrical conductor, such as copper, contains charges (electrons) that are not bound to any atom and are free to move about within the material. When there is no net motion of charge within the conductor, the conductor is in **electrostatic equilibrium.** As we shall see, a conductor in electrostatic equilibrium has the following properties:

- The electric field is zero everywhere inside the conductor.
- Any charge on an isolated conductor resides on its surface.
- The electric field just outside a charged conductor is perpendicular to the

Properties of a conductor in electrostatic equilibrium

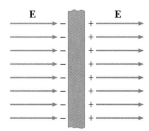

FIGURE 24.16 A conducting slab in an external electric field **E**. The charges induced on the surfaces of the slab produce an electric field that opposes the external field, giving a resultant field of zero inside the conductor.

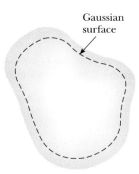

FIGURE 24.17 An insulated conductor of arbitrary shape. The broken line represents a gaussian surface just inside the conductor.

  surface of the conductor and has a magnitude σ/ϵ_0, where σ is the charge per unit area at that point.

- On an irregularly shaped conductor, charge tends to accumulate at locations where the radius of curvature of the surface is the smallest, that is, at sharp points.

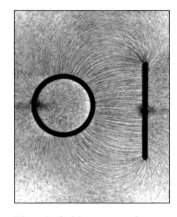

Electric field pattern of a charged conducting plate near an oppositely charged conducting cylinder. Small pieces of thread suspended in oil align with the electric field lines. Note that (1) the electric field lines are perpendicular to the conductors and (2) there are no lines inside the cylinder ($E = 0$). *(Courtesy of Harold M. Waage, Princeton University)*

  The first property can be understood by considering a conducting slab placed in an external field **E** (Fig. 24.16). In electrostatic equilibrium, the electric field inside the conductor must be zero. If this were not the case, the free charges would accelerate under the action of the field. Before the external field is applied, the electrons are uniformly distributed throughout the conductor. When the external field is applied, the free electrons accelerate to the left, causing a buildup of negative charge on the left surface (excess electrons) and of positive charge on the right (where electrons have been removed). These charges create their own internal electric field, which opposes the external field. The surface charge density increases until the magnitude of the internal electric field equals that of the external field, giving a net field of zero inside the conductor. In a good conductor, the time it takes the conductor to reach equilibrium is of the order of 10^{-16} s, which for most purposes can be considered instantaneous.

  We can use Gauss's law to verify the second and third properties of a conductor in electrostatic equilibrium. Figure 24.17 shows an arbitrarily shaped insulated conductor. A gaussian surface is drawn inside the conductor and can be as close to the surface as we wish. As we have just shown, the electric field everywhere inside the conductor is zero when it is in electrostatic equilibrium. Therefore, the electric field must also be zero at every point on the gaussian surface, so that the net flux through this surface is zero. From this result and Gauss's law, we conclude that the net charge inside the gaussian surface is zero. Since there can be no net charge inside the gaussian surface (which is arbitrarily close to the conductor's surface), *any net charge on the conductor must reside on its surface.* Gauss's law does not tell us how this excess charge is distributed on the surface. In Section 25.6 we prove the fourth property of a conductor in electrostatic equilibrium.

  We can use Gauss's law to relate the electric field just outside the surface of a charged conductor in equilibrium to the charge distribution on the conductor. To do this, it is convenient to draw a gaussian surface in the shape of a small cylinder with end faces parallel to the surface (Fig. 24.18). Part of the cylinder is just outside the conductor, and part is inside. There is no flux through the face on the inside of the cylinder because $E = 0$ inside the conductor. Furthermore, the field is normal to the surface. If E had a tangential component, the free charges would move along the surface creating surface currents, and the conductor would not be in equilibrium. There is no flux through the cylindrical part of the gaussian surface because E is tangent to this part. Hence, the net flux through the gaussian surface is $E_n A$, where E_n is the electric field just outside the conductor. Applying Gauss's law to this surface gives

$$\Phi_c = \oint E_n \, dA = E_n A = \frac{q_{in}}{\epsilon_0} = \frac{\sigma A}{\epsilon_0}$$

We have used the fact that the charge inside the gaussian surface is $q_{in} = \sigma A$, where A is the area of the cylinder's face and σ is the (local) charge per unit area. Solving for E_n gives

$$E_n = \frac{\sigma}{\epsilon_0} \qquad (24.9)$$

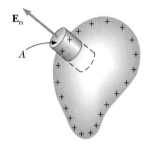

FIGURE 24.18   A gaussian surface in the shape of a small cylinder is used to calculate the electric field just outside a charged conductor. The flux through the gaussian surface is $E_n A$. Note that E is zero inside the conductor.

EXAMPLE 24.10   A Sphere Inside a Spherical Shell

A solid conducting sphere of radius a has a net positive charge $2Q$ (Fig. 24.19). A conducting spherical shell of inner radius b and outer radius c is concentric with the solid sphere and has a *net* charge $-Q$. Using Gauss's law, find the electric field in the regions labeled ①, ②, ③, and ④ and the charge distribution on the spherical shell.

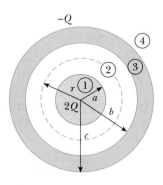

FIGURE 24.19   (Example 24.10) A solid conducting sphere of radius a and charge $2Q$ surrounded by a conducting spherical shell of charge $-Q$.

Reasoning and Solution   First note that the charge distribution on both spheres has spherical symmetry, since they are concentric. To determine the electric field at various distances r from the center, we construct spherical gaussian surfaces of radius r.

To find E inside the solid sphere of radius a (region ①), consider a gaussian surface of radius $r < a$. Since there can be no charge inside a conductor in electrostatic equilibrium, we see that $q_{in} = 0$, and so from Gauss's law and symmetry,

$E_1 = 0$ for $r < a$. Thus, we conclude that the net charge $2Q$ on the solid sphere is distributed on its outer surface.

In region ② between the spheres, where $a < r < b$, we construct a spherical gaussian surface of radius r and note that the charge inside this surface is $+2Q$ (the charge on the inner sphere). Because of the spherical symmetry, the electric field lines must be radial outward and constant in magnitude on the gaussian surface. Following Example 24.4 and using Gauss's law, we find that

$$E_2 A = E_2 (4\pi r^2) = \frac{q_{in}}{\epsilon_0} = \frac{2Q}{\epsilon_0}$$

$$E_2 = \frac{2Q}{4\pi\epsilon_0 r^2} = \frac{2k_e Q}{r^2} \qquad \text{(for } a < r < b\text{)}$$

In region ④, where $r > c$, the spherical gaussian surface surrounds a total charge of $q_{in} = 2Q + (-Q) = Q$. Therefore, Gauss's law applied to this surface gives

$$E_4 = \frac{k_e Q}{r^2} \qquad \text{(for } r > c\text{)}$$

Finally, consider region ③, where $b < r < c$. The electric field must be zero in this region because the spherical shell is also a conductor in equilibrium. If we construct a gaussian surface of this radius, we see that q_{in} must be zero since $E_3 = 0$. From this argument, we conclude that the charge on the inner surface of the spherical shell must be $-2Q$ to cancel the charge $+2Q$ on the solid sphere. (The charge $-2Q$ is induced by the charge $+2Q$.) Furthermore, since the net charge on the shell is $-Q$, we conclude that the outer surface of the shell must have a charge equal to $+Q$.

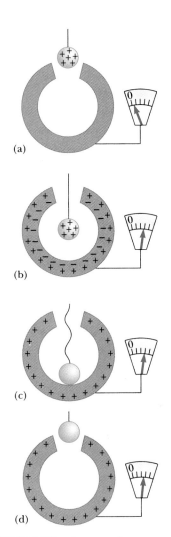

(a)

(b)

(c)

(d)

FIGURE 24.20   An experiment showing that any charge transferred to a conductor resides on its surface in electrostatic equilibrium. The hollow conductor is insulated from ground, and the small metal ball is supported by an insulating thread.

*24.5   EXPERIMENTAL PROOF OF GAUSS'S LAW AND COULOMB'S LAW

When a net charge is placed on a conductor, the charge distributes itself on the surface in such a way that the electric field inside is zero. Since $E = 0$ inside a conductor in electrostatic equilibrium, Gauss's law shows that there can be no net charge inside the conductor. We have seen that Gauss's law is a consequence of Coulomb's law (Example 24.4). Hence, it is possible to test the validity of the inverse-square law of force by attempting to detect a net charge inside a conductor. If a net charge is detected anywhere but on the conductor's surface, Gauss's law, and hence Coulomb's law, are invalid. Many experiments, including early work by Faraday, Cavendish, and Maxwell, have been performed to show that the net charge on a conductor resides on its surface. In all reported cases, no electric field could be detected in a closed conductor. Experiments by Williams, Faller, and Hill in 1971 showed that the exponent of r in Coulomb's law is $(2 + \delta)$, where $\delta = (2.7 \pm 3.1) \times 10^{-16}$!

The following experiment can be performed to verify that the net charge on a conductor resides on its surface. A positively charged metal ball at the end of a silk thread is lowered into an uncharged, hollow conductor through a small opening[2] (Fig. 24.20a). The hollow conductor is insulated from ground. The positively charged ball induces a negative charge on the inner wall of the hollow conductor, leaving an equal positive charge on the outer wall (Fig. 24.20b). The presence of positive charge on the outer wall is indicated by the deflection of an electrometer (a device used to measure charge). The deflection of the electrometer remains unchanged when the ball touches the inner surface of the hollow conductor (Fig. 24.20c). When the ball is removed, the electrometer reading remains the same and the ball is found to be uncharged (Fig. 24.20d). This experiment shows that charge is transferred from the ball to the hollow conductor. Furthermore, *the charge on the hollow conductor resides on its outer surface.* A small charged metal ball now lowered into the center of the charged hollow conductor is not attracted or repelled by the hollow conductor. This shows that $\mathbf{E} = 0$ at the center of the hollow conductor. A small positively charged ball placed near the outside of the conductor is repelled by the conductor, showing that $\mathbf{E} \neq 0$ outside the conductor.

*24.6   DERIVATION OF GAUSS'S LAW

One way of deriving Gauss's law involves the concept of the *solid angle.* Consider a spherical surface of radius r containing an area element ΔA. The solid angle $\Delta \Omega$ subtended by this element at the center of the sphere is defined to be

$$\Delta \Omega \equiv \frac{\Delta A}{r^2}$$

From this expression, we see that $\Delta \Omega$ has no dimensions, since ΔA and r^2 both have the dimension of L^2. The dimensionless unit of a solid angle is the **steradian.** Since the total surface area of a sphere is $4\pi r^2$, the total solid angle subtended by the sphere at the center is

$$\Omega = \frac{4\pi r^2}{r^2} = 4\pi \text{ steradians}$$

---

[2] The experiment is often referred to as *Faraday's ice-pail experiment,* since it was first performed by Faraday using an ice pail for the hollow conductor.

Now consider a point charge q surrounded by a closed surface of arbitrary shape (Fig. 24.21). The total flux through this surface can be obtained by evaluating $\mathbf{E} \cdot \Delta\mathbf{A}$ for each element of area and summing over all elements of the surface. The flux through the element of area ΔA is

$$\Delta\Phi = \mathbf{E} \cdot \Delta\mathbf{A} = E \cos\theta \, \Delta A = k_e q \frac{\Delta A \cos\theta}{r^2}$$

where we have used the fact that $E = k_e Q/r^2$ for a point charge. But the quantity $\Delta A \cos\theta/r^2$ is equal to the solid angle $\Delta\Omega$ subtended at the charge q by the surface element ΔA. From Figure 24.22 we see that $\Delta\Omega$ is equal to the solid angle subtended by the element of a spherical surface of radius r. Since the total solid angle at a point is 4π steradians, we see that the total flux through the closed surface is

$$\Phi_c = k_e q \oint \frac{dA \cos\theta}{r^2} = k_e q \oint d\Omega = 4\pi k_e q = \frac{q}{\epsilon_0}$$

Thus we have derived Gauss's law, Equation 24.6. Note that this result is independent of the shape of the closed surface and independent of the position of the charge within the surface.

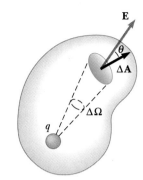

FIGURE 24.21 A closed surface of arbitrary shape surrounds a point charge q. The net flux through the surface is independent of the shape of the surface.

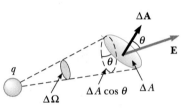

FIGURE 24.22 The area element ΔA subtends a solid angle $\Delta\Omega = (\Delta A \cos\theta)/r^2$ at the charge q.

SUMMARY

Electrix flux is represented by the number of electric field lines that penetrate a surface. If the electric field is uniform and makes an angle θ with the normal to the surface, the electric flux through the surface is

$$\Phi = EA \cos\theta \qquad (24.2)$$

TABLE 24.1 Typical Electric Field Calculations Using Gauss's Law

Charge Distribution	Electric Field	Location
Insulating sphere of radius R, uniform charge density, and total charge Q	$k_e \dfrac{Q}{r^2}$	$r > R$
	$k_e \dfrac{Q}{R^3} r$	$r < R$
Thin spherical shell of radius R and total charge Q	$k_e \dfrac{Q}{r^2}$	$r > R$
	0	$r < R$
Line charge of infinite length and charge per unit length λ	$2k_e \dfrac{\lambda}{r}$	Outside the line charge
Nonconducting, infinite charged plane with charge per unit area σ	$\dfrac{\sigma}{2\epsilon_0}$	Everywhere outside the plane
Conductor of surface charge per unit area σ	$\dfrac{\sigma}{\epsilon_0}$	Just outside the conductor
	0	Inside the conductor

In general, the electric flux through a surface is

$$\Phi = \int\limits_{\text{surface}} \mathbf{E} \cdot dA \tag{24.3}$$

Gauss's law says that the net electric flux, Φ_c, through any closed gaussian surface is equal to the *net* charge inside the surface divided by ϵ_0:

$$\Phi_c = \oint \mathbf{E} \cdot d\mathbf{A} = \frac{q_{\text{in}}}{\epsilon_0} \tag{24.6}$$

Using Gauss's law, one can calculate the electric field due to various symmetric charge distributions. Table 24.1 lists some typical results.

A conductor in electrostatic equilibrium has the following properties:

• The electric field is zero everywhere inside it.
• Any excess charge on it resides entirely on its surface.
• The electric field just outside it is perpendicular to its surface and has a magnitude σ/ϵ_0, where σ is the charge per unit area at that point.
• On an irregularly shaped conductor, charge tends to accumulate where the radius of curvature of the surface is the smallest, that is, at sharp points.

Problem-Solving Strategy and Hints
Applying Gauss's Law

Gauss's law may seem mysterious to you, and it is usually one of the most difficult concepts to understand in introductory physics. However, as we have seen, it is very powerful in solving problems having a high degree of symmetry. In this chapter, you will encounter only problems with three kinds of symmetry: planar, cylindrical, and spherical. It is important to review Examples 24.4 through 24.10 and to use the following procedure:

• First, select a gaussian surface that *has a symmetry to match the charge distribution.* For point charges or spherically symmetric charge distributions, the gaussian surface should be a sphere centered on the charge as in Examples 24.4, 24.5, 24.6, and 24.10. For uniform line charges or uniformly charged cylinders, your choice of a gaussian surface should be a cylindrical surface that is coaxial with the line charge or cylinder as in Example 24.7. For sheets of charge having plane symmetry, the gaussian surface should be a cylinder that straddles the sheet as in Example 24.8. Note that in all cases, the gaussian surface is selected such that the electric field has the same magnitude everywhere on the surface and is directed perpendicularly to the surface. This enables you to easily evaluate the surface integral that appears on the left side of Gauss's law, which represents the total electric flux through that surface.
• Now evaluate the right side of Gauss's law, which amounts to calculating the total electric charge, q_{in}, inside the gaussian surface. If the charge density is uniform, as is usually the case (that is, if λ, σ, or ρ is constant), simply multiply that charge density by the length, area, or volume enclosed by the gaussian surface. However, if the charge distribution is *nonuniform,* you must integrate the charge density over the region enclosed by the gaussian surface. For example, if the charge is distributed along a line, you would integrate the expression $dq = \lambda\, dx$, where dq is the charge on an

infinitesimal element dx and λ is the charge per unit length. For a plane of charge, you would integrate $dq = \sigma \, dA$, where σ is the charge per unit area and dA is an infinitesimal element of area. Finally, for a volume of charge you would integrate $dq = \rho \, dV$, where ρ is the charge per unit volume and dV is an infinitesimal element of volume.

• Once the left and right sides of Gauss's law have been evaluated, you can calculate the electric field on the gaussian surface assuming the charge distribution is given in the problem. Conversely, if the electric field is known, you can calculate the charge distribution that produces the field.

QUESTIONS

1. If the electric field in a region of space is zero, can you conclude there are no electric charges in that region? Explain.
2. If there are more electric field lines leaving a gaussian surface than entering, what can you conclude about the net charge enclosed by that surface?
3. A uniform electric field exists in a region of space in which there are no charges. What can you conclude about the net electric flux through a gaussian surface placed in this region of space?
4. If the total charge inside a closed surface is known but the distribution of the charge is unspecified, can you use Gauss's law to find the electric field? Explain.
5. Explain why the electric flux through a closed surface with a given enclosed charge is independent of the size or shape of the surface.
6. Consider the electric field due to a nonconducting infinite plane having a uniform charge density. Explain why the electric field does not depend on the distance from the plane in terms of the spacing of the electric field lines.
7. Use Gauss's law to explain why electric field lines must begin and end on electric charges. (*Hint:* Change the size of the gaussian surface.)
8. A point charge is placed at the center of an uncharged metallic spherical shell insulated from ground. As the point charge is moved off center, describe what happens to (a) the total induced charge on the shell and (b) the distribution of charge on the interior and exterior surfaces of the shell.

9. Explain why excess charge on an isolated conductor must reside on its surface, using the repulsive nature of the force between like charges and the freedom of motion of charge within the conductor.
10. A person is placed in a large hollow metallic sphere that is insulated from ground. If a large charge is placed on the sphere, will the person be harmed upon touching the inside of the sphere? Explain what will happen if the person also has an initial charge whose sign is opposite that of the charge on the sphere.
11. How would the observations described in Figure 24.20 differ if the hollow conductor were grounded? How would they differ if the small charged ball were an insulator rather than a conductor?
12. What other experiment might be performed on the ball in Figure 24.20 to show that its charge was transferred to the hollow conductor?
13. What would happen to the electrometer reading if the charged ball in Figure 24.20 touched the inner wall of the conductor? the outer wall?
14. Two solid spheres, both of radius R, carry identical total charges, Q. One sphere is a good conductor while the other is an insulator. If the charge on the insulating sphere is uniformly distributed throughout its interior volume, how do the electric fields outside these two spheres compare? Are the fields identical inside the two spheres?

PROBLEMS

Review Problem

A solid insulating sphere of radius a has a net positive charge $3Q$. Concentric with this sphere is a conducting spherical shell of inner radius b and outer radius c, and having

a net negative charge $-Q$ as in the figure. (a) Construct a spherical gaussian surface of radius $r > c$ and find the net charge enclosed by this surface. (b) What is the direction of the electric field at $r > c$? (c) Find the electric field at $r \geq c$. (d) Construct a spherical gaussian sur-

□ indicates problems that have full solutions available in the Student Solutions Manual and Study Guide.

face of radius *r*, where $b < r < c$, and find the net charge enclosed by this surface. (e) Find the electric field in the region $b < r < c$. (f) Construct a spherical gaussian surface of radius *r*, where $a < r < b$. What is the net charge enclosed by this surface? (g) Use your result to part (f) and Gauss's law to find the electric field in the region $a < r < b$. (h) Construct a spherical gaussian surface of radius $r < a$ and find an expression for the net charge inside that surface as a function of *r*. Note that the charge inside this surface is less than $3Q$. (i) Use your result to part (h) and Gauss's law to find the electric field in the region $r < a$. (j) From what you have learned in the previous parts, determine the net charge on the inner surface of the conducting shell and the net charge on the outer surface of the conducting shell. (k) Make a plot of the magnitude of the electric field versus *r* in the interior and exterior regions of the spherical shell.

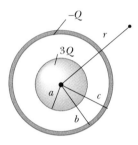

Section 24.1   Electric Flux

1. A spherical shell is placed in a uniform electric field. Determine the total electric flux through the shell.
2. An electric field of magnitude 3.5×10^3 N/C is applied along the *x* axis. Calculate the electric flux through a rectangular plane 0.35 m wide and 0.70 m long if the plane (a) is parallel to the *yz* plane, (b) is parallel to the *xy* plane, and (c) contains the *y* axis and its normal makes an angle of 40° with the *x* axis.
3. A uniform electric field $a\mathbf{i} + b\mathbf{j}$ intersects a surface of area *A*. What is the flux through this area if the surface lies (a) in the *yz* plane? (b) in the *xz* plane? (c) in the *xy* plane?
4. Consider a closed triangular box resting within a horizontal electric field of magnitude $E = 7.8 \times 10^4$

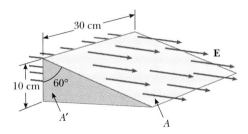

FIGURE P24.4

N/C as in Figure P24.4. Calculate the electric flux through (a) the vertical surface, (b) the slanted surface, and (c) the entire surface of the box.

5. A 40-cm-diameter loop is rotated in a uniform electric field until the position of maximum electric flux is found. The flux in this position is measured to be 5.2×10^5 N·m²/C. What is the electric field strength?

5A. A loop of diameter *d* is rotated in a uniform electric field until the position of maximum electric flux is found. The flux in this position is measured to be Φ. What is the electric field strength?

6. A point charge *q* is located at the center of a uniform ring having linear charge density λ and radius *a*. Determine the total electric flux through a sphere centered at the point charge and having radius *R*, where $R < a$ (Fig. P24.6).

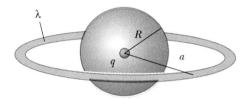

FIGURE P24.6

7. A cone of base radius *R* and height *h* is located on a horizontal table, and a horizontal uniform electric field *E* penetrates the cone, as in Figure P24.7. Determine the electric flux entering the cone.

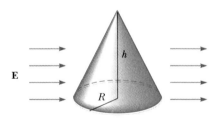

FIGURE P24.7

8. An electric field of magnitude 2.0×10^4 N/C and directed perpendicular to the Earth's surface exists on a day when a thunderstorm is brewing. A car that can be approximated as a rectangle 6.0 m by 3.0 m is traveling along a road that is inclined 10° relative to the ground. Determine the electric flux through the bottom of the car.
9. A pyramid with a 6.0-m-square base and height of 4.0 m is placed in a vertical electric field of 52 N/C. Calculate the total electric flux through the pyramid's four slanted surfaces.

Section 24.2   Gauss's Law

10. Four closed surfaces, S_1 through S_4, together with the charges $-2Q$, Q, and $-Q$ are sketched in Figure P24.10. Find the electric flux through each surface.

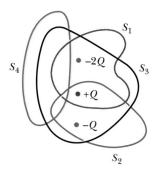

FIGURE P24.10

11. (a) A point charge q is located a distance d from an infinite plane. Determine the electric flux through the plane due to the point charge. (b) A point charge q is located a *very small* distance from the center of a *very large* square on the line perpendicular to the square and going through its center. Determine the approximate electric flux through the square due to the point charge. (c) Explain why the answers to parts (a) and (b) are identical.

12. If the constant electric field in Figure P24.12 has a magnitude E_0, calculate the total electric flux through the paraboloidal surface.

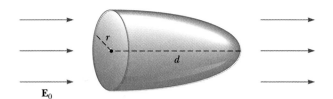

FIGURE P24.12

13. A point charge of 12 μC is placed at the center of a spherical shell of radius 22 cm. What is the total electric flux through (a) the surface of the shell and (b) any hemispherical surface of the shell? (c) Do the results depend on the radius? Explain.

13A. A point charge Q is placed at the center of a spherical shell of radius R. What is the total electric flux through (a) the surface of the shell and (b) any hemispherical surface of the shell? (c) Do the results depend on the radius? Explain.

14. A charge of 12 μC is at the geometric center of a cube. What is the electric flux through one of the faces?

15. The following charges are located inside a submarine: 5.0 μC, -9.0 μC, 27 μC, and -84 μC. Calculate the net electric flux through the submarine. Compare the number of electric field lines leaving the submarine with the number entering it.

16. A point charge of 0.0462 μC is inside a pyramid. Determine the total electric flux through the surface of the pyramid.

17. An infinitely long line of charge having a uniform charge per unit length λ lies a distance d from a point O, as in Figure P24.17. Determine the total electric flux through the surface of a sphere of radius R centered at O. (*Hint*: Consider both $R < d$ and $R > d$.)

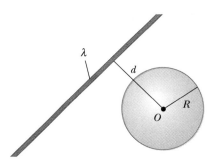

FIGURE P24.17

18. A point charge $Q = 5.0$ μC is located at the center of a cube of side $L = 0.10$ m. Six other point charges, each carrying a charge $q = -1.0$ μC, are positioned symmetrically around Q as in Figure P24.18. Determine the electric flux through one face of the cube.

18A. A point charge Q is located at the center of a cube of side L. Six other point charges, each carrying a charge $-q$, are positioned symmetrically around Q as in Figure P24.18. Determine the electric flux through one face of the cube.

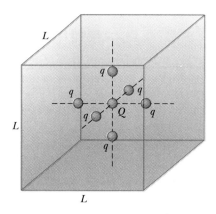

FIGURE P24.18

19. A 10.0-μC charge located at the origin of a cartesian coordinate system is surrounded by a nonconducting hollow sphere of radius 10.0 cm. A drill with a radius of 1.00 mm is aligned along the z axis, and a hole is drilled in the sphere. Calculate the electric flux through the hole.

20. A charge of 170 μC is at the center of a cube of side 80.0 cm. (a) Find the total flux through each face of the cube. (b) Find the flux through the whole surface of the cube. (c) Would your answers to parts (a) or (b) change if the charge were not at the center? Explain.

20A. A charge Q is at the center of a cube of side L. (a) Find the total flux through each face of the cube. (b) Find the flux through the whole surface of the cube. (c) Would your answers to parts (a) or (b) change if the charge were not at the center? Explain.

21. The total electric flux through a closed surface in the shape of a cylinder is 8.60×10^4 N·m²/C. (a) What is the net charge within the cylinder? (b) From the information given, what can you say about the charge within the cylinder? (c) How would your answers to parts (a) and (b) change if the net flux were -8.60×10^4 N·m²/C?

22. The line ag in Figure P24.22 is a diagonal of the cube, and a point charge q is located very close to vertex a (on the extension of ag) as in Figure P24.22. Determine the electric flux through each side of the cube which contains the point a.

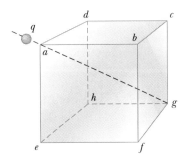

FIGURE P24.22

23. A point charge Q is located just above the center of the flat face of a hemisphere of radius R as in Figure P24.23. What is the electric flux (a) through the curved surface and (b) through the flat face?

Section 24.3   Application of Gauss's Law to Charged Insulators

24. On a clear, sunny day, there is a vertical electrical field of about 130 N/C pointing down over flat ground or water. What is the surface charge density on the ground for these conditions?

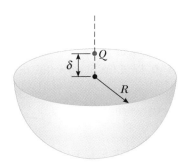

FIGURE P24.23

25. Consider a thin spherical shell of radius 14.0 cm with a total charge of 32.0 μC distributed uniformly on its surface. Find the electric field (a) 10.0 cm and (b) 20.0 cm from the center of the charge distribution.

26. An inflated balloon in the shape of a sphere of radius 12.0 cm has a total charge of 7.00 μC uniformly distributed on its surface. Calculate the magnitude of the electric field (a) 10.0 cm, (b) 12.5 cm, and (c) 30.0 cm from the center of the balloon.

27. An insulating sphere is 8.00 cm in diameter and carries a 5.70-μC charge uniformly distributed throughout its interior volume. Calculate the charge enclosed by a concentric spherical surface with radius (a) $r = 2.00$ cm and (b) $r = 6.00$ cm.

28. Consider an infinitely long line of charge having uniform charge per unit length λ. Determine the total electric flux through a closed right circular cylinder of length L and radius R that is parallel to the line, if the distance between the axis of the cylinder and the line is d. (*Hint:* Consider both when $R < d$ and $R > d$.)

29. A solid sphere of radius 40.0 cm has a total positive charge of 26.0 μC uniformly distributed throughout its volume. Calculate the magnitude of the electric field (a) 0 cm, (b) 10.0 cm, (c) 40.0 cm, and (d) 60.0 cm from the center of the sphere.

30. A sphere of radius a carries a volume charge density $\rho = \rho_0(r/a)^2$ for $r < a$. Calculate the electric field inside and outside the sphere.

31. A spherically symmetric charge distribution has a charge density given by $\rho = a/r$, where a is constant. Find the electric field as a function of r. (See the note in Problem 54.)

32. The charge per unit length on a long, straight filament is -90.0 μC/m. Find the electric field (a) 10.0 cm, (b) 20.0 cm, and (c) 100 cm from the filament, where distances are measured perpendicular to the length of the filament.

33. A uniformly charged, straight filament 7.00 m in length has a total positive charge of 2.00 μC. An uncharged cardboard cylinder 2.00 cm in length and 10.0 cm in radius surrounds the filament at its

center, with the filament as the axis of the cylinder. Using any reasonable approximations, find (a) the electric field at the surface of the cylinder and (b) the total electric flux through the cylinder.

34. An infinitely long cylindrical insulating shell of inner radius a and outer radius b has a uniform volume charge density ρ (C/m^3). A line of charge density λ (C/m) is placed along the axis of the shell. Determine the electric field intensity everywhere.

35. Consider a long cylindrical charge distribution of radius R with a uniform charge density ρ. Find the electric field at distance r from the axis where $r < R$.

36. A nonconducting wall carries a uniform charge density of 8.6 μC/cm^2. What is the electric field 7.0 cm in front of the wall? Does your result change as the distance from the wall is varied?

37. A large flat sheet of charge has a charge per unit area of 9.0 μC/m^2. Find the electric field intensity just above the surface of the sheet, measured from its midpoint.

Section 24.4 Conductors in Electrostatic Equilibrium

38. A conducting spherical shell of radius 15 cm carries a net charge of -6.4 μC uniformly distributed on its surface. Find the electric field at points (a) just outside the shell and (b) inside the shell.

39. A long, straight metal rod has a radius of 5.00 cm and a charge per unit length of 30.0 nC/m. Find the electric field (a) 3.00 cm, (b) 10.0 cm, and (c) 100 cm from the axis of the rod, where distances are measured perpendicular to the rod.

40. A charge q is placed on a conducting sheet that has a finite but very small thickness and area A. What is the approximate magnitude of the electric field at an external point that is a very small distance above the center point?

41. A thin conducting plate 50.0 cm on a side lies in the xy plane. If a total charge of 4.00×10^{-8} C is placed on the plate, find (a) the charge density on the plate, (b) the electric field just above the plate, and (c) the electric field just below the plate.

42. Two identical conducting spheres each having a radius of 0.500 cm are connected by a light 2.00-m-long conducting wire. Determine the tension in the wire if 60.0 μC is placed on one of the conductors. (*Hint:* Assume that the surface distribution of charge on each sphere is uniform.)

42A. Two identical conducting spheres each having a radius R are connected by a light conducting wire of length L, where $L \gg R$. Determine the tension in the wire if a charge Q is placed on one of the conductors. (*Hint:* Assume that the surface distribution of charge on each sphere is uniform.)

43. A conducting spherical shell having an inner radius of 4.0 cm and outer radius of 5.0 cm carries a net charge of $+10$ μC. If a $+2.0$-μC point charge is placed at the center of this shell, determine the surface charge density on (a) the inner surface and (b) the outer surface.

43A. A conducting spherical shell having an inner radius a and outer radius b carries a net charge Q. If a point charge q is placed at the center of this shell, determine the surface charge density on (a) the inner surface and (b) the outer surface.

44. A hollow conducting sphere is surrounded by a larger concentric, spherical, conducting shell. The inner sphere has a charge $-Q$, and the outer sphere has a charge $3Q$. The charges are in electrostatic equilibrium. Using Gauss's law, find the charges and the electric fields everywhere.

45. A solid conducting sphere of radius 2.0 cm has a charge 8.0 μC. A conducting spherical shell of inner radius 4.0 cm and outer radius 5.0 cm is concentric with the solid sphere and has a charge -4.0 μC. Find the electric field at (a) $r = 1.0$ cm, (b) $r = 3.0$ cm, (c) $r = 4.5$ cm, and (d) $r = 7.0$ cm from the center of this charge configuration.

46. Two identical metal blocks resting on a frictionless horizontal surface are connected by a light metal spring for which the spring constant is $k = 100$ N/m and the unstretched length is 0.30 m as in Figure P24.46a. A charge Q is slowly placed on the system causing the spring to stretch to an equilibrium length of 0.40 m as in Figure P24.46b. Determine the value of Q, assuming that all the charge resides on the blocks and that the blocks can be treated as point charges.

46A. Two identical metal blocks resting on a frictionless horizontal surface are connected by a light metal spring having constant k and unstretched length L_0 as in Figure P24.46a. A charge Q is slowly placed on

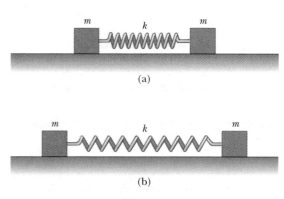

(a)

(b)

FIGURE P24.46

the system, causing the spring to stretch to an equilibrium length L as in Figure P24.46b. Determine the value of Q, assuming that all the charge resides on the blocks and that the blocks can be treated as point charges.

47. A long, straight wire is surrounded by a hollow metal cylinder whose axis coincides with that of the wire. The wire has a charge per unit length of λ, and the cylinder has a net charge per unit length of 2λ. From this information, use Gauss's law to find (a) the charge per unit length on the inner and outer surfaces of the cylinder and (b) the electric field outside the cylinder, a distance r from the axis.

48. Consider two identical conducting spheres whose surfaces are separated by a small distance. One sphere is given a large net positive charge while the other is given a small net positive charge. It is found that the force between them is attractive even though both spheres have net charges of the same sign. Explain how this is possible.

Section 24.6   Derivation of Gauss's Law

49. A sphere of radius R surrounds a point charge Q, located at its center. (a) Show that the electric flux through a circular cap of half-angle θ (Fig. P24.49) is

$$\Phi = \frac{Q}{2\epsilon_0}(1 - \cos\theta)$$

What is the flux for (b) $\theta = 90°$ and (c) $\theta = 180°$?

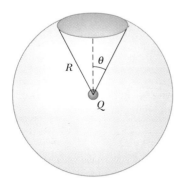

FIGURE P24.49

ADDITIONAL PROBLEMS

50. For the configuration shown in Figure P24.50, suppose that $a = 5.0$ cm, $b = 20$ cm, and $c = 25$ cm. Furthermore, suppose that the electric field at a point 10 cm from the center is measured to be 3.6×10^3 N/C radially inward while the electric field at a point 50 cm from the center is 2.0×10^2 N/C radially outward. From this information, find (a) the

charge on the insulating sphere, (b) the net charge on the hollow conducting sphere, and (c) the total charge on the inner and outer surfaces of the hollow conducting sphere.

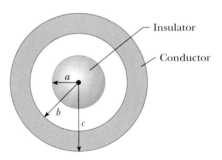

FIGURE P24.50

51. A solid insulating sphere of radius a has a uniform charge density ρ and a total charge Q. Concentric with this sphere is an uncharged, conducting hollow sphere whose inner and outer radii are b and c, as in Figure P24.50. (a) Find the magnitude of the electric field in the regions $r < a$, $a < r < b$, $b < r < c$, and $r > c$. (b) Determine the induced charge per unit area on the inner and outer surfaces of the hollow sphere.

52. Consider an insulating sphere of radius R and having a uniform volume charge density ρ. Plot the magnitude of the electric field E as a function of the distance from the center of the sphere, r. Let r range over the interval $0 < r < 3R$ and plot E in units of $\rho R/\epsilon_0$.

53. An early (incorrect) model of the hydrogen atom, suggested by J. J. Thomson, proposed that a positive cloud of charge $+e$ was uniformly distributed throughout the volume of a sphere of radius R, with the electron an equal-magnitude negative point charge $-e$ at the center. (a) Using Gauss's law, show that the electron would be in equilibrium at the center and, if displaced from the center a distance $r < R$, would experience a restoring force of the form $F = -Kr$, where K is a constant. (b) Show that $K = k_e^2 e^2/R^3$. (c) Find an expression for the frequency f of simple harmonic oscillations that an electron would undergo if displaced a short distance ($< R$) from the center and released. (d) Calculate a numerical value for R that would result in a frequency of 2.47×10^{15} Hz, the most intense line in the hydrogen spectrum.

54. Consider a solid insulating sphere of radius b with nonuniform charge density $\rho = Cr$ for $0 < r \leq b$. Find the charge contained within the radius when (a) $r < b$ and (b) $r > b$. (*Note:* The volume element dV for a spherical shell of radius r and thickness dr is equal to $4\pi r^2\, dr$.)

55. A solid insulating sphere of radius R has a nonuniform charge density that varies with r according to the expression $\rho = Ar^2$, where A is a constant and $r < R$ is measured from the center of the sphere. (a) Show that the electric field outside $(r > R)$ the sphere is $E = AR^5/5\epsilon_0 r^2$. (b) Show that the electric field inside $(r < R)$ the sphere is $E = Ar^3/5\epsilon_0$. (*Hint:* Note that the total charge Q on the sphere is equal to the integral of $\rho\, dV$, where r extends from 0 to R; also note that the charge q within a radius $r < R$ is less than Q. To evaluate the integrals, note that the volume element dV for a spherical shell of radius r and thickness dr is equal to $4\pi r^2\, dr$.)

56. An infinitely long insulating cylinder of radius R has a volume charge density that varies with the radius as

$$\rho = \rho_0 \left(a - \frac{r}{b} \right)$$

where ρ_0, a, and b are positive constants and r is the distance from the axis of the cylinder. Use Gauss's law to determine the magnitude of the electric field at radial distances (a) $r < R$ and (b) $r > R$.

57. (a) Using the fact that Newton's law of gravitation is mathematically similar to Coulomb's law, show that Gauss's law for gravitation can be written

$$\oint \mathbf{g} \cdot d\mathbf{A} = -4\pi G m_{\text{in}}$$

where m_{in} is the net mass inside the gaussian surface and $\mathbf{g} = \mathbf{F}_g/m$ is the gravitational field at any point on the surface. (b) Determine the gravitational field at a point a distance r from the center of the Earth, where $r < R_E$, assuming that the Earth's mass density is uniform.

58. Two infinite, nonconducting sheets of charge are parallel to each other as in Figure P24.58. The sheet on the left has a uniform surface charge density σ, and the one on the right has a uniform charge density $-\sigma$. Calculate the value of the electric field at points (a) to the left of, (b) in between, and (c) to the right of the two sheets. (*Hint:* See Example 24.8.)

59. Repeat the calculations for Problem 58 when both sheets have positive uniform charge densities σ.

60. A closed surface with dimensions $a = b = 0.40$ m and $c = 0.60$ m is located as in Figure P24.60. The electric field throughout the region is nonuniform and given by $\mathbf{E} = (3.0 + 2.0x^2)\mathbf{i}$ N/C, where x is in meters. Calculate the net electric flux leaving the closed surface. What net charge is enclosed by the surface?

60A. A closed surface with dimensions a, b, and c is located as in Figure P24.60. The electric field throughout the region is nonuniform and given by $\mathbf{E} = (A + Bx^2)\mathbf{i}$ N/C, where A and B are constants and x is in meters. Calculate the net electric flux leaving the closed surface. What net charge is enclosed by the surface?

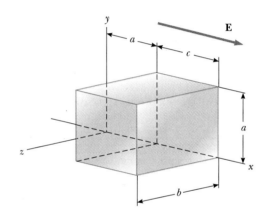

FIGURE P24.60

61. A slab of insulating material (infinite in two of its three dimensions) has a uniform positive charge density ρ. An edge view of the slab is shown in Figure P24.61. (a) Show that the electric field a distance x from its center and inside the slab is $E = \rho x/\epsilon_0$. (b) Suppose an electron of charge $-e$ and mass m is placed inside the slab. If it is released from rest at a distance x from the center, show that the electron exhibits simple harmonic motion with a frequency

$$f = \frac{1}{2\pi}\sqrt{\frac{\rho e}{m\epsilon_0}}$$

62. A slab of insulating material has a nonuniform positive charge density $\rho = Cx^2$, where x is measured from the center of the slab as in Figure P24.61, and C is a constant. The slab is infinite in the y and z directions. Derive expressions for the electric field in (a) the exterior regions and (b) the interior region of the slab $(-d/2 < x < d/2)$.

σ

$-\sigma$

FIGURE P24.58

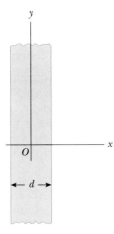

FIGURE P24.61

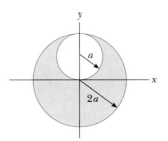

FIGURE P24.63

64. A point charge Q is located on the axis of a disk of radius R at a distance b from the plane of the disk (Fig. P24.64). Show that if one fourth of the electric flux from the charge passes through the disk, then $R = \sqrt{3}b$.

63. A sphere of radius $2a$ is made of a nonconducting material that has a uniform volume charge density ρ. (Assume that the material does not affect the electric field.) A spherical cavity of radius a is now removed from the sphere as shown in Figure P24.63. Show that the electric field within the cavity is uniform and is given by $E_x = 0$ and $E_y = \rho a/3\epsilon_0$. (*Hint:* The field within the cavity is the superposition of the field due to the original uncut sphere, plus the field due to a sphere the size of the cavity with a uniform negative charge density $-\rho$.)

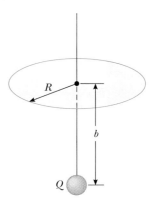

FIGURE P24.64

CHAPTER 25

Electric Potential

Jennifer is holding on to a charged sphere that reaches a potential of about 100 000 volts. The device that generates this high potential is called a Van de Graaff generator. Why do you suppose Jennifer's hair stands on end like the needles of a porcupine? Why is it important that she stand on a pedestal insulated from ground?
(Courtesy of Henry Leap and Jim Lehman)

The concept of potential energy was first introduced in Chapter 8 in connection with such conservative forces as the force of gravity and the elastic force of a spring. By using the law of energy conservation, we were often able to avoid working directly with forces when solving various mechanical problems. In this chapter we see that the energy concept is also of great value in the study of electricity. Since the electrostatic force given by Coulomb's law is conservative, electrostatic phenomena can be described conveniently in terms of an electrical potential energy. This idea enables us to define a scalar quantity called *electric potential*. Because the potential is a scalar function of position, it offers a simpler way of describing electrostatic phenomena than does the electric field. In later chapters we shall see that the concept of the electric potential is of great practical value. In fact, the measured voltage between any two points in an electrical circuit is simply the difference in electric potential between the points.

25.1 POTENTIAL DIFFERENCE AND ELECTRIC POTENTIAL

When a test charge q_0 is placed in an electric field **E**, the electric force on the test charge is $q_0\mathbf{E}$. This force is the vector sum of the individual forces exerted on q_0 by the various charges producing the field **E**. It follows that the force $q_0\mathbf{E}$ is conservative, because the individual forces governed by Coulomb's law are conservative. When a charge is moved within an electric field, the work done on q_0 by the electric field is equal to the negative of the work done by the external agent causing the displacement. For an infinitesimal displacement $d\mathbf{s}$, the work done by the electric field is $\mathbf{F}\cdot d\mathbf{s} = q_0\mathbf{E}\cdot d\mathbf{s}$. This decreases the potential energy of the electric field by an amount $dU = -q_0\mathbf{E}\cdot d\mathbf{s}$. For a finite displacement of the test charge between points A and B, the change in potential energy $\Delta U = U_B - U_A$ is

Change in potential energy	$$\Delta U = -q_0 \int_A^B \mathbf{E}\cdot d\mathbf{s} \qquad (25.1)$$

The integration is performed along the path by which q_0 moves from A to B, and the integral is called either a *path integral* or a *line integral*. Since the force $q_0\mathbf{E}$ is conservative, *this line integral does not depend on the path taken between A and B.*

The potential energy per unit charge, U/q_0, is independent of the value of q_0 and has a unique value at every point in an electric field. The quantity U/q_0 is called the **electric potential** (or simply the **potential**), V. Thus, the electric potential at any point in an electric field is

$$V = \frac{U}{q_0} \qquad (25.2)$$

Because potential energy is a scalar quantity, electric potential is also a scalar quantity.

The **potential difference**, $\Delta V = V_B - V_A$, between the points A and B is defined as the change in potential energy divided by the test charge q_0:

Potential difference	$$\Delta V = \frac{\Delta U}{q_0} = -\int_A^B \mathbf{E}\cdot d\mathbf{s} \qquad (25.3)$$

Potential difference should not be confused with difference in potential energy. The potential difference is proportional to the change in potential energy, and we see from Equation 25.3 that the two are related by $\Delta U = q_0\,\Delta V$. The potential is a scalar characteristic of the field, independent of the charges that may be placed in the field. The potential energy resides in the field, also. However, because we are interested in the potential at the location of a charge, and in the potential energy caused by the interaction of the charge with the field, we follow the common convention of speaking of the potential energy as if it belonged to the charge, except when we specifically require information about transfer of energy between the field and the charge.

Because, as already noted, the change in potential energy of the charge is the negative of the work done by the electric force, the potential difference ΔV equals the work per unit charge that an external agent must perform to move a test charge from A to B without a change in kinetic energy of the test charge.

Equation 25.3 defines a potential difference only. That is, only *differences* in V are meaningful. The electric potential function is often taken to be zero at some convenient point. We arbitrarily set the potential to be zero for a point that is infinitely remote from the charges producing the electric field. With this choice, we can say that the *electric potential at an arbitrary point equals the work required per unit charge to bring a positive test charge from infinity to that point.* Thus, if we take $V_A = 0$ at infinity in Equation 25.3, then the potential at any point P is

$$V_P = -\int_{\infty}^{P} \mathbf{E} \cdot d\mathbf{s} \qquad (25.4)$$

In reality, V_P represents the potential difference between the point P and a point at infinity. (Equation 25.4 is a special case of Eq. 25.3.)

Since potential difference is a measure of energy per unit charge, the SI unit of potential is joules per coulomb, defined to be equal to a unit called the **volt (V)**:

$$1\,V \equiv 1\,J/1\,C$$

Definition of a volt

That is, 1 J of work must be done to take a 1-C charge through a potential difference of 1 V. Equation 25.3 shows that the potential difference also has units of electric field times distance. From this, it follows that the SI unit of electric field (N/C) can also be expressed as volts per meter:

$$\frac{N}{C} = \frac{V}{m}$$

A unit of energy commonly used in atomic and nuclear physics is the **electron volt (eV)**, which is defined as *the energy that an electron (or proton) gains or loses by moving through a potential difference of 1 V.* Since $1\,V = 1\,J/1\,C$ and since the fundamental charge is equal to 1.60×10^{-19} C, we see that the electron volt (eV) is related to the joule as follows:

The electron volt

$$1\,eV = 1.60 \times 10^{-19}\,C \cdot V = 1.60 \times 10^{-19}\,J \qquad (25.5)$$

For instance, an electron in the beam of a typical television picture tube (or cathode ray tube) has a speed of 5.0×10^7 m/s. This corresponds to a kinetic energy of 1.1×10^{-15} J, which is equivalent to 7.1×10^3 eV. Such an electron has to be accelerated from rest through a potential difference of 7.1 kV to reach this speed.

25.2 POTENTIAL DIFFERENCES IN A UNIFORM ELECTRIC FIELD

In this section, we describe the potential difference between any two points in a uniform electric field. The potential difference is independent of the path between these two points; that is, the work done in taking a test charge from point A to point B is the same along all paths. This confirms that a static, uniform electric field is conservative.

First, consider a uniform electric field directed along the negative y axis, as in Figure 25.1a. Let us calculate the potential difference between two points, A and B, separated by a distance d, where d is measured parallel to the field lines. If we apply Equation 25.3 to this situation, we get

$$V_B - V_A = \Delta V = -\int_{A}^{B} \mathbf{E} \cdot d\mathbf{s} = -\int_{A}^{B} E \cos 0° \, ds = -\int_{A}^{B} E \, ds$$

Since E is constant, it can be removed from the integral sign, giving

$$\Delta V = -E \int_{A}^{B} ds = -Ed \qquad (25.6)$$

Potential difference in a uniform **E** field

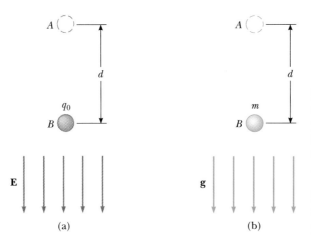

FIGURE 25.1 (a) When the electric field **E** is directed downward, point *B* is at a lower electric potential than point *A*. A positive test charge that moves from *A* to *B* loses electric potential energy. (b) A mass *m* moving downward in the direction of the gravitational field **g** loses gravitational potential energy.

The minus sign results from the fact that point *B* is at a lower potential than point *A*; that is, $V_B < V_A$. *Electric field lines always point in the direction of decreasing electric potential,* as in Figure 25.1a.

Now suppose that a test charge q_0 moves from *A* to *B*. The change in its potential energy can be found from Equations 25.3 and 25.6:

$$\Delta U = q_0 \, \Delta V = -q_0 E d \tag{25.7}$$

From this result, we see that if q_0 is positive, ΔU is negative. This means that *an electric field does work on a positive charge when the positive charge moves in the direction of the electric field.* (This is analogous to the work done by the gravitational field on a falling mass, as in Fig. 25.1b.) If a positive test charge is released from rest in this electric field, it experiences an electric force $q_0 \mathbf{E}$ in the direction of **E** (downward in Fig. 25.1a). Therefore, it accelerates downward, gaining kinetic energy. *As the charged particle gains kinetic energy, the field loses an equal amount of potential energy.*

If the test charge q_0 is negative, then ΔU is positive and the situation is reversed. *A negative charge gains electric potential energy when it moves in the direction of the electric field.* If a negative charge is released from rest in the field **E**, it accelerates in a direction opposite the electric field.

Now consider the more general case of a charged particle moving between any two points in a uniform electric field directed along the *x* axis, as in Figure 25.2. If **s** represents the displacement vector between points *A* and *B*, Equation 25.3 gives

$$\Delta V = -\int_A^B \mathbf{E} \cdot d\mathbf{s} = -\mathbf{E} \cdot \int_A^B d\mathbf{s} = -\mathbf{E} \cdot \mathbf{s} \tag{25.8}$$

where again we are able to remove **E** from the integral since it is constant. Further, the change in potential energy of the charge is

$$\Delta U = q_0 \, \Delta V = -q_0 \mathbf{E} \cdot \mathbf{s} \tag{25.9}$$

Finally, our results show that all points in a plane perpendicular to a uniform electric field are at the same potential. This can be seen in Figure 25.2, where the potential difference $V_B - V_A$ is equal to $V_C - V_A$. Therefore, $V_B = V_C$.

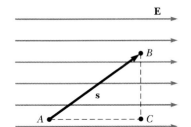

FIGURE 25.2 A uniform electric field directed along the positive *x* axis. Point *B* is at a lower potential than point *A*. Points *B* and *C* are at the *same* potential.

An equipotential surface

The name **equipotential surface** is given to any surface consisting of a continuous distribution of points having the same electric potential.

The line *CB* in Figure 25.2 is actually the cross-section of an equipotential surface, which in this case is a plane perpendicular to the electric field. Note that since $\Delta U = q_0 \Delta V$, no work is done in moving a test charge between any two points on an equipotential surface. The equipotential surfaces of a uniform electric field consist of a family of planes all perpendicular to the field. Equipotential surfaces for fields with other symmetries are described in later sections.

CONCEPTUAL EXAMPLE 25.1

If a proton is released from rest in a uniform electric field, does the electric potential increase or decrease? What about its electric potential energy?

Reasoning The proton moves in the direction of the electric field to a position of lower potential and lower potential energy. The decrease in electric potential energy is accompanied by an equal increase in kinetic energy as required by the principle of conservation of energy. An electron moves in the direction opposite to the electric field so its electric potential increases, but the electric potential energy decreases.

EXAMPLE 25.2 The Electric Field Between Two Parallel Plates of Opposite Charge

A 12-V battery is connected between two parallel plates as in Figure 25.3. The separation between the plates is 0.30 cm, and the electric field is assumed to be uniform. (This assumption is reasonable if the plate separation is small relative to the plate size and if we do not consider points near the edges of the plates.) Find the magnitude of the electric field between the plates.

Solution The electric field is directed from the positive plate toward the negative plate. We see that the positive plate is at a higher potential than the negative plate. Note that the potential difference between plates must equal the potential difference between the battery terminals. This can be understood by noting that all points on a conductor in equilibrium are at the same potential,[1] and hence there is no potential difference between a terminal of the battery and any portion of the plate to which it is connected. Therefore, the magnitude of the electric field between the plates is

$$ E = \frac{|V_B - V_A|}{d} = \frac{12\ \text{V}}{0.30 \times 10^{-2}\ \text{m}} = 4.0 \times 10^3\ \text{V/m} $$

This configuration, which is called a *parallel-plate capacitor,* is examined in more detail in the next chapter.

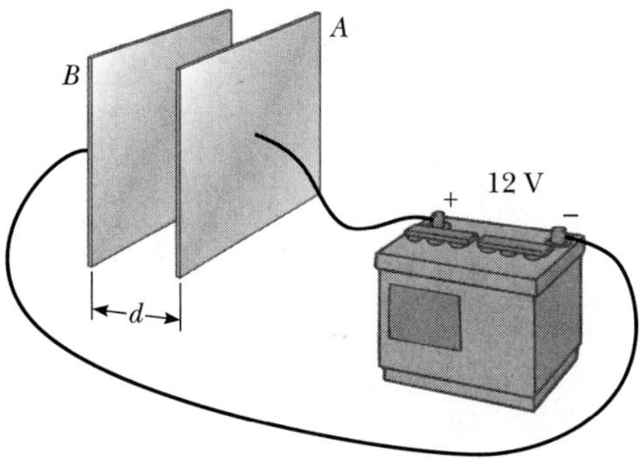

FIGURE 25.3 (Example 25.2) A 12-V battery connected to two parallel plates. The electric field between the plates has a magnitude given by the potential difference divided by the plane separation *d*.

[1] The electric field vanishes within a conductor in electrostatic equilibrium, and so the path integral $\int \mathbf{E} \cdot d\mathbf{s}$ between any two points within the conductor must be zero. A fuller discussion of this point is given in Section 25.6.

EXAMPLE 25.3 Motion of a Proton in a Uniform Electric Field

A proton is released from rest in a uniform electric field of magnitude 8.0×10^4 V/m directed along the positive *x* axis (Fig. 25.4). The proton undergoes a displacement of 0.50 m in the direction of **E**. (a) Find the change in the electric potential between the points *A* and *B*.

Solution From Equation 25.6 we have

$$ \Delta V = -Ex = -\left(8.0 \times 10^4\ \frac{\text{V}}{\text{m}}\right)(0.50\ \text{m}) $$

$$ = -4.0 \times 10^4\ \text{V} $$

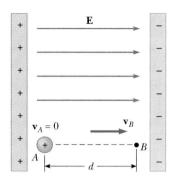

FIGURE 25.4   (Example 25.3) A proton accelerates from A to B in the direction of the electric field.

This negative result tells us that the electric potential of the proton decreases as it moves from A to B.

(b) Find the change in potential energy of the proton for this displacement.

Solution

$$\Delta U = q_0\,\Delta V = e\,\Delta V$$
$$= (1.6 \times 10^{-19}\,\text{C})(-4.0 \times 10^4\,\text{V})$$
$$= -6.4 \times 10^{-15}\,\text{J}$$

The negative sign here means that the potential energy of the proton decreases as it moves in the direction of the electric field. This makes sense since as the proton accelerates in the direction of the field, it gains kinetic energy and at the same time (the field) loses electrical potential energy (energy is conserved).

Exercise   Apply the principle of energy conservation to find the speed of the proton after it has moved 0.50 m, starting from rest.

Answer 2.77×10^6 m/s.

25.3   ELECTRIC POTENTIAL AND POTENTIAL ENERGY DUE TO POINT CHARGES

Consider an isolated positive point charge q (Fig. 25.5). Recall that such a charge produces an electric field that is radially outward from the charge. In order to find the electric potential at a field point located a distance r from the charge, we begin with the general expression for the potential difference:

$$V_B - V_A = -\int_A^B \mathbf{E}\cdot d\mathbf{s}$$

Since the electric field due to the point charge is given by $\mathbf{E} = k_e q\hat{\mathbf{r}}/r^2$, where $\hat{\mathbf{r}}$ is a unit vector directed from the charge to the field point, the quantity $\mathbf{E}\cdot d\mathbf{s}$ can be expressed as

$$\mathbf{E}\cdot d\mathbf{s} = k_e\frac{q}{r^2}\hat{\mathbf{r}}\cdot d\mathbf{s}$$

The dot product $\hat{\mathbf{r}}\cdot d\mathbf{s} = ds\cos\theta$, where θ is the angle between $\hat{\mathbf{r}}$ and $d\mathbf{s}$ as in Figure 25.5. Furthermore, note that $ds\cos\theta$ is the projection of $d\mathbf{s}$ onto r, so that $ds\cos\theta = dr$. That is, any displacement of the charge $d\mathbf{s}$ produces a change dr in the magnitude of $\mathbf{r}$. With these substitutions, we find that $\mathbf{E}\cdot d\mathbf{s} = (k_e q/r^2)\,dr$, so that the expression for the potential difference becomes

$$V_B - V_A = -\int E_r\,dr = -k_e q\int_{r_A}^{r_B}\frac{dr}{r^2} = \frac{k_e q}{r}\Big]_{r_A}^{r_B}$$

$$V_B - V_A = k_e q\left[\frac{1}{r_B} - \frac{1}{r_A}\right] \tag{25.10}$$

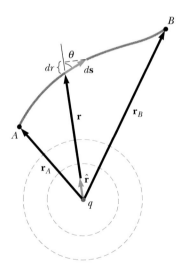

FIGURE 25.5   The potential difference between points A and B due to a point charge q depends *only* on the initial and final radial coordinates, r_A and r_B, respectively. The two dashed circles represent cross-sections of spherical equipotential surfaces.

The integral of $\mathbf{E}\cdot d\mathbf{s}$ is *independent* of the path between A and B—as it must be, because the electric field of a point charge is a conservative field. Furthermore, Equation 25.10 expresses the important result that the potential difference between any two points A and B depends only on the radial coordinates r_A and r_B. It is customary to choose the reference of potential to be zero at $r_A = \infty$. (This is quite natural because then $V \propto 1/r_A$ and as $r_A \rightarrow \infty$, $V \rightarrow 0$.) With this choice, the electric potential due to a point charge at any distance r from the charge is

$$V = k_e \frac{q}{r} \qquad (25.11)$$

Electric potential of a point charge

From this we see that V is constant on any spherical surface when the point charge is at its center. Hence, we conclude that *the equipotential surfaces (surfaces on which V remains constant) for an isolated point charge consist of a family of spheres concentric with the charge*, as shown in Figure 25.5. Note that the blue dashed lines in Figure 25.5 are cross-sections of spherical equipotential surfaces that are perpendicular to the lines of electric force, as was the case for a uniform electric field.

The electric potential of two or more point charges is obtained by applying the superposition principle. That is, the total potential at some point P due to several point charges is the sum of the potentials due to the individual charges. For a group of charges, we can write the total potential at P in the form

$$V = k_e \sum_i \frac{q_i}{r_i} \qquad (25.12)$$

The electric potential of several point charges

where the potential is again taken to be zero at infinity and r_i is the distance from the point P to the charge q_i. Note that the sum in Equation 25.12 is an algebraic sum of scalars rather than a vector sum (which is used to calculate the electric field of a group of charges). Thus, it is much easier to evaluate V than to evaluate $\mathbf{E}$.

We now consider the potential energy of interaction of a system of charged particles. If V_1 is the electric potential at a point P due to charge q_1, then the work required to bring a second charge q_2 from infinity to the point P without acceleration is $q_2 V_1$. By definition, this work equals the potential energy U of the two-particle system when the particles are separated by a distance r_{12} (Fig. 25.6). Therefore, we can express the potential energy as

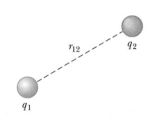

$$U = q_2 V_1 = k_e \frac{q_1 q_2}{r_{12}} \qquad (25.13)$$

FIGURE 25.6   If two point charges are separated by a distance r_{12}, the potential energy of the pair of charges is given by $kq_1 q_2 / r_{12}$.

Note that if the charges are of the same sign, U is positive.[2] This is consistent with the fact that like charges repel, and so positive work must be done on the system to bring the two charges near one another. If the charges are of opposite sign, the force is attractive and U is negative. This means that negative work must be done to bring the unlike charges near one another.

If there are more than two charged particles in the system, the total potential energy can be obtained by calculating U for every pair of charges and summing the terms algebraically. As an example, the total potential energy of the three charges shown in Figure 25.7 is

$$U = k_e \left(\frac{q_1 q_2}{r_{12}} + \frac{q_1 q_3}{r_{13}} + \frac{q_2 q_3}{r_{23}} \right) \qquad (25.14)$$

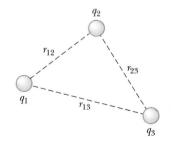

Physically, we can interpret this as follows: Imagine that q_1 is fixed at the position shown in Figure 25.7, but q_2 and q_3 are at infinity. The work required to bring q_2

FIGURE 25.7   Three point charges are fixed at the positions shown. The potential energy of this system of charges is given by Equation 25.14.

---

[2] The expression for the electric potential energy for two point charges, Equation 25.13, is of the *same* form as the gravitational potential energy of two point masses given by $Gm_1 m_2 / r$ (Chapter 14). The similarity is not surprising in view of the fact that both are derived from an inverse-square force law.

from infinity to its position near q_1 is $k_e q_1 q_2 / r_{12}$, which is the first term in Equation 25.14. The last two terms in Equation 25.14 represent the work required to bring q_3 from infinity to its position near q_1 and q_2. (The result is independent of the order in which the charges are transported.)

CONCEPTUAL EXAMPLE 25.4

If the electric potential at some point is zero, can you conclude that there are no charges in the vicinity of that point?

Reasoning   No. Suppose there are several charges in the vicinity of the point in question. If some charges are positive and some negative, their contributions to the potential at the point may cancel. For example, the electric potential at the midpoint of two equal but opposite charges is zero.

EXAMPLE 25.5   The Potential Due to Two Point Charges

A 2.00-μC point charge is located at the origin, and a second point charge of -6.00 μC is located on the y axis at the position (0, 3.00) m, as in Figure 25.8a. (a) Find the total electric potential due to these charges at the point P, whose coordinates are (4.00, 0) m.

Solution   For two charges, the sum in Equation 25.12 gives

$$V_P = k_e \left(\frac{q_1}{r_1} + \frac{q_2}{r_2} \right)$$

In this example, $q_1 = 2.00$ μC, $r_1 = 4.00$ m, $q_2 = -6.00$ μC, and $r_2 = 5.00$ m. Therefore, V_P reduces to

$$V_P = 8.99 \times 10^9 \frac{\text{N} \cdot \text{m}^2}{\text{C}^2} \left(\frac{2.00 \times 10^{-6} \text{ C}}{4.00 \text{ m}} - \frac{6.00 \times 10^{-6} \text{ C}}{5.00 \text{ m}} \right)$$

$$= -6.29 \times 10^3 \text{ V}$$

(b) How much work is required to bring a 3.00-μC point charge from infinity to the point P?

Solution

$$W = q_3 V_P = (3.00 \times 10^{-6} \text{ C})(-6.29 \times 10^3 \text{ V})$$

$$= -18.9 \times 10^{-3} \text{ J}$$

The negative sign means that work is done by the field on the charge as it is displaced from infinity to P. Therefore, positive work would have to be done by an external agent to remove the charge from P back to infinity.

Exercise   Find the total potential energy of the system of three charges in the configuration shown in Figure 25.8b.

Answer -5.48×10^{-2} J.

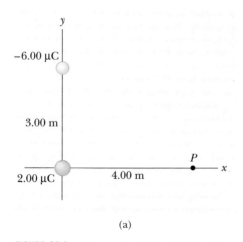

(a)

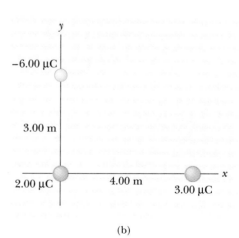

(b)

FIGURE 25.8   (Example 25.5) (a) The electric potential at the point P due to the two point charges q_1 and q_2 is the algebraic sum of the potentials due to the individual charges. (b) What is the potential energy of the system of three charges?

25.4 OBTAINING E FROM THE ELECTRIC POTENTIAL

The electric field **E** and the potential V are related as shown in Equation 25.3. Both quantities are determined by a specific charge distribution. We now show how to calculate the electric field if the electric potential is known in a certain region.

From Equation 25.3 we can express the potential difference dV between two points a distance ds apart as

$$dV = -\mathbf{E} \cdot d\mathbf{s} \qquad (25.15)$$

If the electric field has only one component, E_x, then $\mathbf{E} \cdot d\mathbf{s} = E_x\, dx$. Therefore, Equation 25.15 becomes $dV = -E_x\, dx$, or

$$E_x = -\frac{dV}{dx} \qquad (25.16)$$

That is, the electric field is equal to the negative of the derivative of the potential with respect to some coordinate. Note that the potential change is zero for any displacement perpendicular to the electric field. This is consistent with the notion of equipotential surfaces being perpendicular to the field, as in Figure 25.9a.

If the charge distribution has spherical symmetry, where the charge density depends only on the radial distance r, then the electric field is radial. In this case, $\mathbf{E} \cdot d\mathbf{s} = E_r\, dr$, and so we can express dV in the form $dV = -E_r\, dr$. Therefore,

$$E_r = -\frac{dV}{dr} \qquad (25.17)$$

For example, the potential of a point charge is $V = k_e q/r$. Since V is a function of r only, the potential function has spherical symmetry. Applying Equation 25.17, we find that the electric field due to the point charge is $E_r = k_e q/r^2$, a familiar result. Note that the potential changes only in the radial direction, not in a direction

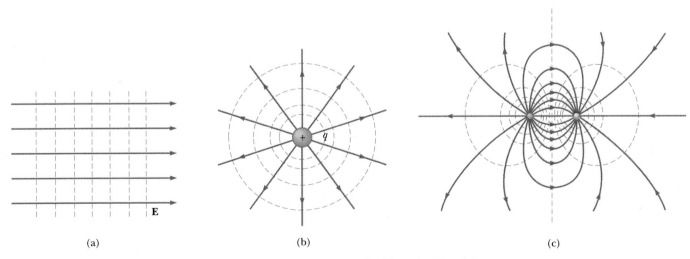

(a)   (b)   (c)

FIGURE 25.9 Equipotential surfaces (dashed blue lines) and electric field lines (red lines) for (a) a uniform electric field produced by an infinite sheet of charge, (b) a point charge, and (c) an electric dipole. In all cases, the equipotential surfaces are *perpendicular* to the electric field lines at every point. A more accurate computer-generated plot is shown on page 717.

perpendicular to r. Thus V (like E_r) is a function only of r. Again, this is consistent with the idea that *equipotential surfaces are perpendicular to field lines*. In this case the equipotential surfaces are a family of spheres concentric with the spherically symmetric charge distribution (Figure 25.9b).

The equipotential surfaces for an electric dipole are sketched in Figure 25.9c. When a test charge is displaced by a vector $d\mathbf{s}$ that lies within any equipotential surface, then by definition $dV = -\mathbf{E} \cdot d\mathbf{s} = 0$. This shows that the equipotential surfaces must *always be perpendicular* to the electric field lines.

In general, the electric potential is a function of all three spatial coordinates. If $V(r)$ is given in terms of the rectangular coordinates, the electric field components E_x, E_y, and E_z can readily be found from $V(x, y, z)$:

$$E_x = -\frac{\partial V}{\partial x} \qquad E_y = -\frac{\partial V}{\partial y} \qquad E_z = -\frac{\partial V}{\partial z}$$

In these expressions, the derivatives are called *partial derivatives*. In the operation $\partial V / \partial x$, we take a derivative with respect to x while y and z are held constant.[3] For example, if $V = 3x^2 y + y^2 + yz$, then

$$\frac{\partial V}{\partial x} = \frac{\partial}{\partial x}(3x^2 y + y^2 + yz) = \frac{\partial}{\partial x}(3x^2 y) = 3y \frac{d}{dx}(x^2) = 6xy$$

[3] In vector notation, $\mathbf{E}$ is often written

$$\mathbf{E} = -\nabla V = -\left(\mathbf{i}\frac{\partial}{\partial x} + \mathbf{j}\frac{\partial}{\partial y} + \mathbf{k}\frac{\partial}{\partial z} \right) V \text{ where } \nabla \text{ is called the } \textit{gradient operator.}$$

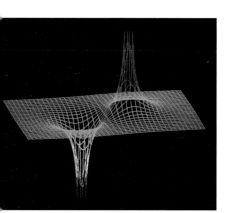

Computer-generated plot of the electric potential associated with an electric dipole. The changes lie in the horizontal plane, at the centers of the potential spikes. The contour lines help visualize the size of the potential, whose values are plotted vertically. *(Richard Megna 1990, Fundamental Photographs)*

CONCEPTUAL EXAMPLE 25.6

If the electric potential is constant in some region, what can you conclude about the electric field in that region? If the electric field is zero in some region, what can you say about the electric potential in that region?

Reasoning If V is constant in some region, the electric field must be zero in that region. In a one-dimensional situation, $E = -dV/dx$, so if $V = $ constant, $E = 0$. Likewise, if $E = 0$ in some region, one can only conclude that V is a constant in that region.

EXAMPLE 25.7 The Electric Potential of a Dipole

An electric dipole consists of two equal and opposite charges separated by a distance $2a$, as in Figure 25.10. The dipole is along the x axis and is centered at the origin. Calculate the electric potential and the electric field at P.

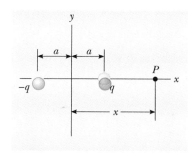

FIGURE 25.10 (Example 25.7) An electric dipole located on the x axis.

Solution

$$V = k_e \sum \frac{q_i}{r_i} = k_e \left(\frac{q}{x - a} - \frac{q}{x + a} \right) = \frac{2 k_e q a}{x^2 - a^2}$$

If P is far from the dipole, so that $x \gg a$, then a^2 can be neglected in the term $x^2 - a^2$ and V becomes

$$V \approx \frac{2 k_e q a}{x^2} \qquad (x \gg a)$$

Using Equation 25.16 and this result, we calculate the electric field at P:

$$E = -\frac{dV}{dx} = \frac{4 k_e q a}{x^3} \qquad \text{for } x \gg a$$

25.5 ELECTRIC POTENTIAL DUE TO CONTINUOUS CHARGE DISTRIBUTIONS

The electric potential due to a continuous charge distribution can be calculated in two ways. If the charge distribution is known, we can start with Equation 25.11 for the potential of a point charge. We then consider the potential due to a small charge element dq, treating this element as a point charge (Fig. 25.11). The potential dV at some point P due to the charge element dq is

$$dV = k_e \frac{dq}{r} \tag{25.18}$$

This simulator can be used to map the electric field lines and electric potential for an arbitrary collection of fixed point charges. After arranging these point charges in an appropriate manner, you will be able to map the electric fields and lines of equal potential for configurations such as line charges, charges on a ring, and geometries that you can create.

Mapping the Electric Field

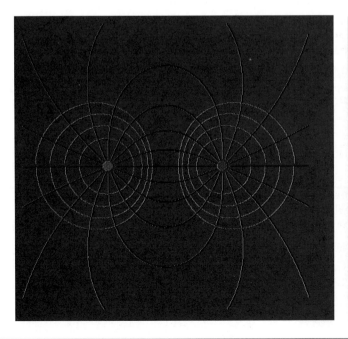

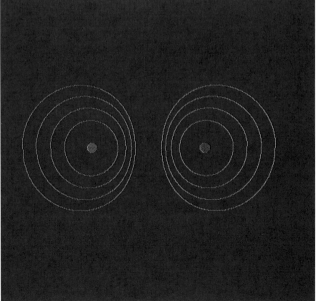

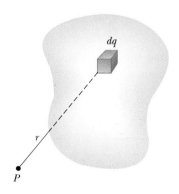

FIGURE 25.11   The electric potential at the point *P* due to a continuous charge distribution can be calculated by dividing the charged body into segments of charge *dq* and summing the potential contributions over all segments.

where *r* is the distance from the charge element to the point *P*. To get the total potential at *P*, we integrate Equation 25.18 to include contributions from all elements of the charge distribution. Since each element is, in general, at a different distance from *P* and since k_e is a constant, we can express *V* as

$$V = k_e \int \frac{dq}{r} \qquad (25.19)$$

In effect, we have replaced the sum in Equation 25.12 with an integral. Note that this expression for *V* uses a particular reference: The potential is taken to be zero when *P* is infinitely far from the charge distribution.

The second method for calculating the potential of a continuous charge distribution makes use of Equation 25.3. This procedure is useful when the electric field is already known from other considerations, such as Gauss's law. If the charge distribution is highly symmetric, we first evaluate **E** at any point using Gauss's law and then substitute the value obtained into Equation 25.3 to determine the potential difference between any two points. We then choose *V* to be zero at some convenient point. Let us illustrate both methods with several examples.

EXAMPLE 25.8   Potential Due to a Uniformly Charged Ring

Find the electric potential at a point *P* located on the axis of a uniformly charged ring of radius *a* and total charge *Q*. The plane of the ring is chosen perpendicular to the *x* axis (Fig. 25.12).

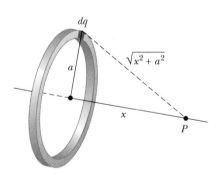

FIGURE 25.12   (Example 25.8) A uniformly charged ring of radius *a*, whose plane is perpendicular to the *x* axis. All segments of the ring are at the same distance from any axial point *P*.

Reasoning and Solution   Let us take *P* to be at a distance *x* from the center of the ring, as in Figure 25.12. The charge element *dq* is at a distance equal to $\sqrt{x^2 + a^2}$ from the point *P*. Hence, we can express *V* as

$$V = k_e \int \frac{dq}{r} = k_e \int \frac{dq}{\sqrt{x^2 + a^2}}$$

In this case, each element *dq* is at the same distance from *P*. Therefore, the term $\sqrt{x^2 + a^2}$ can be removed from the integral, and *V* reduces to

$$V = \frac{k_e}{\sqrt{x^2 + a^2}} \int dq = \frac{k_e Q}{\sqrt{x^2 + a^2}} \qquad (25.20)$$

The only variable in this expression for *V* is *x*. This is not surprising, since our calculation is valid only for points along the *x* axis, where *y* and *z* are both zero. From the symmetry, we see that along the *x* axis **E** can have only an *x* component. Therefore, we can use Equation 25.16 to find the electric field at *P*:

$$E_x = -\frac{dV}{dx} = -k_e Q \frac{d}{dx} (x^2 + a^2)^{-1/2}$$

$$= -k_e Q(-\tfrac{1}{2})(x^2 + a^2)^{-3/2}(2x)$$

$$= \frac{k_e Q x}{(x^2 + a^2)^{3/2}} \qquad (25.21)$$

This result agrees with that obtained by direct integration (see Example 23.11). Note that $E_x = 0$ at $x = 0$ (the center of the ring). Could you have guessed this from Coulomb's law?

Exercise   What is the electric potential at the center of the uniformly charged ring? What does the field at the center imply about this result?

Answer $V = k_e Q/a$ at $x = 0$. Because $E = 0$, *V* must have a maximum or minimum value; it is in fact a maximum.

EXAMPLE 25.9 Potential of a Uniformly Charged Disk

Find the electric potential along the axis of a uniformly charged disk of radius a and charge per unit area σ (Fig. 25.13).

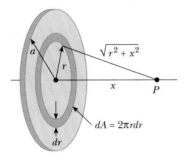

FIGURE 25.13 (Example 25.9) A uniformly charged disk of radius a, whose plane is perpendicular to the x axis. The calculation of the potential at an axial point P is simplified by dividing the disk into rings of area $2\pi r \, dr$.

Reasoning and Solution Again we choose the point P to be at a distance x from the center of the disk and take the plane of the disk perpendicular to the x axis. The problem is simplified by dividing the disk into a series of charged rings. The potential of each ring is given by Equation 25.20 in Example 25.8. Consider one such ring of radius r and width dr,

as indicated in Figure 25.13. The area of the ring is $dA = 2\pi r \, dr$ (the circumference multiplied by the width), and the charge on the ring is $dq = \sigma \, dA = \sigma 2\pi r \, dr$. Hence, the potential at the point P due to this ring is

$$dV = \frac{k_e \, dq}{\sqrt{r^2 + x^2}} = \frac{k_e \sigma 2\pi r \, dr}{\sqrt{r^2 + x^2}}$$

To find the *total* potential at P, we sum over all rings making up the disk. That is, we integrate dV from $r = 0$ to $r = a$:

$$V = \pi k_e \sigma \int_0^a \frac{2r \, dr}{\sqrt{r^2 + x^2}} = \pi k_e \sigma \int_0^a (r^2 + x^2)^{-1/2} 2r \, dr$$

This integral is of the form $u^n \, du$ and has the value $u^{n+1}/(n + 1)$, where $n = -\frac{1}{2}$ and $u = r^2 + x^2$. This gives the result

$$V = 2\pi k_e \sigma [(x^2 + a^2)^{1/2} - x] \qquad (25.22)$$

As in Example 25.8, we can find the electric field at any axial point by taking the negative of the derivative of V with respect to x:

$$E_x = -\frac{dV}{dx} = 2\pi k_e \sigma \left(1 - \frac{x}{\sqrt{x^2 + a^2}} \right) \qquad (25.23)$$

The calculation of V and E for an arbitrary point off the axis is more difficult to perform.

EXAMPLE 25.10 Potential of a Finite Line of Charge

A rod of length ℓ located along the x axis has a uniform charge per unit length and a total charge Q. Find the electric potential at a point P along the y axis a distance d from the origin (Figure 25.14).

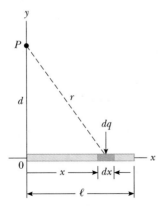

FIGURE 25.14 (Example 25.10) A uniform line charge of length ℓ located along the x axis. To calculate the potential at P, the line charge is divided into segments each of length dx, having a charge $dq = \lambda \, dx$.

Solution The element of length dx has a charge $dq = \lambda \, dx$, where λ is the charge per unit length, Q/ℓ. Since this element is a distance $r = \sqrt{x^2 + d^2}$ from P, we can express the potential at P due to this element as

$$dV = k_e \frac{dq}{r} = k_e \frac{\lambda \, dx}{\sqrt{x^2 + d^2}}$$

To get the total potential at P, we integrate this expression over the limits $x = 0$ to $x = \ell$. Noting that k_e, λ, and d are constants, we find that

$$V = k_e \lambda \int_0^\ell \frac{dx}{\sqrt{x^2 + d^2}} = k_e \frac{Q}{\ell} \int_0^\ell \frac{dx}{\sqrt{x^2 + d^2}}$$

This integral, found in most integral tables, has the value

$$\int \frac{dx}{\sqrt{x^2 + d^2}} = \ln(x + \sqrt{x^2 + d^2})$$

Evaluating V, we find that

$$V = \frac{k_e Q}{\ell} \ln\left(\frac{\ell + \sqrt{\ell^2 + d^2}}{d} \right) \qquad (25.24)$$

EXAMPLE 25.11   Potential of a Uniformly Charged Sphere

An insulating solid sphere of radius R has a uniform positive charge density with total charge Q (Fig. 25.15). (a) Find the electric potential at a point outside the sphere, that is, for $r > R$. Take the potential to be zero at $r = \infty$.

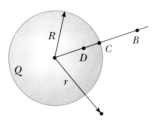

FIGURE 25.15   (Example 25.11) A uniformly charged insulating sphere of radius R and total charge Q. The electric potentials at points B and C are equivalent to those produced by a point charge Q located at the center of the sphere.

Solution   In Example 24.5, we found from Gauss's law that the magnitude of the electric field outside a uniformly charged sphere is

$$E_r = k_e \frac{Q}{r^2}   \text{(for } r > R)$$

where the field is directed radially outward when Q is positive. To obtain the potential at an exterior point, such as B in Figure 25.15, we substitute this expression for E into Equation 25.4. Since $\mathbf{E} \cdot d\mathbf{s} = E_r \, dr$ in this case, we get

$$V_B = -\int_\infty^r E_r \, dr = -k_e Q \int_\infty^r \frac{dr}{r^2}$$

$$V_B = k_e \frac{Q}{r}   \text{(for } r > R)$$

Note that the result is identical to that for the electric potential due to a point charge. Since the potential must be continuous at $r = R$, we can use this expression to obtain the potential at the surface of the sphere. That is, the potential at a point such as C in Figure 25.15 is

$$V_C = k_e \frac{Q}{R}   \text{(for } r = R)$$

(b) Find the potential at a point inside the charged sphere, that is, for $r < R$.

Solution   In Example 24.5 we found that the electric field inside a uniformly charged sphere is

$$E_r = \frac{k_e Q}{R^3} r   \text{(for } r < R)$$

We can use this result and Equation 25.3 to evaluate the potential difference $V_D - V_C$, where D is an interior point:

$$V_D - V_C = -\int_R^r E_r \, dr = -\frac{k_e Q}{R^3} \int_R^r r \, dr = \frac{k_e Q}{2R^3} (R^2 - r^2)$$

Substituting $V_C = k_e Q / R$ into this expression and solving for V_D, we get

$$V_D = \frac{k_e Q}{2R} \left(3 - \frac{r^2}{R^2} \right)   \text{(for } r < R)   (25.25)$$

At $r = R$, this expression gives a result for the potential that agrees with that for the potential at the surface, that is, V_C. A plot of V versus r for this charge distribution is given in Figure 25.16.

Exercise   What are the electric field and the electric potential at the center of a uniformly charged sphere?

Answer $E = 0$ and $V_0 = 3k_e Q/2R$.

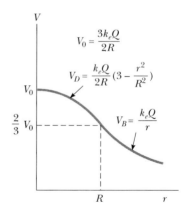

FIGURE 25.16   (Example 25.11) A plot of the electric potential V versus the distance r from the center of a uniformly charged, insulating sphere of radius R. The curve for V_D inside the sphere is parabolic and joins smoothly with the curve for V_B outside the sphere, which is a hyperbola. The potential has a maximum value V_0 at the center of the sphere.

25.6   POTENTIAL OF A CHARGED CONDUCTOR

In the previous chapter we found that when a solid conductor in equilibrium carries a net charge, the charge resides on the outer surface of the conductor. Furthermore, we showed that the electric field just outside the surface of a con-

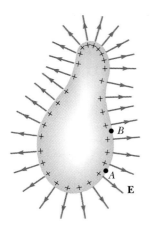

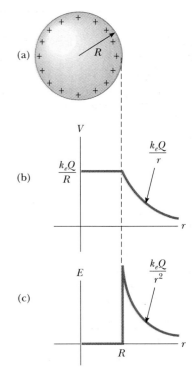

FIGURE 25.17 An arbitrarily shaped conductor with an excess positive charge. When the conductor is in electrostatic equilibrium, all of the charge resides at the surface, $E = 0$ inside the conductor, and the electric field just outside the conductor is perpendicular to the surface. The potential is constant inside the conductor and is equal to the potential at the surface. The surface charge density is nonuniform.

ductor in equilibrium is perpendicular to the surface while the field inside the conductor is zero. If the electric field had a component parallel to the surface, this would cause surface charges to move, creating a current and a nonequilibrium situation.

We now show that *every point on the surface of a charged conductor in equilibrium is at the same potential.* Consider two points A and B on the surface of a charged conductor, as in Figure 25.17. Along a surface path connecting these points, E is always perpendicular to the displacement ds; therefore, $\mathbf{E} \cdot d\mathbf{s} = 0$. Using this result and Equation 25.3, we conclude that the potential difference between A and B is necessarily zero:

$$V_B - V_A = -\int_A^B \mathbf{E} \cdot d\mathbf{s} = 0$$

This result applies to any two points on the surface. Therefore, V is constant everywhere on the surface of a charged conductor in equilibrium. That is,

> the surface of any charged conductor in equilibrium is an equipotential surface. Furthermore, since the electric field is zero inside the conductor, we conclude that the potential is constant everywhere inside the conductor and equal to its value at the surface.

FIGURE 25.18 (a) The excess charge on a conducting sphere of radius R is uniformly distributed on its surface. (b) The electric potential versus the distance r from the center of the charged conducting sphere. (c) The electric field intensity versus the distance r from the center of the charged conducting sphere.

Therefore, no work is required to move a test charge from the interior of a charged conductor to its surface. (Note that the potential is not zero inside the conductor even though the electric field is zero.)

For example, consider a solid metal sphere of radius R and total positive charge Q, as shown in Figure 25.18a. The electric field outside the charged sphere is $k_e Q/r^2$ and points radially outward. Following Example 25.11, we see that the potential at the interior and surface of the sphere must be $k_e Q/R$ relative to infinity. The potential outside the sphere is $k_e Q/r$. Figure 25.18b is a plot of the potential as a function of r, and Figure 25.18c shows the variations of the electric field with r.

When a net charge is placed on a spherical conductor, the surface charge density is uniform, as indicated in Figure 25.18a. However, if the conductor is nonspherical, as in Figure 25.17, the surface charge density is high where the radius of curvature is small and convex and low where the radius of curvature is

The surface of a charged conductor is an equipotential surface

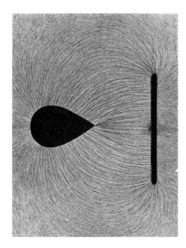

Electric field pattern of a charged conducting plate near an oppositely charged pointed conductor. Small pieces of thread suspended in oil align with the electric field lines. Note that the electric field is most intense near the pointed part of the conductor and at other points where the radius of curvature is small. *(Courtesy of Harold M. Waage, Princeton University)*

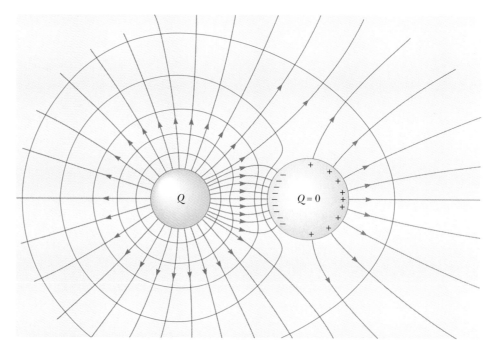

FIGURE 25.19 The electric field lines (in red) around two spherical conductors. The smaller sphere on the left has a net charge Q, and the sphere on the right has zero net charge. The blue lines represent the edges of the equipotential surfaces. *(From E. Purcell, Electricity and Magnetism, New York, McGraw-Hill, 1965, with permission of the Education Development Center, Inc.)*

small and concave. Since the electric field just outside a charged conductor is proportional to the surface charge density, σ, we see that *the electric field is large near points having small convex radii of curvature and reaches very high values at sharp points.*

Figure 25.19 shows the electric field lines around two spherical conductors, one with a net charge Q and a larger one with zero net charge. In this case, the surface charge density is not uniform on either conductor. The sphere having zero net charge has negative charges induced on its side that faces the charged sphere and positive charge on its side opposite the charged sphere. The blue lines in Figure 25.19 represent the boundaries of the equipotential surfaces for this charge configuration. Again, at all points the field lines are perpendicular to the conducting surfaces. Furthermore, the equipotential surfaces are perpendicular to the field lines at the boundaries of the conductor and everywhere else in space.

A Cavity Within a Conductor

Now consider a conductor of arbitrary shape containing a cavity as in Figure 25.20. Let us assume there are no charges inside the cavity. *The electric field inside the cavity must be zero,* regardless of the charge distribution on the outside surface of the conductor. Furthermore, the field in the cavity is zero even if an electric field exists outside the conductor.

In order to prove this point, we use the fact that every point on the conductor is at the same potential, and therefore any two points A and B on the surface of the cavity must be at the same potential. Now imagine that a field $\mathbf{E}$ exists in the cavity, and evaluate the potential difference $V_B - V_A$ defined by the expression

$$V_B - V_A = -\int_A^B \mathbf{E} \cdot d\mathbf{s}$$

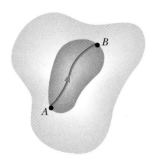

FIGURE 25.20 A conductor in electrostatic equilibrium containing an empty cavity. The electric field in the cavity is *zero*, regardless of the charge on the conductor.

If **E** is nonzero, we can always find a path between A and B for which $\mathbf{E} \cdot d\mathbf{s}$ is always a positive number, and so the integral must be positive. However, since $V_B - V_A = 0$, the integral must also be zero. This contradiction can be reconciled only if $\mathbf{E} = 0$ inside the cavity. Thus, we conclude that a cavity surrounded by conducting walls is a field-free region as long as there are no charges inside the cavity.

This result has some interesting applications. For example, it is possible to shield an electronic circuit or even an entire laboratory from external fields by surrounding it with conducting walls. Shielding is often necessary when performing highly sensitive electrical measurements.

Corona Discharge

A phenomenon known as **corona discharge** is often observed near sharp points of a conductor raised to a high potential. The discharge appears as a greenish glow visible to the naked eye. In this process, air becomes a conductor as a result of the ionization of air molecules in regions of high electric fields. At standard temperature and pressure, this discharge occurs at electric field strengths equal to or greater than approximately 3×10^6 V/m. Because air contains a small number of ions (produced, for example, by cosmic rays), a charged conductor attracts ions of the opposite sign from the air. Near sharp points, where the field is very high, the ions in the air are accelerated to high speeds. These energetic ions collide with other air molecules, producing more ions and an increase in conductivity of the air. The discharge of the conductor is often accompanied by a visible glow surrounding the sharp points.

EXAMPLE 25.12 Two Connected Charged Spheres

Two spherical conductors of radii r_1 and r_2 are separated by a distance much larger than the radius of either sphere. The spheres are connected by a conducting wire as in Figure 25.21. If the charges on the spheres in equilibrium are q_1 and q_2, respectively, find the ratio of the field strengths at the surfaces of the spheres.

Solution Since the spheres are connected by a conducting wire, they must both be at the same potential

$$V = k_e \frac{q_1}{r_1} = k_e \frac{q_2}{r_2}$$

Therefore, the ratio of charges is

$$(1) \qquad \frac{q_1}{q_2} = \frac{r_1}{r_2}$$

Since the spheres are very far apart, their surfaces are uniformly charged, and we can express the magnitude of the electric fields at their surfaces as

$$E_1 = k_e \frac{q_1}{r_1^2} \quad \text{and} \quad E_2 = k_e \frac{q_2}{r_2^2}$$

Taking the ratio of these two fields and making use of (1), we find that

$$(2) \qquad \boxed{\frac{E_1}{E_2} = \frac{r_2}{r_1}}$$

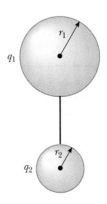

FIGURE 25.21 (Example 25.12) Two charged spherical conductors connected by a conducting wire. The spheres are at the *same* potential, V.

Hence, the field is more intense in the vicinity of the smaller sphere.

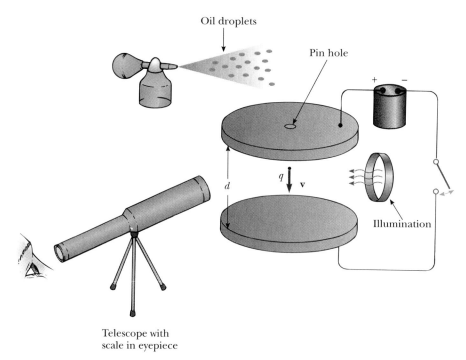

FIGURE 25.22   A schematic view of the Millikan oil-drop apparatus.

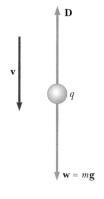

(a) Field off

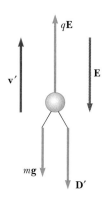

(b) Field on

FIGURE 25.23   The forces on a charged oil droplet in the Millikan experiment.

*25.7   THE MILLIKAN OIL-DROP EXPERIMENT

During the period 1909 to 1913, Robert A. Millikan (1868–1953) performed a brilliant set of experiments in which he measured the elementary charge on an electron, e, and demonstrated the quantized nature of the electronic charge. The apparatus used by Millikan, diagrammed in Figure 25.22, contains two parallel metal plates. Charged oil droplets from an atomizer are allowed to pass through a small hole in the upper plate. A light beam directed horizontally is used to illuminate the oil droplets, which are viewed by a telescope whose axis is at right angles to the light beam. When the droplets are viewed in this manner, they appear as shining stars against a dark background, and the rate of fall of individual drops may be determined.[4]

Let us assume a single drop having a mass m and carrying a charge q is being viewed, and that its charge is negative. If there is no electric field present between the plates, the two forces acting on the charge are the force of gravity, $m\mathbf{g}$, acting downward, and an upward viscous drag force $\mathbf{D}$, as indicated in Figure 25.23a. The drag force is proportional to the speed of the drop. When the drop reaches its terminal speed v, the two forces balance each other ($mg = D$).

Now suppose that an electric field is set up between the plates by connecting a battery such that the upper plate is at the higher potential. In this case, a third force $q\mathbf{E}$ acts on the charged drop. Since q is negative and $\mathbf{E}$ is downward, this electric force is directed upward as in Figure 25.23b. If this force is large enough, the drop moves upward and the drag force $\mathbf{D}'$ acts downward. When the upward

---

[4] At one time, the oil droplets were termed "Millikan's Shining Stars." Perhaps this description has lost its popularity because of the generations of physics students who have experienced hallucinations, near blindness, migraine headaches, and so forth while repeating this experiment!

electric force qE balances the sum of the force of gravity and the drag force, both acting downward, the drop reaches a new terminal speed v'.

With the field turned on, a drop moves slowly upward, typically at rates of hundredths of a centimeter per second. The rate of fall in the absence of a field is comparable. Hence, a single droplet with constant mass and radius may be followed for hours, alternately rising and falling, by simply turning the electric field on and off.

After making measurements on thousands of droplets, Millikan and his co-workers found that all droplets, to within about 1% precision, had a charge equal to some integer multiple of the elementary charge e:

$$q = ne \qquad n = 0, -1, -2, -3, \ldots$$

where $e = 1.60 \times 10^{-19}$ C. Millikan's experiment is conclusive evidence that charge is quantized. He was awarded the Nobel Prize in Physics in 1923 for this work.

*25.8   APPLICATIONS OF ELECTROSTATICS

The principles of electrostatics have been used in various applications, a few of which we briefly discuss in this section. Some of the more practical applications include electrostatic precipitators, used to reduce atmospheric pollution from coal-burning power plants, and xerography, the process that has revolutionized imaging process technology. Scientific applications of electrostatic principles include electrostatic generators for accelerating elementary charged particles and the field-ion microscope, which is used to image atoms on the surface of metallic samples.

The Van de Graaff Generator

In the previous chapter we described an experiment that demonstrates a method for transferring charge to a hollow conductor (the Faraday ice-pail experiment). When a charged conductor is placed in contact with the inside of a hollow conductor, all of the charge of the first conductor is transferred to the hollow conductor. In principle, the charge on the hollow conductor and its potential can be increased without limit by repeating the process.

In 1929, Robert J. Van de Graaff used this principle to design and build an electrostatic generator. This type of generator is used extensively in nuclear physics research. The basic idea is described in Figure 25.24. Charge is delivered continuously to a high-voltage electrode on a moving belt of insulating material. The high-voltage electrode is a hollow conductor mounted on an insulating column. The belt is charged at A by means of a corona discharge between comb-like metallic needles and a grounded grid. The needles are maintained at a positive potential of typically 10^4 V. The positive charge on the moving belt is transferred to the high-voltage electrode by a second comb of needles at B. Since the electric field inside the hollow conductor is negligible, the positive charge on the belt easily transfers to the high-voltage electrode, regardless of its potential. In practice, it is possible to increase the potential of the high-voltage electrode until electrical discharge occurs through the air. Since the "breakdown" electric field in air is equal to about 3×10^6 V/m, a sphere 1 m in radius can be raised to a maximum potential of 3×10^6 V. The potential can be increased further by increasing the radius of the hollow conductor and by placing the entire system in a container filled with high-pressure gas.

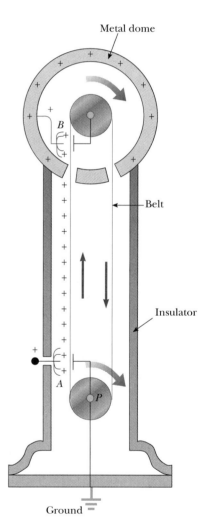

FIGURE 25.24   Schematic diagram of a Van de Graaff generator. Charge is transferred to the hollow conductor at the top by means of a moving belt. The charge is deposited on the belt at point A and is transferred to the hollow conductor at point B.

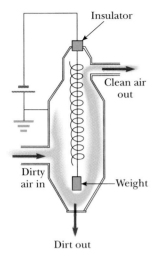

FIGURE 25.25 Schematic diagram of an electrostatic precipitator. The high negative voltage maintained on the central wire creates an electrical discharge in the vicinity of the wire.

Van de Graaff generators can produce potential differences as high as 20 million volts. Protons accelerated through such potential differences receive enough energy to initiate nuclear reactions between themselves and various target nuclei.

The Electrostatic Precipitator

One important application of electrical discharge in gases is a device called an *electrostatic precipitator*. This device is used to remove particulate matter from combustion gases, thereby reducing air pollution. They are especially useful in coal-burning power plants and in industrial operations that generate large quantities of smoke. Current systems are able to eliminate more than 99% of the ash and dust (by weight) from the smoke.

Figure 25.25 shows the basic idea of the electrostatic precipitator. A high voltage (typically 40 kV to 100 kV) is maintained between a wire running down the center of a duct and the outer wall, which is grounded. The wire is maintained at a negative potential with respect to the walls, and so the electric field is directed toward the wire. The electric field near the wire reaches high enough values to cause a corona discharge around the wire and the formation of positive ions, electrons, and negative ions, such as O_2^-. As the electrons and negative ions are accelerated toward the outer wall by the nonuniform electric field, the dirt particles in the streaming gas become charged by collisions and ion capture. Since most of the charged dirt particles are negative, they are also drawn to the outer wall by the electric field. By periodically shaking the duct, the particles fall loose and are collected at the bottom.

In addition to reducing the level of particulate matter in the atmosphere, the electrostatic precipitator recovers valuable materials from the stack in the form of metal oxides.

Xerography

The process of xerography is widely used for making photocopies of letters, documents, and other printed materials. The basic idea for the process was developed by Chester Carlson, for which he was granted a patent in 1940. The one idea that makes the process unique is the use of a photoconductive material to form an image. (A photoconductor is a material that is a poor conductor in the dark but becomes a good electrical conductor when exposed to light.)

The process is illustrated in Figure 25.26. First, the surface of a plate or drum is coated with a thin film of the photoconductive material (usually selenium or some compound of selenium), and the photoconductive surface is given a positive electrostatic charge in the dark. The page to be copied is then projected onto the charged surface. The photoconducting surface becomes conducting only in areas where light strikes. In these areas, the light produces charge carriers in the photoconductor, which neutralize the positively charged surface. However, the charges remain on those areas of the photoconductor not exposed to light, leaving a latent (hidden) image of the object in the form of a positive surface charge distribution.

Next, a negatively charged powder called a *toner* is dusted onto the photoconducting surface. The charged powder adheres only to those areas of the surface that contain the positively charged image. At this point, the image becomes visible. The image is then transferred to the surface of a sheet of positively charged paper.

Finally, the toner material is "fixed" to the surface of the paper through the application of heat. This results in a permanent copy of the original.

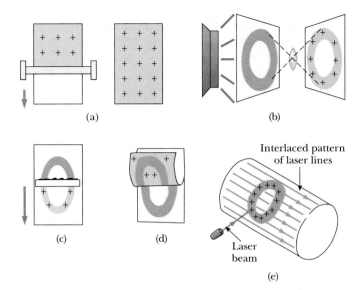

(a)

(b)

(c)

(d)

Interlaced pattern
of laser lines

Laser
beam

(e)

FIGURE 25.26 The xerographic process: (a) The photoconductive surface is positively charged. (b) Through the use of a light source and lens, an image is formed on the surface in the form of hidden positive charges. (c) The surface containing the image is covered with a charged powder, which adheres only to the image area. (d) A piece of paper is placed over the surface and given a charge. This transfers the visible image to the paper, which is then heat-treated to "fix" the powder to the paper. (e) A laser printer operates similarly except the image is produced by turning a laser beam on and off as it sweeps across the selenium-coated drum.

The Field-Ion Microscope

In Section 25.6 we pointed out that the electric field intensity can be very high in the vicinity of a sharp point on a charged conductor. A device that makes use of this intense field is the *field-ion microscope,* invented in 1956 by E. W. Mueller of the Pennsylvania State University. The purpose of this device is to look at individual atoms on the surface of a very small specimen.

The basic construction is shown in Figure 25.27. A specimen to be studied is fabricated from a fine wire, and a sharp needle-shaped tip is formed, usually by etching the wire in an acid. Typically, the diameter of the tip is about 0.1 μm. The specimen is placed at the center of an evacuated glass tube containing a fluorescent screen. Next, a small amount of helium is introduced into the vessel. A very high voltage (potential difference) is applied between the specimen and the screen, producing a very intense electric field near the tip of the specimen. The helium atoms in the vicinity of this high-field region are ionized, stripped of an electron. This leaves the helium positively charged. The positively charged He^+ ions then accelerate to the negatively charged fluorescent screen. This results in a pattern on the screen that represents an image of the tip of the specimen.

It is important to cool the tip of the specimen to at least the temperature of liquid nitrogen to slow down the atoms and obtain pictures. Under the proper conditions (low specimen temperature and high vacuum), the images of the individual atoms on the surface of the sample are visible, and the atomic arrangement on the surface can be studied. Unfortunately, the high electric fields also set up large mechanical stresses near the tip of the specimen, which limits the application of the technique to strong metallic elements, such as tungsten and rhenium. Figure 25.28 represents a typical field-ion microscope pattern of a platinum crystal.

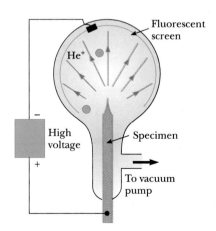

FIGURE 25.27 Schematic diagram of a field-ion microscope. The electric field is very intense at the tip of the needle-shaped specimen.

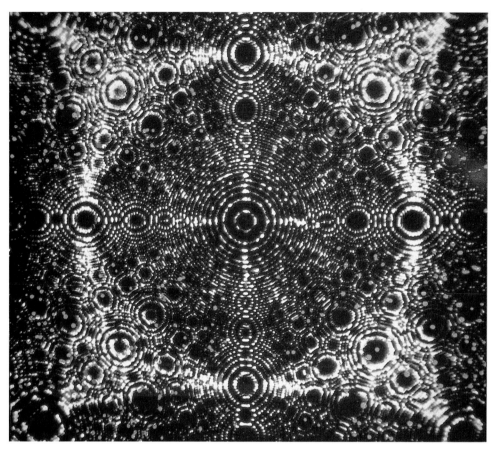

FIGURE 25.28 Field-ion microscope image of the surface of a platinum crystal with a magnification of 1 000 000×. Individual atoms can be seen on surface layers using this technique. *(Manfred Kage/Peter Arnold, Inc.)*

SUMMARY

When a positive test charge q_0 is moved between points A and B in an electric field **E**, the **change in the potential energy** is

$$\Delta U = -q_0 \int_A^B \mathbf{E} \cdot d\mathbf{s} \tag{25.1}$$

The **potential difference** ΔV between points A and B in an electric field **E** is defined as

$$\Delta V = \frac{\Delta U}{q_0} = -\int_A^B \mathbf{E} \cdot d\mathbf{s} \tag{25.3}$$

where the electric potential V is a scalar and has the units of J/C, where $1\,\text{J/C} \equiv 1\,\text{V}$.

The potential difference between two points A and B in a uniform electric field **E** is

$$\Delta V = -Ed \tag{25.6}$$

where d is the displacement in the direction parallel to **E**.

Equipotential surfaces are surfaces on which the electric potential remains constant. Equipotential surfaces are perpendicular to electric field lines. The potential due to a point charge q at any distance r from the charge is

$$V = k_e \frac{q}{r} \tag{25.11}$$

The potential due to a group of point charges is obtained by summing the potentials due to the individual charges. Since V is a scalar, the sum is a simple algebraic operation.

The **potential energy of a pair of point charges** separated by a distance r_{12} is

$$U = k_e \frac{q_1 q_2}{r_{12}} \tag{25.13}$$

This energy represents the work required to bring the charges from an infinite separation to the separation r_{12}. The potential energy of a distribution of point charges is obtained by summing terms like Equation 25.13 over all pairs of particles.

If the electric potential is known as a function of coordinates x, y, z, the components of the electric field can be obtained by taking the negative derivative of the potential with respect to the coordinates. For example, the x component of the electric field is

$$E_x = -\frac{dV}{dx} \tag{25.16}$$

The **electric potential due to a continuous charge distribution** is

$$V = k_e \int \frac{dq}{r} \tag{25.19}$$

Every point on the surface of a charged conductor in electrostatic equilibrium is at the same potential. Furthermore, the potential is constant everywhere inside the conductor and equal to its value at the surface. Table 25.1 lists potentials due to several charge distributions.

TABLE 25.1 Potentials Due to Various Charge Distributions

Charge Distribution	Electrical Potential	Location
Uniformly charged ring of radius a	$V = k_e \dfrac{Q}{\sqrt{x^2 + a^2}}$	Along the axis of the ring, a distance x from its center
Uniformly charged disk of radius a	$V = 2\pi k_e \sigma [(x^2 + a^2)^{1/2} - x]$	Along the axis of the disk, a distance x from its center
Uniformly charged, *insulating* solid sphere of radius R and total charge Q	$\begin{cases} V = k_e \dfrac{Q}{r} \\ V = \dfrac{k_e Q}{2R}\left(3 - \dfrac{r^2}{R^2}\right) \end{cases}$	$r \geq R$ $\qquad$ $r < R$

Problem-Solving Strategy and Hints
Calculating the Electric Potential

- When working problems involving electric potential, remember that potential is a scalar quantity and so there are no components to worry about. Therefore, when using the superposition principle to evaluate the electric potential at a point due to a system of point charges, you simply take the algebraic sum of the potentials due to each charge. However, you must keep track of signs. The potential for each positive charge ($V = k_e q/r$) is positive, while the potential for each negative charge is negative.

- Just as in mechanics, only *changes* in potential are significant; hence, the point where you choose the potential to be zero is arbitrary. When dealing with point charges or a finite-sized charge distribution, we usually define $V = 0$ to be at a point infinitely far from the charges. However, if the charge distribution itself extends to infinity, or if the problem concerns the potential difference between two charge distributions, some other nearby point must be selected as the reference point.

- The electric potential at some point P due to a continuous distribution of charge can be evaluated by dividing the charge distribution into infinitesimal elements of charge dq located at a distance r from the point P. You then treat this element as a point charge, so that the potential at P due to the element is $dV = k_e \, dq/r$. The total potential at P is obtained by integrating dV over the entire charge distribution. In performing the integration for most problems, it is necessary to express dq and r in terms of a single variable. In order to simplify the integration, it is important to give careful consideration of the geometry involved in the problem. You should review Examples 25.9 through 25.11 as guides for using this method.

- Another method that can be used to obtain the potential due to a finite continuous charge distribution is to start with the definition of the potential difference given by Equation 25.3. If E is known or can be obtained easily (say from Gauss's law), then the line integral of $\mathbf{E} \cdot d\mathbf{s}$ can be evaluated. An example of this method is given in Example 25.11.

- Once you know the electric potential at a point, it is possible to obtain the electric field at that point by remembering that the electric field is equal to the negative of the derivative of the potential with respect to some coordinate. Example 25.8 illustrates how to use this procedure.

QUESTIONS

1. Distinguish between electric potential and electrical potential energy.
2. A negative charge moves in the direction of a uniform electric field. Does the potential energy of the charge increase or decrease? Does it move to a position of higher or lower potential?
3. Give a physical explanation of the fact that the potential energy of a pair of like charges is positive whereas the potential energy of a pair of unlike charges is negative.
4. A uniform electric field is parallel to the x axis. In what direction can a charge be displaced in this field without any external work being done on the charge?
5. Explain why equipotential surfaces are always perpendicular to electric field lines.
6. Describe the equipotential surfaces for (a) an infinite line of charge and (b) a uniformly charged sphere.
7. Explain why, under static conditions, all points in a conductor must be at the same electric potential.

8. The electric field inside a hollow, uniformly charged sphere is zero. Does this imply that the potential is zero inside the sphere? Explain.

9. The potential of a point charge is defined to be zero at an infinite distance. Why can we not define the potential of an infinite line of charge to be zero at $r = \infty$?

10. Two charged conducting spheres of different radii are connected by a conducting wire as in Figure 25.21. Which sphere has the greater charge density?

11. What determines the maximum potential to which the dome of a Van de Graaff generator can be raised?

12. In what type of weather would a car battery be more likely to discharge and why?

13. Explain the origin of the glow sometimes observed around the cables of a high-voltage power line.

14. Why is it important to avoid sharp edges or points on conductors used in high-voltage equipment?

15. How would you shield an electronic circuit or laboratory from stray electric fields? Why does this work?

16. Why is it relatively safe to stay in an automobile with a metal body during a severe thunderstorm?

17. Walking across a carpet and then touching someone can result in a shock. Explain why this occurs.

PROBLEMS

Review Problem

A uniformly charged insulating sphere of radius R has a total positive charge Q. (a) Use Gauss's law to find the magnitude of the electric field at a point outside the sphere, that is, for $r > R$. (b) Use Gauss's law to find the magnitude of the electric field at a point inside the sphere, that is, for $r < R$. (c) Use the result to part (a) and find an expression for the electric potential at a point outside the sphere, taking the potential to be zero at $r = \infty$. (d) Use the results to (b) and (c) to find the electric potential at a point inside the sphere. (e) Sketch graphs of the electric field versus r and the electric potential versus r. (f) If a negative point charge $- q$ having mass m is located at an exterior point, what is the electric force on the charge? (g) When the negative point charge is at an exterior point, what is the potential energy of the system? (h) If the negative point charge is released from an exterior point, find its speed when it reaches the surface of the sphere.

Section 25.1   Potential Difference and Electric Potential

1. The gap between electrodes in a spark plug is 0.060 cm. To produce an electric spark in a gasoline-air mixture, an electric field of 3.0×10^6 V/m must be achieved. When starting the car, what minimum voltage must be supplied by the ignition circuit?

2. What change in potential energy does a 12-μC charge experience when it is moved between two points for which the potential difference is 65 V? Express the answer in electron volts.

3. (a) Calculate the speed of a proton that is accelerated from rest through a potential difference of 120 V. (b) Calculate the speed of an electron that is accelerated through the same potential difference.

4. Through what potential difference would an electron need to be accelerated for it to achieve a speed of 40% of the speed of light ($c = 3.0 \times 10^8$ m/s), starting from rest?

5. A deuteron (a nucleus that consists of one proton and one neutron) is accelerated through a 2.7-kV potential difference. (a) How much energy does it gain? (b) How fast is it going if it starts from rest?

6. What potential difference is needed to stop an electron having an initial speed of 4.2×10^5 m/s?

7. An ion accelerated through a potential difference of 115 V experiences an increase in kinetic energy of 7.37×10^{-17} J. Calculate the charge on the ion.

8. In a Van de Graaff accelerator a proton is accelerated through a potential difference of 14×10^6 V. Assuming that the proton starts from rest, calculate its (a) final kinetic energy in joules, (b) final kinetic energy in electron volts, and (c) final speed.

9. A positron has the same mass as an electron. When a positron is accelerated from rest between two points at a fixed potential difference, it acquires a speed that is 30% of the speed of light. What speed is achieved by a proton accelerated from rest between the same two points?

Section 25.2   Potential Differences in a Uniform Electric Field

10. Consider two points in an electric field. The potential at P_1 is $V_1 = - 30$ V, and the potential at P_2 is $V_2 = + 150$ V. How much work is done by an external force in moving a charge $q = - 4.7 \ \mu$C from P_2 to P_1?

11. How much work is done (by a battery, generator, or other source of electrical energy) in moving Avoga-

☐ indicates problems that have full solutions available in the Student Solutions Manual and Study Guide.

dro's number of electrons from an initial point where the electric potential is 9 V to a point where the potential is -5 V? (The potential in each case is measured relative to a common reference point.)

12. Two parallel plates are separated by 0.30 mm. If a 20-V potential difference is maintained between those plates, calculate the electric field strength in the region between them.

13. The magnitude of the electric field between two charged parallel plates separated by 1.8 cm is 2.4×10^4 N/C. Find the potential difference between the two plates. How much kinetic energy is gained by a deuteron in accelerating from the positive to the negative plate?

14. On planet Tehar, the gravitational field strength is the same as that on Earth but on Tehar there is also a strong downward electric field that is uniform close to the planet's surface. A 2.00-kg ball carrying a charge of 5.00 μC is thrown upward at 20.1 m/s and hits the ground after 4.10 s. What is the potential difference between the starting point and the top point of the trajectory?

14A. On planet Tehar, the gravitational field strength is the same as that on Earth but on Tehar there is also a strong downward electric field that is uniform close to the planet's surface. A ball of mass m carrying a charge q is thrown upward at a speed v and hits the ground after an interval t. What is the potential difference between the starting point and the top point of the trajectory?

15. An electron moving parallel to the x axis has an initial speed of 3.7×10^6 m/s at the origin. Its speed is reduced to 1.4×10^5 m/s at the point $x = 2.0$ cm. Calculate the potential difference between the origin and this point. Which point is at the higher potential?

16. A positron has the same charge as a proton but the same mass as an electron. Suppose a positron moves 5.2 cm in the direction of a uniform 480-V/m electric field. (a) How much potential energy does it gain or lose? (b) How much kinetic energy?

17. An electron in the beam of a typical television picture tube is accelerated through a potential difference of 20 kV before striking the face of the tube. (a) What is the energy of this electron, in electron volts, and what is its speed when it strikes the screen? (b) How much momentum is imparted to the screen by the electron?

18. A 4.00-kg block carrying a charge $Q = 50.0$ μC is connected to a spring for which $k = 100$ N/m. The block lies on a frictionless horizontal track, the system is immersed in a uniform electric field of magnitude $E = 5.00 \times 10^5$ V/m and is directed as in Figure P25.18. If the block is released from rest when the spring is unstretched (at $x = 0$), (a) by what max-

mum amount does the spring expand? (b) What will be the equilibrium position of the block? (c) Show that the block's motion is simple harmonic, and determine its period. (d) Repeat part (a) if the coefficient of kinetic friction between block and surface is 0.200.

18A. A block having mass m and charge Q is connected to a spring having constant k. The block lies on a frictionless horizontal track, the system is immersed in a uniform electric field of magnitude E and is directed as in Figure P25.18. If the block is released from rest when the spring is unstretched (at $x = 0$), (a) by what maximum amount does the spring expand? (b) What is the equilibrium position of the block? (c) Show that the block's motion is simple harmonic, and determine its period. (d) Repeat part (a) if the coefficient of kinetic friction between block and surface is μ.

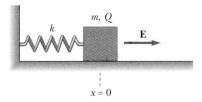

FIGURE P25.18

19. An insulating rod having linear charge density $\lambda = 40.0$ μC/m and linear mass density $\mu = 0.100$ kg/m is released from rest in a uniform electric field $E = 100$ V/m and directed perpendicular to the rod (Fig. P25.19). (a) Determine the speed of the rod after it has traveled 2.00 m. (b) How does your answer to part (a) change if the electric field is not perpendicular to the rod? Explain.

19A. An insulating rod having linear charge density λ and linear mass density μ is released from rest in a uniform electric field E and directed perpendicular to the rod (Fig. P25.19). (a) Determine the speed of the rod after it has traveled a distance d. (b) How does your answer to part (a) change if the electric field is not perpendicular to the rod? Explain.

20. A particle having charge $q = +2.0$ μC and mass $m = 0.01$ kg is connected to a string that is $L = 1.5$ m long and is tied to the pivot point P in Figure P25.20. The particle, string, and pivot point all lie on a horizontal table. The particle is released from rest when the string makes an angle $\theta = 60°$ with a uniform electric field of magnitude $E = 300$ V/m. Determine the speed of the particle when the string is parallel to the electric field (point a in Fig. P25.20).

20A. A particle having charge q and mass m in Figure P25.20 is connected to a string of length L and tied to

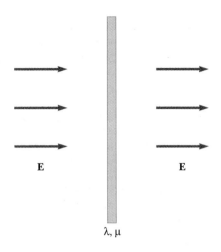

FIGURE P25.19

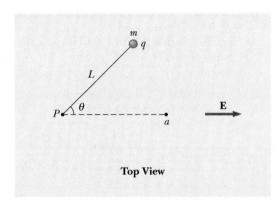

Top View

FIGURE P25.20

the pivot point *P*. The particle, string, and pivot point all lie on a horizontal table. The particle is released from rest when the string makes an angle θ with a uniform electric field of magnitude *E*. Determine the speed of the particle when the string is parallel to the electric field (point *a* in Fig. P25.20).

Section 25.3   Electric Potential and Potential Energy Due to Point Charges

(Note: Unless stated otherwise, assume a reference $V = 0$ at $r = \infty$.)

21. At what distance from a point charge of 8.0 μC does the electric potential equal 3.6×10^4 V?

22. A small spherical object carries a charge of 8.0 nC. At what distance from the center of the object is the potential equal to 100 V? 50 V? 25 V? Is the spacing of the equipotentials proportional to the change in V?

23. At a distance *r* away from a point charge *q*, the elec-

tric potential is $V = 400$ V and the magnitude of the electric field is $E = 150$ N/C. Determine the values of *q* and *r*.

24. Given two 2.00-μC charges, as in Figure P25.24, and a positive test charge $q = 1.28 \times 10^{-18}$ C at the origin, (a) what is the net force exerted on *q* by the two 2.00-μC charges? (b) What is the electric field at the origin due to the two 2.00-μC charges? (c) What is the electric potential at the origin due to the two 2.00-μC charges?

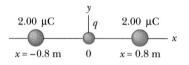

FIGURE P25.24

25. The electrostatic potential due to a set of point charges on a Cartesian grid is

$$V = \frac{36}{\sqrt{(x+1)^2 + y^2}} - \frac{45}{\sqrt{x^2 + (y-2)^2}}$$

where *V* is in volts. Determine the position and magnitude of all charges in this distribution.

26. A charge $+q$ is at the origin. A charge $-2q$ is at $x = 2.0$ m on the *x* axis. For what finite value(s) of *x* is (a) the electric field zero? (b) the electric potential zero?

27. The three charges in Figure P25.27 are at the vertices of an isosceles triangle. Calculate the electric potential at the midpoint of the base, taking $q = 7.00$ μC.

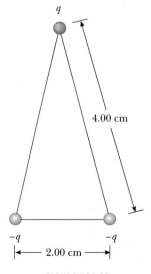

FIGURE P25.27

28. In Rutherford's famous scattering experiments that led to the planetary model of the atom, alpha parti-

cles (charge $+2e$, mass $= 6.6 \times 10^{-27}$ kg) were fired at a gold nucleus (charge $+79e$). An alpha particle initially very far from the gold nucleus is fired at 2.0×10^7 m/s directly toward the center of the nucleus. How close does the alpha particle get to this center before turning around?

29. Two point charges, $Q_1 = +5.00$ nC and $Q_2 = -3.00$ nC, are separated by 35.0 cm. (a) What is the potential energy of the pair? What is the significance of the algebraic sign of your answer? (b) What is the electric potential at a point midway between the charges?

30. An electron starts from rest 3.00 cm from the center of a uniformly charged insulating sphere of radius 2.00 cm and total charge of 1.00 nC. What is the speed of the electron when it reaches the surface of the sphere?

30A. An electron starts from rest a distance d from the center of a uniformly charged insulating sphere of radius R and total charge Q. If $d > R$, what is the speed of the electron when it reaches the surface of the sphere?

31. The Bohr model of the hydrogen atom states that the electron can exist only in certain allowed orbits. The radius of each Bohr orbit is $r = n^2(0.0529$ nm) where $n = 1, 2, 3, \ldots$. Calculate the electric potential energy of a hydrogen atom when the electron is in the (a) first allowed orbit, $n = 1$, (b) second allowed orbit, $n = 2$, and (c) when the electron has escaped from the atom, $r = \infty$. Express your answers in electron volts.

32. Calculate the energy required to assemble the array of charges shown in Figure P25.32, where $a = 0.20$ m, $b = 0.40$ m, and $q = 6.0$ μC.

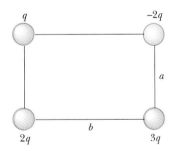

FIGURE P25.32

33. Show that the amount of work required to assemble four identical point charges of magnitude Q at the corners of a square of side s is $5.41 k_e Q^2/s$.

34. Two insulating spheres having radii 0.30 cm and 0.50 cm, masses 0.10 kg and 0.70 kg, and charges -2.0 μC and 3.0 μC are released from rest when their centers are separated by 1.0 m. (a) How fast is

each moving when they collide? (*Hint:* Consider conservation of energy and conservation of linear momentum.) (b) If the spheres are conductors, will the speeds calculated in part (a) be larger or smaller? Explain.

34A. Two insulating spheres having radii r_1 and r_2, masses m_1 and m_2, and charges $-q_1$ and q_2 are released from rest when their centers are separated by a distance d. (a) How fast is each moving when they collide? (*Hint:* Consider conservation of energy and conservation of linear momentum.) (b) If the spheres are conductors, will the speeds calculated in part (a) be larger or smaller? Explain.

35. Four identical particles each have charge $q = 0.50$ μC and mass 0.010 kg. They are released from rest at the vertices of a square of side 0.10 m. How fast is each charge moving when their distance from the center of the square doubles?

35A. Four identical particles each have charge q and mass m. They are released from rest at the vertices of a square of side L. How fast is each charge moving when their distance from the center of the square doubles?

36. How much work is required to assemble eight identical point charges, each of magnitude q, at the corners of a cube of side s?

Section 25.4   Obtaining E from the Electric Potential

37. An infinite sheet of charge that has a surface charge density of 25.0 nC/m^2 lies in the yz plane, passes through the origin, and is at a potential of 1.0 kV. A long wire having a linear charge density of 80.0 nC/m lies parallel to the y axis and intersects the x axis at $x = 3.0$ m. (a) Determine, as a function of x, the potential along the x axis between wire and sheet. (b) What is the potential energy of a 2.0-nC charge placed at $x = 0.8$ m?

37A. An infinite sheet of charge with a surface charge density σ lies in the yz plane, passes through the origin, and is at a potential V_0. A long wire having a linear charge density λ lies parallel to the y axis and intersects the x axis at $x = d$. (a) Determine the potential along the x axis between the wire and the sheet as a function of x. (b) What is the potential energy of a charge q placed at $x = d/4$?

38. The electric potential in a certain region is $V = 4xz - 5y + 3z^2$ V. Find the magnitude of the electric field at $(+2, -1, +3)$, where all distances are in meters.

39. Over a certain region of space, the electric potential is $V = 5x - 3x^2y + 2yz^2$. Find the expressions for the x, y, and z components of the electric field over

this region. What is the magnitude of the field at the point P, which has coordinates $(1, 0, -2)$ m?

40. The electric potential in a certain region is $V = ax^2 + bx + c$, where $a = 12$ V/m^2, $b = -10$ V/m, and $c = 62$ V. Determine (a) the magnitude and direction of the electric field at $x = +2.0$ m and (b) the position where the electric field is zero.

41. The potential in a region between $x = 0$ and $x = 6.0$ m is $V = a + bx$ where $a = 10$ V and $b = -7.0$ V/m. Determine (a) the potential at $x = 0$, 3.0 m, and 6.0 m and (b) the magnitude and direction of the electric field at $x = 0$, 3.0 m, and 6.0 m.

42. The electric potential inside a charged spherical conductor of radius R is given by $V = k_e Q/R$ and outside the potential is given by $V = k_e Q/r$. Using $E_r = -dV/dr$, derive the electric field (a) inside and (b) outside this charge distribution.

43. When an uncharged conducting sphere of radius a is placed at the origin of an xyz coordinate system that lies in an initially uniform electric field $\mathbf{E} = E_0\mathbf{k}$, the resulting electrostatic potential is $V(x, y, z) = V_0$ for points inside the sphere, and

$$V(x, y, z) = V_0 - E_0 z + \frac{E_0 a^3 z}{(x^2 + y^2 + z^2)^{3/2}}$$

for points outside the sphere, where V_0 is the (constant) electrostatic potential on the conductor. Use this equation to determine the x, y, and z components of the resulting electric field.

44. An uncharged, infinitely long conducting cylinder of radius a is placed in an initially uniform electric field $\mathbf{E} = E_0\mathbf{i}$, such that the cylinder's axis lies along the z axis. The resulting electrostatic potential is $V(x, y, z) = V_0$ for points inside the cylinder, and

$$V(x, y, z) = V_0 - E_0 x + \frac{E_0 a^2 x}{x^2 + y^2}$$

for points outside the cylinder, where V_0 is the (constant) electrostatic potential on the conductor. Use this equation to determine the x, y, and z components of the resulting electric field.

Section 25.5 Electric Potential Due to Continuous Charge Distributions

45. Consider a ring of radius R with total charge Q spread uniformly over its perimeter. What is the potential difference between the point at the center of the ring and a point on its axis a distance $2R$ from the center?

46. Consider two coaxial rings of 30.0-cm radius and separated by 30.0 cm. (a) Calculate the electric potential at a point on their common axis midway between the two rings, assuming that each ring carries a uniformly distributed charge of 5.00 μC. (b) What is the potential at this point if the two rings carry equal and opposite charges?

47. A rod of length L (Fig. P25.47) lies along the x axis with its left end at the origin and has a nonuniform charge density $\lambda = \alpha x$ (where α is a positive constant). (a) What are the units of α? (b) Calculate the electric potential at A.

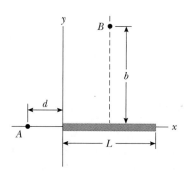

FIGURE P25.47

48. For the arrangement described in the previous problem, calculate the electric potential at point B that lies on the perpendicular bisector of the rod a distance b above the x axis.

49. Calculate the electric potential at point P on the axis of the annulus shown in Figure P25.49, which has a uniform charge density σ.

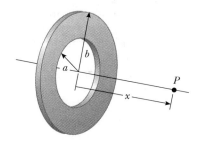

FIGURE P25.49

50. A wire that has a uniform linear charge density λ is bent into the shape shown in Figure P25.50. Find the electrical potential at point O.

FIGURE P25.50

Section 25.6 Potential of a Charged Conductor

51. How many electrons should be removed from an initially uncharged spherical conductor of radius 0.300 m to produce a potential of 7.50 kV at the surface?

52. Calculate the surface charge density, σ (in C/m^2), for a solid spherical conductor of radius $R = 0.250$ m if the potential 0.500 m from the center of the sphere is 1.30 kV.

53. A spherical conductor has a radius of 14.0 cm and charge of 26.0 μC. Calculate the electric field and the electric potential (a) $r = 10.0$ cm, (b) $r = 20.0$ cm, and (c) $r = 14.0$ cm from the center.

54. Two concentric spherical conducting shells of radii $a = 0.400$ m and $b = 0.500$ m are connected by a thin wire as in Figure P25.54. If a total charge $Q = 10.0$ μC is placed on the system, how much charge settles on each sphere?

54A. Two concentric spherical conducting shells of radii a and b are connected by a thin wire as in Figure P25.54. If a total charge Q is placed on the system, how much charge settles on each sphere?

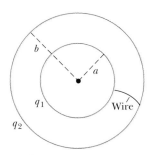

FIGURE P25.54

55. Two charged spherical conductors are connected by a long conducting wire, and a charge of 20.0 μC is placed on the combination. (a) If one sphere has a radius of 4.00 cm and the other has a radius of 6.00 cm, what is the electric field near the surface of each sphere? (b) What is the electrical potential of each sphere?

56. An egg-shaped conductor has a charge of 43 nC placed on its surface. It has a total surface area of 38 cm². What are (a) the average surface charge density, (b) the electric field inside the conductor, and (c) the (average) electric field just outside the conductor?

*Section 25.8   Applications of Electrostatics

57. Consider a Van de Graaff generator with a 30.0-cm-diameter dome operating in dry air. (a) What is the maximum potential of the dome? (b) What is the maximum charge on the dome?

58. (a) Calculate the largest amount of charge possible on the surface of a Van de Graaff generator that has a 40.0-cm-diameter dome surrounded by air. (b) What is the potential of this dome when it carries this charge?

59. What charge must be placed on the surface of a Van de Graaff generator, whose dome has a radius of 15 cm, to produce a spark across a 10-cm air gap?

ADDITIONAL PROBLEMS

60. Three point charges having magnitudes of 8.00 μC, -3.00 μC, and 5.00 μC are located at corners of a triangle whose sides are each 9.00 cm long. Calculate the electric potential at the center of this triangle.

61. At a certain distance from a point charge, the magnitude of the electric field is 500 V/m and the electric potential is -3.00 kV. (a) What is the distance to the charge? (b) What is the magnitude of the charge?

62. Two parallel plates having equal but opposite charge are separated by 12.0 cm. Each plate has a surface charge density of 36.0 nC/m^2. A proton is released from rest at the positive plate. Determine (a) the potential difference between the plates, (b) the energy of the proton when it reaches the negative plate, (c) the speed of the proton just before it strikes the negative plate, (d) the acceleration of the proton, and (e) the force on the proton. (f) From the force, find the electric field intensity and show that it is equal to the electric field intensity found from the charge densities on the plates.

63. A Van de Graaff generator is operated until the spherical dome has a measured potential of 6.0×10^5 V and an electric field of maximum value for a dome surrounded by air (3.0×10^6 V/m). Determine (a) the charge on the dome and (b) the radius of the dome.

64. (a) Consider a uniformly charged cylindrical shell having total charge Q, radius R, and height h. Determine the electrostatic potential at a point a distance d from the right side of the cylinder as in Figure P25.64. (*Hint:* Use the result of Example 25.8 by treating the cylinder as a collection of ring charges.) (b) Use the result of Example 25.9 to solve the same problem for a solid cylinder.

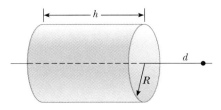

FIGURE P25.64

65. Equal charges ($q = 2.0$ μC) are placed at 30° intervals around the equator of a sphere that has a radius of 1.2 m. What is the electric potential (a) at the center of the sphere and (b) at its north pole?

66. The charge distribution shown in Figure P25.66 is referred to as a linear quadrupole. (a) Show that the potential at a point on the x axis where $x > d$ is

$$V = \frac{2k_e Q d^2}{x^3 - xd^2}$$

(b) Show that the expression obtained in (a) when $x \gg d$ reduces to

$$V = \frac{2k_e Q d^2}{x^3}$$

66A. Use the exact result from Problem 66a to evaluate the potential for the linear quadrupole at $x = 3d$ if $d = 2.00$ mm and $Q = 3.00$ μC. Compare this answer with what you obtain when you use the approximate result (Problem 66b) valid when $x \gg d$.

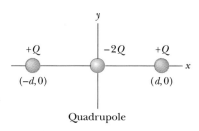

Quadrupole

FIGURE P25.66

67. (a) Use the exact result from Problem 66 to find the electric field at any point along the axis of the linear quadrupole for $x > d$. (b) Evaluate E at $x = 3d$ if $d = 2.00$ mm and $Q = 3.00$ μC.

68. A ring of radius 0.20 m carries a uniformly distributed positive charge, as in Figure P25.68. The linear charge density of the ring is 0.10 μC/m, and an electron is located 0.10 above the plane of the ring on the central perpendicular. If this electron is released from rest, what is its speed when it reaches the center of the ring?

68A. A ring of radius R carries a uniformly distributed positive charge, as in Figure P25.68. The linear charge density of the ring is λ, and an electron is located a distance d above the plane of the ring on the central perpendicular axis. If this electron is released from rest, what is its speed when it reaches the center of the ring?

69. Two point charges of equal magnitude are located along the y axis equal distances above and below the x axis, as in Figure P25.69. (a) Plot a graph of the potential at points along the x axis over the interval $-3a < x < 3a$. You should plot the potential in units of $k_e Q / a$. (b) Let the charge located at $-a$ be negative and plot the potential along the y axis over the interval $-4a < y < 4a$.

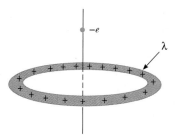

FIGURE P25.68

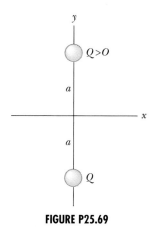

FIGURE P25.69

70. The liquid-drop model of the nucleus suggests that high-energy oscillations of certain nuclei can split the nucleus into two unequal fragments plus a few neutrons. The fragments acquire kinetic energy from their mutual Coulomb repulsion. Calculate the electric potential energy (in electron volts) of two spherical fragments from a uranium nucleus having the following charges and radii: $38e$ and 5.5×10^{-15} m; $54e$ and 6.2×10^{-15} m. Assume that the charge is distributed uniformly throughout the volume of each spherical fragment and that their surfaces are initially in contact at rest. (The electrons surrounding the nucleus can be neglected.)

71. Two identical raindrops, each carrying surplus electrons on its surface to give a net charge $-q$ on each, collide and form a single drop of larger size. Before the collision, the characteristics of each drop are as follows: (a) surface charge density σ_0, (b) electric field $\mathbf{E}_0$ at the surface, (c) electric potential V_0 at the surface (where $V = 0$ at $r = \infty$). For the combined drop, find these three quantities in terms of their original values.

72. Use the results to Example 25.11 and $E_r = -dV/dr$ to derive the electric field (a) inside and (b) outside a uniformly charged insulating sphere.

73. Calculate the work that must be done to charge a spherical shell of radius R to a total charge Q.

74. A point charge q is located at $x = -R$, and a point charge $-2q$ is located at the origin. Prove that the equipotential surface that has zero potential is a sphere centered at $(-4R/3, 0, 0)$ and having a radius $r = 2R/3$.

75. From Gauss's law, the electric field set up by a uniform line of charge is

$$\mathbf{E} = \left(\frac{\lambda}{2\pi\epsilon_0 r}\right)\hat{\mathbf{r}}$$

where $\hat{\mathbf{r}}$ is a unit vector pointing radially away from the line and λ is the charge per meter along the line. Derive an expression for the potential difference between $r = r_1$ and $r = r_2$.

76. Consider two thin, conducting, spherical shells as in Figure P25.76. The inner shell has a radius $r_1 = 15$ cm and a charge of 10 nC. The outer shell has a radius $r_2 = 30$ cm and a charge of -15 nC. Find (a) the electric field $\mathbf{E}$ and (b) the electric potential V in regions A, B, and C, with $V = 0$ at $r = \infty$.

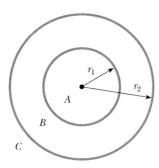

FIGURE P25.76

77. The x axis is the symmetry axis of a uniformly charged ring of radius R and charge Q (Fig. P25.77). A point charge Q of mass M is located at the center of the ring. When it is displaced slightly, the point charge accelerates along the x axis to infinity. Show that the ultimate speed of the point charge is

$$v = \left(\frac{2k_e Q^2}{MR}\right)^{1/2}$$

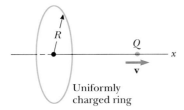

FIGURE P25.77

78. The thin, uniformly charged rod shown in Figure P25.78 has a linear charge density λ. Find an expression for the electric potential at P.

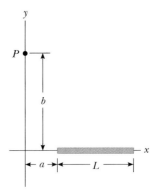

FIGURE P25.78

79. It is shown in Example 25.10 that the potential at a point P a distance d above one end of a uniformly charged rod of length ℓ lying along the x axis is

$$V = \frac{k_e Q}{\ell} \ln\left(\frac{\ell + \sqrt{\ell^2 + d^2}}{d}\right)$$

Use this result to derive an expression for the y component of the electric field at P. (*Hint:* Replace d with y.)

80. Figure P25.80 shows several equipotential lines each labeled by its potential in volts. The distance between the lines of the square grid represents 1 cm. (a) Is the magnitude of the field bigger at A or at B? Why? (b) What is $\mathbf{E}$ at B? (c) Represent what the field looks like by drawing at least eight field lines.

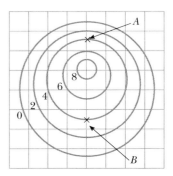

FIGURE P25.80

81. A dipole is located along the y axis as in Figure P25.81. (a) At a point P, which is far from the dipole $(r \gg a)$, the electric potential is

$$V = k_e \frac{p\cos\theta}{r^2}$$

where $p = 2qa$. Calculate the radial component of the associated electric field, E_r, and the perpendicular component, E_θ. Note that $E_\theta = -\dfrac{1}{r}\left(\dfrac{\partial V}{\partial \theta}\right)$. Do these results seem reasonable for $\theta = 90°$ and $0°$? for $r = 0$? (b) For the dipole arrangement shown, express V in terms of rectangular coordinates using $r = (x^2 + y^2)^{1/2}$ and

$$\cos \theta = \frac{y}{(x^2 + y^2)^{1/2}}$$

Using these results and taking $r \gg a$, calculate the field components E_x and E_y.

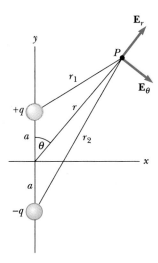

FIGURE P25.81

82. A disk of radius R has a nonuniform surface charge density $\sigma = Cr$, where C is a constant and r is measured from the center of the disk (Fig. P25.82). Find (by direct integration) the potential at P.

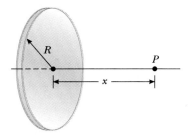

FIGURE P25.82

83. A solid sphere of radius R has a uniform charge density ρ and total charge Q. Derive an expression for its total electric potential energy. (*Hint:* Imagine that the sphere is constructed by adding successive layers

of concentric shells of charge $dq = (4\pi r^2 \, dr)\rho$ and use $dU = V \, dq$.)

84. A Geiger-Müller counter is a radiation detector that essentially consists of a hollow cylinder (the cathode) of inner radius r_a and a coaxial cylindrical wire (the anode) of radius r_b (Fig. P25.84). The charge per unit length on the anode is λ, while the charge per unit length on the cathode is $-\lambda$. (a) Show that the magnitude of the potential difference between the wire and the cylinder in the sensitive region of the detector is

$$V = 2k_e\lambda \ln\left(\frac{r_a}{r_b}\right)$$

(b) Show that the magnitude of the electric field over that region is given by

$$E = \frac{V}{\ln(r_a/r_b)}\left(\frac{1}{r}\right)$$

where r is the distance from the center of the anode to the point where the field is to be calculated.

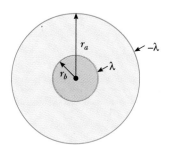

FIGURE P25.84

85. Three identical charges lie at the vertices of an equilateral triangle having sides 2.000 m long (Fig. P25.85). Locate positions of electrostatic equilibrium within the triangle.

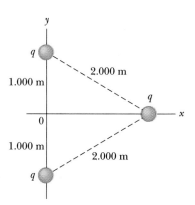

FIGURE P25.85

SPREADSHEET PROBLEMS

S1. Spreadsheet 25.1 calculates the electrical potential in the two-dimensional region around two charges. The region is divided into a 10 × 10 grid. The upper left corner of the grid corresponds to $x = 1.0$ m, $y = 1.0$ m, and the lower-right corner corresponds to $x = 10$ m, $y = 10$ m. The two charges can be placed anywhere in this grid. The first two tables calculate the distances from each charge to each grid point. The spreadsheet then calculates the electric potential at each grid point. Place charges of $+2.0$ μC at $x = 3.0$ m, $y = 5.0$ m and $x = 7.0$ m, $y = 5.0$ m. Print out the electric potential matrix. The location of the point charges will appear on the grid in the cells denoted by *ERR* (in Lotus 1-2-3) or *#DIV/0* (in Excel) since the potential is infinite at the location of the point charges. Sketch by hand the equipotential lines for $V = 20$ kV, 15 kV, and 10 kV. Sketch in a representative set of electric-field lines. (*Hint:* By adjusting the cell width on the spreadsheet and the printer line spacing, you can get the grid to print out approximately as a square.)

S2. Repeat Problem S1 with one charge replaced by -2.0 μC. Print out the electric potential matrix. Sketch the equipotential lines for $V = \pm 20$ kV, ± 15 kV, and ± 10 kV. Sketch in a representative set of electric-field lines.

S3. Place two charges anywhere in the grid in Problem S1. Choose any values for the charges. Print out the electric potential matrix. Sketch representative equipotentials and electric-field lines.

S4. Modify Spreadsheet 25.1 to include additional charges. Choose locations and values for each charge. Sketch the equipotentials and the electric-field lines. Place a row of charges together. Are the field lines for this case uniform? If not, why not?

S5. Spreadsheet 14.1 calculates the gravitational potential energy of a mass moving along the x axis in the gravitational field of four fixed point masses. Rework this spreadsheet to calculate the electrical potential along the x axis for four fixed point charges at the same locations as the four point masses. Find the electric field on the x axis as well. (*Hint:* $GM_1 m$ must be replaced by $k_e Q_1$, and so forth.) Investigate various choices for the charges and their locations.

CHAPTER 26

Capacitance and Dielectrics

Electrical discharge visible in a section of the Particle Beam Fusion Accelerator II, the nation's most powerful x-ray source, at Sandia National Laboratories. The discharges are due to air breakdown at the surface of the water that covers this section. At the center of the machine, high-energy electrons are converted to x-rays, which are used to determine their effect on weapons systems and other components. *(Courtesy of Sandia National Laboratories. Photo by Walter Dickenman)*

This chapter is concerned with the properties of capacitors, which are devices that store charge. Capacitors are commonly used in a variety of electrical circuits. For instance, they are used (1) to tune the frequency of radio receivers, (2) as filters in power supplies, (3) to eliminate sparking in automobile ignition systems, and (4) as energy-storing devices in electronic flash units.

A capacitor basically consists of two conductors separated by an insulator. We shall see that the capacitance of a given device depends on its geometry and on the material separating the charged conductors, called a *dielectric*.

26.1 DEFINITION OF CAPACITANCE

Consider two conductors having a potential difference V between them. Let us assume that the conductors have equal and opposite charges as in Figure 26.1. Such a combination of two conductors is called a **capacitor**. The potential differ-

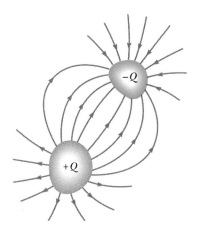

FIGURE 26.1 A capacitor consists of two conductors electrically isolated from each other and their surroundings. Once the capacitor is charged, the two conductors carry equal but opposite charges.

ence V is proportional to the magnitude of the charge Q on the capacitor.[1]

> The **capacitance**, C, of a capacitor is defined as the ratio of the magnitude of the charge on either conductor to the magnitude of the potential difference between them:

$$C \equiv \frac{Q}{V} \tag{26.1}$$

Note that by definition *capacitance is always a positive quantity*. Furthermore, since the potential difference increases as the stored charge increases, the ratio Q/V is constant for a given capacitor. Therefore, the capacitance of a device is a measure of its ability to store charge and electrical potential energy.

From Equation 26.1, we see that capacitance has the SI unit coulomb per volt. The SI unit of capacitance is the **farad** (F), in honor of Michael Faraday:

$$[\text{Capacitance}] = 1 \text{ F} = \frac{1 \text{ C}}{1 \text{ V}}$$

The farad is a very large unit of capacitance. In practice, typical devices have capacitances ranging from microfarads to picofarads. As a practical note, capacitors are often labeled mF for microfarads and mmF for micromicrofarads (picofarads).

As we show in the next section, the capacitance of a device depends, among other things, on the geometrical arrangement of the conductors. To illustrate this point, let us calculate the capacitance of an isolated spherical conductor of radius R and charge Q. (The second conductor can be taken as a concentric hollow conducting sphere of infinite radius.) Since the potential of the sphere is simply $k_e Q/R$ (where $V = 0$ at infinity), its capacitance is

$$C = \frac{Q}{V} = \frac{Q}{k_e Q/R} = \frac{R}{k_e} = 4\pi\epsilon_0 R \tag{26.2}$$

This shows that the capacitance of an isolated charged sphere is proportional to its radius and is independent of both the charge and the potential difference. For example, an isolated metallic sphere of radius 0.15 m has a capacitance of

$$C = 4\pi\epsilon_0 R = 4\pi(8.85 \times 10^{-12} \text{ C}^2/\text{N} \cdot \text{m}^2)(0.15 \text{ m}) = 17 \text{ pF}$$

26.2 CALCULATION OF CAPACITANCE

The capacitance of a pair of oppositely charged conductors can be calculated in the following manner. A charge of magnitude Q is assumed, and the potential difference is calculated using the techniques described in the previous chapter. One then simply uses $C = Q/V$ to evaluate the capacitance. As you might expect, the calculation is relatively easy to perform if the geometry of the capacitor is simple.

Let us illustrate this with three geometries that we are familiar with, namely, two parallel plates, two coaxial cylinders, and two concentric spheres. In these

---

[1] The proportionality between the potential difference and charge on the conductors can be proved from Coulomb's law or by experiment.

examples, we assume that the charged conductors are separated by a vacuum. The effect of a dielectric material placed between the conductors is treated in Section 26.5.

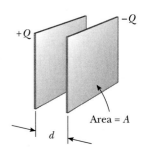

The Parallel-Plate Capacitor

Two parallel plates of equal area A are separated by a distance d as in Figure 26.2. One plate has a charge Q, the other, charge $-Q$. The charge per unit area on either plate is $\sigma = Q/A$. If the plates are very close together (compared with their length and width), we can neglect edge effects and assume that the electric field is uniform between the plates and zero elsewhere. According to Example 24.8, the electric field between the plates is

$$E = \frac{\sigma}{\epsilon_0} = \frac{Q}{\epsilon_0 A}$$

FIGURE 26.2 A parallel-plate capacitor consists of two parallel plates each of area A, separated by a distance d. When the capacitor is charged, the plates carry equal charges of opposite sign.

where ϵ_0 is the permittivity of free space. The potential difference between the plates equals Ed; therefore,

$$V = Ed = \frac{Qd}{\epsilon_0 A}$$

Substituting this result into Equation 26.1, we find that the capacitance is

$$C = \frac{Q}{V} = \frac{Q}{Qd/\epsilon_0 A}$$

$$C = \frac{\epsilon_0 A}{d} \qquad (26.3)$$

That is, *the capacitance of a parallel-plate capacitor is proportional to the area of its plates and inversely proportional to the plate separation.*

EXAMPLE 26.1 Parallel-Plate Capacitor

A parallel-plate capacitor has an area $A = 2.00 \times 10^{-4}$ m^2 and a plate separation $d = 1.00$ mm. Find its capacitance.

Solution   From Equation 26.3, we find

$$C = \epsilon_0 \frac{A}{d} = \left(8.85 \times 10^{-12} \frac{C^2}{N \cdot m^2}\right)\left(\frac{2.00 \times 10^{-4} \text{ m}^2}{1.00 \times 10^{-3} \text{ m}}\right)$$

$$= 1.77 \times 10^{-12} \text{ F} = \boxed{1.77 \text{ pF}}$$

Exercise   If the plate separation is increased to 3.00 mm, find the capacitance.

Answer   0.590 pF.

As you can see from the definition of capacitance, $C = Q/V$, the amount of charge a given capacitor is able to store for a given potential difference across its plates increases as the capacitance increases. Therefore, it seems reasonable that a capacitor constructed from plates having a large area should be able to store a large charge. The amount of charge needed to produce a given potential difference increases with decreasing plate separation.

A careful inspection of the electric field lines for a parallel-plate capacitor

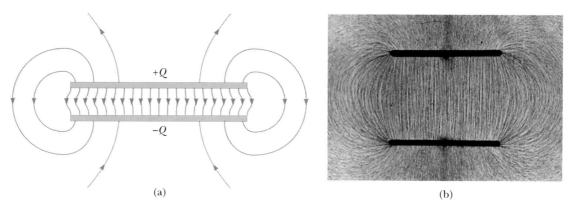

(a)

(b)

FIGURE 26.3   (a) The electric field between the plates of a parallel-plate capacitor is uniform near its center, but is nonuniform near its edges. (b) Electric field pattern of two oppositely charged conducting parallel plates. Small pieces of thread on an oil surface align with the electric field. Note the nonuniform nature of the electric field at the ends of the plates. Such end effects can be neglected if the plate separation is small compared to the length of the plates.   *(Courtesy of Harold M. Waage, Princeton University)*

reveals that the field is uniform in the central region between the plates as shown in Figure 26.3a. However, the field is nonuniform at the edges of the plates. Figure 26.3b is a photograph of the electric field pattern of a parallel-plate capacitor showing the nonuniform field lines at its edges.

EXAMPLE 26.2   The Cylindrical Capacitor

A cylindrical conductor of radius a and charge Q is coaxial with a larger cylindrical shell of radius b and charge $-Q$ (Fig. 26.4a). Find the capacitance of this cylindrical capacitor if its length is ℓ.

Reasoning and Solution   If we assume that ℓ is long compared with a and b, we can neglect end effects. In this case, the field is perpendicular to the axis of the cylinders and is confined to the region between them (Fig. 26.4b). We must first calculate the potential difference between the two cylinders, which is given in general by

$$V_b - V_a = -\int_a^b \mathbf{E} \cdot d\mathbf{s}$$

where $\mathbf{E}$ is the electric field in the region $a < r < b$. In Chapter 24, we showed using Gauss's law that the electric field of a cylinder of charge per unit length λ is $E = 2k_e\lambda/r$. The same result applies here, since the outer cylinder does not contribute to the electric field inside it. Using this result and noting that $\mathbf{E}$ is along r in Figure 26.4b, we find that

$$V_b - V_a = -\int_a^b E_r\, dr = -2k_e\lambda \int_a^b \frac{dr}{r} = -2k_e\lambda \ln\!\left(\frac{b}{a}\right)$$

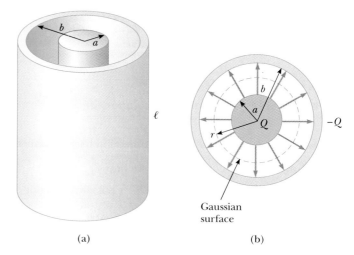

(a)

(b)

FIGURE 26.4   (Example 26.2) (a) A cylindrical capacitor consists of a cylindrical conductor of radius a and length ℓ surrounded by a coaxial cylindrical shell of radius b. (b) The end view of a cylindrical capacitor. The dashed line represents the end of the cylindrical gaussian surface of radius r and length ℓ.

Substituting this into Equation 26.1 and using the fact that $\lambda = Q/\ell$, we get

$$C = \frac{Q}{V} = \frac{Q}{\dfrac{2k_e Q}{\ell} \ln\left(\dfrac{b}{a}\right)} = \frac{\ell}{2k_e \ln\left(\dfrac{b}{a}\right)} \qquad (26.4)$$

where V is the magnitude of the potential difference, given by $2k_e\lambda \ln(b/a)$, a positive quantity. That is, $V = V_a - V_b$ is positive because the inner cylinder is at the higher potential. Our result for C makes sense because it shows that the capacitance is proportional to the length of the cylinders. As you might expect, the capacitance also depends on the radii of the two cylindrical conductors. As an example, a coaxial cable consists of two concentric cylindrical conductors of radii a and b separated by an insulator. The cable carries currents in opposite directions in the inner and outer conductors. Such a geometry is especially useful for shielding an electrical signal from external influences. From Equation 26.4, we see that the capacitance per unit length of a coaxial cable is

$$\frac{C}{\ell} = \frac{1}{2k_e \ln\left(\dfrac{b}{a}\right)}$$

EXAMPLE 26.3 The Spherical Capacitor

A spherical capacitor consists of a spherical conducting shell of radius b and charge $-Q$ that is concentric with a smaller conducting sphere of radius a and charge Q (Fig. 26.5). Find its capacitance.

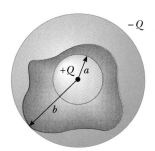

FIGURE 26.5 (Example 26.3) A spherical capacitor consists of an inner sphere of radius a surrounded by a concentric spherical shell of radius b. The electric field between the spheres is radial outward if the inner sphere is positively charged.

Reasoning and Solution As we showed in Chapter 24, the field outside a spherically symmetric charge distribution is radial and given by $k_e Q/r^2$. In this case, this corresponds to the field between the spheres ($a < r < b$). (The field is zero elsewhere.) From Gauss's law we see that only the inner sphere contributes to this field. Thus, the potential difference between the spheres is given by

$$V_b - V_a = -\int_a^b E_r\, dr = -k_e Q \int_a^b \frac{dr}{r^2} = k_e Q \left[\frac{1}{r}\right]_a^b$$

$$= k_e Q \left(\frac{1}{b} - \frac{1}{a}\right)$$

The magnitude of the potential difference is

$$V = V_a - V_b = kQ \frac{(b - a)}{ab}$$

Substituting this into Equation 26.1, we get

$$C = \frac{Q}{V} = \frac{ab}{k_e(b - a)} \qquad (26.5)$$

Exercise Show that as the radius b of the outer sphere approaches infinity, the capacitance approaches the value $a/k_e = 4\pi\epsilon_0 a$. This is consistent with Equation 26.2.

26.3 COMBINATIONS OF CAPACITORS

Two or more capacitors are often combined in circuits in several ways. The equivalent capacitance of certain combinations can be calculated using methods described in this section. The circuit symbols for capacitors and batteries, together with their color codes, are given in Figure 26.6. The positive terminal of the battery is at the higher potential and is represented by the longer vertical line in the battery symbol.

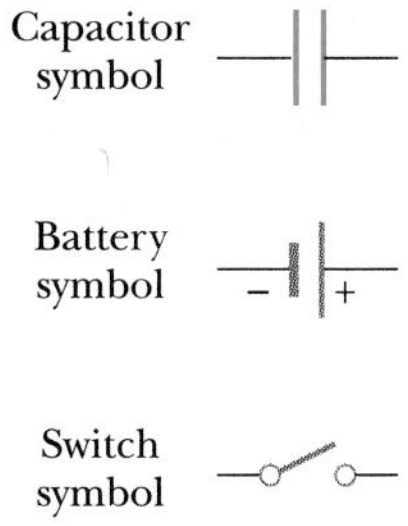

Parallel Combination

Two capacitors connected as shown in Figure 26.7a are known as a *parallel combination* of capacitors. The left plates of the capacitors are connected by a conducting wire to the positive terminal of the battery and are therefore both at the same

Capacitor symbol

Battery symbol

Switch symbol

FIGURE 26.6 Circuit symbols for capacitors, batteries, and switches. Note that capacitors are in blue, and batteries and switches are in red.

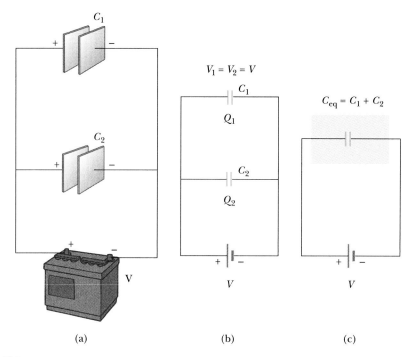

FIGURE 26.7 (a) A parallel combination of two capacitors. (b) The circuit diagram for the parallel combination. (c) The potential difference is the same across each capacitor, and the equivalent capacitance is $C_{eq} = C_1 + C_2$.

potential as the positive terminal. Likewise, the right plates are connected to the negative terminal of the battery and are therefore both at the same potential as the negative terminal. When the capacitors are first connected in the circuit, electrons are transferred through the battery from the left plates to the right plates, leaving the left plates positively charged and the right plates negatively charged. The energy source for this charge transfer is the internal chemical energy stored in the battery, which is converted to electrical energy. The flow of charge ceases when the voltage across the capacitors is equal to that of the battery. The capacitors reach their maximum charge when the flow of charge ceases. Let us call the maximum charges on the two capacitors Q_1 and Q_2. Then the *total charge, Q*, stored by the two capacitors is

$$Q = Q_1 + Q_2 \qquad (26.6)$$

Suppose we wish to replace these two capacitors by one equivalent capacitor having a capacitance C_{eq}. This equivalent capacitor must have exactly the same external effect on the circuit as the original two. That is, it must store Q units of charge. We see from Figure 26.7b that

the potential difference across each capacitor in the parallel circuit is the same and is equal to the voltage of the battery, V.

From Figure 26.7c, we see that the voltage across the equivalent capacitor is also V.

Thus, we have

$$Q_1 = C_1 V \qquad Q_2 = C_2 V$$

and, for the equivalent capacitor,

$$Q = C_{eq} V$$

Substituting these relationships into Equation 26.6 gives

$$C_{eq} V = C_1 V + C_2 V$$

or

$$C_{eq} = C_1 + C_2 \qquad \left(\begin{array}{l}\text{parallel}\\\text{combination}\end{array}\right)$$

If we extend this treatment to three or more capacitors connected in parallel, the equivalent capacitance is found to be

$$C_{eq} = C_1 + C_2 + C_3 + \cdots \qquad \left(\begin{array}{l}\text{parallel}\\\text{combination}\end{array}\right) \qquad (26.7)$$

Thus we see that *the equivalent capacitance of a parallel combination of capacitors is larger than any of the individual capacitances.*

Series Combination

Now consider two capacitors connected in *series,* as illustrated in Figure 26.8a.

> For this series combination of capacitors, the magnitude of the charge must be the same on all the plates.

To see why this must be true, let us consider the charge transfer process in some detail. We start with uncharged capacitors and follow what happens just after a

When the key on a computer keyboard is depressed, the spacing between the plates of a capacitor beneath the key changes, causing a change in capacitance. An electrical signal derived from this capacitance change is used to register the keystroke. *(Ray Serway)*

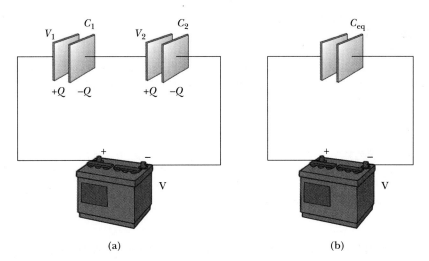

(a)   (b)

FIGURE 26.8 A series combination of two capacitors. The charge on each capacitor is the same, and the equivalent capacitance can be calculated from the relationship

$$1/C_{eq} = 1/C_1 + 1/C_2$$

battery is connected to the circuit. When the battery is connected, electrons are transferred from the left plate of C_1 to the right plate of C_2 through the battery. As this negative charge accumulates on the right plate of C_2, an equivalent amount of negative charge is forced off the left plate of C_2, leaving it with an excess positive charge. The negative charge leaving the left plate of C_2 accumulates on the right plate of C_1, where again an equivalent amount of negative charge leaves the left plate. The result of this is that *all of the right plates gain a charge of $-Q$ while all of the left plates have a charge of $+Q$.*

Suppose an equivalent capacitor performs the same function as the series combination. After it is fully charged, *the equivalent capacitor must have a charge of $-Q$ on its right plate and $+Q$ on its left plate.* By applying the definition of capacitance to the circuit shown in Figure 26.8b, we have

$$V = \frac{Q}{C_{eq}}$$

where V is the potential difference between the terminals of the battery and C_{eq} is the equivalent capacitance. From Figure 26.8a, we see that

$$V = V_1 + V_2 \tag{26.8}$$

where V_1 and V_2 are the potential differences across capacitors C_1 and C_2. In general, the potential difference across any number of capacitors in series is equal to the sum of the potential differences across the individual capacitors. Since $Q = CV$ can be applied to each capacitor, the potential difference across each is

$$V_1 = \frac{Q}{C_1} \qquad V_2 = \frac{Q}{C_2}$$

Substituting these expressions into Equation 26.8, and noting that $V = Q/C_{eq}$, we have

$$\frac{Q}{C_{eq}} = \frac{Q}{C_1} + \frac{Q}{C_2}$$

Cancelling Q, we arrive at the relationship

$$\frac{1}{C_{eq}} = \frac{1}{C_1} + \frac{1}{C_2} \qquad \left(\begin{array}{c}\text{series}\\\text{combination}\end{array}\right)$$

If this analysis is applied to three or more capacitors connected in series, the equivalent capacitance is found to be

$$\frac{1}{C_{eq}} = \frac{1}{C_1} + \frac{1}{C_2} + \frac{1}{C_3} + \cdots \qquad \left(\begin{array}{c}\text{series}\\\text{combination}\end{array}\right) \tag{26.9}$$

This shows that *the equivalent capacitance of a series combination is always less than any individual capacitance in the combination.*

EXAMPLE 26.4   Equivalent Capacitance

Find the equivalent capacitance between a and b for the combination of capacitors shown in Figure 26.9a. All capacitances are in microfarads.

Solution   Using Equations 26.7 and 26.9, we reduce the combination step by step as indicated in the figure. The 1.0-μF and 3.0-μF capacitors are in parallel and combine according to $C_{eq} = C_1 + C_2$. Their equivalent capacitance is 4.0 μF. Likewise, the 2.0-μF and 6.0-μF capacitors are also in parallel and have an equivalent capacitance of 8.0 μF. The upper branch in Figure 26.9b now consists of two 4.0-μF capacitors in series, which combine according to

$$\frac{1}{C_{eq}} = \frac{1}{C_1} + \frac{1}{C_2} = \frac{1}{4.0\ \mu F} + \frac{1}{4.0\ \mu F} = \frac{1}{2.0\ \mu F}$$

$$C_{eq} = 2.0\ \mu F$$

Likewise, the lower branch in Figure 26.9b consists of two

8.0-μF capacitors in *series,* which give an equivalent of 4.0 μF. Finally, the 2.0-μF and 4.0-μF capacitors in Figure 26.9c are in parallel and have an equivalent capacitance of 6.0 μF. Hence, the equivalent capacitance of the circuit is 6.0 μF, as shown in Figure 26.9d.

Exercise   Consider three capacitors having capacitances of 3.0 μF, 6.0 μF, and 12 μF. Find their equivalent capacitance if they are connected (a) in parallel and (b) in series.

Answer   (a) 21 μF, (b) 1.7 μF.

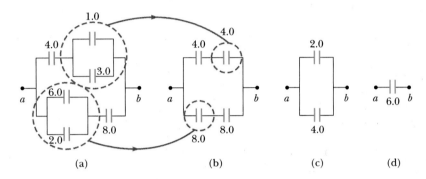

FIGURE 26.9   (Example 26.4) To find the equivalent combination of the capacitors in (a), the various combinations are reduced in steps as indicated in (b), (c), and (d), using the series and parallel rules described in the text.

26.4   ENERGY STORED IN A CHARGED CAPACITOR

If the plates of a charged capacitor are connected together by a conductor, such as a wire, charge moves from one plate to the other until the two are uncharged. The discharge can often be observed as a visible spark. If you should accidentally touch the opposite plates of a charged capacitor, your fingers act as a pathway by which the capacitor could discharge, and the result is an electric shock. The degree of shock you receive depends on the capacitance and voltage applied to the capacitor. Such a shock could be fatal where high voltages are present, such as in the power supply of a television set.

Consider a parallel-plate capacitor that is initially uncharged, so that the initial potential difference across the plates is zero. Now imagine that the capacitor is connected to a battery which supplies it with charge Q. We assume that the capacitor is charged slowly so that the problem can be considered as an electrostatic system. The final potential difference across the capacitor is $V = Q/C$. Because the initial potential difference is zero, the average potential difference during the charging process is $V/2 = Q/2C$. From this we might conclude that the work needed to charge the capacitor is $W = QV/2 = Q^2/2C$. Although this result is correct, a more detailed proof is desirable and is now given.

Suppose that q is the charge on the capacitor at some instant during the charging process. At the same instant, the potential difference across the capacitor is $V = q/C$. The work necessary[2] to transfer an increment of charge dq from the plate

---

[2] One mechanical analog of this process is the work required to raise a mass through some vertical distance in the presence of gravity.

of charge $-q$ to the plate of charge q (which is at the higher potential) is

$$dW = V \, dq = \frac{q}{C} \, dq$$

Thus, the total work required to charge the capacitor from $q = 0$ to some final charge $q = Q$ is

$$W = \int_0^Q \frac{q}{C} \, dq = \frac{Q^2}{2C}$$

But the work done in charging the capacitor can be considered as potential energy U stored in the capacitor. Using $Q = CV$, we can express the electrostatic potential energy stored in a charged capacitor in the following alternative forms:

Energy stored in a charged
capacitor

$$U = \frac{Q^2}{2C} = \tfrac{1}{2}QV = \tfrac{1}{2}CV^2 \tag{26.10}$$

This result applies to any capacitor, regardless of its geometry. We see that for a given capacitance, the stored energy increases as the charge increases and as the potential difference increases. In practice, there is a limit to the maximum energy (or charge) that can be stored. This is because electrical discharge ultimately occurs between the plates of the capacitor at a sufficiently large value of V. For this reason, capacitors are usually labeled with a maximum operating voltage.

The energy stored in a capacitor can be considered as being stored in the electric field created between the plates as the capacitor is charged. This description is reasonable in view of the fact that the electric field is proportional to the charge on the capacitor. For a parallel-plate capacitor, the potential difference is related to the electric field through the relationship $V = Ed$. Furthermore, its capacitance is $C = \epsilon_0 A/d$. Substituting these expressions into Equation 26.10 gives

Energy stored in a parallel-plate
capacitor

$$U = \tfrac{1}{2} \frac{\epsilon_0 A}{d} (E^2 d^2) = \tfrac{1}{2}(\epsilon_0 Ad)E^2 \tag{26.11}$$

Since the volume occupied by the electric field is Ad, the *energy per unit volume* $u_E = U/Ad$, called the *energy density*, is

Energy density in an electric field

$$u_E = \tfrac{1}{2}\epsilon_0 E^2 \tag{26.12}$$

Although Equation 26.12 was derived for a parallel-plate capacitor, the expression is generally valid. That is, the *energy density in any electric field is proportional to the square of the electric field in the unit volume.*

EXAMPLE 26.5   Rewiring Two Charged Capacitors

Two capacitors C_1 and C_2 (where $C_1 > C_2$) are charged to the same potential difference V_0, but with opposite polarity. The charged capacitors are removed from the battery, and their plates are connected as shown in Figure 26.10a. The switches S_1 and S_2 are then closed as in Figure 26.10b. (a) Find the final potential difference between a and b after the switches are closed.

Solution   The charges on the left-hand plates of the capacitors before the switches are closed are

$$Q_1 = C_1 V_0 \quad \text{and} \quad Q_2 = -C_2 V_0$$

The negative sign for Q_2 is necessary since this capacitor's polarity is opposite that of capacitor C_1. After the switches are closed, the charges on the plates redistribute until the total charge Q shared by the capacitors is

$$Q = Q_1 + Q_2 = (C_1 - C_2)V_0$$

The two capacitors are now in parallel, and so the final po-

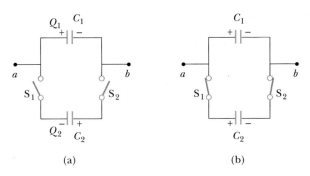

(a)   (b)

FIGURE 26.10   (Example 26.5).

tential difference across each is the same:

$$V = \frac{Q}{C_1 + C_2} = \left(\frac{C_1 - C_2}{C_1 + C_2}\right) V_0$$

(b) Find the total energy stored in the capacitors before and after the switches are closed.

Solution   Before the switches are closed, the total energy stored in the capacitors is

$$U_i = \tfrac{1}{2} C_1 V_0^2 + \tfrac{1}{2} C_2 V_0^2 = \tfrac{1}{2}(C_1 + C_2) V_0^2$$

After the switches are closed and the capacitors have reached an equilibrium charge, the total energy stored in them is

$$U_f = \tfrac{1}{2} C_1 V^2 + \tfrac{1}{2} C_2 V^2 = \tfrac{1}{2}(C_1 + C_2) V^2$$

$$= \tfrac{1}{2}(C_1 + C_2)\left(\frac{C_1 - C_2}{C_1 + C_2}\right)^2 V_0^2 = \left(\frac{C_1 - C_2}{C_1 + C_2}\right)^2 U_i$$

Therefore, the ratio of the final to the initial energy stored is

$$\frac{U_f}{U_i} = \left(\frac{C_1 - C_2}{C_1 + C_2}\right)^2$$

This shows that the final energy is less than the initial energy. At first, you might think that energy conservation has been violated, but this is not the case. Part of the missing energy appears as thermal energy in the connecting wires, and part is radiated away in the form of electromagnetic waves (Chapter 34).

26.5   CAPACITORS WITH DIELECTRICS

A **dielectric** is a nonconducting material, such as rubber, glass, or waxed paper. When a dielectric material is inserted between the plates of a capacitor, the capacitance increases. If the dielectric completely fills the space between the plates, the capacitance increases by a dimensionless factor κ, called the **dielectric constant.**

The following experiment can be performed to illustrate the effect of a dielectric in a capacitor. Consider a parallel-plate capacitor of charge Q_0 and capacitance C_0 in the absence of a dielectric. The potential difference across the capacitor as measured by a voltmeter is $V_0 = Q_0/C_0$ (Fig. 26.11a). Notice that the capacitor

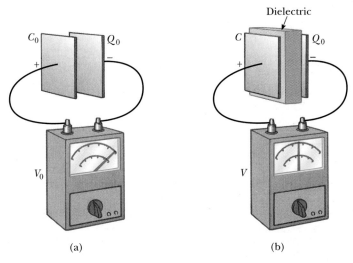

(a)   (b)

FIGURE 26.11   When a dielectric is inserted between the plates of a charged capacitor, the charge on the plates remains unchanged, but the potential difference as recorded by an electrostatic voltmeter is reduced from V_0 to $V = V_0/\kappa$. Thus, the capacitance *increases* in the process by the factor κ.

Sparks leap between two brass spheres connected to an electrostatic generator. The potential difference between the spheres is approximately 4000 V. *(Courtesy of Central Scientific Co.)*

circuit is open, that is, the plates of the capacitor are not connected to a battery and charge cannot flow through an ideal voltmeter. (We discuss the voltmeter further in Chapter 28.) Hence, there is no path by which charge can flow and alter the charge on the capacitor. If a dielectric is now inserted between the plates as in Figure 26.11b, it is found that the voltmeter reading decreases by a factor κ to a value V, where

$$V = \frac{V_0}{\kappa}$$

Since $V < V_0$, we see that $\kappa > 1$.

Since the charge Q_0 on the capacitor *does not change*, we conclude that the capacitance must change to the value

$$C = \frac{Q_0}{V} = \frac{Q_0}{V_0/\kappa} = \kappa \frac{Q_0}{V_0}$$

$$C = \kappa C_0 \tag{26.13}$$

where C_0 is the capacitance in the absence of the dielectric. That is, the capacitance *increases* by the factor κ when the dielectric completely fills the region between the plates.[3] For a parallel-plate capacitor, where $C_0 = \epsilon_0 A/d$ (Eq. 26.3), we can express the capacitance when the capacitor is filled with a dielectric as

$$C = \kappa \frac{\epsilon_0 A}{d} \tag{26.14}$$

The capacitance of a filled capacitor is greater than that of an empty one by a factor κ.

TABLE 26.1   Dielectric Constants and Dielectric Strengths of Various Materials at Room Temperature

Material	Dielectric Constant κ	Dielectric Strength[a] (V/m)
Vacuum	1.00000	—
Air (dry)	1.00059	3×10^6
Bakelite	4.9	24×10^6
Fused quartz	3.78	8×10^6
Pyrex glass	5.6	14×10^6
Polystyrene	2.56	24×10^6
Teflon	2.1	60×10^6
Neoprene rubber	6.7	12×10^6
Nylon	3.4	14×10^6
Paper	3.7	16×10^6
Strontium titanate	233	8×10^6
Water	80	—
Silicone oil	2.5	15×10^6

[a] The dielectric strength equals the maximum electric field that can exist in a dielectric without electrical breakdown.

---

[3] If another experiment is performed in which the dielectric is introduced while the potential difference remains constant by means of a battery, the charge increases to a value $Q = \kappa Q_0$. The additional charge is supplied by the battery and the capacitance still increases by the factor κ.

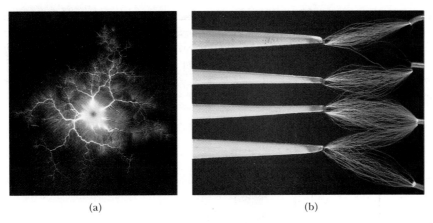

(a)   (b)

(a) Kirlian photograph created by dropping a steel ball into a high-energy electric field. This technique is also known as electrophotography.   *(Henry Dakin/Science Photo Library)* (b) Sparks from static electricity discharge between a fork and four electrodes. Many sparks were used to make this image, because only one spark will form for a given discharge. Each spark follows the line of least resistance through the air at the time. Note that the bottom prong of the fork forms discharges to both electrodes at bottom right. The light of each spark is created by the excitations of gas atoms along its path.   *(Adam Hart-Davis/Science Photo Library)*

From Equations 26.3 and 26.14, it would appear that the capacitance could be made very large by decreasing d, the distance between the plates. In practice, the lowest value of d is limited by the electrical discharge that could occur through the dielectric medium separating the plates. For any given separation d, the maximum voltage that can be applied to a capacitor without causing a discharge depends on the *dielectric strength* (maximum electric field strength) of the dielectric, which for air is equal to 3×10^6 V/m. If the field strength in the medium exceeds the dielectric strength, the insulating properties break down and the medium begins to conduct. Most insulating materials have dielectric strengths and dielectric constants greater than that of air, as Table 26.1 indicates. Thus, we see that a dielectric provides the following advantages:

- Increases the capacitance of a capacitor
- Increases the maximum operating voltage of a capacitor
- May provide mechanical support between the conducting plates

Types of Capacitors

Commercial capacitors are often made using metal foil interlaced with thin sheets of paraffin-impregnated paper or Mylar, which serves as the dielectric material. These alternate layers of metal foil and dielectric are then rolled into a cylinder to form a small package (Fig. 26.12a). High-voltage capacitors commonly consist of a number of interwoven metal plates immersed in silicone oil (Fig. 26.12b). Small capacitors are often constructed from ceramic materials. Variable capacitors (typically 10 to 500 pF) usually consist of two interwoven sets of metal plates, one fixed and the other movable, with air as the dielectric.

An *electrolytic capacitor* is often used to store large amounts of charge at relatively low voltages. This device, shown in Figure 26.12c, consists of a metal foil in contact

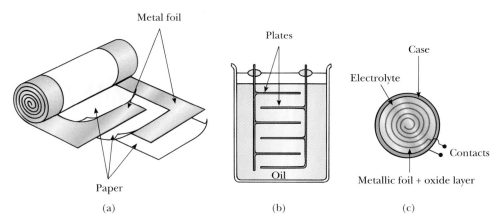

FIGURE 26.12   Three commercial capacitor designs. (a) A tubular capacitor whose plates are separated by paper and then rolled into a cylinder. (b) A high-voltage capacitor consists of many parallel plates separated by insulating oil. (c) An electrolytic capacitor.

with an electrolyte — a solution that conducts electricity by virtue of the motion of ions contained in the solution. When a voltage is applied between the foil and the electrolyte, a thin layer of metal oxide (an insulator) is formed on the foil, and this layer serves as the dielectric. Very large values of capacitance can be obtained because the dielectric layer is very thin and thus the plate separation is very small.

When electrolytic capacitors are used in circuits, the polarity (the plus and minus signs on the device) must be installed properly. If the polarity of the applied voltage is opposite what is intended, the oxide layer is removed and the capacitor conducts electricity rather than stores charge.

EXAMPLE 26.6   A Paper-Filled Capacitor

A parallel-plate capacitor has plates of dimensions 2.0 cm × 3.0 cm separated by a 1.0-mm thickness of paper. (a) Find the capacitance of this device.

Solution   Since $\kappa = 3.7$ for paper (Table 26.1), we get

$$C = \kappa \frac{\epsilon_0 A}{d} = 3.7 \left(8.85 \times 10^{-12} \, \frac{C^2}{N \cdot m^2} \right) \left(\frac{6.0 \times 10^{-4} \, m^2}{1.0 \times 10^{-3} \, m} \right)$$

$$= 20 \times 10^{-12} \, F = \boxed{20 \, pF}$$

(b) What is the maximum charge that can be placed on the capacitor?

Solution   From Table 26.1 we see that the dielectric strength of paper is 16×10^6 V/m. Since the thickness of the paper is 1.0 mm, the maximum voltage that can be applied before breakdown is

$$V_{max} = E_{max}d = \left(16 \times 10^6 \, \frac{V}{m} \right) (1.0 \times 10^{-3} \, m)$$

$$= 16 \times 10^3 \, V$$

Hence, the maximum charge is

$$Q_{max} = CV_{max} = (20 \times 10^{-12} \, F)(16 \times 10^3 \, V) = \boxed{0.32 \, \mu C}$$

Exercise   What is the maximum energy that can be stored in the capacitor?

Answer 2.5×10^{-3} J.

EXAMPLE 26.7   Energy Stored Before and After

A parallel-plate capacitor is charged with a battery to a charge Q_0, as in Figure 26.13a. The battery is then removed, and a slab of material that has a dielectric constant κ is in-serted between the plates, as in Figure 26.13b. Find the energy stored in the capacitor before and after the dielectric is inserted.

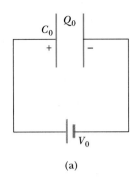

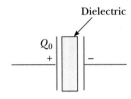

(b)

FIGURE 26.13 (Example 26.7).

Solution The energy stored in the capacitor in the absence of the dielectric is

$$U_0 = \tfrac{1}{2} C_0 V_0^2$$

Since $V_0 = Q_0/C_0$, this can be expressed as

$$U_0 = \frac{Q_0^2}{2C_0}$$

After the battery is removed and the dielectric is inserted between the plates, the *charge on the capacitor remains the same.* Hence, the energy stored in the presence of the dielectric is

$$U = \frac{Q_0^2}{2C}$$

But the capacitance in the presence of the dielectric is $C = \kappa C_0$, and so U becomes

$$U = \frac{Q_0^2}{2\kappa C_0} = \boxed{\frac{U_0}{\kappa}}$$

Since $\kappa > 1$, we see that the final energy is less than the initial energy by the factor $1/\kappa$. This missing energy can be accounted for by noting that when the dielectric is inserted into the capacitor, it gets pulled into the device. An external agent must do negative work to keep the slab from accelerating. This work is simply the difference $U - U_0$. (Alternatively, the positive work done by the system on the external agent is $U_0 - U$.)

Exercise Suppose that the capacitance in the absence of a dielectric is 8.50 pF, and the capacitor is charged to a potential difference of 12.0 V. If the battery is disconnected, and a slab of polystyrene ($\kappa = 2.56$) is inserted between the plates, calculate the energy difference $U - U_0$.

Answer 373 pJ.

As we have seen, the energy of a capacitor is lowered when a dielectric is inserted between the plates, which means that work is done on the dielectric. This, in turn, implies that a force must be acting on the dielectric that draws it into the capacitor. This force originates from the nonuniform nature of the electric field of the capacitor near its edges, as indicated in Figure 26.14. The horizontal compo-

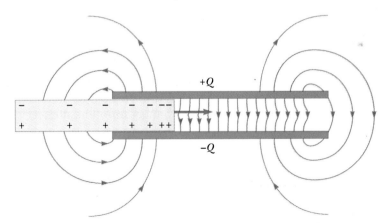

FIGURE 26.14 The nonuniform electric field near the edges of a parallel-plate capacitor causes a dielectric to be pulled into the capacitor. Note that the field acts on the induced surface charges on the dielectric that are nonuniformly distributed.

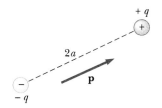

FIGURE 26.15 An electric dipole consists of two equal and opposite charges separated by a distance $2a$. The electric dipole moment **p** is directed from $-q$ to $+q$.

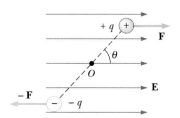

FIGURE 26.16 An electric dipole in a uniform electric field. The dipole moment **p** is at an angle θ with the field, and the dipole experiences a torque.

Torque on an electric dipole in an external electric field

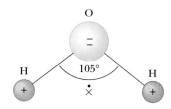

FIGURE 26.17 The water molecule, H_2O, has a permanent polarization resulting from its bent geometry. The center of positive charge is at the point x.

nent of this fringe field acts on the induced charges on the surface of the dielectric, producing a net horizontal force directed into the capacitor.

*26.6 ELECTRIC DIPOLE IN AN EXTERNAL ELECTRIC FIELD

The electric dipole, discussed briefly in Example 23.9, consists of two equal and opposite charges separated by a distance $2a$, as in Figure 26.15. Let us define the **electric dipole moment** of this configuration as the vector **p** that is directed from $-q$ to $+q$ along the line joining the charges, and whose magnitude is $2aq$:

$$p \equiv 2aq \tag{26.15}$$

Now suppose an electric dipole is placed in a uniform electric field **E** as in Figure 26.16, where the dipole moment makes an angle θ with the field. The forces on the two charges are equal and opposite as shown, each having a magnitude

$$F = qE$$

Thus, we see that the net force on the dipole is zero. However, the two forces produce a net torque on the dipole, and the dipole tends to rotate such that its axis is aligned with the field. The torque due to the force on the positive charge about an axis through O is $Fa \sin \theta$, where $a \sin \theta$ is the moment arm of F about O. In Figure 26.16, this force tends to produce a clockwise rotation. The torque about O on the negative charge is also $Fa \sin \theta$, and so the net torque about O is

$$\tau = 2Fa \sin \theta$$

Because $F = qE$ and $p = 2aq$, we can express τ as

$$\tau = 2aqE \sin \theta = pE \sin \theta \tag{26.16}$$

It is convenient to express the torque in vector form as the cross product of the vectors **p** and **E**:

$$\boldsymbol{\tau} = \mathbf{p} \times \mathbf{E} \tag{26.17}$$

We can also determine the potential energy of an electric dipole as a function of its orientation with respect to the external electric field. In order to do this, you should recognize that work must be done by an external agent to rotate the dipole through a given angle in the field. The work done increases the potential energy in the system, which consists of the dipole and the external field. The work dW required to rotate the dipole through an angle $d\theta$ is $dW = \tau \, d\theta$ (Chapter 10). Because $\tau = pE \sin \theta$, and because the work is transformed to potential energy U, we find that for a rotation from θ_0 to θ, the change in potential energy is

$$U - U_0 = \int_{\theta_0}^{\theta} \tau \, d\theta = \int_{\theta_0}^{\theta} pE \sin \theta \, d\theta = pE \int_{\theta_0}^{\theta} \sin \theta \, d\theta$$

$$U - U_0 = pE[-\cos \theta]_{\theta_0}^{\theta} = pE(\cos \theta_0 - \cos \theta)$$

The term involving $\cos \theta_0$ is a constant that depends on the initial orientation of the dipole. It is convenient to choose $\theta_0 = 90°$, so that $\cos \theta_0 = \cos 90° = 0$. Furthermore, let us choose $U_0 = 0$ at $\theta_0 = 90°$ as our reference of potential energy. Hence, we can express U as

$$U = -pE \cos \theta \tag{26.18}$$

This can be written as the dot product of the vectors **p** and **E**:

$$U = -\mathbf{p} \cdot \mathbf{E} \qquad (26.19)$$

Molecules are said to be polarized when there is a separation between the "center of gravity" of the negative charges and that of the positive charges on the molecule. In some molecules, such as water, this condition is always present. This can be understood by inspecting the geometry of the water molecule. The molecule is arranged so that the oxygen atom is bonded to the hydrogen atoms with an angle of 105° between the two bonds (Fig. 26.17). The center of negative charge is near the oxygen atom, and the center of positive charge lies at a point midway along the line joining the hydrogen atoms (point x in the diagram). Materials composed of molecules that are permanently polarized in this fashion have large dielectric constants. For example, the dielectric constant of water is quite large ($\kappa = 80$).

A symmetrical molecule (Fig. 26.18a) might have no permanent polarization, but a polarization can be induced by an external electric field. A field directed to the left, as in Figure 26.18b, would cause the center of positive charge to shift to the right from its initial position and the center of negative charge to shift to the left. This *induced polarization* is the effect that predominates in most materials used as dielectrics in capacitors.

Potential energy of a dipole in an electric field

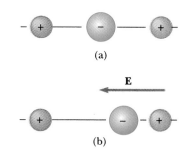

(a)

(b)

FIGURE 26.18 (a) A symmetric molecule has no permanent polarization. (b) An external electric field induces a polarization in the molecule.

EXAMPLE 26.8   The H₂O Molecule

The H_2O molecule has a dipole moment of 6.3×10^{-30} C·m. A sample contains 10^{21} such molecules, whose dipole moments are all oriented in the direction of an electric field of 2.5×10^5 N/C. How much work is required to rotate the dipoles from this orientation ($\theta = 0°$) to one in which all of the moments are perpendicular to the field ($\theta = 90°$)?

Solution   The work required to rotate one molecule by 90° is equal to the difference in potential energy between the 90° orientation and the 0° orientation. Using Equation 26.18

gives

$$
\begin{aligned}
W &= U_{90} - U_0 = (-pE \cos 90°) - (-pE \cos 0°) \\
&= pE = (6.3 \times 10^{-30} \text{ C·m})(2.5 \times 10^5 \text{ N/C}) \\
&= 1.6 \times 10^{-24} \text{ J}
\end{aligned}
$$

Since there are 10^{21} molecules in the sample, the *total* work required is

$$W_{\text{total}} = (10^{21})(1.6 \times 10^{-24} \text{ J}) = \boxed{1.6 \times 10^{-3} \text{ J}}$$

---

*26.7   AN ATOMIC DESCRIPTION OF DIELECTRICS

In Section 26.5 we found that the potential difference between the plates of a capacitor is reduced by the factor κ when a dielectric is introduced. Since the potential difference between the plates equals the product of the electric field and the separation d, the electric field is also reduced by the factor κ. Thus, if $\mathbf{E}_0$ is the electric field without the dielectric, the field in the presence of a dielectric is

$$\mathbf{E} = \frac{\mathbf{E}_0}{\kappa} \qquad (26.20)$$

This relationship can be understood by noting that a dielectric can be polarized. At the atomic level, a polarized material is one in which the positive and negative charges are slightly separated. If the molecules of the dielectric possess permanent electric dipole moments in the absence of an electric field, they are called **polar molecules** (water is an example). The dipoles are randomly oriented in the ab-

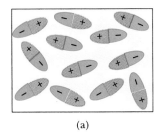

(a)

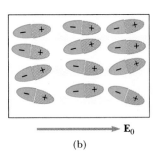

$\mathbf{E}_0$

(b)

FIGURE 26.19 (a) Molecules with a permanent dipole moment are randomly oriented in the absence of an external electric field. (b) When an external field is applied, the dipoles are partially aligned with the field.

sence of an electric field, as shown in Figure 26.19a. When an external field $\mathbf{E}_0$ is applied, a torque is exerted on the dipoles, causing them to be partially aligned with the field, as in Figure 26.19b. The degree of alignment depends on temperature and on the magnitude of the applied field. In general, the alignment increases with decreasing temperature and with increasing electric field strength. The partially aligned dipoles produce an internal electric field that opposes the external field, thereby causing a reduction in the net field within the dielectric.

If the molecules of the dielectric do not possess a permanent dipole moment, they are called **nonpolar molecules.** In this case, an external electric field produces some charge separation and an induced dipole moment. These induced dipole moments tend to align with the external field, causing a reduction in the internal electric field.

With these ideas in mind, consider a slab of dielectric material in a uniform electric field $\mathbf{E}_0$ as in Figure 26.20a. The external electric field in the capacitor is directed toward the right and exerts forces on the molecules of the dielectric material. Under the influence of these forces, electrons in the dielectric are shifted from their equilibrium positions toward the left. Hence, the applied electric field polarizes the dielectric. The net effect on the dielectric is the formation of an "induced" positive surface charge density σ_i on the right face and an equal negative surface charge density on the left face, as in Figure 26.20b. These induced surface charges on the dielectric give rise to an induced internal electric field $\mathbf{E}_i$ that opposes the external field $\mathbf{E}_0$. Therefore, the net electric field $\mathbf{E}$ in the dielectric has a magnitude given by

$$E = E_0 - E_i \tag{26.21}$$

In the parallel-plate capacitor shown in Figure 26.21, the external field E_0 is related to the free charge density σ on the plates through the relationship $E_0 = \sigma/\epsilon_0$. The induced electric field in the dielectric is related to the induced charge density σ_i through the relationship $E_i = \sigma_i/\epsilon_0$. Since $E = E_0/\kappa = \sigma/\kappa\epsilon_0$, substitution into Equation 26.21 gives

$$\frac{\sigma}{\kappa\epsilon_0} = \frac{\sigma}{\epsilon_0} - \frac{\sigma_i}{\epsilon_0}$$

$$\sigma_i = \left(\frac{\kappa - 1}{\kappa}\right)\sigma \tag{26.22}$$

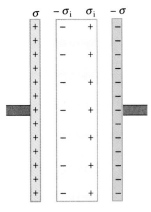

FIGURE 26.21 Induced charge on a dielectric placed between the plates of a charged capacitor. Note that the induced charge density on the dielectric is *less* than the free charge density on the plates.

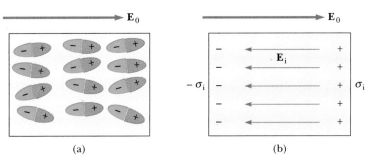

(a)   (b)

FIGURE 26.20 (a) When a dielectric is polarized, the molecular dipole moments in the dielectric are partially aligned with the external field $\mathbf{E}_0$. (b) This polarization causes an induced negative surface charge on one side of the dielectric and an equal positive surface charge on the opposite side. This results in a reduction in the net electric field within the dielectric.

Because $\kappa > 1$, this expression shows that the charge density σ_i induced on the dielectric is less than the free charge density σ on the plates. For instance, if $\kappa = 3$, we see that the induced charge density on the dielectric is two-thirds the free charge density on the plates. If there is no dielectric present, $\kappa = 1$ and $\sigma_i = 0$ as expected. However, if the dielectric is replaced by an electrical conductor, for which $E = 0$, then Equation 26.21 shows that $E_0 = E_i$, corresponding to $\sigma_i = \sigma$. That is, the surface charge induced on the conductor is equal to and opposite that on the plates, resulting in a net field of zero in the conductor.

EXAMPLE 26.9   A Partially Filled Capacitor

A parallel-plate capacitor has a capacitance C_0 in the absence of a dielectric. A slab of dielectric material of dielectric constant κ and thickness $\frac{1}{3}d$ is inserted between the plates (Fig. 26.22a). What is the new capacitance when the dielectric is present?

Reasoning   This capacitor is equivalent to two parallel-plate capacitors of the same area A connected in series, one with a plate separation $d/3$ (dielectric filled) and the other with a plate separation $2d/3$ and air between the plates (Fig. 26.22b). (This breaking-into-two step is permissible because there is no potential difference between the lower plate of C_1 and the upper plate of C_2.)[4]

From Equations 26.3 and 26.13, the two capacitances are

$$C_1 = \frac{\kappa \epsilon_0 A}{d/3} \quad \text{and} \quad C_2 = \frac{\epsilon_0 A}{2d/3}$$

Solution   Using Equation 26.9 for two capacitors combined in series, we get

$$\frac{1}{C} = \frac{1}{C_1} + \frac{1}{C_2} = \frac{d/3}{\kappa \epsilon_0 A} + \frac{2d/3}{\epsilon_0 A}$$

$$\frac{1}{C} = \frac{d}{3\epsilon_0 A}\left(\frac{1}{\kappa} + 2\right) = \frac{d}{3\epsilon_0 A}\left(\frac{1 + 2\kappa}{\kappa}\right)$$

$$C = \left(\frac{3\kappa}{2\kappa + 1}\right)\frac{\epsilon_0 A}{d}$$

Since the capacitance without the dielectric is $C_0 = \epsilon_0 A/d$, we see that

$$C = \left(\frac{3\kappa}{2\kappa + 1}\right)C_0$$

[4] You could also imagine placing two thin metallic plates (with a coiled-up conducting wire between them) at the lower surface of the dielectric in Figure 26.22a and then pulling the assembly out until it becomes like Figure 26.22b.

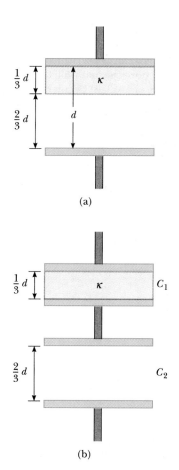

(a)

(b)

FIGURE 26.22   (Example 26.9) (a) A parallel-plate capacitor of plate separation d partially filled with a dielectric of thickness $d/3$. (b) The equivalent circuit of the capacitor consists of two capacitors connected in series.

EXAMPLE 26.10   Effect of a Metal Slab

A parallel-plate capacitor has a plate separation d and plate area A. An uncharged metal slab of thickness a is inserted midway between the plates, as shown in Figure 26.23a. Find the capacitance of the device.

Reasoning   This problem can be solved by noting that any charge that appears on one plate of the capacitor must induce an equal and opposite charge on the metal slab, as in Figure 26.23a. Consequently, the net charge on the metal

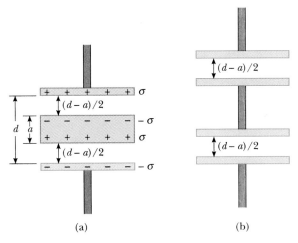

FIGURE 26.23   (Example 26.10) (a) A parallel-plate capacitor of plate separation d partially filled with a metal slab of thickness a. (b) The equivalent circuit of the device in (a) consists of two capacitors in series, each with a plate separation $(d - a)/2$.

slab remains zero, and the field inside the slab is zero. Hence, the capacitor is equivalent to two capacitors in series, each having a plate separation $(d - a)/2$, as in Figure 26.23b.

Solution   Using the rule for adding two capacitors in series we get

$$\frac{1}{C} = \frac{1}{C_1} + \frac{1}{C_2} = \frac{1}{\dfrac{\epsilon_0 A}{(d - a)/2}} + \frac{1}{\dfrac{\epsilon_0 A}{(d - a)/2}}$$

$$C = \frac{\epsilon_0 A}{d - a}$$

Note that C approaches infinity as a approaches d. Why?

SUMMARY

A *capacitor* consists of two equal and oppositely charged conductors separated by a distance that is very small compared with the dimensions of the plates. The **capacitance** C of any capacitor is defined to be the ratio of the charge Q on either conductor to the potential difference V between them:

$$C \equiv \frac{Q}{V} \tag{26.1}$$

The SI unit of capacitance is coulomb per volt, or farad (F), and 1 F = 1 C/V.

The capacitance of several capacitors is summarized in Table 26.2. The formulas apply when the charged conductors are separated by a vacuum.

TABLE 26.2   Capacitance and Geometry

Geometry	Capacitance	Equation
Isolated charged sphere of radius R	$C = 4\pi\epsilon_0 R$	(26.2)
Parallel-plate capacitor of plate area A and plate separation d	$C = \epsilon_0 \dfrac{A}{d}$	(26.3)
Cylindrical capacitor of length ℓ and inner and outer radii a and b, respectively	$C = \dfrac{\ell}{2k_e \ln\left(\dfrac{b}{a}\right)}$	(26.4)
Spherical capacitor with inner and outer radii a and b, respectively	$C = \dfrac{ab}{k_e(b - a)}$	(26.5)

If two or more capacitors are connected in parallel, the potential difference is the same across all of them. The equivalent capacitance of a parallel combination of capacitors is

$$C_{eq} = C_1 + C_2 + C_3 + \cdots \tag{26.7}$$

If two or more capacitors are connected in series, the charge is the same on all of them, and the equivalent capacitance of the series combination is

$$\frac{1}{C_{eq}} = \frac{1}{C_1} + \frac{1}{C_2} + \frac{1}{C_3} + \cdots \tag{26.9}$$

Work is required to charge a capacitor, since the charging process consists of transferring charges from one conductor at a lower potential to another conductor at a higher potential. The work done in charging the capacitor to a charge Q equals the electrostatic potential energy U stored in the capacitor, where

$$U = \frac{Q^2}{2C} = \tfrac{1}{2}QV = \tfrac{1}{2}CV^2 \tag{26.10}$$

When a dielectric material is inserted between the plates of a capacitor, the capacitance generally increases by a dimensionless factor κ called the **dielectric constant**:

$$C = \kappa C_0 \tag{26.13}$$

where C_0 is the capacitance in the absence of the dielectric. The increase in capacitance is due to a decrease in the electric field in the presence of the dielectric and to a corresponding decrease in the potential difference between the plates — assuming the charging battery is removed from the circuit before the dielectric is inserted. The decrease in E arises from an internal electric field produced by aligned dipoles in the dielectric. This internal field produced by the dipoles opposes the original applied field, and the result is a reduction in the net electric field.

An *electric dipole* consists of two equal and opposite charges separated by a distance $2a$. The **electric dipole moment p** of this configuration has a magnitude

$$p \equiv 2aq \tag{26.15}$$

The **torque** acting on an electric dipole in a uniform electric field E is

$$\tau = \mathbf{p} \times \mathbf{E} \tag{26.17}$$

The **potential energy** of an electric dipole in a uniform external electric field E is

$$U = -\mathbf{p} \cdot \mathbf{E} \tag{26.19}$$

Problem-Solving Strategy and Hints
Capacitors

- Be careful with your choice of units. To calculate capacitance in farads, make sure that distances are in meters and use the SI value of ϵ_0. When checking consistency of units, remember that the units for electric fields can be either N/C or V/m.

- When two or more unequal capacitors are connected in series, they carry the same charge, but the potential differences are not the same. Their capacitances add as reciprocals, and the equivalent capacitance of the combination is always less than the smallest individual capacitor.
- When two or more capacitors are connected in parallel, the potential difference across each is the same. The charge on each capacitor is proportional to its capacitance; hence, the capacitances add directly to give the equivalent capacitance of the parallel combination.
- The effect of a dielectric is to increase the capacitance of a capacitor by a factor κ (the dielectric constant) over its empty capacitance. The reason for this is that induced surface charges on the dielectric reduce the electric field inside the material from E to E/κ.
- Be careful about problems in which you may be connecting or disconnecting a battery to a capacitor. It is important to note whether modifications to the capacitor are being made while the capacitor is connected to the battery or after it has been disconnected. If the capacitor remains connected to the battery, the voltage across the capacitor necessarily remains the same (equal to the battery voltage), and the charge is proportional to the capacitance *however it may be modified* (say, by inserting a dielectric). If you disconnect the capacitor from the battery before making any modifications to the capacitor, then its charge remains the same. In this case, as you vary the capacitance, the voltage across the plates changes as $V = Q/C$.

QUESTIONS

1. What happens to the charge on a capacitor if the potential difference between the conductors is doubled?

2. The plates of a capacitor are connected to a battery. What happens to the charge on the plates if the connecting wires are removed from the battery? What happens to the charge if the wires are removed from the battery and connected to each other?

3. A farad is a very large unit of capacitance. Calculate the length of one side of a square, air-filled capacitor that has a plate separation of 1 m. Assume it has a capacitance of 1 F.

4. A pair of capacitors are connected in parallel while an identical pair are connected in series. Which pair would be more dangerous to handle after being connected to the same voltage source? Explain.

5. If you are given three different capacitors C_1, C_2, C_3, how many different combinations of capacitance can you produce?

6. What advantage might there be in using two identical capacitors in parallel connected in series with another identical parallel pair, rather than using a single capacitor?

7. Is it always possible to reduce a combination of capacitors to one equivalent capacitor with the rules we have developed? Explain.

8. Since the net charge in a capacitor is always zero, what does a capacitor store?

9. Since the charges on the plates of a parallel-plate capacitor are equal and opposite, they attract each other. Hence, it would take positive work to increase the plate separation. What happens to the external work done in this process?

10. Explain why the work needed to move a charge Q through a potential difference V is $W = QV$ whereas the energy stored in a charged capacitor is $U = \frac{1}{2}QV$. Where does the $\frac{1}{2}$ factor come from?

11. If the potential difference across a capacitor is doubled, by what factor does the energy stored change?

12. Why is it dangerous to touch the terminals of a high-voltage capacitor even after the applied voltage has been turned off? What can be done to make the capacitor safe to handle after the voltage source has been removed?

13. If you want to increase the maximum operating voltage of a parallel-plate capacitor, describe how you can do this for a fixed plate separation.

14. An air-filled capacitor is charged, then disconnected from the power supply, and finally connected to a voltmeter. Explain how and why the voltage reading changes when a dielectric is inserted between the plates of the capacitor.

15. Using the polar molecule description of a dielectric, explain how a dielectric affects the electric field inside a capacitor.

16. Explain why a dielectric increases the maximum operating voltage of a capacitor although the physical size of the capacitor does not change.
17. What is the difference between dielectric strength and the dielectric constant?
18. Explain why a water molecule is permanently polarized. What type of molecule has no permanent polarization?
19. If a dielectric-filled capacitor is heated, how will its capacitance change? (Neglect thermal expansion and assume that the dipole orientations are temperature dependent.)
20. In terms of induced charges, explain why a charged comb attracts small bits of paper.
21. If you were asked to design a capacitor where small size and large capacitance were required, what factors would be important in your design?

PROBLEMS

Section 26.1 Definition of Capacitance

1. The excess charge on each conductor of a parallel-plate capacitor is 53.0 μC. What is the potential difference between the conductors if the capacitance of the system is 4.00×10^{-3} μF?
2. If a drop of liquid had a capacitance of 1.0 pF in air, (a) what is its radius? (b) If its radius is 2.0 mm, what is its capacitance? (c) What is the charge on the smaller drop if its potential is 100 V?
3. Two conductors having net charges of $+10.0$ μC and -10.0 μC have a potential difference of 10.0 V. Determine (a) the capacitance of the system and (b) the potential difference between the two conductors if the charges on each are increased to $+100.0$ μC and -100.0 μC.
4. Two conductors insulated from each other are charged by transferring electrons from one conductor to the other. After 1.6×10^{12} electrons have been transferred, the potential difference between the conductors is 14 V. What is the capacitance of the system?
5. A parallel-plate capacitor has a capacitance of 19.0 μF. What charge on each plate produces a potential difference of 36.0 V between the plates?
6. By what factor does the capacitance of a metal sphere increase if its volume is tripled?
7. An isolated charged conducting sphere of radius 12.0 cm creates an electric field of 4.90×10^4 N/C at a distance 21.0 cm from its center. (a) What is its surface charge density? (b) What is its capacitance?
8. Two conducting spheres with diameters of 0.40 m and 1.0 m are separated by a distance that is large compared with the diameters. The spheres are connected by a thin wire and are charged to 7.0 μC. (a) How is this total charge shared between the spheres? (Neglect any charge on the wire.) (b) What is the potential of the system of spheres when the reference potential is taken to be $V = 0$ at $r = \infty$?
9. Two spherical conductors with radii $R_1 = 0.15$ cm and $R_2 = 0.23$ cm are separated by a distance large enough to make induction effects negligible. The spheres are connected by a thin conducting wire and are brought to the same potential of 775 V relative to $V = 0$ at $r = \infty$. (a) Determine the capacitance of the system. (b) What is the charge ratio Q_1/Q_2?
9A. Two spherical conductors with radii R_1 and R_2 are separated by a distance large enough to make induction effects negligible. The spheres are connected by a thin conducting wire and are brought to the same potential V relative to $V = 0$ at $r = \infty$. (a) Determine the capacitance C of the system, where $C = (Q_1 + Q_2)/V$. (b) What is the charge ratio Q_1/Q_2?

Section 26.2 Calculation of Capacitance

10. An air-filled parallel-plate capacitor is to have a capacitance of 1.00 F. If the distance between the plates is 1.00 mm, calculate the required surface area of each plate. Convert your answer to square miles.
11. A parallel-plate capacitor has a plate area of 12.0 cm² and a capacitance of 7.00 pF. What is the plate separation?
12. The plates of a parallel-plate capacitor are separated by 0.20 mm. If the space between the plates is air, what plate area is required to provide a capacitance of 9.0 pF?
13. When a potential difference of 150 V is applied to the plates of a parallel-plate capacitor, the plates carry a surface charge density of 30 nC/cm². What is the spacing between the plates?
14. A small object with a mass of 350 mg carries a charge of 30 nC and is suspended by a thread between the vertical plates of a parallel-plate capacitor. The plates are separated by 4.0 cm. If the thread makes an angle of 15° with the vertical, what is the potential difference between the plates?
14A. A small object of mass m carries a charge q and is suspended by a thread between the vertical plates of

---

☐ indicates problems that have full solutions available in the Student Solutions Manual and Study Guide.

a parallel-plate capacitor. The plate separation is *d*. If the thread makes an angle θ with the vertical, what is the potential difference between the plates?

15. An air-filled capacitor consists of two parallel plates, each with an area of 7.60 cm², separated by a distance of 1.80 mm. If a 20.0-V potential difference is applied to these plates, calculate (a) the electric field between the plates, (b) the surface charge density, (c) the capacitance, and (d) the charge on each plate.

16. A 1-megabit computer memory chip contains many 60-fF capacitors. Each capacitor has a plate area of 21×10^{-12} m². Determine the plate separation of such a capacitor (assume a parallel-plate configuration). The characteristic atomic diameter is 10^{-10} m = 1 Å. Express the plate separation in Å.

17. A variable air capacitor used in tuning circuits is made of 10 semicircular plates each of radius 2.5 cm and positioned 0.80 cm from each other. A second identical set that is free to rotate is enmeshed with the first set of plates (Fig. P26.17). Determine the capacitance as a function of the angle of rotation θ, where $\theta = 0$ corresponds to the maximum capacitance.

17A. A variable air capacitor used in tuning circuits is made of *N* semicircular plates each of radius *R* and positioned a distance *d* from each other. A second identical set of plates that is free to rotate is enmeshed with the first set (Fig. P26.17). Determine the capacitance as a function of the angle of rotation θ, where $\theta = 0$ corresponds to the maximum capacitance.

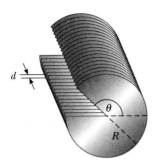

FIGURE P26.17

18. A capacitor is constructed of interlocking plates as shown in Figure P26.18 (a cross-sectional view). The separation between adjacent plates is 0.80 mm, and the total effective area of all plates combined is 7.0 cm². Ignoring side effects, calculate the capacitance of the unit.

FIGURE P26.18

19. A 2.0-μF spherical capacitor is composed of two metal spheres, one having a radius twice as large as the other. If the region between the spheres is a vacuum, determine the volume of this region.

19A. A spherical capacitor having a capacitance *C* is composed of two metal spheres, one having a radius twice as large as the other. If the region between the spheres is a vacuum, determine the volume of this region.

20. An air-filled cylindrical capacitor has a capacitance of 10 pF and is 6.0 cm in length. If the radius of the outside conductor is 1.5 cm, what is the required radius of the inner conductor?

21. A 50.0-m length of coaxial cable has an inner conductor that has a diameter of 2.58 mm and carries a charge of 8.10 μC. The surrounding conductor has an inner diameter of 7.27 mm and a charge of -8.10 μC. (a) What is the capacitance of this cable? (b) What is the potential difference between the two conductors? Assume the region between the conductors is air.

22. A cylindrical capacitor has outer and inner conductors whose radii are in the ratio of $b/a = 4/1$. The inner conductor is to be replaced by a wire whose radius is one-half the radius of the original inner conductor. By what factor should the length be increased in order to obtain a capacitance equal to that of the original capacitor?

23. An air-filled spherical capacitor is constructed with inner and outer shell radii of 7.00 and 14.0 cm, respectively. (a) Calculate the capacitance of the device. (b) What potential difference between the spheres results in a charge of 4.00 μC on the capacitor?

24. Find the capacitance of the Earth. (*Hint:* The outer conductor of the "spherical capacitor" may be considered as a conducting sphere at infinity where $V \equiv 0$.)

25. A spherical capacitor consists of a conducting ball of radius 10.0 cm that is centered inside a grounded conducting spherical shell of inner radius 12.0 cm. What capacitor charge is required to achieve a potential of 1000 V on the ball?

26. Estimate the maximum voltage to which a smooth, metallic sphere 10 cm in diameter can be charged without exceeding the dielectric strength of the dry air around the sphere.

Section 26.3   Combinations of Capacitors

27. (a) Two capacitors, $C_1 = 2.00$ μF and $C_2 = 16.0$ μF, are connected in parallel. What is the equivalent capacitance of the combination? (b) Calculate the equivalent capacitance of the two capacitors in part (a) if they are connected in series.

28. Two capacitors when connected in parallel give an equivalent capacitance of 9.0 pF and an equivalent capacitance of 2.0 pF when connected in series. What is the capacitance of each capacitor?

28A. Two capacitors give an equivalent capacitance C_p and an equivalent capacitance C_s when connected in series. What is the capacitance of each capacitor?

29. (a) Determine the equivalent capacitance for the capacitor network shown in Figure P26.29. (b) If the network is connected to a 12-V battery, calculate the potential difference across each capacitor and the charge on each capacitor.

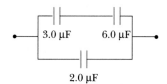

FIGURE P26.29

30. Evaluate the equivalent capacitance of the configuration shown in Figure P26.30. All the capacitors are identical, and each has capacitance C.

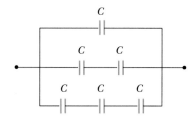

FIGURE P26.30

31. Four capacitors are connected as shown in Figure P26.31. (a) Find the equivalent capacitance between points a and b. (b) Calculate the charge on each capacitor if $V_{ab} = 15$ V.

32. For three 2.0-μF capacitors, sketch the arrangement that gives (a) the largest equivalent capacitance,

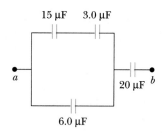

FIGURE P26.31

(b) the smallest equivalent capacitance, (c) an equivalent capacitance of 3.0 μF.

33. Consider the circuit shown in Figure P26.33, where $C_1 = 6.00$ μF, $C_2 = 3.00$ μF, and $V = 20.0$ V. Capacitor C_1 is first charged by the closing of switch S_1. Switch S_1 is then opened, and the charged capacitor is connected to the uncharged capacitor by the closing of S_2. Calculate the initial charge acquired by C_1 and the final charge on each.

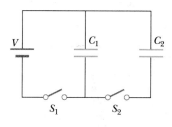

FIGURE P26.33

34. The circuit in Figure P26.34 consists of two identical parallel metal plates connected by identical metal springs to a 100-V battery. With the switch open, the plates are uncharged, are separated by a distance $d = 8.0$ mm, and have a capacitance $C = 2.0$ μF. When the switch is closed, the distance between the

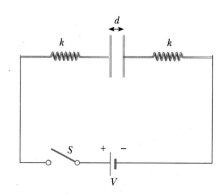

FIGURE P26.34

plates decreases by a factor of 0.5. (a) How much charge collects on each plate and (b) what is the spring constant for each spring? (*Hint:* Use the result of Problem 51.)

34A. The circuit in Figure P26.34 consists of two identical parallel metal plates connected by identical metal springs to a battery of voltage *V*. With the switch open, the plates are uncharged, are separated by a distance *d*, and have a capacitance *C*. When the switch is closed, the distance between the plates decreases by a factor of 0.5. (a) How much charge collects on each plate and (b) what is the spring constant for each spring? (*Hint:* Use the result of Problem 51.)

35. Figure P26.35 shows six concentric conducting spheres, A, B, C, D, E, and F, having radii R, $2R$, $3R$, $4R$, $5R$, and $6R$, respectively. Spheres B and C are connected by a conducting wire as are spheres D and E. Determine the equivalent capacitance of this system.

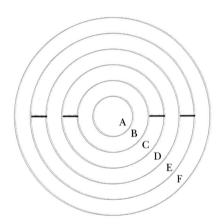

FIGURE P26.35

36. How many 0.25-pF capacitors must be connected in parallel in order to store 1.2 μC of charge when connected to a battery providing a potential difference of 10 V?

37. A group of identical capacitors is connected first in series and then in parallel. The combined capacitance in parallel is 100 times larger than for the series connection. How many capacitors are in the group?

38. Find the equivalent capacitance between points a and b for the group of capacitors connected as shown in Figure P26.38 if $C_1 = 5.00$ μF, $C_2 = 10.0$ μF, and $C_3 = 2.00$ μF.

39. For the network described in the previous problem if the potential between points a and b is 60.0 V, what charge is stored on C_3?

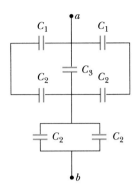

FIGURE P26.38

40. Determine the equivalent capacitance between points a and b in Figure P26.40.

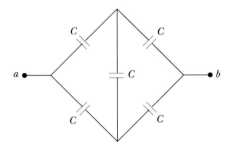

FIGURE P26.40

41. Find the equivalent capacitance between points a and b in the combination of capacitors shown in Figure P26.41.

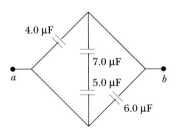

FIGURE P26.41

42. How should four 2.0-μF capacitors be connected to have a total capacitance of (a) 8.0 μF, (b) 2.0 μF, (c) 1.5 μF, and (d) 0.50 μF?

43. A conducting slab of thickness d and area A is inserted into the space between the plates of a parallel-plate capacitor with spacing s and surface area A, as in Figure P26.43. What is the capacitance of the system?

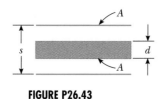

FIGURE P26.43

Section 26.4   Energy Stored in a Charged Capacitor

44. A certain storm cloud has a potential difference of 1.00×10^8 V relative to a tree. If, during a lightning storm, 50.0 C of charge is transferred through this potential difference and 1 percent of the energy is absorbed by the tree, how much water (sap in the tree) initially at 30°C can be boiled away? Water has a specific heat of 4186 J/kg·°C, a boiling point of 100°C, and a heat of vaporization of 2.26×10^6 J/kg.

45. Calculate the energy stored in an 18.0-μF capacitor when it is charged to a potential of 100 V.

46. The energy stored in a particular capacitor is increased fourfold. What is the accompanying change in (a) the charge and (b) the potential difference across the capacitor?

47. The energy stored in a 12.0-μF capacitor is 130 μJ. Determine (a) the charge on the capacitor and (b) the potential difference across it.

48. Einstein said that energy is associated with mass according to the famous relationship, $E = mc^2$. Estimate the radius of an electron, assuming that its charge is distributed uniformly over the surface of a sphere of radius R and that the mass-energy of the electron is equal to the total energy stored in the resulting nonzero electric field between R and infinity. (See Problem 53.)

49. A 16.0-pF parallel-plate capacitor is charged by a 10.0-V battery. If each plate of the capacitor has an area of 5.00 cm², what is the energy stored in the capacitor? What is the energy density (energy per unit volume) in the electric field of the capacitor if the plates are separated by air?

50. The energy stored in a 52.0-μF capacitor is used to melt a 6.00-mg sample of lead. To what voltage must the capacitor be initially charged, assuming that the initial temperature of the lead is 20.0°C? Lead has a specific heat of 128 J/kg·°C, a melting point of 327.3°C, and a latent heat of fusion of 24.5 kJ/kg.

51. A parallel-plate capacitor has a charge Q and plates of area A. Show that the force exerted on each plate by the other is $F = Q^2/2\epsilon_0 A$. (*Hint:* Let $C = \epsilon_0 A/x$ for an arbitrary plate separation x; then, require that the work done in separating the two charged plates be $W = \int F \, dx$.)

52. A uniform electric field $E = 3000$ V/m exists within a certain region. What volume of space contains an energy equal to 1.00×10^{-7} J? Express your answer in cubic meters and in liters.

53. Show that the energy associated with a conducting sphere of radius R and charge Q surrounded by a vacuum is $U = k_e Q^2/2R$.

54. Plate a of a parallel-plate, air-filled capacitor is connected to a spring having force constant k, and plate b is fixed. They rest on a table top as shown (top view) in Figure P26.54. If a charge $+ Q$ is placed on plate a and a charge $- Q$ is placed on plate b, by how much does the spring expand?

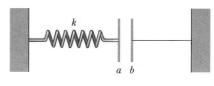

FIGURE P26.54

Section 26.5   Capacitors with Dielectrics
*Section 26.7   An Atomic Description of Dielectrics

55. A parallel-plate capacitor in air has a plate separation of 1.50 cm and a plate area of 25.0 cm². The plates are charged to a potential difference of 250 V and disconnected from the source. The capacitor is then immersed in distilled water. Determine (a) the charge on the plates before and after immersion, (b) the capacitance and voltage after immersion, and (c) the change in energy of the capacitor. Neglect the conductance of the water.

55A. A parallel-plate capacitor in air has a plate separation d and a plate area A. The plates are charged to a potential difference V and disconnected from the source. The capacitor is then immersed in a liquid of dielectric constant κ. Determine (a) the charge on the plates before and after immersion, (b) the capacitance and voltage after immersion and (c) the change in energy of the capacitor.

56. A parallel-plate capacitor is to be constructed using paper as a dielectric. If a maximum voltage before breakdown of 2500 V is desired, what thickness of dielectric is needed? (See Table 26.1 for other dielectric properties.)

57. A parallel-plate capacitor has a plate area of 0.64 cm². When the plates are in a vacuum, the capacitance of the device is 4.9 pF. (a) Calculate the value of the capacitance if the space between the plates is filled with nylon. (b) What is the maximum potential difference that can be applied to the plates without causing dielectric breakdown?

58. A capacitor is constructed from two square metal plates of side length L and separated by a distance d (Fig. P26.58). One half of the space between the plates (top to bottom) is filled with polystyrene ($\kappa = 2.56$), and the other half is filled with neoprene rubber ($\kappa = 6.7$). Calculate the capacitance of the device, taking $L = 2.0$ cm and $d = 0.75$ mm. (*Hint:* The capacitor can be considered as two capacitors connected in parallel.)

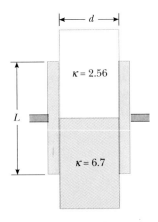

FIGURE P26.58

59. A commercial capacitor is constructed as in Figure 26.12a. This particular capacitor is rolled from two strips of aluminum separated by two strips of paraffin-coated paper. Each strip of foil and paper is 7.0 cm wide. The foil is 0.0040 mm thick, and the paper is 0.025 mm thick and has a dielectric constant of 3.7. What length should the strips be if a capacitance of 9.5×10^{-8} F is desired? (Use the parallel-plate formula.)

60. A detector of radiation called a Geiger tube consists of a closed, hollow, conducting cylinder with a fine wire along its axis. Suppose that the internal diameter of the cylinder is 2.5 cm and that the wire along the axis has a diameter of 0.20 mm. If the dielectric strength of the gas between the central wire and the cylinder is 1.2×10^6 V/m, calculate the maximum voltage that can be applied between the wire and the cylinder before breakdown occurs in the gas.

61. The plates of an isolated, charged capacitor are 1.0 mm apart, and the potential difference across them is V_0. The plates are now separated to 4.0 mm (while the charge on them is preserved), and a slab of dielectric material is inserted, filling the space between the plates. The potential difference across the capacitor is now $V_0/2$. Find the dielectric constant of the material.

62. (a) What is the capacitance of a square parallel-plate capacitor measuring 5.0 cm on a side and having a

0.20-mm gap between the plates if this gap is filled with Teflon? (b) What maximum voltage can this capacitor withstand? (c) What maximum energy can this capacitor store?

63. Each capacitor in the combination shown in Figure P26.63 has a breakdown voltage of 15.0 V. What is the breakdown voltage of the combination?

63A. Each capacitor in the combination shown in Figure P26.63 has a breakdown voltage V. What is the breakdown voltage of the combination?

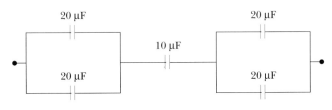

FIGURE P26.63

64. A conducting spherical shell has inner radius a and outer radius c. The space between these two surfaces is filled with a dielectric for which the dielectric constant is κ_1 between a and b and κ_2 between b and c (Fig. P26.64). Determine the capacitance of this system.

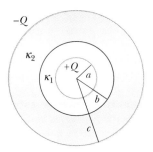

FIGURE P26.64

65. A sheet of 0.10-mm-thick paper is inserted between the plates of a 340-pF air-filled capacitor that has a plate separation of 0.40 mm. Calculate the new capacitance.

66. A wafer of titanium dioxide ($\kappa = 173$) has an area of 1.0 cm^2 and a thickness of 0.10 mm. Aluminum is evaporated on the parallel faces to form a parallel-plate capacitor. (a) Calculate the capacitance. (b) When the capacitor is charged with a 12-V battery, what is the magnitude of charge delivered to each plate? (c) For the situation in part (b), what are the free and induced surface charge densities? (d) What is the electric field strength E?

ADDITIONAL PROBLEMS

67. When two capacitors are connected in parallel, the equivalent capacitance is 4.00 μF. If the same capacitors are reconnected in series, the equivalent capacitance is one-fourth the capacitance of one of the two capacitors. Determine the two capacitances.

68. For the system of capacitors shown in Figure P26.68, find (a) the equivalent capacitance of the system, (b) the potential across each capacitor, (c) the charge on each capacitor, and (d) the total energy stored by the group.

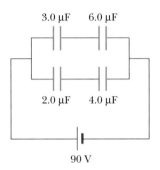

3.0 μF   6.0 μF

2.0 μF   4.0 μF

90 V

FIGURE P26.68

69. (a) Two spheres have radii a and b and their centers are a distance d apart. Show that the capacitance of this system is

$$C \approx \frac{4\pi\epsilon_0}{\dfrac{1}{a} + \dfrac{1}{b} - \dfrac{2}{d}}$$

provided that d is large compared with a and b. (*Hint:* Since the spheres are very far apart, assume that the potential on each equals the sum of the potentials due to each sphere, and when calculating those potentials, assume that $V = k_e Q/r$ applies.) (b) Show that as d approaches $+\infty$, the above result reduces to that of two spherical capacitors in series.

70. A parallel-plate capacitor with air between its plates has a capacitance C_0. A slab of dielectric material with a dielectric constant κ and a thickness equal to a fraction f of the separation of the plates is inserted between the plates in contact with one plate. Find the capacitance C in terms of f, κ, and C_0. Check your result by first letting f approach zero and then letting it approach unity.

71. When a certain air-filled parallel-plate capacitor is connected across a battery, it acquires a charge (on each plate) of 150 μC. While the battery connection is maintained, a dielectric slab is inserted into and fills the region between the plates. This results in the accumulation of an *additional* charge of 200 μC on each plate. What is the dielectric constant of the slab?

71A. When a certain air-filled parallel-plate capacitor is connected across a battery, it acquires a charge (on each plate) of q_0. While the battery connection is maintained, a dielectric slab is inserted into and fills the region between the plates. This results in the accumulation of an *additional* charge q on each plate. What is the dielectric constant of the slab?

72. A capacitor is constructed from two square plates of sides ℓ and separation d. A material of dielectric constant κ is inserted a distance x into the capacitor, as in Figure P26.72. (a) Find the equivalent capacitance of the device. (b) Calculate the energy stored in the capacitor if the potential difference is V. (c) Find the direction and magnitude of the force exerted on the dielectric, assuming a constant potential difference V. Neglect friction and edge effects. (d) Obtain a numerical value for the force assuming that $\ell = 5.0$ cm, $V = 2000$ V, $d = 2.0$ mm, and the dielectric is glass ($\kappa = 4.5$). (*Hint:* The system can be considered as two capacitors connected in *parallel.*)

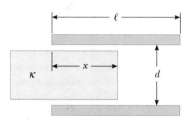

ℓ

κ x d

FIGURE P26.72

73. Three capacitors—8.0 μF, 10.0 μF, and 14 μF—are connected to the terminals of a 12-V battery. How much energy does the battery supply if the capacitors are connected (a) in series and (b) in parallel?

74. When considering the energy supply for an automobile, the energy per unit mass of the energy source is an important parameter. Using the following data, compare the energy per unit mass (J/kg) for gasoline, lead-acid batteries, and capacitors.

- *Gasoline:* 126 000 Btu/gal; density = 670 kg/m^3
- *Lead-acid battery:* 12 V; 100 A·h; mass = 16 kg
- *Capacitor:* potential difference at full charge = 12 V; capacitance = 0.10 F; mass = 0.10 kg

75. An isolated capacitor of unknown capacitance has been charged to a potential difference of 100 V. When the charged capacitor is then connected in parallel to an uncharged 10-μF capacitor, the voltage across the combination is 30 V. Calculate the unknown capacitance.

75A. An isolated capacitor of unknown capacitance has been charged to a potential difference V_0. When the charged capacitor is then connected in parallel to an uncharged capacitor C, the voltage across the combination is $V < V_0$. Calculate the unknown capacitance.

76. A certain electronic circuit calls for a capacitor having a capacitance of 1.2 pF and a breakdown potential of 1000 V. If you have a supply of 6.0-pF capacitors, each having a breakdown potential of 200 V, how could you meet this circuit requirement?

77. A 2.0-μF capacitor and a 3.0-μF capacitor have the same maximum voltage rating V_{max}. Due to this voltage limitation, the maximum potential difference that can be applied to a series combination of these capacitors is 800 V. Calculate the maximum voltage rating of the individual capacitors.

78. A 2.0-nF parallel-plate capacitor is charged to an initial potential difference $V_i = 100$ V and then isolated. The dielectric material between the plates is mica ($\kappa = 5.0$). (a) How much work is required to withdraw the mica sheet? (b) What is the potential difference of the capacitor after the mica is withdrawn?

79. A parallel-plate capacitor is constructed using a dielectric material whose dielectric constant is 3.0 and whose dielectric strength is 2.0×10^8 V/m. The desired capacitance is 0.25 μF, and the capacitor must withstand a maximum potential difference of 4000 V. Find the minimum area of the capacitor plates.

80. A parallel-plate capacitor is constructed using three dielectric materials, as in Figure P26.80. (a) Find an expression for the capacitance of the device in terms of the plate area A and d, κ_1, κ_2, and κ_3. (b) Calculate the capacitance using the values $A = 1.0$ cm^2, $d = 2.00$ mm, $\kappa_1 = 4.9$, $\kappa_2 = 5.6$, and $\kappa_3 = 2.1$.

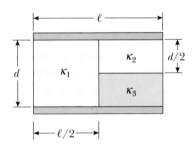

FIGURE P26.80

81. In the arrangement shown in Figure P26.81, a potential V is applied, and C_1 is adjusted so that the voltmeter between points b and d reads zero. This "balance" occurs when $C_1 = 4.00$ μF. If $C_3 = 9.00$ μF and $C_4 = 12.0$ μF, calculate the value of C_2.

82. It is possible to obtain large potential differences by first charging a group of capacitors connected in parallel and then activating a switch arrangement that in

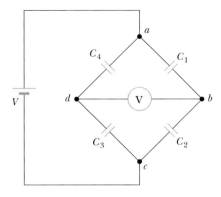

FIGURE P26.81

effect disconnects the capacitors from the charging source and from each other and reconnects them in a series arrangement. The group of charged capacitors is then discharged in series. What is the maximum potential difference that can be obtained in this manner by using ten capacitors each of 500 μF and a charging source of 800 V?

83. A parallel-plate capacitor of plate separation d is charged to a potential difference V_0. A dielectric slab of thickness d and dielectric constant κ is introduced between the plates *while the battery remains connected to the plates*. (a) Show that the ratio of energy stored after the dielectric is introduced to the energy stored in the empty capacitor is $U/U_0 = \kappa$. Give a physical explanation for this increase in stored energy. (b) What happens to the charge on the capacitor? (Note that this situation is not the same as Example 26.7, in which the battery was removed from the circuit before the dielectric was introduced.)

84. A parallel-plate capacitor with plates of area A and plate separation d has the region between the plates filled with two dielectric materials as in Figure P26.84. (a) Determine the capacitance, and (b) show that when $\kappa_1 = \kappa_2 = \kappa$, your result becomes the same as that for a capacitor containing a single dielectric: $C = \kappa \epsilon_0 A / d$.

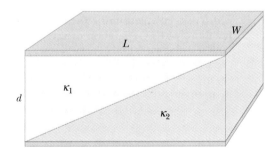

FIGURE P26.84

85. A vertical parallel-plate capacitor is half filled with a dielectric for which the dielectric constant is 2.0 (Fig.

P26.85a). When this capacitor is positioned horizontally, what fraction of it should be filled with the same dielectric (Fig. P26.85b) in order for the two capacitors to have equal capacitance?

(a)   (b)

FIGURE P26.85

86. Capacitors $C_1 = 6.00 \ \mu F$ and $C_2 = 2.00 \ \mu F$ are charged as a parallel combination across a 250-V battery. The capacitors are disconnected from the battery and from each other. They are then connected positive plate to negative plate and negative plate to positive plate. Calculate the resulting charge on each capacitor.

87. A stack of N plates has alternate plates connected to form a capacitor similar to that shown in Figure P26.18. Adjacent plates are separated by a dielectric of thickness d. The dielectric constant is κ, and the area of overlap of adjacent plates is A. Show that the capacitance of this stack of plates is $C = \frac{\kappa \epsilon_0 A}{d} (N - 1).$

88. A coulomb balance is constructed of two parallel plates, each 10.0 cm square. The upper plate is movable. A 25.0-mg mass is placed on the upper plate and the plate is observed to lower; the mass is then removed. When a potential difference is applied to the plates, it is found that the applied voltage must be 375 V to cause the upper plate to lower the same amount as it lowered when the mass was on it. If the force exerted on each plate by the other is $F = Q^2/2\epsilon_0 A$, calculate the following, assuming an applied voltage of 375 V: (a) the charge on the plates, (b) the electric field between them, (c) their separation distance, and (d) the capacitance of this capacitor.

89. The inner conductor of a coaxial cable has a radius of 0.80 mm, and the outer conductor's inside radius is 3.0 mm. The space between the conductors is filled with polyethylene, which has a dielectric constant of 2.3 and a dielectric strength of 18×10^6 V/m. What is the maximum potential difference that this cable can withstand?

90. You are optimizing coaxial cable design for a major manufacturer. Show that for a given outer conductor radius b, maximum potential difference capability is attained when the radius of the inner conductor is $a = b/e$ where e is the base of natural logarithms.

91. Calculate the equivalent capacitance between the points a and b in Figure P26.91. Note that this is not a simple series or parallel combination. (*Hint:* Assume a potential difference V between points a and b. Write expressions for V_{ab} in terms of the charges and capacitances for the various possible pathways from a to b, and require conservation of charge for those capacitor plates that are connected to each other.)

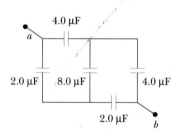

FIGURE P26.91

92. Determine the effective capacitance of the combination shown in Figure P26.92. (*Hint:* Consider the symmetry involved!)

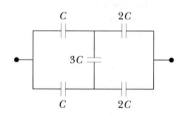

FIGURE P26.92

93. Consider two *long*, parallel, and oppositely charged wires of radius d with their centers separated by a distance D. Assuming the charge is distributed uniformly on the surface of each wire, show that the capacitance per unit length of this pair of wires is

$$\frac{C}{\ell} = \frac{\pi \epsilon_0}{\ln \left(\dfrac{D - d}{d} \right)}$$

CHAPTER 27

Current and Resistance

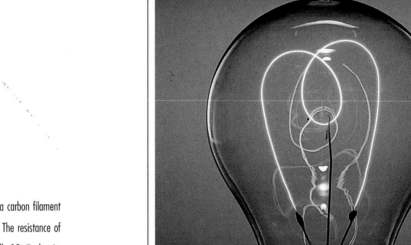

Photograph of a carbon filament incandescent lamp. The resistance of such a lamp is typically 10 Ω, but its value changes with temperature. Most modern lightbulbs use tungsten filaments, whose resistance increases with increasing temperature. *(Courtesy of Central Scientific Co.)*

Thus far our discussion of electrical phenomena has been confined to charges at rest, or electrostatics. We now consider situations involving electric charges in motion. The term *electric current,* or simply *current,* is used to describe the rate of flow of charge through some region of space. Most practical applications of electricity deal with electric currents. For example, the battery of a flashlight supplies current to the filament of the bulb when the switch is turned on. A variety of home appliances operate on alternating current. In these common situations, the flow of charge takes place in a conductor, such as a copper wire. It is also possible for currents to exist outside of a conductor. For instance, a beam of electrons in a TV picture tube constitutes a current.

In this chapter we first define current and current density. A microscopic description of current is given, and some of the factors that contribute to the resistance to the flow of charge in conductors are discussed. Mechanisms responsible for the electrical resistance of various materials depend on the composition of the material and on temperature. A classical model is used to describe electrical conduction in metals, and some of the limitations of this model are pointed out.

27.1 ELECTRIC CURRENT

Whenever electric charges of like sign move, a *current* is established. To define current more precisely, suppose the charges are moving perpendicular to a surface of area A as in Figure 27.1. (This area could be the cross-sectional area of a wire, for example.) The **current** is *the rate at which charge flows through this surface.* If ΔQ is the amount of charge that passes through this area in a time interval Δt, the **average current,** I_{av}, is equal to the charge that passes through A per unit time:

$$I_{av} = \frac{\Delta Q}{\Delta t} \qquad (27.1)$$

If the rate at which charge flows varies in time, the current also varies in time and we define the **instantaneous current** I as the differential limit of Equation 27.1:

$$I \equiv \frac{dQ}{dt} \qquad (27.2)$$

As we learned in Section 23.3, the SI unit of current is the **ampere** (A):

$$1A = \frac{1\ C}{1\ s} \qquad (27.3)$$

That is, 1 A of current is equivalent to 1 C of charge passing through the surface area in 1 s.

The charges passing through the surface in Figure 27.1 can be positive, negative, or both. *It is conventional to give the current the same direction as the flow of positive charge.* In a conductor such as copper, the current is due to the motion of negatively charged electrons. Therefore, when we speak of current in an ordinary conductor, such as a copper wire, *the direction of the current is opposite the direction of flow of electrons.* On the other hand, if a beam of positively charged protons in an accelerator is considered, the current is in the direction of motion of the protons. In some cases—gases and electrolytes, for instance—the current is the result of the flow of both positive and negative charges. It is common to refer to a moving charge (whether it is positive or negative) as a mobile *charge carrier.* For example, the charge carriers in a metal are electrons.

It is instructive to relate current to the motion of the charged particles. To illustrate this point, consider the current in a conductor of cross-sectional area A (Fig. 27.2). The volume of an element of the conductor of length Δx (the shaded region in Fig. 27.2) is $A\ \Delta x$. If n represents the number of mobile charge carriers per unit volume, then the number of mobile charge carriers in the volume element is $nA\ \Delta x$. Therefore, the charge ΔQ in this element is

$$\Delta Q = \text{number of charges} \times \text{charge per particle} = (nA\ \Delta x)q$$

where q is the charge on each particle. If the charge carriers move with a speed v_d, the distance they move in a time Δt is $\Delta x = v_d\ \Delta t$. Therefore, we can write ΔQ in the form

$$\Delta Q = (nAv_d\ \Delta t)q$$

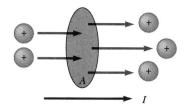

FIGURE 27.1 Charges in motion through an area A. The time rate of flow of charge through the area is defined as the current I. The direction of the current is the direction in which positive charge would flow if free to do so.

Electric current

The direction of the current

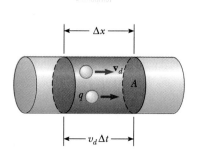

FIGURE 27.2 A section of a uniform conductor of cross-sectional area A. The charge carriers move with a speed v_d, and the distance they travel in a time Δt is given by $\Delta x = v_d\ \Delta t$. The number of mobile charge carriers in the section of length Δx is given by $nAv_d\ \Delta t$, where n is the number of mobile carriers per unit volume.

If we divide both sides of this equation by Δt, we see that the current in the conductor is given by

$$I = \frac{\Delta Q}{\Delta t} = nqv_d A \tag{27.4}$$

The speed of the charge carriers, v_d, is actually an average speed and is called the **drift speed**. To understand its meaning, consider a conductor in which the charge carriers are free electrons. If the conductor is isolated, these electrons undergo random motion similar to that of gas molecules. When a potential difference is applied across the conductor (say, by means of a battery), an electric field is set up in the conductor, and this field creates an electric force on the electrons and hence a current. In reality, the electrons do not move in straight lines along the conductor. Instead, they undergo repeated collisions with the metal atoms, and the result is a complicated zigzag motion (Fig. 27.3). The energy transferred from the electrons to the metal atoms during collision causes an increase in the vibrational energy of the atoms and a corresponding increase in the temperature of the conductor. However, despite the collisions, the electrons move slowly along the conductor (in a direction opposite $\mathbf{E}$) at the drift velocity, $\mathbf{v}_d$. The work done by the field on the electrons exceeds the average loss in energy due to collisions, and this provides a steady current. One can think of the collisions of the electrons within a conductor as being an effective internal friction (or drag force), similar to that experienced by the molecules of a liquid flowing through a pipe stuffed with steel wool.

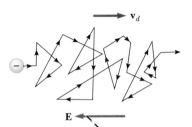

FIGURE 27.3 A schematic representation of the zigzag motion of a charge carrier in a conductor. The changes in direction are due to collisions with atoms in the conductor. Note that the net motion of electrons is opposite the direction of the electric field. The zigzag paths are actually parabolic segments.

EXAMPLE 27.1   Drift Speed in a Copper Wire

A copper wire of cross-sectional area 3.00×10^{-6} m² carries a current of 10.0 A. Find the drift speed of the electrons in this wire. The density of copper is 8.95 g/cm³.

Solution   From the periodic table of the elements in Appendix C, we find that the atomic mass of copper is 63.5 g/mol. Recall that one atomic mass of any substance contains Avogadro's number of atoms, 6.02×10^{23} atoms. Knowing the density of copper enables us to calculate the volume occupied by 63.5 g of copper:

$$V = \frac{m}{\rho} = \frac{63.5 \text{ g}}{8.95 \text{ g/cm}^3} = 7.09 \text{ cm}^3$$

If we now assume that each copper atom contributes one free electron to the body of the material, we have

$$n = \frac{6.02 \times 10^{23} \text{ electrons}}{7.09 \text{ cm}^3}$$

$$= 8.48 \times 10^{22} \text{ electrons/cm}^3$$

$$= \left(8.48 \times 10^{22} \frac{\text{electrons}}{\text{cm}^3}\right)\left(10^6 \frac{\text{cm}^3}{\text{m}^3}\right)$$

$$= 8.48 \times 10^{28} \text{ electrons/m}^3$$

From Equation 27.4, we find that the drift speed is

$$v_d = \frac{I}{nqA}$$

$$= \frac{10.0 \text{ C/s}}{(8.48 \times 10^{28} \text{ m}^{-3})(1.60 \times 10^{-19} \text{ C})(3.00 \times 10^{-6} \text{ m}^2)}$$

$$= 2.46 \times 10^{-4} \text{ m/s}$$

Example 27.1 shows that typical drift speeds are very small. In fact, the drift speed is much smaller than the average speed between collisions. For instance, electrons traveling with this drift speed would take approximately 68 min to travel 1 m! In view of this low speed, you might wonder why a light turns on almost instantaneously when a switch is thrown. This can be explained by considering the flow of water through a pipe. If a drop of water is forced in one end of a pipe that is already filled with water, a drop must be pushed out the other end. While it may take individual drops of water a long time to make it through the pipe, a flow initiated at one end produces a similar flow at the other end very quickly. In a conductor, the electric field that drives the free electrons travels through the conductor with a speed close to that of light. Thus, when you flip a light switch, the message for the electrons to start moving through the wire (the electric field) reaches them at a speed on the order of 10^8 m/s.

27.2 RESISTANCE AND OHM'S LAW

Earlier, we found that there can be no electric field inside a conductor. However, this statement is true *only* if the conductor is in static equilibrium. The purpose of this section is to describe what happens when the charges are allowed to move in the conductor.

Charges move in a conductor to produce a current under the action of an electric field inside the conductor. An electric field can exist in the conductor in this case because we are dealing with charges in motion, a *nonelectrostatic* situation.

Consider a conductor of cross-sectional area A carrying a current I. The **current density** J in the conductor is defined to be the current per unit area. Since the current $I = nqv_dA$, the current density is

$$J \equiv \frac{I}{A} = nqv_d \tag{27.5}$$

where J has SI units of A/m^2. This expression is valid only if the current density is uniform and only if the surface of cross-sectional area A is perpendicular to the direction of the current. In general, the current density is a *vector quantity:*

$$\mathbf{J} = nq\mathbf{v}_d \tag{27.6}$$

Current density

From this definition, we see once again that the current density, like the current, is in the direction of charge motion for positive charge carriers and opposite the direction of motion for negative charge carriers.

A current density $\mathbf{J}$ *and an electric field* $\mathbf{E}$ *are established in a conductor when a potential difference is maintained across the conductor.* If the potential difference is constant, the current is also constant. Very often, the current density is proportional to the electric field:

$$\mathbf{J} = \sigma\mathbf{E} \tag{27.7}$$

Ohm's law

where the constant of proportionality σ is called the **conductivity** of the conductor.[1] Materials that obey Equation 27.7 are said to follow Ohm's law, named after Georg Simon Ohm (1787–1854). More specifically, **Ohm's law** states that

> for many materials (including most metals), the ratio of the current density to the electric field is a constant, σ, that is independent of the electric field producing the current.

Materials that obey Ohm's law and hence demonstrate this linear behavior between $\mathbf{E}$ and $\mathbf{J}$ are said to be *ohmic.* The electrical behavior of most materials is quite

---

[1] Do not confuse the conductivity σ with the surface charge density, for which the same symbol is used.

linear for very small changes in the current. Experimentally, it is found that not all materials have this property, however. Materials that do not obey Ohm's law are said to be *nonohmic*. Ohm's law is not a fundamental law of nature but rather an empirical relationship valid only for certain materials.

A form of Ohm's law useful in practical applications can be obtained by considering a segment of a straight wire of cross-sectional area A and length ℓ, as in Figure 27.4. A potential difference $V = V_b - V_a$ is maintained across the wire, creating an electric field in the wire and a current. If the electric field in the wire is assumed to be uniform, the potential difference is related to the electric field through the relationship[2]

$$V = E\ell$$

Therefore, we can express the magnitude of the current density in the wire as

$$J = \sigma E = \sigma \frac{V}{\ell}$$

Since $J = I/A$, the potential difference can be written

$$V = \frac{\ell}{\sigma} J = \left(\frac{\ell}{\sigma A}\right) I$$

The quantity $\ell/\sigma A$ is called the **resistance** R of the conductor. From the last expression, we can define the resistance as the ratio of the potential difference across the conductor to the current:

$$R = \frac{\ell}{\sigma A} \equiv \frac{V}{I} \qquad (27.8)$$

From this result we see that resistance has SI units of volts per ampere. One volt per ampere is defined to be one ohm (Ω):

$$1\ \Omega \equiv \frac{1\ \text{V}}{1\ \text{A}} \qquad (27.9)$$

That is, if a potential difference of 1 V across a conductor causes a current of 1 A, the resistance of the conductor is 1 Ω. For example, if an electrical appliance connected to a 120-V source carries a current of 6 A, its resistance is 20 Ω.

The inverse of conductivity is **resistivity** ρ:

$$\rho \equiv \frac{1}{\sigma} \qquad (27.10)$$

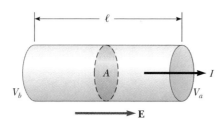

FIGURE 27.4 A uniform conductor of length ℓ and cross-sectional area A. A potential difference $V_b - V_a$ maintained across the conductor sets up an electric field **E** in the conductor, and this field produces a current I that is proportional to the potential difference.

[2] This result follows from the definition of potential difference:

$$V_b - V_a = -\int_a^b \mathbf{E} \cdot d\mathbf{s} = E \int_0^\ell dx = E\ell$$

Using this definition and Equation 27.8, we can express the resistance as

$$R = \rho \frac{\ell}{A}$$

(27.11)

Resistance of a uniform conductor

where ρ has the units ohm-meters ($\Omega \cdot m$). (The symbol ρ for resistivity should not be confused with the same symbol used earlier in the text for mass density or charge density.) Every ohmic material has a characteristic resistivity that depends on the properties of the material and on temperature. On the other hand, as you can see from Equation 27.11, the resistance of a substance depends on simple geometry as well as on resistivity. Good electrical conductors have very low resistivity (or high conductivity), and good insulators have very high resistivity (low conductivity). Table 27.1 gives the resistivities of a variety of materials at 20°C. Note the enormous range in resistivities, from very low values for good conductors, such as copper and silver, to very high values for good insulators, such as glass and rubber. An ideal, or "perfect," conductor would have zero resistivity, and an ideal insulator would have infinite resistivity.

Equation 27.11 shows that the resistance of a given cylindrical conductor is proportional to its length and inversely proportional to its cross-sectional area. If the length of a wire is doubled, its resistance doubles. If its cross-sectional area is doubled, its resistance drops by one half. The situation is analogous to the flow of a liquid through a pipe. As the length of the pipe is increased, the resistance to flow increases. As its cross-sectional area is increased, the pipe can more readily transport liquid.

An assortment of resistors used for various applications in electronic circuits.   *(Henry Leap and Jim Lehman)*

TABLE 27.1   Resistivities and Temperature Coefficients of Resistivity for Various Materials

Material	Resistivity[a] ($\Omega \cdot m$)	Temperature Coefficient $\alpha[(°C)^{-1}]$
Silver	1.59×10^{-8}	3.8×10^{-3}
Copper	1.7×10^{-8}	3.9×10^{-3}
Gold	2.44×10^{-8}	3.4×10^{-3}
Aluminum	2.82×10^{-8}	3.9×10^{-3}
Tungsten	5.6×10^{-8}	4.5×10^{-3}
Iron	10×10^{-8}	5.0×10^{-3}
Platinum	11×10^{-8}	3.92×10^{-3}
Lead	22×10^{-8}	3.9×10^{-3}
Nichrome[b]	1.50×10^{-6}	0.4×10^{-3}
Carbon	3.5×10^{-5}	-0.5×10^{-3}
Germanium	0.46	-48×10^{-3}
Silicon	640	-75×10^{-3}
Glass	$10^{10} - 10^{14}$	
Hard rubber	$\approx 10^{13}$	
Sulfur	10^{15}	
Quartz (fused)	75×10^{16}	

[a] All values at 20°C.

[b] A nickel-chromium alloy commonly used in heating elements.

TABLE 27.2 **Color Code for Resistors**

Color	Number	Multiplier	Tolerance (%)
Black	0	1	
Brown	1	10^1	
Red	2	10^2	
Orange	3	10^3	
Yellow	4	10^4	
Green	5	10^5	
Blue	6	10^6	
Violet	7	10^7	
Gray	8	10^8	
White	9	10^9	
Gold		10^{-1}	5%
Silver		10^{-2}	10%
Colorless			20%

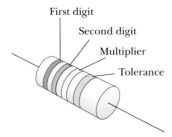

First digit
Second digit
Multiplier
Tolerance

FIGURE 27.5 The colored bands on a resistor represent a code for determining the value of its resistance. The first two colors give the first two digits in the resistance value. The third color represents the power of ten for the multiplier of the resistance value. The last color is the tolerance of the resistance value. As an example, if the four colors are orange, blue, yellow, and gold, the resistance value is $36 \times 10^4 \ \Omega$ or 360 kΩ, with a tolerance value of 18 kΩ (5%).

Most electric circuits make use of devices called **resistors** to control the current level in the various parts of the circuit. Two common types of resistors are the composition resistor containing carbon, which is a semiconductor, and the wirewound resistor, which consists of a coil of wire. Resistors are normally color coded to give their values in ohms, as shown in Figure 27.5 and Table 27.2.

Ohmic materials have a linear current-voltage relationship over a large range of applied voltage (Fig. 27.6a). The slope of the *I* versus *V* curve in the linear region yields a value for *R*. Nonohmic materials have a nonlinear current-voltage relationship. One common semiconducting device that has nonlinear *I* versus *V* characteristics is the diode (Fig. 27.6b). The resistance of this device (inversely proportional to the slope of its *I* versus *V* curve) is small for currents in one direction (positive *V*) and large for currents in the reverse direction (negative *V*). In fact, most modern electronic devices, such as transistors, have nonlinear current-voltage relationships; their proper operation depends on the particular way in which they violate Ohm's law.

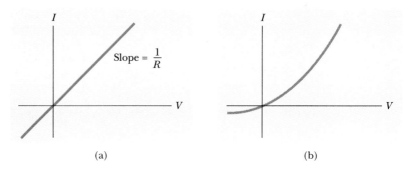

(a)   (b)

FIGURE 27.6 (a) The current-voltage curve for an ohmic material. The curve is linear, and the slope gives the resistance of the conductor. (b) A nonlinear current-voltage curve for a semiconducting diode. This device does not obey Ohm's law.

CONCEPTUAL EXAMPLE 27.2   Is There a Paradox?

We have seen that an electric field must exist inside a conductor that carries a current. How is this possible in view of the fact that in electrostatics we concluded that the electric field is zero inside a conductor?

Reasoning   In the electrostatic case where charges are stationary (Chapters 23 and 24), the internal electric field must be zero because a nonzero field would produce a current (by interacting with the free electrons in the conductor), which would violate the condition of static equilibrium. In this chapter we deal with conductors that carry current, a non-electrostatic situation. The current arises because of a potential difference applied between the ends of the conductor, which produces an internal electric field. So there is no paradox.

EXAMPLE 27.3   The Resistance of a Conductor

Calculate the resistance of an aluminum cylinder that is 10.0 cm long and has a cross-sectional area of 2.00×10^{-4} m². Repeat the calculation for a glass cylinder of resistivity 3.0×10^{10} Ω·m.

Solution   From Equation 27.11 and Table 27.1, we can calculate the resistance of the aluminum cylinder:

$$R = \rho \frac{L}{A} = (2.82 \times 10^{-8} \ \Omega \cdot m)\left(\frac{0.100 \ m}{2.00 \times 10^{-4} \ m^2}\right)$$

$$= 1.41 \times 10^{-5} \ \Omega$$

Similarly, for glass we find

$$R = \rho \frac{L}{A} = (3.0 \times 10^{10} \ \Omega \cdot m)\left(\frac{0.100 \ m}{2.00 \times 10^{-4} \ m^2}\right)$$

$$= 1.5 \times 10^{13} \ \Omega$$

As you might expect, aluminum has a much lower resistance than glass. This is why aluminum is considered a good electrical conductor and glass is a poor conductor.

EXAMPLE 27.4   The Resistance of Nichrome Wire

(a) Calculate the resistance per unit length of a 22-gauge Nichrome wire, which has a radius of 0.321 mm.

Solution   The cross-sectional area of this wire is

$$A = \pi r^2 = \pi (0.321 \times 10^{-3} \ m)^2 = 3.24 \times 10^{-7} \ m^2$$

The resistivity of Nichrome is 1.5×10^{-6} Ω·m (Table 27.1). Thus, we can use Equation 27.11 to find the resistance per unit length:

$$\frac{R}{\ell} = \frac{\rho}{A} = \frac{1.5 \times 10^{-6} \ \Omega \cdot m}{3.24 \times 10^{-7} \ m^2} = 4.6 \ \Omega/m$$

(b) If a potential difference of 10 V is maintained across a 1.0-m length of the nichrome wire, what is the current in the wire?

Solution   Since a 1.0-m length of this wire has a resistance of 4.6 Ω, Ohm's law gives

$$I = \frac{V}{R} = \frac{10 \ V}{4.6 \ \Omega} = 2.2 \ A$$

Note from Table 27.1 that the resistivity of nichrome wire is about 100 times that of copper. Therefore, a copper wire of the same radius would have a resistance per unit length of only 0.052 Ω/m. A 1.0-m length of copper wire of the same radius would carry the same current (2.2 A) with an applied voltage of only 0.11 V.

Because of its high resistivity and its resistance to oxidation, Nichrome is often used for heating elements in toasters, irons, and electric heaters.

Exercise   What is the resistance of a 6.0-m length of 22-gauge Nichrome wire? How much current does it carry when connected to a 120-V source?

Answer   28 Ω, 4.3 A.

Exercise   Calculate the current density and electric field in the wire assuming that it carries a current of 2.2 A.

Answer 6.7×10^6 A/m²; 10 N/C.

EXAMPLE 27.5   The Resistance of a Coaxial Cable

A coaxial cable consists of two cylindrical conductors. The gap between the conductors is completely filled with silicon as in Figure 27.7a. The radius of the inner conductor is $a = 0.500$ cm, the radius of the outer one is $b = 1.75$ cm, and their length is $L = 15.0$ cm. Calculate the total resistance of the silicon when measured between the inner and outer conductors.

Reasoning   In this type of problem, we must divide the object whose resistance we are calculating into elements of infinitesimal thickness over which the area may be considered constant. We start by using the differential form of Equation 27.11, which is $dR = \rho \, d\ell / A$, where dR is the resistance of a section of silicon of thickness $d\ell$ and area A. In this example, we take as our element a hollow cylinder of thickness dr and length L as in Figure 27.7b. Any current that passes between the inner and outer conductors must pass radially through such elements, and the area through which this current passes is $A = 2\pi rL$. (This is the surface area of our hollow cylinder neglecting the area of its ends.) Hence, we can write

the resistance of our hollow cylinder as

$$dR = \frac{\rho}{2\pi rL}\, dr$$

Solution   Since we wish to know the total resistance of the silicon, we must integrate this expression over dr from $r = a$ to $r = b$:

$$R = \int_a^b dR = \frac{\rho}{2\pi L}\int_a^b \frac{dr}{r} = \frac{\rho}{2\pi L}\ln\left(\frac{b}{a}\right)$$

Substituting in the values given, and using $\rho = 640 \ \Omega \cdot$ m for silicon, we get

$$R = \frac{640 \ \Omega \cdot \text{m}}{2\pi(0.150 \ \text{m})}\ln\left(\frac{1.75 \ \text{cm}}{0.500 \ \text{cm}}\right) = \boxed{851 \ \Omega}$$

Exercise   If a potential difference of 12.0 V is applied between the inner and outer conductors, calculate the total current that passes between them.

Answer   14.1 mA.

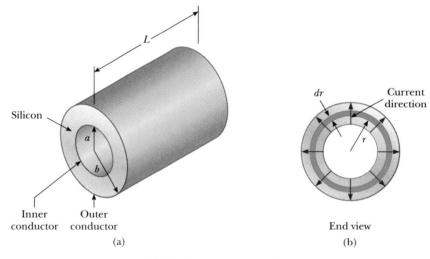

Silicon
a
b
Inner conductor   Outer conductor
(a)

dr Current direction
r
End view
(b)

FIGURE 27.7   (Example 27.5).

27.3   RESISTANCE AND TEMPERATURE

Resistivity depends on a number of factors, one of which is temperature. For all metals, resistivity increases with increasing temperature. The resistivity of a conductor varies approximately linearly with temperature over a limited temperature range according to the expression

Variation of ρ with temperature

$$\rho = \rho_0[1 + \alpha(T - T_0)] \tag{27.12}$$

where ρ is the resistivity at some temperature T (in °C), ρ_0 is the resistivity at some reference temperature T_0 (usually taken to be 20°C), and α is called the **temperature coefficient of resistivity**. From Equation 27.12, we see that the temperature coefficient of resistivity can also be expressed as

$$\alpha = \frac{1}{\rho_0} \frac{\Delta\rho}{\Delta T} \tag{27.13}$$

where $\Delta\rho = \rho - \rho_0$ is the change in resistivity in the temperature interval $\Delta T = T - T_0$. (The temperature coefficients for various materials are given in Table 27.1.)

Since resistance is proportional to resistivity according to Equation 27.11, the variation of resistance with temperature can be written as

$$R = R_0[1 + \alpha(T - T_0)] \tag{27.14}$$

Precise temperature measurements are often made using this property, as shown in the following example.

EXAMPLE 27.6 A Platinum Resistance Thermometer

A resistance thermometer, which measures temperature by measuring the change in resistance of a conductor, is made from platinum and has a resistance of 50.0 Ω at 20.0°C. When immersed in a vessel containing melting indium, its resistance increases to 76.8 Ω. What is the melting point of indium?

Solution Solving Equation 27.14 for ΔT, and getting α from Table 27.1, we get

$$\Delta T = \frac{R - R_0}{\alpha R_0} = \frac{76.8\ \Omega - 50.0\ \Omega}{[3.92 \times 10^{-3}\ (°\text{C})^{-1}](50.0\ \Omega)} = 137°\text{C}$$

Since $T_0 = 20.0°\text{C}$, we find that $T = 157°\text{C}$.

For several metals, resistivity is nearly proportional to temperature, as shown in Figure 27.8. In reality, however, there is always a nonlinear region at very low temperatures, and the resistivity usually approaches some finite value near absolute zero (see magnified insert in Fig. 27.8). This residual resistivity near absolute zero is due primarily to collisions of electrons with impurities and imperfections in the metal. In contrast, the high-temperature resistivity (the linear region) is dominated by collisions of electrons with the metal atoms. We describe this process in more detail in Section 27.5.

The resistivity of semiconductors decreases with increasing temperature, corresponding to a negative temperature coefficient of resistivity (Fig. 27.9). This

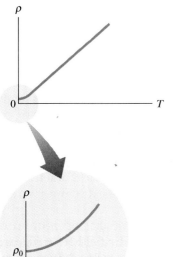

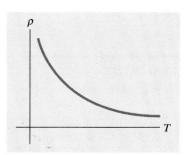

FIGURE 27.8 Resistivity versus temperature for a normal metal, such as copper. The curve is linear over a wide range of temperatures, and ρ increases with increasing temperature. As T approaches absolute zero (insert), the resistivity approaches a finite value ρ_0.

FIGURE 27.9 Resistivity versus temperature for a pure semiconductor, such as silicon or germanium.

behavior is due to the increase in the density of charge carriers at the higher temperatures. Since the charge carriers in a semiconductor are often associated with impurity atoms, the resistivity is very sensitive to the type and concentration of such impurities. The **thermistor** is a semiconducting thermometer that makes use of the large changes in its resistivity with temperature. We shall return to the study of semiconductors in the extended version of this text, Chapter 43.

27.4 SUPERCONDUCTORS

There is a class of metals and compounds whose resistance goes to zero below a certain temperature, T_c, called the *critical temperature*. These materials are known as **superconductors**. The resistance-temperature graph for a superconductor follows that of a normal metal at temperatures above T_c (Fig. 27.10). When the temperature is at or below T_c, the resistivity drops suddenly to zero. This phenomenon was discovered in 1911 by the Dutch physicist Heike Kamerlingh-Onnes as he worked with mercury, which is a superconductor below 4.2 K. Recent measurements have shown that the resistivities of superconductors below T_c are less than $4 \times 10^{-25}\ \Omega \cdot m$, which is around 10^{17} times smaller than the resistivity of copper and considered to be zero in practice.

Today there are thousands of known superconductors, and Table 27.3 lists the critical temperatures of several. The value of T_c is sensitive to chemical composition, pressure, and crystalline structure. It is interesting to note that copper, silver, and gold, which are excellent conductors, do not exhibit superconductivity.

One of the truly remarkable features of superconductors is that once a current is set up in them, it persists *without any applied voltage* (since $R = 0$). In fact, steady currents have been observed to persist in superconducting loops for several years with no apparent decay!

One of the most important recent developments in physics that has created much excitement in the scientific community has been the discovery of high-temperature copper-oxide superconductors. The excitement began with a 1986 publication by George Bednorz and K. Alex Müller, two scientists working at the IBM Zurich Research Laboratory, who reported evidence for superconductivity near 30 K in an oxide of barium, lanthanum, and copper. Bednorz and Müller were awarded the Nobel Prize in 1987 for their remarkable and important discovery. Shortly thereafter, a new family of compounds was open for investigation, and research activity in the field of superconductivity proceeded vigorously. In early 1987, groups at the University of Alabama at Huntsville and the University of Houston announced the discovery of superconductivity at about 92 K in an oxide of yttrium, barium, and copper ($YBa_2Cu_3O_7$). Late in 1987, teams of scientists from Japan and the United States reported superconductivity at 105 K in an oxide of bismuth, strontium, calcium, and copper. Most recently, scientists have reported superconductivity as high as 134 K in the compound. At this point, the possibility of room temperature superconductivity cannot be ruled out, and the search for novel superconducting materials continues. These developments are very exciting and important both for scientific reasons and because practical applications become more probable and widespread as the critical temperature is raised.

An important and useful application of superconductivity has been the construction of superconducting magnets in which the magnetic field strengths are about ten times greater than those of the best normal electromagnets. Such superconducting magnets are being considered as a means of storing energy. The idea of using superconducting power lines for transmitting power efficiently is also

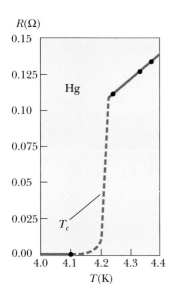

FIGURE 27.10 Resistance versus temperature for mercury. The graph follows that of a normal metal above the critical temperature, T_c. The resistance drops to zero at the critical temperature, which is 4.2 K for mercury.

TABLE 27.3 Critical Temperatures for Various Superconductors

Material	T_c(K)
$YBa_2Cu_3O_{7-\delta}$	92
Bi-Sr-Ca-Cu-O	105
Tl-Ba-Ca-Cu-O	125
$HgBa_2Ca_2Cu_3O_8$	134
Nb_3Ge	23.2
Nb_3Sn	18.05
Nb	9.46
Pb	7.18
Hg	4.15
Sn	3.72
Al	1.19
Zn	0.88

receiving some consideration. Modern superconducting electronic devices consisting of two thin-film superconductors separated by a thin insulator have been constructed. They include magnetometers (a magnetic-field measuring device) and various microwave devices.

27.5 A MODEL FOR ELECTRICAL CONDUCTION

In this section we describe a classical model of electrical conduction in metals. This model leads to Ohm's law and shows that resistivity can be related to the motion of electrons in metals.

Consider a conductor as a regular array of atoms containing free electrons (sometimes called *conduction* electrons). These electrons are free to move through the conductor and are approximately equal in number to the number of atoms. In the absence of an electric field, the free electrons move in random directions through the conductor with average speeds of the order of 10^6 m/s. The situation is similar to the motion of gas molecules confined in a vessel. In fact, some scientists refer to conduction electrons in a metal as an *electron gas*. The conduction electrons are not totally free because they are confined to the interior of the conductor and undergo frequent collisions with the atoms. These electron-atom collisions are the predominant mechanism for the resistivity of a metal at normal temperatures. Note that there is no current through a conductor in the absence of an electric field because the drift velocity of the free electrons is zero. That is, on the average, just as many electrons move in one direction as in the opposite direction, and so there is no net flow of charge.

The situation is modified when an electric field is applied to the conductor. In addition to the random motion just described, the free electrons drift slowly in a direction opposite that of the electric field, with an average drift speed v_d, that is much smaller (typically 10^{-4} m/s) than the average speed between collisions (typically 10^6 m/s). Figure 27.11 provides a crude description of the motion of free electrons in a conductor. In the absence of an electric field, there is no net displacement after many collisions (Fig. 27.11a). An electric field E modifies the random motion and causes the electrons to drift in a direction opposite that of E (Fig. 27.11b). The slight curvature in the paths in Figure 27.11b results from the acceleration of the electrons between collisions, caused by the applied field. One

Photograph of a small permanent magnet levitated above a disk of the superconductor $YBa_2Cu_3O_{7\text{-}\delta}$, which is at 77 K. *(Tony Stone/Worldwide)*

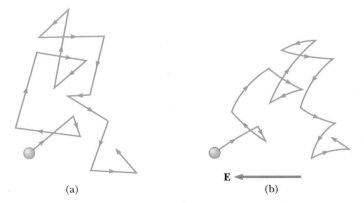

(a)   E ⟵   (b)

FIGURE 27.11 (a) A schematic diagram of the random motion of a charge carrier in a conductor in the absence of an electric field. The drift velocity is zero. (b) The motion of a charge carrier in a conductor in the presence of an electric field. Note that the random motion is modified by the field, and the charge carrier has a drift velocity.

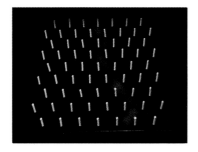

FIGURE 27.12 A mechanical system somewhat analogous to the motion of charge carriers in the presence of an electric field. The collisions of the ball with the pegs represent the resistance to the ball's motion down the incline. (*Jim Lehman*)

mechanical system somewhat analogous to this situation is a ball rolling down a slightly inclined plane through an array of closely spaced, fixed pegs (Fig. 27.12). The ball represents a conduction electron, the pegs represent defects in the crystal lattice, and the component of the gravitational force along the incline represents the electric force $e\mathbf{E}$.

In our model, we assume that the excess energy acquired by the electrons in the electric field is lost to the conductor in the collision process. The energy given up to the atoms in the collisions increases the vibrational energy of the atoms, causing the conductor to heat up. The model also assumes that the motion of an electron after a collision is independent of its motion before the collision.

We are now in a position to obtain an expression for the drift velocity. When a free electron of mass m and charge q is subjected to an electric field $\mathbf{E}$, it experiences a force $q\mathbf{E}$. Since $\mathbf{F} = m\mathbf{a}$, we conclude that the acceleration of the electron is

$$\mathbf{a} = \frac{q\mathbf{E}}{m} \tag{27.15}$$

This acceleration, which occurs for only a short time between collisions, enables the electron to acquire a small drift velocity. If t is the time since the last collision and $\mathbf{v}_0$ is the initial velocity, then the velocity of the electron after a time t is

$$\mathbf{v} = \mathbf{v}_0 + \mathbf{a}t = \mathbf{v}_0 + \frac{q\mathbf{E}}{m}t \tag{27.16}$$

We now take the average value of $\mathbf{v}$ over all possible times t and all possible values of $\mathbf{v}_0$. If the initial velocities are assumed to be randomly distributed in space, we see that the average value of $\mathbf{v}_0$ is zero. The term $(q\mathbf{E}/m)\,t$ is the velocity added by the field during one trip between atoms. If the electron starts with zero velocity, the average value of the second term of Equation 27.16 is $(q\mathbf{E}/m)\,\tau$, where τ is the *average time interval between successive collisions*. Because the average of $\mathbf{v}$ is equal to the drift velocity,[3] we have

Drift velocity

$$\mathbf{v}_d = \frac{q\mathbf{E}}{m}\,\tau \tag{27.17}$$

Substituting this result into Equation 27.6, we find that the magnitude of the current density is

Current density

$$J = nqv_d = \frac{nq^2E}{m}\,\tau \tag{27.18}$$

Comparing this expression with Ohm's law, $J = \sigma E$, we obtain the following relationships for conductivity and resistivity:

Conductivity

$$\sigma = \frac{nq^2\tau}{m} \tag{27.19}$$

Resistivity

$$\rho = \frac{1}{\sigma} = \frac{m}{nq^2\tau} \tag{27.20}$$

---

[3] Since the collision process is random, each collision event is *independent* of what happened earlier. This is analogous to the random process of throwing a die. The probability of rolling a particular number on one throw is independent of the result of the previous throw. On the average, it would take six throws to come up with that number, starting at any arbitrary time.

According to this classical model, conductivity and resistivity do not depend on the electric field. This feature is characteristic of a conductor obeying Ohm's law. The average time between collisions is related to the average distance between collisions ℓ (the mean free path, Section 21.7) and the average speed $\bar{v}$ through the expression

$$\tau = \frac{\ell}{\bar{v}} \tag{27.21}$$

EXAMPLE 27.7   Electron Collisions in Copper

(a) Using the data and results from Example 27.1 and the classical model of electron conduction, estimate the average time between collisions for electrons in copper at 20°C.

Solution   From Equation 27.20 we see that

$$\tau = \frac{m}{nq^2\rho}$$

where $\rho = 1.7 \times 10^{-8}$ $\Omega \cdot$m for copper and the carrier density $n = 8.48 \times 10^{28}$ electrons/m^3 for the wire described in Example 27.1. Substitution of these values into the expression above gives

$$\tau = \frac{(9.11 \times 10^{-31} \text{ kg})}{(8.48 \times 10^{28} \text{ m}^{-3})(1.6 \times 10^{-19} \text{ C})^2(1.7 \times 10^{-8} \text{ }\Omega \cdot \text{m})}$$

$$= 2.5 \times 10^{-14} \text{ s}$$

(b) Assuming the average speed for free electrons in copper to be 1.6×10^6 m/s and using the result from part (a), calculate the mean free path for electrons in copper.

Solution

$$\ell = \bar{v}\tau = (1.6 \times 10^6 \text{ m/s})(2.5 \times 10^{-14} \text{ s})$$

$$= 4.0 \times 10^{-8} \text{ m}$$

which is equivalent to 40 nm (compared with atomic spacings of about 0.2 nm). Thus, although the time between collisions is very short, the electrons travel about 200 atomic distances before colliding with an atom.

Although this classical model of conduction is consistent with Ohm's law, it is not satisfactory for explaining some important phenomena. For example, classical calculations for $\bar{v}$ using the ideal-gas model are about a factor of 10 smaller than the true values. Furthermore, according to Equations 27.20 and 27.21, the temperature variation of the resistivity is predicted to vary as $\bar{v}$, which according to an ideal-gas model (Chapter 21) is proportional to $\sqrt{T}$. This is in disagreement with the linear dependence of resistivity with temperature for pure metals (Fig. 27.8). It is possible to account for such observations only by using a quantum mechanical model, which we shall describe briefly.

According to quantum mechanics, electrons have wave-like properties. If the array of atoms is regularly spaced (that is, periodic), the wave-like character of the electrons makes it possible for them to move freely through the conductor, and a collision with an atom is unlikely. For an idealized conductor, there would be no collisions, the mean free path would be infinite, and the resistivity would be zero. Electron waves are scattered only if the atomic arrangement is irregular (not periodic) as a result of, for example, structural defects or impurities. At low temperatures, the resistivity of metals is dominated by scattering caused by collisions between the electrons and impurities. At high temperatures, the resistivity is dominated by scattering caused by collisions between the electrons and the atoms of the conductor, which are continuously displaced as a result of thermal agitation. The thermal motion of the atoms causes the structure to be irregular (compared with an atomic array at rest), thereby reducing the electron's mean free path.

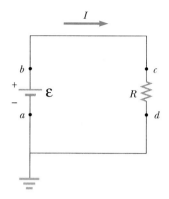

FIGURE 27.13 A circuit consisting of a battery of emf $\mathcal{E}$ and resistance R. Positive charge flows in the clockwise direction, from the negative to the positive terminal of the battery. Points a and d are grounded.

27.6 ELECTRICAL ENERGY AND POWER

If a battery is used to establish an electric current in a conductor, there is a continuous transformation of chemical energy stored in the battery to kinetic energy of the charge carriers. This kinetic energy is quickly lost as a result of collisions between the charge carriers and the atoms making up the conductor, resulting in an increase in the temperature of the conductor. Therefore, we see that the chemical energy stored in the battery is continuously transformed to thermal energy.

Consider a simple circuit consisting of a battery whose terminals are connected to a resistor R, as shown in Figure 27.13. (Resistors are designated by the symbol $-\wedge\wedge\wedge\wedge-$.) Now imagine following a positive quantity of charge ΔQ moving around the circuit from point a through the battery and resistor and back to a. Point a is a reference point that is grounded (ground symbol $\perp$), and its potential is taken to be zero. As the charge moves from a to b through the battery, its electrical potential energy *increases* by an amount $V \Delta Q$ (where V is the potential at b) while the chemical potential energy in the battery *decreases* by the same amount. (Recall from Eq. 25.9 that $\Delta U = q \Delta V$.) However, as the charge moves from c to d through the resistor, it *loses* this electrical potential energy as it undergoes collisions with atoms in the resistor, thereby producing thermal energy. If we neglect the resistance of the interconnecting wires, there is no loss in energy for paths bc and da. When the charge returns to point a, it must have the same potential energy (zero) as it had at the start.[4]

The rate at which the charge ΔQ loses potential energy in going through the resistor is

$$\frac{\Delta U}{\Delta t} = \frac{\Delta Q}{\Delta t} V = IV$$

where I is the current in the circuit. Of course, the charge regains this energy when it passes through the battery. Since the rate at which the charge loses energy equals the power P dissipated in the resistor, we have

Power

$$P = IV \tag{27.22}$$

In this case, the power is supplied to a resistor by a battery. However, Equation 27.22 can be used to determine the power transferred to *any* device carrying a current I and having a potential difference V between its terminals.

Using Equation 27.22 and the fact that $V = IR$ for a resistor, we can express the power dissipated by the resistor in the alternative forms

Power loss in a conductor

$$P = I^2 R = \frac{V^2}{R} \tag{27.23}$$

When I is in amperes, V in volts, and R in ohms, the SI unit of power is the watt.

---

[4] Note that when the current reaches its steady-state value, there is *no* change with time in the kinetic energy associated with the current.

The power lost as heat in a conductor of resistance R is called *joule heat*[5]; however, it is often referred to as an I^2R loss.

A battery or any other device that provides electrical energy is called a source of *electromotive force*, usually referred to as an *emf*. The concept of emf is discussed in more detail in Chapter 28. (The phrase *electromotive force* is an unfortunate one, because it describes not a force but rather a potential difference in volts.) *Neglecting the internal resistance of the battery, the potential difference between points a and b in Figure 27.13 is equal to the emf ε of the battery.* That is, $V = V_b - V_a = \varepsilon$, and the current in the circuit is $I = V/R = \varepsilon/R$. Since $V = \varepsilon$, the power supplied by the emf can be expressed as $P = I\varepsilon$, which, of course, equals the power dissipated in the resistor, I^2R.

CONCEPTUAL EXAMPLE 27.8

Two lightbulbs A and B are connected across the same potential difference as in Figure 27.14. The resistance of A is twice that of B. Which lightbulb dissipates more power? Which carries the greater current?

Reasoning Because the voltage across each lightbulb is the same, and the power dissipated by a conductor is $P = V^2/R$, the conductor with the lower resistance will dissipate more power. In this case, the power dissipated by B is twice that of A and provides twice as much illumination. Furthermore, because $P = IV$, we see that the current carried by B is twice that of A.

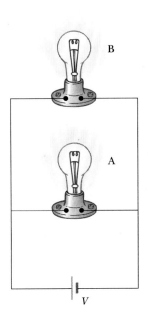

FIGURE 27.14 (Conceptual Example 27.8) Two bulbs connected across the same potential difference.

EXAMPLE 27.9 Power in an Electric Heater

An electric heater is constructed by applying a potential difference of 110 V to a Nichrome wire of total resistance 8.00 Ω. Find the current carried by the wire and the power rating of the heater.

Solution Since $V = IR$, we have

$$I = \frac{V}{R} = \frac{110 \text{ V}}{8.00 \text{ }\Omega} = \boxed{13.8 \text{ A}}$$

We can find the power rating using $P = I^2R$:

$$P = I^2R = (13.8 \text{ A})^2(8.00 \text{ }\Omega) = \boxed{1.52 \text{ kW}}$$

If we doubled the applied voltage, the current would double but the power would quadruple.

---

[5] It is called *joule heat* even though its dimensions are *energy per unit time*, which are dimensions of power.

EXAMPLE 27.10   Electrical Rating of a Lightbulb

A lightbulb is rated at 120 V/75 W, which means its operating voltage is 120 V and it has a power rating of 75.0 W. The bulb is powered by a 120-V direct-current power supply. Find the current in the bulb and its resistance.

Solution   Since the power rating of the bulb is 75.0 W and the operating voltage is 120 V, we can use $P = IV$ to find the current:

$$I = \frac{P}{V} = \frac{75.0 \text{ W}}{120 \text{ V}} = \boxed{0.625 \text{ A}}$$

Using Ohm's law, $V = IR$, the resistance is calculated to be

$$R = \frac{V}{I} = \frac{120 \text{ V}}{0.625 \text{ A}} = \boxed{192 \ \Omega}$$

Exercise   What would the resistance be in a lamp rated at 120 V and 100 W?

Answer   144 Ω.

EXAMPLE 27.11   The Cost of Operating a Lightbulb

How much does it cost to burn a 100-W lightbulb for 24 h if electricity costs eight cents per kilowatt hour?

Solution   Since the energy consumed equals power × time, the amount of energy you must pay for, expressed in kWh, is

$$\text{Energy} = (0.10 \text{ kW})(24 \text{ h}) = 2.4 \text{ kWh}$$

If energy is purchased at eight cents per kWh, the cost is

$$\text{Cost} = (2.4 \text{ kWh})(\$0.080/\text{kWh}) = \boxed{\$0.19}$$

That is, it costs 19 cents to operate the lightbulb for one day. This is a small amount, but when larger and more complex devices are being used, the costs go up rapidly.

Demands on our energy supplies have made it necessary to be aware of the energy requirements of our electric devices. This is true not only because they are becoming more expensive to operate but also because, with the dwindling of the coal and oil resources that ultimately supply us with electrical energy, increased awareness of conservation becomes necessary. On every electric appliance is a label that contains the information you need to calculate the power requirements of the appliance. The power consumption in watts is often stated directly, as on a lightbulb. In other cases, the amount of current used by the device and the voltage at which it operates are given. This information and Equation 27.22 are sufficient to calculate the operating cost of any electric device.

Exercise   If electricity costs eight cents per kilowatt hour, what does it cost to operate an electric oven, which operates at 20.0 A and 220 V, for 5.00 h?

Answer $1.76.

EXAMPLE 27.12   Current in an Electron Beam

In a certain accelerator, electrons emerge with energies of 40.0 MeV (1 MeV = 1.60×10^{-13} J). The electrons do not emerge in a steady stream, but in pulses that repeat 250 times per second. This corresponds to a time between each pulse of 4.00 ms in Figure 27.15. Each pulse lasts for 200 ns and the electrons in the pulse constitute a current of 250 mA. The current is zero between pulses. (a) How many electrons are delivered by the accelerator per pulse?

Solution   We can use Equation 27.2 in the form $dQ = I\, dt$, and integrate to find the charge per pulse. While the pulse is on, the current is constant, therefore

$$Q_{\text{pulse}} = I\int dt = It = (250 \times 10^{-3} \text{ A})(200 \times 10^{-9} \text{ s})$$

$$= 5.00 \times 10^{-8} \text{ C}$$

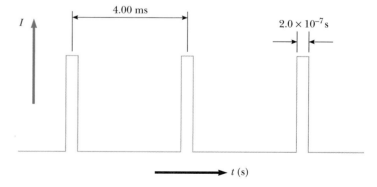

FIGURE 27.15   (Example 27.12) Current versus time for a pulsed beam of electrons.

This quantity of charge per pulse divided by the electronic charge gives the number of electrons per pulse:

$$\text{No. of electrons per pulse} = \frac{5.00 \times 10^{-8} \text{ C/pulse}}{1.60 \times 10^{-19} \text{ C/electron}}$$

$$= 3.13 \times 10^{11} \text{ electrons/pulse}$$

(b) What is the average current delivered by the accelerator?

Solution The average current is given by Equation 27.1, $I = \Delta Q/\Delta t$. Since the duration of one pulse is 4.00 ms, and the charge per pulse is known from part (a), we get

$$I_{av} = \frac{Q_{pulse}}{\Delta t} = \frac{5.00 \times 10^{-8} \text{ C}}{4.00 \times 10^{-3} \text{ s}} = \boxed{12.5 \ \mu A}$$

This represents only 0.0005% of the peak current.

(c) What is the maximum power delivered by the electron beam?

Solution By definition, power is the energy delivered per unit time. Thus, the maximum power is equal to the energy delivered by the beam during the pulse period:

$$P = \frac{E}{\Delta t} = \frac{(3.13 \times 10^{11} \text{ electrons/pulse})(40.0 \text{ MeV/electron})}{2.00 \times 10^{-7} \text{ s/pulse}}$$

$$= (6.26 \times 10^{19} \text{ MeV/s})(1.60 \times 10^{-13} \text{ J/MeV})$$

$$= 1.00 \times 10^{7} \text{ W} = \boxed{10.0 \text{ MW}}$$

SUMMARY

The **electric current** I in a conductor is defined as

$$I \equiv \frac{dQ}{dt} \tag{27.2}$$

where dQ is the charge that passes through a cross-section of the conductor in a time dt. The SI unit of current is the ampere (A), where 1 A = 1 C/s.

The current in a conductor is related to the motion of the charge carriers through the relationship

$$I = nqv_d A \tag{27.4}$$

where n is the density of charge carriers, q is their charge, v_d is the drift speed, and A is the cross-sectional area of the conductor.

The **current density** $\mathbf{J}$ in a conductor is defined as the current per unit area:

$$\mathbf{J} = nq\mathbf{v}_d \tag{27.6}$$

The current density in a conductor is proportional to the electric field according to the expression

$$\mathbf{J} = \sigma \mathbf{E} \tag{27.7}$$

The constant σ is called the **conductivity** of the material. The inverse of σ is called the **resistivity**, ρ. That is, $\rho = 1/\sigma$.

A material is said to obey Ohm's law if its conductivity is independent of the applied field.

The **resistance** R of a conductor is defined as the ratio of the potential difference across the conductor to the current:

$$R \equiv \frac{V}{I} \tag{27.8}$$

If the resistance is independent of the applied voltage, the conductor obeys Ohm's law.

If the conductor has a uniform cross-sectional area A and a length ℓ, its resistance is

$$R = \frac{\ell}{\sigma A} = \rho \frac{\ell}{A} \qquad (27.11)$$

The SI unit of resistance is volt per ampere, which is defined to be 1 ohm (Ω). That is, $1 \, \Omega = 1 \, V/A$.

The resistivity of a conductor varies with temperature in an approximately linear fashion, that is

$$\rho = \rho_0 [1 + \alpha(T - T_0)] \qquad (27.12)$$

where α is the temperature coefficient of resistivity and ρ_0 is the resistivity at some reference temperature T_0.

In a classical model of electronic conduction in a metal, the electrons are treated as molecules of a gas. In the absence of an electric field, the average velocity of the electrons is zero. When an electric field is applied, the electrons move (on the average) with a **drift velocity** v_d, which is opposite the electric field and given by

$$v_d = \frac{qE}{m} \tau \qquad (27.17)$$

where τ is the average time between collisions with the atoms of the metal. The resistivity of the material according to this model is

$$\rho = \frac{m}{nq^2 \tau} \qquad (27.20)$$

where n is the number of free electrons per unit volume.

If a potential difference V is maintained across a resistor, the **power,** or rate at which energy is supplied to the resistor, is

$$P = IV \qquad (27.22)$$

Since the potential difference across a resistor is given by $V = IR$, we can express the power dissipated in a resistor in the form

$$P = I^2 R = \frac{V^2}{R} \qquad (27.23)$$

The electrical energy supplied to a resistor appears in the form of internal energy (thermal energy) in the resistor.

QUESTIONS

1. In an analogy between traffic flow and electrical current, what would correspond to the charge Q? What would correspond to the current I?
2. What factors affect the resistance of a conductor?
3. What is the difference between resistance and resistivity?
4. Two wires A and B of circular cross-section are made of the same metal and have equal lengths, but the resistance of wire A is three times greater than that of wire B. What is the ratio of their cross-sectional areas? How do their radii compare?

5. What is required in order to maintain a steady current in a conductor?
6. Do all conductors obey Ohm's law? Give examples to justify your answer.
7. When the voltage across a certain conductor is doubled, the current is observed to increase by a factor of 3. What can you conclude about the conductor?
8. In the water analogy of an electric circuit, what corresponds to the power supply, resistor, charge, and potential difference?

9. Why might a "good" electrical conductor also be a "good" thermal conductor?
10. Use the atomic theory of matter to explain why the resistance of a material should increase as its temperature increases.
11. How does the resistance change with temperature for copper and silicon? Why are they different?
12. Explain how a current can persist in a superconductor without any applied voltage.
13. What single experimental requirement makes superconducting devices expensive to operate? In principle, can this limitation be overcome?
14. What would happen to the drift velocity of the electrons in a wire and to the current in the wire if the electrons could move freely without resistance through the wire?
15. If charges flow very slowly through a metal, why does it not require several hours for a light to come on when you throw a switch?
16. In a conductor, the electric field that drives the electrons through the conductor propagates with a speed close to the speed of light, although the drift velocity of the electrons is very small. Explain how these can both be true.

Does the same electron move from one end of the conductor to the other?
17. Two conductors of the same length and radius are connected across the same potential difference. One conductor has twice the resistance of the other. Which conductor will dissipate more power?
18. When incandescent lamps burn out, they usually do so just after they are switched on. Why?
19. If you were to design an electric heater using nichrome wire as the heating element, what parameters of the wire could you vary to meet a specific power output, such as 1000 W?
20. Two lightbulbs both operate from 110 V, but one has a power rating of 25 W and the other of 100 W. Which bulb has the higher resistance? Which bulb carries the greater current?
21. A typical monthly utility rate structure might go something like this: $1.60 for the first 16 kWh, 7.05 cents/kWh for the next 34 kWh used, 5.02 cents/kWh for the next 50 kWh, 3.25 cents/kWh for the next 100 kWh, 2.95 cents/kWh for the next 200 kWh, 2.35 cents/kWh for all in excess of 400 kWh. Based on these rates, what would be the charge for 327 kWh?

PROBLEMS

Section 27.1   Electric Current

1. In the Bohr model of the hydrogen atom, an electron in the lowest energy state follows a circular path, 5.29×10^{-11} m from the proton. (a) Show that the speed of the electron is 2.19×10^6 m/s. (b) What is the effective current associated with this orbiting electron?

2. In a particular cathode ray tube, the measured beam current is 30 μA. How many electrons strike the tube screen every 40 s?

3. A small sphere that carries a charge of 8.00 nC is whirled in a circle at the end of an insulating string. The angular frequency of rotation is 100π rad/s. What average current does this rotating charge represent?

3A. A small sphere that carries a charge q is whirled in a circle at the end of an insulating string. The angular frequency of rotation is ω. What average current does this rotating charge represent?

4. The quantity of charge q (in C) passing through a surface of area 2.0 cm^2 varies with time as $q = 4t^3 + 5t + 6$, where t is in seconds. (a) What is the instantaneous current through the surface at $t = 1.0$ s? (b) What is the value of the current density?

5. An electric current is given by $I(t) = 100.0$

$\sin(120\pi t)$, where I is in amperes and t is in seconds. What is the total charge carried by the current from $t = 0$ to $t = 1/240$ s?

6. Suppose that the current through a conductor decreases exponentially with time according to

$$I(t) = I_0 e^{-t/\tau}$$

where I_0 is the initial current (at $t = 0$), and τ is a constant having dimensions of time. Consider a fixed observation point within the conductor. (a) How much charge passes this point between $t = 0$ and $t = \tau$? (b) How much charge passes this point between $t = 0$ and $t = 10\tau$? (c) How much charge passes this point between $t = 0$ and $t = \infty$?

7. A Van de Graaff generator produces a beam of 2.0-MeV deuterons, which are heavy hydrogen nuclei containing a proton and a neutron. (a) If the beam current is 10.0 μA, how far apart are the deuterons in the beam? (b) Is their electrostatic repulsion a factor of beam stability? Explain.

8. Calculate the average drift speed of electrons traveling through a copper wire with a cross-sectional area of 1.00 mm^2 when carrying a current of 1.00 A (values similar to those for the electric wire to your study lamp). It is known that about one electron per atom of copper contributes to the current. The

□ indicates problems that have full solutions available in the Student Solutions Manual and Study Guide.

atomic weight of copper is 63.54, and its density is 8.92 g/cm³.

9. A copper bus bar has a cross-section of 5.0 cm × 15.0 cm and carries a current with a density of 2000 A/cm². (a) What is the total current in the bus bar? (b) How much charge passes a given point in the bar per hour?

10. Figure P27.10 represents a section of a circular conductor of nonuniform diameter carrying a current of 5.0 A. The radius of cross-section A_1 is 0.40 cm. (a) What is the magnitude of the current density across A_1? (b) If the current density across A_2 is one-fourth the value across A_1, what is the radius of the conductor at A_2?

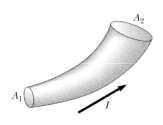

FIGURE P27.10

11. A coaxial conductor with a length of 20 m consists of an inner cylinder with a radius of 3.0 mm and a concentric outer cylindrical tube with an inside radius of 9.0 mm. A uniformly distributed leakage current of 10 μA flows between the two conductors. Determine the leakage current density (in A/m²) through a cylindrical surface (concentric with the conductors) that has a radius of 6.0 mm.

Section 27.2 Resistance and Ohm's Law

12. A conductor of uniform radius 1.2 cm carries a current of 3.0 A produced by an electric field of 120 V/m. What is the resistivity of the material?

13. An electric field of 2100 V/m is applied to a section of silver of uniform cross-section. Calculate the resulting current density if the specimen is at a temperature of 20°C.

14. A solid cube of silver (specific gravity = 10.50) has a mass of 90 g. (a) What is the resistance between opposite faces of the cube? (b) If there is one conduction electron for each silver atom, find the average drift speed of electrons when a potential difference of 1.0×10^{-5} V is applied to opposite faces. The atomic number of silver is 47, and its atomic mass is 107.87.

15. Calculate the resistance at 20°C of a 40-m length of silver wire having a cross-sectional area of 0.40 mm².

16. Eighteen-gauge wire has a diameter of 1.024 mm. Calculate the resistance of 15.0 m of 18-gauge copper wire at 20.0°C.

17. While traveling through Death Valley on a day when the temperature is 58°C, Bill Hiker finds that a certain voltage applied to a copper wire produces a current of 1.000 A. Bill then travels to Antarctica and applies the same voltage to the same wire. What current does he register there if the temperature is −88°C? Assume no change in the wire's shape and size.

18. A circular disk of radius R and thickness d is made of material with resistivity ρ. Show that the resistance between points a and b (Fig. P27.18) is independent of the radius and is given by $R = \pi\rho/2d$.

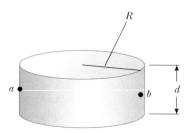

FIGURE P27.18

19. A 12.0-Ω metal wire is cut into three equal pieces that are then connected side by side to form a new wire the length of which is equal to one-third the original length. What is the resistance of this new wire?

19A. A metal wire of resistance R is cut into three equal pieces that are then connected side by side to form a new wire the length of which is equal to one-third the original length. What is the resistance of this new wire?

20. The temperature coefficients of resistivity in Table 27.1 are at 20°C. What would they be at 0°C? (*Hint:* The temperature coefficient of resistivity at 20°C satisfies $\rho = \rho_0[1 + \alpha(T - T_0)]$, where ρ_0 is the resistivity of the material at $T_0 = 20$°C. The temperature coefficient of resistivity, α', at 0°C must satisfy $\rho = \rho_0'[1 + \alpha'T]$, where ρ_0' is the resistivity of the material at 0°C.)

21. A wire with a resistance R is lengthened to 1.25 times its original length by pulling it through a small hole. Find the resistance of the wire after it is stretched.

22. Aluminum and copper wires of equal length are found to have the same resistance. What is the ratio of their radii?

23. Suppose that you wish to fabricate a uniform wire out of 1.0 g of copper. If the wire is to have a resistance of $R = 0.50$ Ω, and all of the copper is to be used, what will be (a) the length and (b) the diameter of this wire?

24. A platinum resistance thermometer, when placed in thermal equilibrium with an object, uses the measured resistance of the platinum to determine the

temperature of the object. If such a thermometer has a resistance of 200.0 Ω when placed in a 0°C ice bath and of 253.8 Ω when immersed in a crucible containing melting potassium, what is the melting point of potassium? (*Hint:* First determine the measured resistance of the thermometer at room temperature, 20°C.)

25. A 0.90-V potential difference is maintained across a 1.5-m length of tungsten wire that has a cross-sectional area of 0.60 mm². What is the current in the wire?

26. The electron beam emerging from a certain high-energy electron accelerator has a circular cross-section of radius 1.00 mm. (a) If the beam current is 8.00 μA, find the current density in the beam, assuming that it is uniform throughout. (b) The speed of the electrons is so close to the speed of light that their speed can be taken as $c = 3.00 \times 10^8$ m/s with negligible error. Find the electron density in the beam. (c) How long does it take for an Avogadro's number of electrons to emerge from the accelerator?

27. A resistor is constructed of a carbon rod that has a uniform cross-sectional area of 5.0 mm². When a potential difference of 15 V is applied across the ends of the rod, there is a current of 4.0×10^{-3} A in the rod. Find (a) the resistance of the rod and (b) the rod's length.

28. A current density of 6.0×10^{-13} A/m² exists in the atmosphere where the electric field (due to charged thunderclouds in the vicinity) is 100 V/m. Calculate the electrical conductivity of the Earth's atmosphere in this region.

Section 27.3   Resistance and Temperature

29. An aluminum wire with a diameter of 0.10 mm has a uniform electric field of 0.20 V/m imposed along its entire length. The temperature of the wire is 50°C. Assume one free electron per atom. (a) Use the information in Table 27.1 and determine the resistivity. (b) What is the current density in the wire? (c) What is the total current in the wire? (d) What is the drift speed of the conduction electrons? (e) What potential difference must exist between the ends of a 2.0-m length of the wire to produce the stated electric field strength?

30. The rod in Figure P27.30 is made of two materials. Both have a square cross-section 3.0 mm on a side. The first material has a resistivity of 4.00×10^{-3} Ω·m and is 25.0 cm long, while the second material has a resistivity of 6.00×10^{-3} Ω·m and is 40.0 cm long. What is the resistance between the ends of the rod?

30A. The rod in Figure P27.30 is made of two materials. Both have a square cross-section with side *d*. The first

material has resistivity ρ_1 and length L_1, while the second material has resistivity ρ_2 and length L_2. What is the resistance between the ends of the rod?

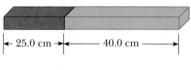

25.0 cm ←→ 40.0 cm

FIGURE P27.30

31. What is the fractional change in the resistance of an iron filament when its temperature changes from 25°C to 50°C?

32. The resistance of a platinum wire is to be calibrated for low-temperature measurements. A platinum wire with resistance 1.00 Ω at 20.0°C is immersed in liquid nitrogen at 77 K (-196°C). If the temperature response of the platinum wire is linear, what is the expected resistance of the platinum wire at -196°C? ($\alpha_{\text{platinum}} = 3.92 \times 10^{-3}$/°C)

33. If a copper wire has a resistance of 18 Ω at 20°C, what resistance will it have at 60°C? (Neglect any change in length or cross-sectional area due to the change in temperature.)

34. A carbon wire and a Nichrome wire are connected in series. If the combination has a resistance of 10.0 kΩ at 0°C, what is the resistance of each wire at 0°C so that the resistance of the combination does not change with temperature?

34A. A carbon wire and a Nichrome wire are connected in series. If the combination has a resistance R at temperature T_0, what is the resistance of each wire at T_0 so that the resistance of the combination does not change with temperature?

35. At what temperature will tungsten have a resistivity four times that of copper? (Assume that the copper is at 20°C.)

36. A segment of Nichrome wire is initially at 20°C. Using the data from Table 27.1, calculate the temperature to which the wire must be heated to double its resistance.

37. At 45.0°C, the resistance of a segment of gold wire is 85.0 Ω. When the wire is placed in a liquid bath, the resistance decreases to 80.0 Ω. What is the temperature of the bath?

38. A 500-W heating coil designed to operate from 110 V is made of Nichrome wire 0.50 mm in diameter. (a) Assuming that the resistivity of the Nichrome remains constant at its 20°C value, find the length of wire used. (b) Now consider the variation of resistivity with temperature. What power will the coil of part (a) actually deliver when it is heated to 1200°C?

Section 27.5   A Model for Electrical Conduction

39. Calculate the current density in a gold wire in which an electric field of 0.74 V/m exists.

40. If the drift velocity of free electrons in a copper wire is 7.84×10^{-4} m/s, calculate the electric field in the conductor.

41. Use data from Example 27.1 to calculate the collision mean free path of electrons in copper if the average thermal speed of conduction electrons is 8.6×10^5 m/s.

42. If the current carried by a conductor is doubled, what happens to the (a) charge carrier density? (b) current density? (c) electron drift velocity? (d) average time between collisions?

Section 27.6   Electrical Energy and Power

43. A 10-V battery is connected to a 120-Ω resistor. Neglecting the internal resistance of the battery, calculate the power dissipated in the resistor.

44. A coil of Nichrome wire is 25.0 m long. The wire has a diameter of 0.40 mm and is at 20.0°C. If it carries a current of 0.50 A, what are (a) the electric field intensity in the wire and (b) the power dissipated in it? (c) If the temperature is increased to 340°C and the voltage across the wire remains constant, what is the power dissipated?

45. Suppose that a voltage surge produces 140 V for a moment. By what percentage will the output of a 120-V, 100-W lightbulb increase, assuming its resistance does not change?

46. A particular type of automobile storage battery is characterized as "360-ampere-hour, 12 V." What total energy can the battery deliver?

47. Batteries are rated in terms of ampere hours (A·h), where a battery rated at 1.0 A·h can produce a current of 1.0 A for 1.0 h. (a) What is the total energy, in kilowatt hours, stored in a 12.0-V battery rated at 55.0 A·h? (b) At $0.06 per kilowatt hour, what is the value of the electricity produced by this battery?

48. In a hydroelectric installation, a turbine delivers 1500 hp to a generator, which in turn converts 80% of the mechanical energy into electrical energy. Under these conditions, what current will the generator deliver at a terminal potential difference of 2000 V?

49. Suppose that you want to install a heating coil that will convert electric energy to heat at a rate of 300 W for a current of 1.5 A. (a) Determine the resistance of the coil. (b) The resistivity of the coil wire is 1.0×10^{-6} Ω·m, and its diameter is 0.30 mm. Determine its length.

50. It is estimated that in the United States (population 250 million) there is one electric clock per person, with each clock using energy at a rate of 2.5 W. To supply this energy, about how many metric tons of coal are burned per hour in coal-fired electric generating plants that are, on average, 25% efficient. The heat of combustion for coal is 33.0 MJ/kg.

51. What is the required resistance of an immersion heater that will increase the temperature of 1.5 kg of water from 10°C to 50°C in 10 min while operating at 110 V?

51A. What is the required resistance of an immersion heater that will increase the temperature of m kg of water from T_1 to T_2 in a time t while operating at a voltage V?

52. The heating element of a coffee maker operates at 120 V and carries a current of 2.0 A. Assuming that all of the heat generated is absorbed by the water, how long does it take to heat 0.50 kg of water from room temperature (23°C) to the boiling point?

53. Compute the cost per day of operating a lamp that draws 1.7 A from a 110-V line if the cost of electrical energy is $0.06/kWh.

54. It requires about 10.0 W of electric power per square foot to heat a room having ceilings 7.5 ft high. At a cost of $0.080/kWh, how much does it cost per day to use electric heat to heat a room 10.0 ft × 15.0 ft?

55. A certain toaster has a heating element made of Nichrome resistance wire. When first connected to a 120-V voltage source (and the wire is at a temperature of 20.0°C) the initial current is 1.80 A but begins to decrease as the resistive element heats up. When the toaster has reached its final operating temperature, the current has dropped to 1.53 A. (a) Find the power the toaster consumes when it is at its operating temperature. (b) What is the final temperature of the heating element?

ADDITIONAL PROBLEMS

56. An electric utility company supplies a customer's house from the main power lines (120 V) with two copper wires, each 50.0 m long and having a resistance of 0.108 Ω per 300 m. (a) Find the voltage at the customer's house for a load current of 110 A. For this load current, find (b) the power the customer is receiving and (c) the power dissipated in the copper wires.

57. The potential difference across the filament of a lamp is maintained at a constant level while equilibrium temperature is being reached. It is observed that the steady-state current in the lamp is only one tenth of the current drawn by the lamp when it is first turned on. If the temperature coefficient of resistivity for the lamp at 20°C is 0.0045 (°C)$^{-1}$, and if the resistance increases linearly with increasing temperature, what is the final operating temperature of the filament?

58. The current in a resistor decreases by 3.0 A when the

voltage applied across the resistor decreases from 12.0 V to 6.0 V. Find the resistance of the resistor.

59. An electric car is designed to run off a bank of 12-V batteries with total energy storage of 2.0×10^7 J. (a) If the electric motor draws 8.0 kW, what is the current delivered to the motor? (b) If the electric motor draws 8.0 kW as the car moves at a steady speed of 20 m/s, how far will the car travel before it is "out of juice"?

60. When a straight wire is heated, its resistance changes according to Equation 27.14, where α is the temperature coefficient of resistivity. (a) Show that a more precise result, one that includes the fact that the length and area of the wire do change when heated, is

$$R = \frac{R_0[1 + \alpha(T - T_0)][1 + \alpha'(T - T_0)]}{[1 - 2\alpha'(T - T_0)]}$$

where α' is the coefficient of linear expansion (Chapter 19). (b) Compare these two results for a 2.00-m-long copper wire of radius 0.100 mm, first initially at 20.0°C and then heated to 100.0°C.

61. A Wheatstone bridge can be used to measure the strain ($\Delta L/L_0$) of a wire (see Section 12.4), where L_0 is the length before stretching, L is the length after stretching, and $\Delta L = L - L_0$. Let $\alpha = \Delta L/L_0$. Show that the resistance is $R = R_0 (1 + 2\alpha + \alpha^2)$ for any length where $R_0 = \rho L_0/A_0$. Assume that the resistivity and volume of the wire stay constant.

62. The current in a wire decreases with time according to the relationship $I = 2.5e^{-at}$ mA where $a = 0.833$ s^{-1}. Determine the total charge that passes through the wire by the time the current has diminished to zero.

63. A resistor is constructed by forming a material of resistivity ρ into the shape of a hollow cylinder of length L and inner and outer radii r_a and r_b, respectively (Fig. P27.63). In use, a potential difference is applied between the ends of the cylinder, producing a current parallel to the axis. (a) Find a general expression for the resistance of such a device in terms of L, ρ, r_a, and r_b. (b) Obtain a numerical value for R when $L = 4.0$ cm, $r_a = 0.50$ cm, $r_b = 1.2$ cm, and the resistivity $\rho = 3.5 \times 10^5$ $\Omega \cdot$m. (c) Suppose now that

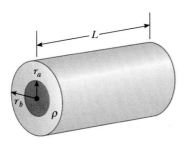

FIGURE P27.63

the potential difference is applied between the inner and outer surfaces so that the resulting current flows radially outward. (a) Find a general expression for the resistance of the device in terms of L, ρ, r_a, and r_b. (d) Calculate the value of R using the parameter values given in part (b).

64. In a certain stereo system, each speaker has a resistance of 4.00 Ω. The system is rated at 60.0 W in each channel, and each speaker circuit includes a fuse rated at 4.00 A. Is this system adequately protected against overload? Explain.

65. A more general definition of the temperature coefficient of resistivity is

$$\alpha = \frac{1}{\rho} \frac{d\rho}{dT}$$

where ρ is the resistivity at temperature T. (a) Assuming that α is constant, show that

$$\rho = \rho_0 e^{\alpha(T - T_0)}$$

where ρ_0 is the resistivity at temperature T_0. (b) Using the series expansion ($e^x \approx 1 + x$; $x \ll 1$), show that the resistivity is given approximately by the expression $\rho = \rho_0[1 + \alpha(T - T_0)]$ for $\alpha(T - T_0) \ll 1$.

66. There is a close analogy between the flow of heat because of a temperature difference (Section 20.7) and the flow of electrical charge because of a potential difference. The thermal energy dQ and the electrical charge dq are both transported by free electrons in the conducting material. Consequently, a good electrical conductor is usually a good heat conductor as well. Consider a thin conducting slab of thickness dx, area A, and electrical conductivity σ, with a potential difference dV between opposite faces. Show that the current $I = dq/dt$ is

Charge conduction	Analogous heat conduction
	(Eq. 20.14)
$\dfrac{dq}{dt} = -\sigma A \dfrac{dV}{dx}$	$\dfrac{dQ}{dt} = -kA \dfrac{dT}{dx}$

In the analogous heat conduction equation, the rate of heat flow dQ/dt (in SI units of joules per second) is due to a temperature gradient dT/dx, in a material of thermal conductivity k. What is the origin of the minus sign in the charge conduction equation?

67. Material with uniform resistivity ρ is formed into a wedge as shown in Figure P27.67. Show that the resistance between face A and face B of this wedge is

$$R = \rho \frac{L}{w(y_2 - y_1)} \ln\left(\frac{y_2}{y_1}\right)$$

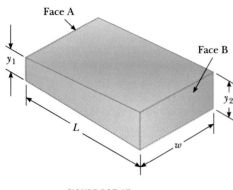

FIGURE P27.67

68. A material of resistivity ρ is formed into the shape of a truncated cone of altitude h as in Figure P27.68. The bottom end has a radius b and the top end has a radius a. Assuming a uniform current density through any circular cross-section of the cone, show that the resistance between the two ends is

$$R = \frac{\rho}{\pi}\left(\frac{h}{ab}\right)$$

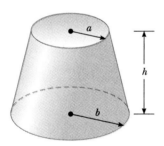

FIGURE P27.68

69. An experiment is conducted to measure the electrical resistivity of nichrome in the form of wires with different lengths and cross-sectional areas. For one set of measurements, a student uses #30-gauge wire, which has a cross-sectional area of $7.3 \times 10^{-8} \text{ m}^2$. The voltage across the wire and the current in the wire are measured with a voltmeter and ammeter, respectively. For each of the measurements given in the table below taken on wires of three different lengths, calculate the resistance of the wires and the corresponding values of the resistivity. What is the average value of the resistivity, and how does it compare with the value given in Table 27.1?

L (m)	V (V)	I (A)	R (Ω)	ρ ($\Omega \cdot$m)
0.54	5.22	0.500		
1.028	5.82	0.276		
1.543	5.94	0.187		

SPREADSHEET PROBLEMS

S1. Spreadsheet 27.1 calculates the average annual lighting cost per bulb for fluorescent and incandescent bulbs and the average yearly savings realized with fluorescent bulbs. It also graphs the average annual lighting cost per bulb versus the cost of electrical energy. (a) Suppose that a fluorescent bulb costs $5, lasts for 5000 h, and consumes 40 W of power, but provides the light intensity of a 100-W incandescent bulb. Assume that a 100-W incandescent bulb costs $0.65 and lasts for 750 h. If the average house has six 100-W incandescent bulbs on at all times and if energy costs 8.3 cents per kilowatt hour, how much does a consumer save each year by switching to fluorescent bulbs? (b) Check with your local electric company for their current rates, and find the cost of bulbs in your area. Would it pay you to switch to fluorescent bulbs? (c) Vary the parameters for bulbs of different wattages and reexamine the annual savings.

S2. The current-voltage characteristic curve for a semiconductor diode as a function of temperature T is given by

$$I = I_0(e^{eV/k_B T} - 1)$$

where e is the charge on the electron, k_B is Boltzmann's constant, and T is the absolute temperature. Set up a spreadsheet to calculate I and $R = V/I$ for $V = 0.40$ V to 0.60 V in increments of 0.05 V. Assume $I_0 = 1.0$ nA. Plot R versus V for $T = 280$ K, 300 K, and 320 K.

CHAPTER 28

Direct Current Circuits

Electrical discharges in tubes filled with neon and other gases are used to produce light of various colors. The characteristic color of each tube depends on the type of gas contained in the tube. As examples, neon gives off reddish light, argon produces violet light, and sodium emits yellow light.

(Dan McCoy/Rainbow)

This chapter is concerned with the analysis of some simple circuits whose elements include batteries, resistors, and capacitors in various combinations. The analysis of these circuits is simplified by the use of two rules known as *Kirchhoff's rules,* both of which follow from the laws of conservation of energy and conservation of charge. Most of the circuits analyzed are assumed to be in *steady state,* which means that the currents are constant in magnitude and direction. In Section 28.4, however, we discuss circuits for which the current varies with time. Finally, a number of common electrical devices and techniques are described for measuring current, potential differences, resistance, and emfs.

28.1 ELECTROMOTIVE FORCE

In the previous chapter we found that a constant current can be maintained in a closed circuit through the use of a source of energy, an *emf* (ee-em-eff), from the historical, but inaccurate, term electromotive force. A source of emf is any device (such as a battery or generator) that produces an electric field and thus may cause charges to move around a circuit. One can think of a source of emf as a "charge

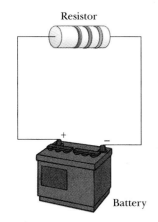

FIGURE 28.1   A circuit consisting of a resistor connected to the terminals of a battery.

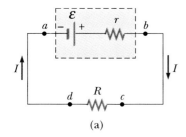

(a)

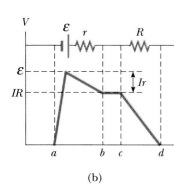

(b)

FIGURE 28.2   (a) Circuit diagram of an emf $\mathcal{E}$ of internal resistance r connected to an external resistor R. (b) Graphical representation showing how the potential changes as the series circuit in part (a) is traversed clockwise.

pump.'' When a potential can be defined, the source moves charges "uphill" to a higher potential. The emf, $\mathcal{E}$, describes the work done per unit charge, and hence the SI unit of emf is the volt.

Consider the circuit shown in Figure 28.1, consisting of a battery connected to a resistor. We assume that the connecting wires have no resistance. The positive terminal of the battery is at a higher potential than the negative terminal. If we neglect the internal resistance of the battery, then the potential difference across it (the terminal voltage) equals its emf. However, because a real battery always has some internal resistance r, the terminal voltage is not equal to the emf. The circuit shown in Figure 28.1 can be described by the circuit diagram in Figure 28.2a. The battery within the dashed rectangle is represented by an emf $\mathcal{E}$ in series with the internal resistance r. Now imagine a positive charge moving from a to b in Figure 28.2a. As the charge passes from the negative to the positive terminal, its potential *increases* by $\mathcal{E}$. However, as it moves through the resistance r, its potential *decreases* by an amount Ir, where I is the current in the circuit. Thus, the terminal voltage of the battery, $V = V_b - V_a$, is[1]

$$V = \mathcal{E} - Ir \tag{28.1}$$

From this expression, note that $\mathcal{E}$ is equivalent to the **open-circuit voltage**, that is, the *terminal voltage when the current is zero*. Figure 28.2b is a graphical representation of the changes in potential as the circuit is traversed in the clockwise direction. By inspecting Figure 28.2a we see that the terminal voltage V must also equal the potential difference across the external resistance R, often called the **load resistance**. That is, $V = IR$. Combining this expression with Equation 28.1, we see that

$$\mathcal{E} = IR + Ir \tag{28.2}$$

Solving for the current gives

$$I = \frac{\mathcal{E}}{R + r} \tag{28.3}$$

This equation shows that the current in this simple circuit depends on both the resistance R external to the battery and the internal resistance r. If R is much greater than r, we can neglect r.

If we multiply Equation 28.2 by the current I, we get

$$I\mathcal{E} = I^2 R + I^2 r \tag{28.4}$$

This equation tells us that, because power $P = IV$ (Eq. 27.22), the total power output of the device emf, $I\mathcal{E}$, is converted to power dissipated as joule heat in the load resistance, $I^2 R$, plus power dissipated in the internal resistance, $I^2 r$. Again, if $r \ll R$, then most of the power delivered by the battery is transferred to the load resistance.

---

[1] The terminal voltage in this case is less than the emf by an amount Ir. In some situations, the terminal voltage may *exceed* the emf by an amount Ir. This happens when the direction of the current is *opposite* that of the emf, as in the case of charging a battery with another source of emf.

EXAMPLE 28.1   Terminal Voltage of a Battery

A battery has an emf of 12.0 V and an internal resistance of 0.05 Ω. Its terminals are connected to a load resistance of 3.00 Ω. (a) Find the current in the circuit and the terminal voltage of the battery.

Solution   Using first Equations 28.3 and then 28.1, we get

$$I = \frac{\mathcal{E}}{R + r} = \frac{12.0 \text{ V}}{3.05 \text{ Ω}} = \boxed{3.93\text{A}}$$

$$V = \mathcal{E} - Ir = 12.0 \text{ V} - (3.93 \text{ A})(0.05 \text{ Ω}) = \boxed{11.8 \text{ V}}$$

As a check of this result, we can calculate the voltage drop across the load resistance R:

$$V = IR = (3.93 \text{ A})(3.00 \text{ Ω}) = 11.8 \text{ V}$$

(b) Calculate the power dissipated in the load resistor, the power dissipated by the internal resistance of the battery, and the power delivered by the battery.

Solution   The power dissipated by the load resistor is

$$P_R = I^2R = (3.93 \text{ A})^2(3.00 \text{ Ω}) = \boxed{46.3 \text{ W}}$$

The power dissipated by the internal resistance is

$$P_r = I^2r = (3.93 \text{ A})^2(0.05 \text{ Ω}) = \boxed{0.772 \text{ W}}$$

Hence, the power delivered by the battery is the sum of these quantities, or 47.1 W. This can be checked using the expression $P = I\mathcal{E}$.

EXAMPLE 28.2   Matching the Load

Show that the maximum power lost in the load resistance R in Figure 28.2a occurs when $R = r$, that is, when the load resistance matches the internal resistance.

Solution   The power dissipated in the load resistance is equal to I^2R, where I is given by Equation 28.3:

$$P = I^2R = \frac{\mathcal{E}^2R}{(R + r)^2}$$

When P is plotted versus R as in Figure 28.3, we find that P reaches a maximum value of $\mathcal{E}^2/4r$ at $R = r$. This can also be proved by differentiating P with respect to R, setting the result equal to zero, and solving for R. The details are left as a problem (Problem 79).

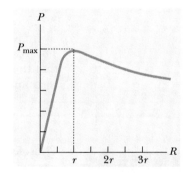

FIGURE 28.3   (Example 28.2) Graph of the power P delivered to a load resistor as a function of R. The power delivered to R is a maximum when the load resistance of the circuit equals the internal resistance of the battery.

28.2   RESISTORS IN SERIES AND IN PARALLEL

When two or more resistors are connected together so that they have only one common point per pair, they are said to be in *series*. Figure 28.4 shows two resistors connected in series. Note that

the current is the same through each resistor because any charge that flows through R_1 must also flow through R_2.

> For a series connection of resistors, the current is the same in each resistor

Since the potential drop from a to b in Figure 28.4b equals IR_1 and the potential drop from b to c equals IR_2, the potential drop from a to c is

$$V = IR_1 + IR_2 = I(R_1 + R_2)$$

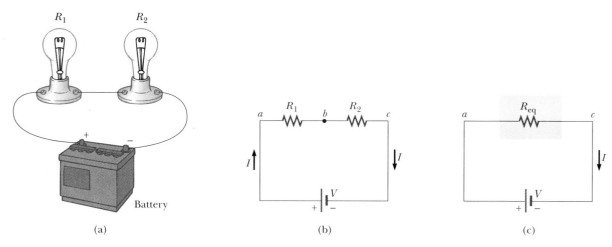

(a)   (b)   (c)

FIGURE 28.4 Series connection of two resistors, R_1 and R_2. The current is the same in each resistor.

Therefore, we can replace the two resistors in series by a single *equivalent resistance* R_{eq} whose value is the *sum* of the individual resistances:

$$R_{eq} = R_1 + R_2 \qquad (28.5)$$

The resistance R_{eq} is equivalent to the series combination $R_1 + R_2$ in the sense that the circuit current is unchanged when R_{eq} replaces $R_1 + R_2$. The equivalent resistance of three or more resistors connected in series is simply

$$R_{eq} = R_1 + R_2 + R_3 + \cdots \qquad (28.6)$$

Therefore, *the equivalent resistance of a series connection of resistors is always greater than any individual resistance.*

Note that if the filament of one lightbulb in Figure 28.4 were to break, or "burn out," the circuit would no longer be complete (an open-circuit condition) and the second bulb would also go out. Some Christmas tree light sets (especially older ones) are connected in this way, and the experience of determining which bulb is burned out was once a familiar one. Frustrating experiences such as this illustrate how inconvenient it would be to have all appliances in a house connected in series. In many circuits, fuses are used in series with other circuit elements for safety purposes. The conductor in the fuse is designed to melt and open the circuit at some maximum current, the value of which depends on the nature of the circuit. If a fuse is not used, excessive currents could damage circuit elements, overheat wires, and perhaps cause a fire. In modern home construction, circuit breakers are used in place of fuses. When the current in a circuit exceeds some value (typically 15 A), the circuit breaker acts as a switch and opens the circuit.

Now consider two resistors connected in *parallel* as shown in Figure 28.5.

In this case, there is an equal potential difference across each resistor.

However, the current in each resistor is in general not the same. When the current I reaches point a, called a *junction*, it splits into two parts, I_1 going through R_1 and

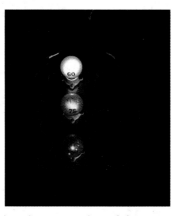

A series connection of three lamps, all rated at 120 V, with power ratings of 60 W, 75 W, and 200 W. Why are the intensities of the lamps different? Which lamp has the greatest resistance? How would their relative intensities differ if they were connected in parallel? *(Henry Leap and Jim Lehman)*

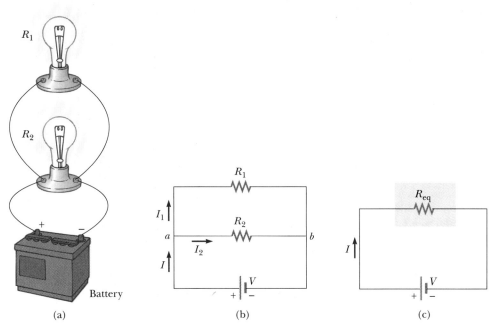

Three incandescent lamps with power ratings of 25 W, 75 W, and 150 W connected in parallel to a voltage source of about 100 V. All lamps are rated at the same voltage. Why do the intensities of the lamps differ? Which lamp draws the most current? Which has the least resistance? *(Henry Leap and Jim Lehman)*

FIGURE 28.5 Parallel connection of two resistors, R_1 and R_2. The potential difference across each resistor is the same, and the equivalent resistance of the combination is given by $R_{eq} = R_1 R_2 / (R_1 + R_2)$.

I_2 going through R_2. (A **junction** is any point in a circuit where a current can split.) If R_1 is greater than R_2, then I_1 will be less than I_2. That is, the moving charge tends to take the path of least resistance. Clearly, since charge must be conserved, the current I that enters point a must equal the total current leaving this point:

$$I = I_1 + I_2$$

Since the potential drop across each resistor must be the same, Ohm's law gives

$$I = I_1 + I_2 = \frac{V}{R_1} + \frac{V}{R_2} = V\left(\frac{1}{R_1} + \frac{1}{R_2}\right) = \frac{V}{R_{eq}}$$

From this result, we see that the equivalent resistance of two resistors in parallel is

$$\frac{1}{R_{eq}} = \frac{1}{R_1} + \frac{1}{R_2} \tag{28.7}$$

$$R_{eq} = \frac{R_1 R_2}{R_1 + R_2}$$

An extension of this analysis to three or more resistors in parallel gives

$$\frac{1}{R_{eq}} = \frac{1}{R_1} + \frac{1}{R_2} + \frac{1}{R_3} + \cdots \tag{28.8}$$

It can be seen from this expression that the equivalent resistance of two or more resistors connected in parallel is always less than the smallest resistance in the group.

This versatile circuit enables the experimenter to examine the properties of circuit elements such as capacitors and resistors and their effect on circuit behavior. *(Courtesy of Central Scientific Company)*

Household circuits are always wired such that the lightbulbs (or appliances, etc.) are connected in parallel. Connected this way, each device operates independently of the others, so that if one is switched off, the others remain on. Equally important, each device operates on the same voltage.

EXAMPLE 28.3   Find the Equivalent Resistance

Four resistors are connected as shown in Figure 28.6a. (a) Find the equivalent resistance between *a* and *c*.

Solution   The circuit can be reduced in steps as shown in Figure 28.6. The 8.0-Ω and 4.0-Ω resistors are in series, and so the equivalent resistance between *a* and *b* is 12 Ω (Eq. 28.5). The 6.0-Ω and 3.0-Ω resistors are in parallel, and so from Equation 28.7 we find that the equivalent resistance from *b* to *c* is 2.0 Ω. Hence, the equivalent resistance from *a* to *c* is 14 Ω.

(b) What is the current in each resistor if a potential difference of 42 V is maintained between *a* and *c*?

Solution   The current in the 8.0-Ω and 4.0-Ω resistors is the same because they are in series. Using Ohm's law and the results from part (a), we get

$$I = \frac{V_{ac}}{R_{eq}} = \frac{42 \text{ V}}{14 \text{ Ω}} = 3.0 \text{ A}$$

When this current enters the junction at *b*, it splits, part passing through the 6.0-Ω resistor (I_1) and part through the 3.0-Ω resistor (I_2). Since the potential difference across these resistors, V_{bc}, is the same (they are in parallel), we see that $6I_1 = 3I_2$, or $I_2 = 2I_1$. Using this result and the fact that $I_1 + I_2 = 3.0$ A, we find that $I_1 = 1.0$ A and $I_2 = 2.0$ A. We could have guessed this from the start by noting that the current through the 3.0-Ω resistor has to be twice the current through the 6.0-Ω resistor in view of their relative resistances and the fact that the same voltage is applied to each of them.

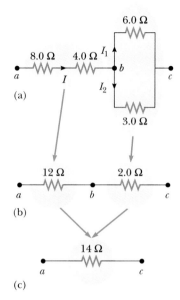

(a)

(b)

(c)

FIGURE 28.6   (Example 28.3) The resistances of the four resistors shown in (a) can be reduced in steps to an equivalent 14-Ω resistor.

As a final check, note that $V_{bc} = 6I_1 = 3I_2 = 6.0$ V and $V_{ab} = 12I = 36$ V; therefore, $V_{ac} = V_{ab} + V_{bc} = 42$ V, as it must.

EXAMPLE 28.4   Three Resistors in Parallel

Three resistors are connected in parallel as in Figure 28.7. A potential difference of 18 V is maintained between points *a* and *b*. (a) Find the current in each resistor.

Solution   The resistors are in parallel, and the potential difference across each is 18 V. Applying $V = IR$ to each resistor gives

$$I_1 = \frac{V}{R_1} = \frac{18 \text{ V}}{3.0 \text{ Ω}} = \boxed{6.0 \text{ A}}$$

$$I_2 = \frac{V}{R_2} = \frac{18 \text{ V}}{6.0 \text{ Ω}} = \boxed{3.0 \text{ A}}$$

$$I_3 = \frac{V}{R_3} = \frac{18 \text{ V}}{9.0 \text{ Ω}} = \boxed{2.0 \text{ A}}$$

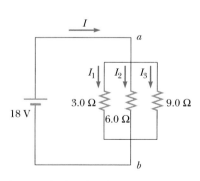

FIGURE 28.7   (Example 28.4) Three resistors connected in parallel. The voltage across each resistor is 18 V.

(b) Calculate the power dissipated by each resistor and the total power dissipated by the three resistors.

Solution Applying $P = I^2R$ to each resistor gives

3.0-Ω: $P_1 = I_1^2R_1 = (6.0\ \text{A})^2(3.0\ \Omega) = \boxed{110\ \text{W}}$

6.0-Ω: $P_2 = I_2^2R_2 = (3.0\ \text{A})^2(6.0\ \Omega) = \boxed{54\ \text{W}}$

9.0-Ω: $P_3 = I_3^2R_3 = (2.0\ \text{A})^2(9.0\ \Omega) = \boxed{36\ \text{W}}$

This shows that the smallest resistor dissipates the most power since it carries the most current. (Note that you can also use $P = V^2/R$ to find the power dissipated by each resis-

tor.) Summing the three quantities gives a total power of 200 W.

(c) Calculate the equivalent resistance of the three resistors. We can use Equation 28.7 to find R_{eq}:

Solution

$$\frac{1}{R_{\text{eq}}} = \frac{1}{3.0} + \frac{1}{6.0} + \frac{1}{9.0}$$

$$R_{\text{eq}} = \frac{18}{11}\ \Omega = \boxed{1.6\ \Omega}$$

Exercise Use R_{eq} to calculate the total power dissipated in the circuit.

Answer 200 W.

EXAMPLE 28.5 Finding R_{eq} by Symmetry Arguments

Consider the five resistors connected as shown in Figure 28.8a. Find the equivalent resistance between points a and b.

Solution In this type of problem, it is convenient to assume a current entering junction a and then apply symmetry arguments. Because of the symmetry in the circuit (all 1-Ω resistors in the outside loop), the currents in branches ac and ad

must be equal; hence, the potentials at points c and d must be equal. Since $V_c = V_d$, points c and d may be connected together without affecting the circuit, as in Figure 28.8b. Thus, the 5-Ω resistor may be moved from the circuit, and the circuit may be reduced as shown in Figures 28.8c and 28.8d. From this reduction, we see that the equivalent resistance of the combination is 1 Ω. Note that the result is 1 Ω regardless of what resistor is connected between c and d.

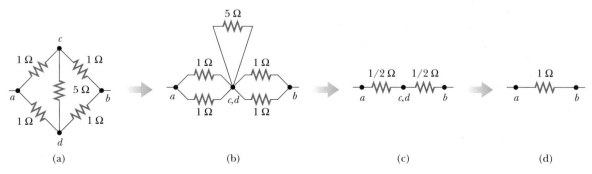

(a)   (b)   (c)   (d)

FIGURE 28.8   (Example 28.5) Because of the symmetry in this circuit, the 5-Ω resistor does not contribute to the resistance between points a and b and can be disregarded.

CONCEPTUAL EXAMPLE 28.6   Operation of a Three-Way Lightbulb

Figure 28.9 illustrates how a three-way lightbulb is constructed to provide three levels of light intensity. The socket of the lamp is equipped with a three-way switch for selecting different light intensities. The bulb contains two filaments. Why are the filaments connected in parallel? Explain how the two filaments are used to provide three different light intensities.

Reasoning If the filaments were connected in series, and one of them were to burn out, no current could pass through the bulb, and the bulb would give no illumination, regardless of the switch position. However, when the filaments are connected in parallel, and one of them (say the 75-W filament) burns out, the bulb would still operate in one of the switch positions as current passes through the other (100 W) filament. The three light intensities are made possible by selecting one of three values of filament resistance, using a single value of 120 V for the applied voltage. The 75-W filament offers one value of resistance, the 100-W filament offers a second value, and the third resistance is obtained by combining the two filaments in parallel. When switch 1 is closed and switch 2 is opened, current passes only through the 75-W filament. When switch 1 is open and switch 2 is closed, current passes only through the 100-W filament. When both switches are closed, current passes through both filaments, and a total illumination of 175 W is obtained.

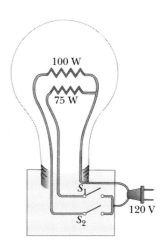

FIGURE 28.9   (Conceptual Example 28.6) Three-way light-bulb.

Georg Simon Ohm (1787–1854).   *(Courtesy of North Wind Picture Archives)*

28.3 KIRCHHOFF'S RULES

As we saw in the previous section, simple circuits can be analyzed using Ohm's law and the rules for series and parallel combinations of resistors. Very often it is not possible to reduce a circuit to a single loop, however. The procedure for analyzing more complex circuits is greatly simplified by the use of two simple rules called **Kirchhoff's rules:**

- The sum of the currents entering any junction must equal the sum of the currents leaving that junction.
- The algebraic sum of the changes in potential across all of the elements around any closed circuit loop must be zero.

The first rule is a statement of conservation of charge. All current that enters a given point in a circuit must leave that point, because charge cannot build up at a point. If we apply this rule to the junction shown in Figure 28.10a, we get

$$I_1 = I_2 + I_3$$

Figure 28.10b represents a mechanical analog to this situation, in which water flows through a branched pipe with no leaks. The flow rate into the pipe equals the total flow rate out of the two branches.

The second rule follows from conservation of energy. A charge that moves around any closed loop in a circuit (the charge starts and ends at the same point) must gain as much energy as it loses if a potential is defined for each point in the circuit. Its energy may decrease in the form of a potential drop, $-IR$, across a resistor or as the result of having the charge move in the reverse direction through an emf. In a practical application of the latter case, electrical energy is converted to chemical energy when a battery is charged; similarly, electrical energy may be converted to mechanical energy for operating a motor. However, Kirchhoff's second rule applies only for circuits in which a potential is defined at each point, which may not be satisfied if there are changing electromagnetic fields.

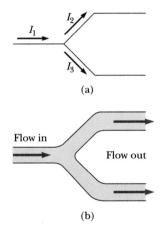

FIGURE 28.10 (a) A schematic diagram illustrating Kirchhoff's junction rule. Conservation of charge requires that all current entering a junction must leave that junction. Therefore, in this case, $I_1 = I_2 + I_3$. (b) A mechanical analog of the junction rule: The flow out must equal the flow in.

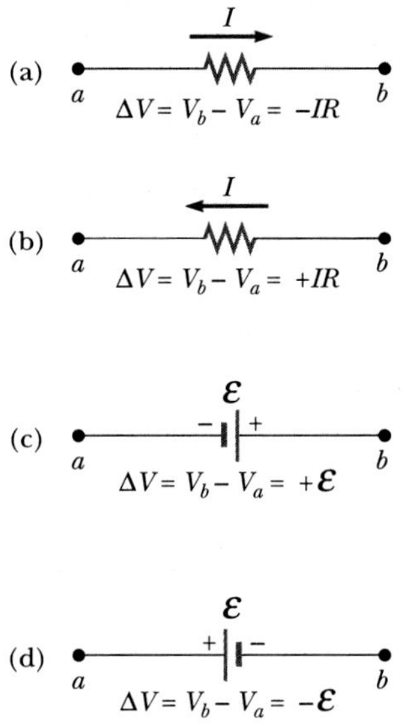

(a) $\Delta V = V_b - V_a = -IR$

(b) $\Delta V = V_b - V_a = +IR$

(c) $\mathcal{E}$ $\Delta V = V_b - V_a = +\mathcal{E}$

(d) $\mathcal{E}$ $\Delta V = V_b - V_a = -\mathcal{E}$

FIGURE 28.11 Rules for determining the potential changes across a resistor and a battery, assuming the battery has no internal resistance.

As an aid in applying the second rule, the following rules should be noted:

- If a resistor is traversed in the direction of the current, the change in potential across the resistor is $-IR$ (Fig. 28.11a).
- If a resistor is traversed in the direction *opposite* the current, the change in potential across the resistor is $+IR$ (Fig. 28.11b).
- If an emf is traversed in the direction of the emf (from $-$ to $+$ on the terminals), the change in potential is $+\mathcal{E}$ (Fig. 28.11c).
- If an emf is traversed in the direction opposite the emf (from $+$ to $-$ on the terminals), the change in potential is $-\mathcal{E}$ (Fig. 28.11d).

There are limitations on the number of times you can use the junction rule and the loop rule. The junction rule can be used as often as needed so long as each time you write an equation, you include in it a current that has not been used in a previous junction rule equation. In general, the number of times the junction rule must be used is one fewer than the number of junction points in the circuit. The loop rule can be used as often as needed so long as a new circuit element (resistor or battery) or a new current appears in each new equation. In general, *the number of independent equations you need equals the number of unknowns in order to solve a particular circuit problem.*

Complex networks with many loops and junctions generate large numbers of independent linear equations and a corresponding large number of unknowns. Such situations can be handled formally using matrix algebra. Computer programs can also be written to solve for the unknowns.

Gustav Robert Kirchhoff (1824–1887)   *(Courtesy of North Wind Picture Archives)*

The following examples illustrate the use of Kirchhoff's rules in analyzing circuits. In all cases, it is assumed that the circuits have reached steady-state conditions, that is, the currents in the various branches are constant. If a capacitor is included, as an example, in one of the branches, *it acts as an open circuit,* that is, the current in the branch containing the capacitor is zero under steady-state conditions.

Problem-Solving Strategy and Hints
Kirchhoff's Rules

- Draw the circuit diagram and label all the known and unknown quantities. You must assign a *direction* to the currents in each part of the circuit. Do not be alarmed if you guess the direction of a current incorrectly; your result will be negative, but *its magnitude will be correct.* Although the assignment of current directions is arbitrary, you must adhere *rigorously* to the assigned directions when applying Kirchhoff's rule.
- Apply the junction rule (Kirchhoff's first rule) to any junction in the circuit that provides a relationship between the various currents.
- Apply Kirchhoff's second rule to as many loops in the circuit as are needed to solve for the unknowns. In order to apply this rule, you must correctly identify the change in potential as you cross each element in traversing the closed loop (either clockwise or counterclockwise). Watch out for signs!
- Solve the equations simultaneously for the unknown quantities.

EXAMPLE 28.7   A Single-Loop Circuit

A single-loop circuit contains two external resistors and two batteries as in Figure 28.12. (Neglect the internal resistances of the batteries.) (a) Find the current in the circuit.

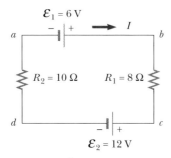

FIGURE 28.12   (Example 28.7) A series circuit containing two batteries and two resistors, where the polarities of the batteries are in opposition to each other.

Reasoning   There are no junctions in this single-loop circuit, and so the current is the same in all elements. Let us assume that the current is in the clockwise direction as shown

in Figure 28.12. Traversing the circuit in this direction, starting at a, we see that $a \rightarrow b$ represents a potential increase of $+ \mathcal{E}_1$, $b \rightarrow c$ represents a potential decrease of $- IR_1$, $c \rightarrow d$ represents a potential decrease of $- \mathcal{E}_2$, and $d \rightarrow a$ represents a potential decrease of $- IR_2$. Applying Kirchhoff's second rule gives

$$\sum_i \Delta V_i = 0$$

$$\mathcal{E}_1 - IR_1 - \mathcal{E}_2 - IR_2 = 0$$

Solution   Solving for I and using the values given in Figure 28.12, we get

$$I = \frac{\mathcal{E}_1 - \mathcal{E}_2}{R_1 + R_2} = \frac{6 \text{ V} - 12 \text{ V}}{8 \ \Omega + 10 \ \Omega} = \boxed{-\frac{1}{3} \text{ A}}$$

The negative sign for I indicates that the direction of the current is opposite the assumed direction.

(b) What is the power lost in each resistor?

Solution

$$P_1 = I^2 R_1 = (\tfrac{1}{3}\,\text{A})^2(8\ \Omega) = \boxed{\dfrac{8}{9}\,\text{W}}$$

$$P_2 = I^2 R_2 = (\tfrac{1}{3}\,\text{A})^2(10\ \Omega) = \boxed{\dfrac{10}{9}\,\text{W}}$$

Hence, the total power lost is $P_1 + P_2 = 2$ W. Note that the 12-V battery delivers $I\mathcal{E}_2 = 4$ W. Half of this power is delivered to the external resistors. The other half is delivered to the 6-V battery, which is being charged by the 12-V battery. If we had included the internal resistances of the batteries, some of the power would be dissipated as heat in the batteries, so that less power would be delivered to the 6-V battery.

EXAMPLE 28.8 Applying Kirchhoff's Rules

Find the currents I_1, I_2, and I_3 in the circuit shown in Figure 28.13.

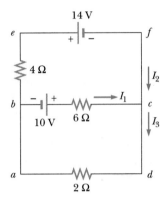

FIGURE 28.13 (Example 28.8) A circuit containing three loops.

Reasoning We choose the directions of the currents as in Figure 28.13. Applying Kirchhoff's first rule to junction c gives

(1) $I_1 + I_2 = I_3$

There are three loops in the circuit, *abcda*, *befcb*, and *aefda* (the outer loop). Therefore, we need only two loop equations to determine the unknown currents. The third loop equation would give no new information. Applying Kirchhoff's second rule to loops *abcda* and *befcb* and traversing these loops in the clockwise direction, we obtain the expressions

(2)   Loop *abcda*: $10\ \text{V} - (6\ \Omega)\,I_1 - (2\ \Omega)\,I_3 = 0$

(3)   Loop *befcb*: $-14\ \text{V} - 10\ \text{V} + (6\ \Omega)\,I_1 - (4\ \Omega)\,I_2 = 0$

Note that in loop *befcb*, a positive sign is obtained when traversing the 6-Ω resistor because the direction of the path is opposite the direction of I_1. A third loop equation for *aefda* gives $-14 = 2I_3 + 4I_2$, which is just the sum of (2) and (3).

Solution Expressions (1), (2), and (3) represent three independent equations with three unknowns. We can solve the problem as follows: Substituting (1) into (2) gives

$$10 - 6I_1 - 2(I_1 + I_2) = 0$$

(4) $10 = 8I_1 + 2I_2$

Dividing each term in (3) by 2 and rearranging the equation gives

(5) $-12 = -3I_1 + 2I_2$

Subtracting (5) from (4) eliminates I_2, giving

$$22 = 11I_1$$

$$I_1 = 2\ \text{A}$$

Using this value of I_1 in (5) gives a value for I_2:

$$2I_2 = 3I_1 - 12 = 3(2) - 12 = -6$$

$$I_2 = -3\ \text{A}$$

Finally, $I_3 = I_1 + I_2 = -1$ A. Hence, the currents have the values

$$I_1 = \boxed{2\ \text{A}} \qquad I_2 = \boxed{-3\ \text{A}} \qquad I_3 = \boxed{-1\ \text{A}}$$

The fact that I_2 and I_3 are both negative indicates only that we chose the wrong direction for these currents. However, the numerical values are correct.

Exercise Find the potential difference between points b and c.

Answer $V_b - V_c = 2$ V.

EXAMPLE 28.9 A Multiloop Circuit

(a) Under steady-state conditions, find the unknown currents in the multiloop circuit shown in Figure 28.14.

Reasoning First note that *the capacitor represents an open circuit, and hence there is no current along path ghab under steady-state*

conditions. Therefore, $I_{gf} = I_1$. Labeling the currents as shown in Figure 28.14 and applying Kirchhoff's first rule to junction c, we get

(1) $I_1 + I_2 = I_3$

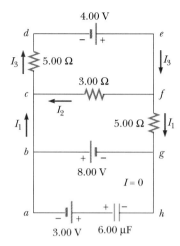

FIGURE 28.14   (Example 28.9) A multiloop circuit. Note that Kirchhoff's loop equation can be applied to *any* closed loop, including one containing the capacitor.

Kirchhoff's second rule applied to loops *defcd* and *cfgbc* gives

(2)   Loop *defcd:* $4.00 \text{ V} - (3.00 \ \Omega) I_2 - (5.00 \ \Omega) I_3 = 0$

(3)   Loop *cfgbc:* $8.00 \text{ V} - (5.00 \ \Omega) I_1 + (3.00 \ \Omega) I_2 = 0$

Solution   From (1) we see that $I_1 = I_3 - I_2$, which when substituted into (3) gives

(4) $8.00 \text{ V} - (5.00 \ \Omega) I_3 + (8.00 \ \Omega) I_2 = 0$

Subtracting (4) from (2), we eliminate I_3 and find

$$I_2 = -\tfrac{4}{11} \text{ A} = -0.364 \text{ A}$$

Since I_2 is negative, we conclude that I_2 is from *c* to *f* through the 3.00-Ω resistor. Using this value of I_2 in (3) and (1) gives the following values for I_1 and I_3:

$$I_1 = \boxed{1.38 \text{ A}} \qquad I_3 = \boxed{1.02 \text{ A}}$$

Under state-steady conditions, the capacitor represents an *open* circuit, and so there is no current in the branch *ghab*.

(b) What is the charge on the capacitor?

Solution   We can apply Kirchhoff's second rule to loop *abgha* (or any other loop that contains the capacitor) to find the potential difference V_c across the capacitor:

$$-8.00 \text{ V} + V_c - 3.00 \text{ V} = 0$$

$$V_c = 11.0 \text{ V}$$

Since $Q = CV_c$, the charge on the capacitor is

$$Q = (6.00 \ \mu\text{F})(11.0 \text{ V}) = \boxed{66.0 \ \mu\text{C}}$$

Why is the left side of the capacitor positively charged?

Exercise   Find the voltage across the capacitor by traversing any other loop.

Answer   11.0 V.

28.4   RC CIRCUITS

So far we have been concerned with circuits with constant currents, or so-called *steady-state circuits*. We now consider circuits containing capacitors, in which the currents may vary in time.

Charging a Capacitor

Consider the series circuit shown in Figure 28.15. Let us assume that the capacitor is initially uncharged. There is no current when the switch S is open (Fig. 28.15b). If the switch is closed at $t = 0$, charges begin to flow, setting up a current in the circuit, and the capacitor begins to charge (Fig. 28.15c). Note that during the charging process, charges do not jump across the plates of the capacitor because the gap between the plates represents an open circuit. Instead, charge is transferred from one plate to the other through the resistor, switch, and battery until the capacitor is fully charged. The value of the maximum charge depends on the voltage of the battery. Once the maximum charge is reached, the current in the circuit is zero.

To put this discussion on a quantitative basis, let us apply Kirchhoff's second rule to the circuit after the switch is closed. Doing so gives

$$\mathcal{E} - IR - \frac{q}{C} = 0 \tag{28.9}$$

where IR is the potential drop across the resistor and q/C is the potential drop

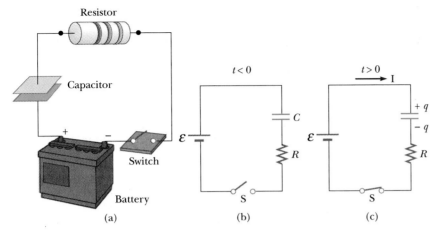

FIGURE 28.15   (a) A capacitor in series with a resistor, battery, and switch. (b) Circuit diagram representing this system before the switch is closed, $t < 0$. (c) Circuit diagram after the switch is closed, $t > 0$.

across the capacitor. Note that q and I are instantaneous values of the charge and current, respectively, as the capacitor is being charged.

We can use Equation 28.9 to find the initial current in the circuit and the maximum charge on the capacitor. At the instant the switch is closed ($t = 0$), the charge on the capacitor is zero, and from Equation 28.9 we find that the initial current in the circuit I_0 is a maximum and equal to

$$I_0 = \frac{\mathcal{E}}{R} \qquad \text{(current at } t = 0\text{)} \qquad\qquad (28.10)$$

Maximum current

At this time, *the potential drop is entirely across the resistor.* Later, when the capacitor is charged to its maximum value Q, charges cease to flow, the current in the circuit is zero, and *the potential drop is entirely across the capacitor.* Substituting $I = 0$ into Equation 28.9 gives

$$Q = C\mathcal{E} \qquad \text{(maximum charge)} \qquad\qquad (28.11)$$

Maximum charge on the capacitor

To determine analytical expressions for the time dependence of the charge and current, we must solve Equation 28.9, a single equation containing two variables, q and I. In order to do this, let us substitute $I = dq/dt$ and rearrange the equation:

$$\frac{dq}{dt} = \frac{\mathcal{E}}{R} - \frac{q}{RC}$$

An expression for q may be found in the following manner. Rearrange the equation by placing terms involving q on the left side and those involving t on the right side. Then integrate both sides:

$$\frac{dq}{(q - C\mathcal{E})} = -\frac{1}{RC}\, dt$$

$$\int_0^q \frac{dq}{(q - C\mathcal{E})} = -\frac{1}{RC}\int_0^t dt$$

$$\ln\left(\frac{q - C\mathcal{E}}{-C\mathcal{E}}\right) = -\frac{t}{RC}$$

From the definition of the natural logarithm, we can write this expression as

$$q(t) = C\mathcal{E}[1 - e^{-t/RC}] = Q[1 - e^{-t/RC}] \qquad (28.12)$$

where e is the base of the natural logarithm.

An expression for the charging current may be found by differentiating Equation 28.12 with respect to time. Using $I = dq/dt$, we find

$$I(t) = \frac{\mathcal{E}}{R} e^{-t/RC} \qquad (28.13)$$

where $I_0 = \mathcal{E}/R$ is the initial current in the circuit.

Plots of charge and current versus time are shown in Figure 28.16. Note that the charge is zero at $t = 0$ and approaches the maximum value of $C\mathcal{E}$ as $t \to \infty$ (Fig. 28.16a). Furthermore, the current has its maximum value $I_0 = \mathcal{E}/R$ at $t = 0$ and decays exponentially to zero as $t \to \infty$ (Fig. 28.16b). The quantity RC, which appears in the exponents of Equations 28.12 and 28.13, is called the **time constant,** τ, of the circuit. It represents the time it takes the current to decrease to $1/e$ of its initial value; that is, in a time τ, $I = e^{-1}I_0 = 0.368I_0$. In a time 2τ, $I = e^{-2}I_0 = 0.135I_0$, and so forth. Likewise, in a time τ the charge increases from zero to $C\mathcal{E}[1 - e^{-1}] = 0.632\,C\mathcal{E}$.

The following dimensional analysis shows that τ has the unit of time:

$$[\tau] = [RC] = \left[\frac{V}{I} \times \frac{Q}{V}\right] = \left[\frac{Q}{Q/T}\right] = [T]$$

The work done by the battery during the charging process is $Q\mathcal{E} = C\mathcal{E}^2$. After the capacitor is fully charged, the energy stored in the capacitor is $\frac{1}{2}Q\mathcal{E} = \frac{1}{2}C\mathcal{E}^2$, which is just half the work done by the battery. It is left as a problem to show that the remaining half of the energy supplied by the battery goes into joule heat in the resistor (Problem 82).

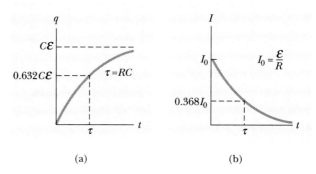

(a)   (b)

FIGURE 28.16   (a) Plot of capacitor charge versus time for the circuit shown in Figure 28.15. After one time constant, τ, the charge is 63.2% of the maximum value, $C\mathcal{E}$. The charge approaches its maximum value as t approaches infinity. (b) Plot of current versus time for the RC circuit shown in Figure 28.15. The current has its maximum value, $I_0 = \mathcal{E}/R$, at $t = 0$ and decays to zero exponentially as t approaches infinity. After one time constant, τ, the current decreases to 36.8% of its initial value.

Discharging a Capacitor

Now consider the circuit in Figure 28.17, consisting of a capacitor with an initial charge Q, a resistor, and a switch. When the switch is open (Fig. 28.17a), there is a potential difference of Q/C across the capacitor and zero potential difference across the resistor since $I = 0$. If the switch is closed at $t = 0$, the capacitor begins to discharge through the resistor. At some time during the discharge, the current in the circuit is I and the charge on the capacitor is q (Fig. 28.17b). From Kirchhoff's second rule, we see that the potential drop across the resistor, IR, must equal the potential difference across the capacitor, q/C:

$$IR = \frac{q}{C} \tag{28.14}$$

However, the current in the circuit must equal the rate of *decrease* of charge on the capacitor. That is, $I = -dq/dt$, and so Equation 28.14 becomes

$$-R\frac{dq}{dt} = \frac{q}{C}$$

$$\frac{dq}{q} = -\frac{1}{RC}\,dt$$

Integrating this expression using the fact that $q = Q$ at $t = 0$ gives

$$\int_Q^q \frac{dq}{q} = -\frac{1}{RC}\int_0^t dt$$

$$\ln\left(\frac{q}{Q}\right) = -\frac{t}{RC}$$

$$q(t) = Qe^{-t/RC} \tag{28.15}$$

Differentiating Equation 28.15 with respect to time gives the current as a function of time:

$$I(t) = -\frac{dq}{dt} = I_0 e^{-t/RC} \tag{28.16}$$

where the initial current $I_0 = Q/RC$. Therefore, we see that both the charge on the capacitor and the current decay exponentially at a rate characterized by the time constant $\tau = RC$.

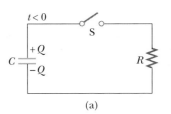

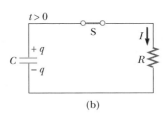

FIGURE 28.17   (a) A charged capacitor connected to a resistor and a switch, which is open at $t < 0$. (b) After the switch is closed, a nonsteady current is set up in the direction shown and the charge on the capacitor decreases exponentially with time.

Charge versus time for a discharging capacitor

Current versus time for a discharging capacitor

CONCEPTUAL EXAMPLE 28.10   Intermittent Windshield Wipers

Many automobiles are equipped with windshield wipers that can be used intermittently during a light rainfall. How does the operation of this feature depend on the charging and discharging of a capacitor?

Reasoning   The wipers are part of an RC circuit whose time constant can be varied by selecting different values of R through a multi-positioned switch. The brief time that the wipers remain on, and the time they are off, is determined by the value of the time constant of the circuit.

EXAMPLE 28.11   Charging a Capacitor in an *RC* Circuit

An uncharged capacitor and a resistor are connected in series to a battery as in Figure 28.18. If $\mathcal{E} = 12.0$ V, $C = 5.00\ \mu$F, and $R = 8.00 \times 10^5\ \Omega$, find the time constant of the circuit, the maximum charge on the capacitor, the maximum current in the circuit, and the charge and current as a function of time.

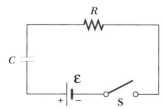

FIGURE 28.18   (Example 28.11) The switch of this series *RC* circuit is closed at $t = 0$.

Solution   The time constant of the circuit is $\tau = RC = (8.00 \times 10^5\ \Omega)(5.00 \times 10^{-6}$ F$) = 4.00$ s.   The maximum charge on the capacitor is $Q = C\mathcal{E} = (5.00 \times 10^{-6}$ F$)$ $(12.0$ V$) = 60.0\ \mu$C. The maximum current in the circuit is $I_0 = \mathcal{E}/R = (12.0$ V$)/(8.00 \times 10^5\ \Omega) = 15.0\ \mu$A. Using these values and Equations 28.12 and 28.13, we find that

$$q(t) = 60.0[1 - e^{-t/4}]\ \mu\text{C}$$

$$I(t) = 15.0e^{-t/4}\ \mu\text{A}$$

Graphs of these functions are given in Figure 28.19.

Exercise   Calculate the charge on the capacitor and the current in the circuit after one time constant has elapsed.

Answer $37.9\ \mu$C, $5.52\ \mu$A.

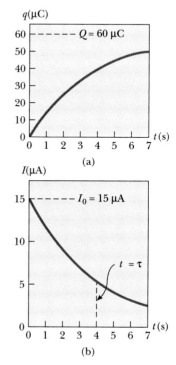

FIGURE 28.19   (Example 28.11) Plots of (a) charge versus time and (b) current versus time for the *RC* circuit shown in Figure 28.18, with $\mathcal{E} = 12.0$ V, $R = 8.00 \times 10^5\ \Omega$, and $C = 5.00\ \mu$F.

EXAMPLE 28.12   Discharging a Capacitor in an *RC* Circuit

Consider a capacitor C being discharged through a resistor R as in Figure 28.17. (a) After how many time constants is the charge on the capacitor one fourth of its initial value?

Solution   The charge on the capacitor varies with time according to Equation 28.15, $q(t) = Qe^{-t/RC}$. To find the time it takes the charge q to drop to one fourth of its initial value, we substitute $q(t) = Q/4$ into this expression and solve for t:

$$\tfrac{1}{4}Q = Qe^{-t/RC}$$

$$\tfrac{1}{4} = e^{-t/RC}$$

Taking logarithms of both sides, we find

$$-\ln 4 = -\frac{t}{RC}$$

$$t = RC \ln 4 = 1.39RC$$

(b) The energy stored in the capacitor decreases with time as it discharges. After how many time constants is this stored energy one fourth of its initial value?

Solution Using Equations 26.10 and 28.15, we can express the energy stored in the capacitor at any time t as

$$U = \frac{q^2}{2C} = \frac{Q^2}{2C} e^{-2t/RC} = U_0 e^{-2t/RC}$$

where U_0 is the initial energy stored in the capacitor. As in part (a), we now set $U = U_0/4$ and solve for t:

$$\tfrac{1}{4}U_0 = U_0 e^{-2t/RC}$$

$$\tfrac{1}{4} = e^{-2t/RC}$$

Again, taking logarithms of both sides and solving for t gives

$$t = \tfrac{1}{2}RC \ln 4 = \boxed{0.693RC}$$

Exercise After how many time constants is the current in the RC circuit one half of its initial value?

Answer $0.693RC$.

EXAMPLE 28.13 Energy Loss in a Resistor

A 5.00-μF capacitor is charged to a potential difference of 800 V and is then discharged through a 25.0-kΩ resistor. How much energy is lost as joule heating in the time it takes to fully discharge the capacitor?

Solution We shall solve this problem in two ways. The first method is to note that the initial energy in the system equals the energy stored in the capacitor, $C\mathcal{E}^2/2$. Once the capacitor is fully discharged, the energy stored in it is zero. Since energy is conserved, the initial energy stored in the capacitor is transformed to thermal energy dissipated in the resistor. Using the given values of C and $\mathcal{E}$, we find

$$\text{Energy} = \tfrac{1}{2}C\mathcal{E}^2 = \tfrac{1}{2}(5.00 \times 10^{-6} \text{ F})(800 \text{ V})^2 = \boxed{1.60 \text{ J}}$$

The second method, which is more difficult but perhaps more instructive, is to note that as the capacitor discharges through the resistor, the rate at which heat is generated in the resistor (or the power loss) is given by RI^2, where I is the instantaneous current given by Equation 28.16. Since power is defined as the rate of change of energy, we conclude that the energy lost in the resistor in the form of heat must equal the time integral of $RI^2\, dt$:

$$\text{Energy} = \int_0^\infty RI^2\, dt = \int_0^\infty R(I_0 e^{-t/RC})^2\, dt$$

To evaluate this integral, we note that the initial current $I_0 = \mathcal{E}/R$ and all parameters are constants except for t. Thus, we find

$$\text{Energy} = \frac{\mathcal{E}^2}{R} \int_0^\infty e^{-2t/RC}\, dt$$

This integral has a value of $RC/2$, and so we find

$$\text{Energy} = \tfrac{1}{2}C\mathcal{E}^2$$

which agrees with the simpler approach, as it must. Note that this second approach can be used to find the energy lost as heat at *any* time after the switch is closed by simply replacing the upper limit in the integral by that specific value of t.

Exercise Show that the integral given in this example has the value of $RC/2$.

---

*28.5 ELECTRICAL INSTRUMENTS

The Ammeter

Current is one of the most important quantities that one would like to measure in an electric circuit. A device that measures current is called an **ammeter.** The current to be measured must pass directly through the ammeter, because the ammeter must be connected in the current, as in Figure 28.20. The wires usually must be cut to make connections to the ammeter. When using an ammeter to measure direct currents, you must be sure to connect it so that current enters the positive terminal of the instrument and exits at the negative terminal. **Ideally, an ammeter should have zero resistance so as not to alter the current being measured.** In the circuit shown in Figure 28.20, this condition requires that the ammeter's resistance be small compared with $R_1 + R_2$. Since any ammeter always has some

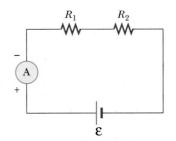

FIGURE 28.20 The current in a circuit can be measured with an ammeter connected in series with the resistor and battery. An ideal ammeter has zero resistance.

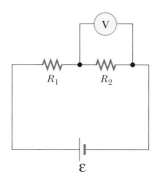

FIGURE 28.21 The potential difference across a resistor can be measured with a voltmeter connected in parallel with the resistor. An ideal voltmeter has infinite resistance and does not affect the circuit.

resistance, its presence in the circuit slightly reduces the current from its value when the ammeter is not present.

The Voltmeter

A device that measures potential differences is called a **voltmeter.** The potential difference between any two points in the circuit can be measured by simply attaching the terminals of the voltmeter between these points without breaking the circuit, as in Figure 28.21. The potential difference across resistor R_2 is measured by connecting the voltmeter in parallel with R_2. Again, it is necessary to observe the polarity of the instrument. The positive terminal of the voltmeter must be connected to the end of the resistor at the higher potential, and the negative terminal to the low-potential end of the resistor. **An ideal voltmeter has infinite resistance so that no current passes through it.** In Figure 28.21, this condition requires that the voltmeter have a resistance that is very large relative to R_2. In practice, if this condition is not met, corrections should be made for the known resistance of the voltmeter.

The Galvanometer

The **galvanometer** is the main component used in the construction of ammeters and voltmeters. The essential features of a common type, called the *D'Arsonval galvanometer,* are shown in Figure 28.22. It consists of a coil of wire mounted so that it is free to rotate on a pivot in a magnetic field provided by a permanent magnet. The basic operation of the galvanometer makes use of the fact that a torque acts on a current loop in the presence of a magnetic field. (The reason for this is discussed in detail in Chapter 29.) The torque experienced by the coil is proportional to the current through it. This means that the larger the current, the larger the torque and the more the coil rotates before the spring tightens enough to stop the rotation. Hence, the amount of deflection is proportional to the current. Once the instrument is properly calibrated, it can be used in conjunction with other circuit elements to measure either currents or potential differences.

A typical off-the-shelf galvanometer is often not suitable for use as an ammeter, mainly because a typical galvanometer has a resistance of about 60 Ω. An ammeter resistance this large considerably alters the current in the circuit in which it is placed. This can be understood by considering the following example. Suppose you construct a simple series circuit containing a 3-V battery and a 3-Ω resistor. The current in such a circuit is 1 A. However, if you insert a 60-Ω galvanometer in the circuit to measure the current, the total resistance of the circuit is 63 Ω and the current is reduced to 0.048 A.

A second factor that limits the use of a galvanometer as an ammeter is the fact that a typical galvanometer gives a full-scale deflection for very low currents, of the order of 1 mA or less. Consequently, such a galvanometer cannot be used directly to measure currents greater than this. However, a galvanometer can be converted to an ammeter by placing a resistor R_p in parallel with the galvanometer as in Figure 28.23a. The value of R_p, sometimes called the *shunt resistor,* must be very small relative to the resistance of the galvanometer so that most of the current to be measured passes through the shunt resistor.

A galvanometer can also be used as a voltmeter by adding an external resistor R_s in series with it, as in Figure 28.23b. In this case, the external resistor must have a value that is very large relative to the resistance of the galvanometer. This ensures that the galvanometer does not significantly alter the voltage to be measured.

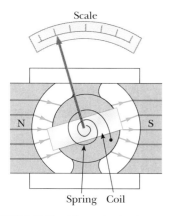

FIGURE 28.22 The principal components of a D'Arsonval galvanometer. When current passes through the coil, situated in a magnetic field, the magnetic torque causes the coil to twist. The angle through which the coil rotates is proportional to the current through it because of the spring's torque.

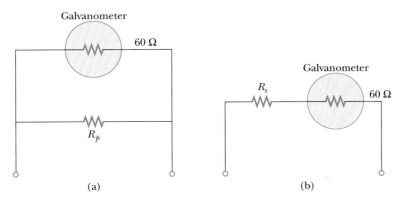

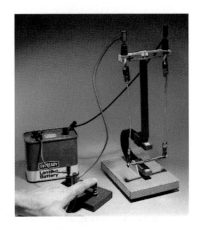

FIGURE 28.23 (a) When a galvanometer is to be used as an ammeter, a resistor, R_p, is connected in parallel with the galvanometer. (b) When the galvanometer is used as a voltmeter, a resistor, R_s, is connected in series with the galvanometer.

Large-scale model of a galvanometer movement. Why does the coil rotate about the vertical axis after the switch is closed?
(Henry Leap and Jim Lehman)

The Wheatstone Bridge

Unknown resistances can be accurately measured using a circuit known as a **Wheatstone bridge** (Fig. 28.24). This circuit consists of the unknown resistance, R_x, three known resistors, R_1, R_2, and R_3 (where R_1 is a calibrated variable resistor), a galvanometer, and a battery. The known resistor R_1 is varied until the galvanometer reading is zero, that is, until there is no current from a to b. Under this condition the bridge is said to be balanced. Since the potential at point a must equal the potential at point b when the bridge is balanced, the potential difference across R_1 must equal the potential difference across R_2. Likewise, the potential difference across R_3 must equal the potential difference across R_x. From these considerations, we see that

$$(1) \qquad I_1 R_1 = I_2 R_2$$

$$(2) \qquad I_1 R_3 = I_2 R_x$$

Dividing (1) by (2) eliminates the currents, and solving for R_x we find

$$R_x = \frac{R_2 R_3}{R_1} \qquad (28.17)$$

Since R_1, R_2, and R_3 are known quantities, R_x can be calculated. There are a number of similar devices that use the null measurement (when the galvanometer reads zero), such as a capacitance bridge used to measure unknown capacitances. These devices do not require the use of calibrated meters and can be used with any voltage source.

When very high resistances are to be measured (above $10^5\ \Omega$), the Wheatstone bridge method becomes difficult for technical reasons. As a result of recent advances in the technology of such solid state devices as the field-effect transistor, modern electronic instruments can measure resistances as high as $10^{12}\ \Omega$. Such instruments have an extremely high resistance between their input terminals. For example, input resistances of $10^{10}\ \Omega$ are common in most digital multimeters. (A multimeter is a device that is used to measure voltage, current, and resistance.)

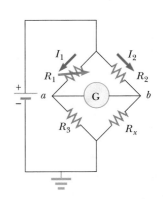

FIGURE 28.24 Circuit diagram for a Wheatstone bridge. This circuit is often used to measure an unknown resistance R_x in terms of known resistances R_1, R_2, and R_3. When the bridge is balanced, there is no current in the galvanometer.

The strain gauge, a device used for experimental stress analysis, consists of a thin coiled wire bonded to a flexible plastic backing. Stresses are measured by detecting changes in resistance of the coil as the strip bends. Resistance measurements are made with the gauge as one element of a Wheatstone bridge. These devices are commonly used in modern electronic balances to measure the mass of an object.

The Potentiometer

A **potentiometer** is a circuit used to measure an unknown emf $\mathcal{E}_x$ by comparison with a known emf. Figure 28.25 shows the essential components of the potentiometer. Point d represents a sliding contact used to vary the resistance (and hence the potential difference) between points a and d. In a common version of the potentiometer, called a **slide-wire potentiometer,** the variable resistor is a wire with the contact point d at some position on the wire. The other required components in this circuit are a galvanometer, a battery with emf $\mathcal{E}$, and the unknown emf $\mathcal{E}_x$.

With the currents in the directions shown in Figure 28.25, we see from Kirchhoff's first rule that the current through the resistor R_x is $I - I_x$, where I is the current in the left branch (through the battery of emf $\mathcal{E}$) and I_x is the current in the right branch. Kirchhoff's second rule applied to loop $abcda$ gives

$$-\mathcal{E}_x + (I - I_x)R_x = 0$$

where R_x is the resistance between points a and d. The sliding contact at d is now adjusted until the galvanometer reads zero (a balanced circuit). Under this condition, the current in the galvanometer and in the unknown cell is zero, and the potential difference between a and d equals the unknown emf $\mathcal{E}_x$. That is,

$$\mathcal{E}_x = IR_x$$

Next, the battery of unknown emf is replaced by a standard battery of known emf $\mathcal{E}_s$ and the above procedure is repeated. That is, the moving contact at d is varied until a balance is obtained. If R_s is the resistance between a and d when balance is achieved, then

$$\mathcal{E}_s = IR_s$$

where it is assumed that I remains the same.

Combining this expression with the previous equation, we see that

$$\mathcal{E}_x = \frac{R_x}{R_s}\mathcal{E}_s \tag{28.18}$$

This result shows that the unknown emf can be determined from a knowledge of the standard-battery emf and the ratio of the two resistances.

Voltages, currents, and resistances are frequently measured by digital multimeters like the one shown in this photograph.
(Henry Leap and Jim Lehman)

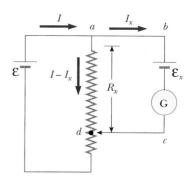

FIGURE 28.25 Circuit diagram for a potentiometer. The circuit is used to measure an unknown emf $\mathcal{E}_x$.

If the resistor is a wire of resistivity ρ, its resistance can be varied using sliding contacts to vary the length of the circuit. With the substitutions $R_s = \rho L_s / A$ and $R_x = \rho L_x / A$, Equation 28.18 reduces to

$$\mathcal{E}_x = \frac{L_x}{L_s} \mathcal{E}_s \qquad (28.19)$$

According to this result, the unknown emf can be obtained from a measurement of the two wire lengths and the magnitude of the standard emf.

*28.6   HOUSEHOLD WIRING AND ELECTRICAL SAFETY

Household circuits represent a practical application of some of the ideas we have presented in this chapter. In our world of electrical appliances, it is useful to understand the power requirements and limitations of conventional electrical systems and the safety measures that should be practiced to prevent accidents.

In a conventional installation, the utilities company distributes electrical power to individual homes with a pair of power lines. Each user is connected in parallel to these lines, as in Figure 28.26. The potential difference between these wires is about 120 V. The voltage alternates in time, with one of the wires connected to ground, and the potential of the other, "live," wire oscillates relative to ground.[2] For the present discussion, we assume a constant voltage (direct current). (Alternating voltages and currents are discussed in Chapter 33.)

A meter and circuit breaker (or in older installations, a fuse) are connected in series with one of the wires entering the house. The wire and circuit breaker are carefully selected to meet the current demands for that circuit. If a circuit is to carry currents as large as 30 A, a heavy wire and appropriate circuit breaker must be selected to handle this current. Other individual household circuits normally used to power lamps and small appliances often require only 15 A. Each circuit has its own circuit breaker to accomodate various load conditions.

As an example, consider a circuit in which a toaster, a microwave oven, and a heater are in the same circuit (corresponding to R_1, R_2, . . . in Figure 28.26). We can calculate the current drawn by each appliance using the expression $P = IV$. The toaster, rated at 1000 W, draws a current of $1000/120 = 8.33$ A. The microwave oven, rated at 800 W, draws 6.67 A, and the electric heater, rated at 1300 W, draws 10.8 A. If the three appliances are operated simultaneously, they draw a total current of 25.8 A. Therefore, the circuit should be wired to handle at least this much current. In order to accomodate a small additional load, such as a 100-W lamp, a 30-A circuit should be installed. Alternatively, the toaster and microwave oven could be operated on one 20-A circuit and the heater on a separate 20-A circuit.

Many heavy-duty appliances, such as electric ranges and clothes dryers, require 240 V for their operation. The power company supplies this voltage by providing a third wire that is 120 V below ground potential (Fig. 28.27). The potential difference between this wire and the other live wire (which is 120 V above ground potential) is 240 V. An appliance that operates from a 240-V line requires half the current of one operating from a 120-V line; therefore, smaller wires can be used in the higher-voltage circuit without overheating becoming a problem.

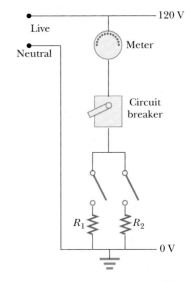

FIGURE 28.26 Wiring diagram for a household circuit. The resistances R_1 and R_2 represent appliances or other electric devices that operate with an applied voltage of 120 V.

FIGURE 28.27 Power connections for a 240-V appliance.

---

[2] The phrase *live wire* is common jargon for a conductor whose potential is above or below ground.

Electrical Safety

When the live wire of an electrical outlet is connected directly to ground, the circuit is completed and a short-circuit condition exists. When this happens accidentally, a properly operating circuit breaker opens the circuit. On the other hand, a person in contact with ground can be electrocuted by touching the live wire of a frayed cord or other exposed conductors. An exceptionally good ground contact is made either by the person's touching a water pipe (normally at ground potential) or by standing on ground with wet feet, since water is a conductor. Such situations should be avoided at all costs.

Electrical shock can result in fatal burns, or it can cause the muscles of vital organs, such as the heart, to malfunction. The degree of damage to the body depends on the magnitude of the current, the length of time it acts, the location of the contact, and the part of the body through which the current passes. Currents of 5 mA or less can cause a sensation of shock, but ordinarily do little or no damage. If the current is larger than about 10 mA, the muscles contract and the person may be unable to release the live wire. If a current of about 100 mA passes through the body for only a few seconds, the result can be fatal. Such large currents paralyze the respiratory muscles and prevent breathing. In some cases, currents of about 1 A through the body can produce serious (and sometimes fatal) burns. In practice, no contact with live wires (voltages above 24 V) is regarded as safe.

Many 120-V outlets are designed to accept a three-pronged power cord. (This feature is required in all new electrical installations.) One of these prongs is the live wire, a second called the "neutral," carries current to ground, and the third, round prong is a safety ground wire that carries no current. The additional grounded wire is an important safety feature with the safety ground wire connected directly to the casing of the appliance. If the live wire is accidentally shorted to the casing (which often occurs when the wire insulation wears off), the current takes the low-resistance path through the appliance to ground. In contrast, if the casing of the appliance is not properly grounded and a short occurs, anyone in contact with the appliance experiences an electric shock because the body provides a low-resistance path to ground.

Special power outlets called ground-fault interrupters (GFIs) are now being used in kitchens, bathrooms, basements, exterior outlets, and other hazardous areas of new homes. These devices are designed to protect persons from electrical shock by sensing small currents (≈ 5 mA) leaking to ground. (The principle of their operation is described in Chapter 31.) When an excessive leakage current is detected, the current is shut off in less than 1 ms.

SUMMARY

The **emf** of a battery is equal to the voltage across its terminals when the current is zero. That is, the emf is equivalent to the open-circuit voltage of the battery.

The **equivalent resistance** of a set of resistors connected in **series** is

$$R_{eq} = R_1 + R_2 + R_3 + \cdots \tag{28.6}$$

The **equivalent resistance** of a set of resistors connected in **parallel** is

$$\frac{1}{R_{eq}} = \frac{1}{R_1} + \frac{1}{R_2} + \frac{1}{R_3} + \cdots \tag{28.8}$$

Complex circuits involving more than one loop are conveniently analyzed using **Kirchhoff's rules:**

- The sum of the currents entering any junction must equal the sum of the currents leaving that junction.
- The sum of the potential differences across each element around any closed-circuit loop must be zero.

The first rule is a statement of **conservation of charge.** The second rule is equivalent to a statement of **conservation of energy.**

When a resistor is traversed in the direction of the current, the change in potential, ΔV, across the resistor is $-IR$. If a resistor is traversed in the direction opposite the current, $\Delta V = +IR$. If a source of emf is traversed in the direction of the emf (negative to positive) the change in potential is $+\mathcal{E}$. If it is traversed opposite the emf (positive to negative), the change in potential is $-\mathcal{E}$.

If a capacitor is charged with a battery through a resistance R, the charge on the capacitor and the current in the circuit vary in time according to the expressions

$$q(t) = Q[1 - e^{-t/RC}] \tag{28.12}$$

$$I(t) = \frac{\mathcal{E}}{R} e^{-t/RC} \tag{28.13}$$

where $Q = C\mathcal{E}$ is the maximum charge on the capacitor. The product RC is called the **time constant** of the circuit.

If a charged capacitor is discharged through a resistance R, the charge and current decrease exponentially in time according to the expressions

$$q(t) = Qe^{-t/RC} \tag{28.15}$$

$$I(t) = I_0 e^{-t/RC} \tag{28.16}$$

where $I_0 = Q/RC$ is the initial current and Q is the initial charge on the capacitor.

QUESTIONS

1. Explain the difference between load resistance and internal resistance for a battery.
2. Under what condition does the potential difference across the terminals of a battery equal its emf? Can the terminal voltage ever exceed the emf? Explain.
3. Is the direction of current through a battery always from negative to positive on the terminals? Explain.
4. Two sets of Christmas-tree lights are available. For set A, when one bulb is removed (or burns out), the remaining bulbs remain illuminated. For set B, when one bulb is removed, the remaining bulbs do not operate. Explain the difference in wiring for the two sets.
5. How would you connect resistors so that the equivalent resistance is larger than the individual resistances? Give an example involving two or three resistors.
6. How would you connect resistors so that the equivalent resistance is smaller than the individual resistances? Give an example involving two or three resistors.
7. Given three lightbulbs and a battery, sketch as many different electric circuits as you can.

8. When resistors are connected in series, which of the following would be the same for each resistor: potential difference, current, power?
9. When resistors are connected in parallel, which of the following would be the same for each resistor: potential difference, current, power?
10. What advantage might there be in using two identical resistors in parallel connected in series with another identical parallel pair, rather than just using a single resistor?
11. Are the two headlights on a car wired in series or in parallel? How can you tell?
12. An incandescent lamp connected to a 120-V source with a short extension cord provides more illumination than the same lamp connected to the same source with a very long extension cord. Explain.
13. Embodied in Kirchhoff's rules are two conservation laws, what are they?
14. When can the potential difference across a resistor be positive?
15. In Figure 28.14, suppose the wire between points g and

h is replaced by a 10-Ω resistor. Explain why this change does not affect the currents calculated in Example 28.9.

16. In Figure 28.28, describe what happens to the lightbulb after the switch is closed. Assume the capacitor has a large capacitance and is initially uncharged, and assume that the light illuminates when connected directly across the battery terminals.

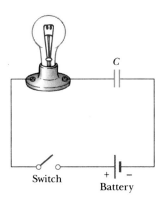

FIGURE 28.28   (Question 16).

17. What is the internal resistance of an ideal ammeter and voltmeter? Do real meters attain this ideal case?

18. Although the internal resistance of the unknown and known emfs was neglected in the treatment of the potentiometer (Section 28.5), it is really not necessary to make this assumption. Explain why the internal resistances play no role in this measurement.

19. Why is it dangerous to turn on a light when you are in the bathtub?

20. Why is it possible for a bird to sit on a high-voltage wire without being electrocuted?

21. Suppose you fall from a building and on the way down grab a high-voltage wire. Assuming that the wire holds you, will you be electrocuted? If the wire then breaks,

should you continue to hold onto an end of the wire as you fall?

22. Would a fuse work successfully if it were placed in parallel with the device it is supposed to protect?

23. What advantage does 120-V operation offer over 240 V? What disadvantages?

24. When electricians work with potentially live wires, they often use the backs of their hands or fingers to move wires. Why do you suppose they use this technique?

25. What procedure would you use to try to save a person who is "frozen" to a live high-voltage wire without endangering your own life?

26. If it is the current flowing through the body that determines how serious a shock will be, why do we see warnings of high voltage rather than high current near electric equipment?

27. Suppose you are flying a kite when it strikes a high-voltage wire. What factors determine how great a shock you receive?

28. A series circuit consists of three identical lamps connected to a battery as in Figure 28.29. When the switch S is closed, what happens (a) to the intensities of lamps A and B; (b) to the intensity of lamp C; (c) to the current in the circuit; and (d) to the voltage drop across the three lamps? (e) Does the power dissipated in the circuit increase, decrease, or remain the same?

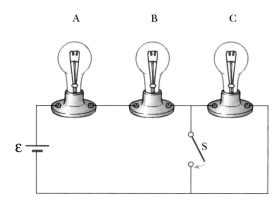

FIGURE 28.29   (Question 28).

PROBLEMS

Review Problem

In the circuit shown, the values of *I* and *R* are known, while the emf and internal resistance of the battery are unknown. When the switch S is closed, the ammeter reads $20I$ before burning out. When the switch is open, find (a) the total exter-

nal resistance, (b) the potential difference between *a* and *b*, (c) the emf of the battery, (d) the internal resistance *r* of the battery, (e) the current in the resistor marked *, and (f) the power dissipated by the resistor marked *. If points 1 and 2 are connected by a wire, find (g) the total resistance of the external circuit, (h) the current in the battery, and (i) the power dissipated in the circuit. (j) In the original circuit, suppose an uncharged capacitor C is inserted between b and d as indicated by the dashed circuit symbol. How long does it take the capacitor to acquire a charge $q = CIR$?

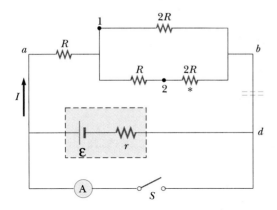

Section 28.1   Electromotive Force

1. A battery with an emf of 12 V and internal resistance of 0.90 Ω is connected across a load resistor R. (a) If the current in the circuit is 1.4 A, what is the value of R? (b) What power is dissipated in the internal resistance of the battery?

2. A 9.00-V battery delivers 117 mA when connected to a 72.0-Ω load. Determine the internal resistance of the battery.

3. (a) What is the current in a 5.6-Ω resistor connected to a battery that has a 0.2-Ω internal resistance if the terminal voltage of the battery is 10 V? (b) What is the emf of the battery?

4. If the emf of a battery is 15 V and a current of 60 A is measured when the battery is shorted, what is the internal resistance of the battery?

5. The current in a loop circuit that has a resistance of R_1 is 2 A. The current is reduced to 1.6 A when an additional resistor $R_2 = 3$ Ω is added in series with R_1. What is the value of R_1?

6. A typical fresh AA dry cell has an emf of 1.50 V and an internal resistance of 0.311 Ω. (a) Find the terminal voltage of the battery when it supplies 58 mA to a circuit. (b) What is the resistance R of the external circuit?

7. A battery has an emf of 15.0 V. The terminal voltage of the battery is 11.6 V when it is delivering 20.0 W of power to an external load resistor R. (a) What is the value of R? (b) What is the internal resistance of the battery?

8. What potential difference is measured across an 18-Ω load resistor when it is connected across a battery of emf 5.0 V and internal resistance 0.45 Ω?

9. Two 1.50-V batteries—with their positive terminals in the same direction—are inserted in series into the barrel of a flashlight. One battery has an internal resistance of 0.255 Ω, the other an internal resistance of 0.153 Ω. When the switch is closed, a current of 600 mA occurs in the lamp. (a) What is the lamp's resistance? (b) What fraction of the power dissipated is dissipated in the batteries?

Section 28.2   Resistors in Series and in Parallel

10. Two circuit elements with fixed resistances R_1 and R_2 are connected in series with a 6.0-V battery and a switch. The battery has an internal resistance of 5.0 Ω, $R_1 = 132$ Ω, and $R_2 = 56$ Ω. (a) What is the current through R_1 when the switch is closed? (b) What is the voltage across R_2 when the switch is closed?

11. Using only three resistors—2.0 Ω, 3.0 Ω, and 4.0 Ω —find 17 resistance values that may be obtained by various combinations of one or more resistors. Tabulate the combinations in order of increasing resistance.

12. (a) You need a 45-Ω resistor, but the stockroom has only 20-Ω and 50-Ω resistors. How can the desired resistance be achieved under these circumstances? (b) What can you do if you need a 35-Ω resistor?

13. The current in a circuit is tripled by connecting a 500-Ω resistor in parallel with the resistance of the circuit. Determine the resistance of the circuit in the absence of the 500-Ω resistor.

14. (a) Find the equivalent resistance between points a and b in Figure P28.14. (b) If a potential difference of 34 V is applied between points a and b, calculate the current in each resistor.

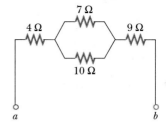

FIGURE P28.14

15. The resistance between terminals a and b in Figure P28.15 is 75 Ω. If the resistors labeled R have the same value, determine R.

16. Four copper wires of equal length are connected in series. Their cross-sectional areas are 1.0 cm², 2.0 cm², 3.0 cm², and 5.0 cm². If a voltage of 120 V is

---

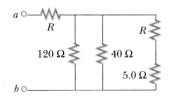

FIGURE P28.15

applied to the arrangement, determine the voltage across the 2.0-cm² wire.

17. The power dissipated in the top part of the circuit in Figure P28.17 does not depend on whether the switch is open or closed. If $R = 1.0 \ \Omega$, determine R'. Neglect the internal resistance of the voltage source.

17A. The power dissipated in the top part of the circuit in Figure P28.17 does not depend on whether the switch is open or closed. Determine R' in terms of R. Neglect the internal resistance of the voltage source.

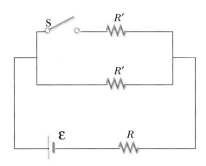

FIGURE P28.17

18. In Figures 28.4 and 28.5, $R_1 = 11 \ \Omega$, $R_2 = 22 \ \Omega$, and the battery has a terminal voltage of 33 V. (a) In the parallel circuit shown in Figure 28.5, which resistor uses more power? (b) Verify that the sum of the power (I^2R) used by each resistor equals the power supplied by the battery (IV). (c) In the series circuit, which resistor uses more power? (d) Verify that the sum of the power (I^2R) used by each resistor equals the power supplied by the battery ($P = IV$). (e) Which circuit configuration uses more power?

19. Calculate the power dissipated in each resistor in the circuit of Figure P28.19.

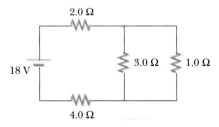

FIGURE P28.19

20. Determine the equivalent resistance between the terminals a and b for the network illustrated in Figure P28.20.

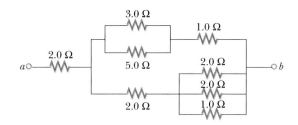

FIGURE P28.20

21. In Figure P28.21, find (a) the current in the 20-Ω resistor and (b) the potential difference between points a and b.

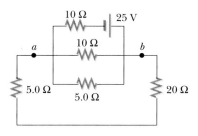

FIGURE P28.21

22. The resistance between points a and b in Figure P28.22 drops to one-half its original value when switch S is closed. Determine the value of R.

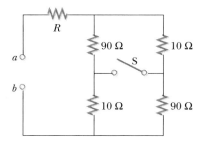

FIGURE P28.22

23. Two resistors connected in series have an equivalent resistance of 690 Ω. When they are connected in parallel, their equivalent resistance is 150 Ω. Find the resistance of each resistor.

23A. Two resistors connected in series have an equivalent resistance of R_s. When they are connected in parallel, their equivalent resistance is R_p. Find the resistance of each resistor.

24. Three 100-Ω resistors are connected as shown in Figure P28.24. The maximum power dissipated in any

one resistor is 25 W. (a) What is the maximum voltage that can be applied to the terminals *a* and *b*? (b) For the voltage determined in part (a), what is the power dissipation in each resistor? What is the total power dissipation?

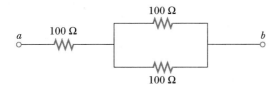

FIGURE P28.24

Section 28.3   Kirchhoff's Rules

(*Note:* The currents are not necessarily in the direction shown for some circuits.)

25. (a) Find the potential difference between points *a* and *b* in Figure P28.25. (b) Find the currents I_1, I_2, and I_3 in Figure P28.25.

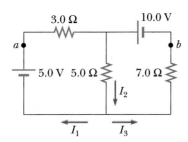

FIGURE P28.25

26. If $R = 1.0$ kΩ and $\mathcal{E} = 250$ V in Figure P28.26, determine the direction and magnitude of the current in the horizontal wire between *a* and *e*.

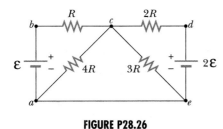

FIGURE P28.26

27. Determine the current in each branch in Figure P28.27.
28. In the circuit of Figure P28.28, determine the current in each resistor and the voltage across the 200-Ω resistor.
29. A dead battery is charged by connecting it to the live battery of another car (Fig. P28.29). Determine the current in the starter and in the dead battery.

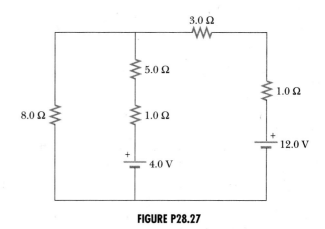

FIGURE P28.27

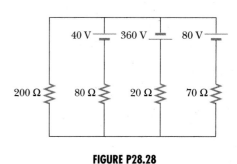

FIGURE P28.28

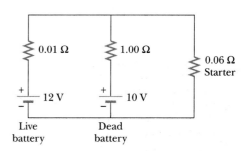

FIGURE P28.29

30. For the network shown in Figure P28.30, show that the resistance $R_{ab} = (27/17)\,\Omega$.

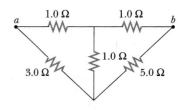

FIGURE P28.30

31. Calculate I_1, I_2, and I_3 in Figure P28.31.

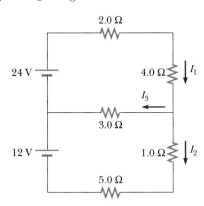

FIGURE P28.31

32. The ammeter in Figure P28.32 reads 2.0 A. Find I_1, I_2, and $\mathcal{E}$.

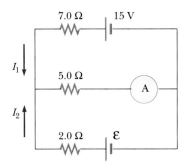

FIGURE P28.32

33. Using Kirchhoff's rules, (a) find the current in each resistor in Figure P28.33. (b) Find the potential difference between points c and f. Which point is at the higher potential?

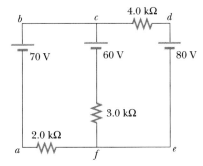

FIGURE P28.33

34. Find I_1, I_2, and I_3 in Figure P28.34.
35. An automobile battery has an emf of 12.6 V and an internal resistance of 0.080 Ω. The headlights have total resistance 5.00 Ω (assumed constant). What is the potential difference across the headlight bulbs

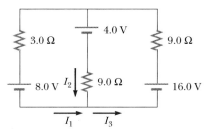

FIGURE P28.34

(a) when they are the only load on the battery and (b) when the starter motor is operated, taking an additional 35.0 A from the battery?
36. In Figure P28.36, calculate (a) the equivalent resistance of the network outside the battery, (b) the current through the battery, and (c) the current in the 6.0-Ω resistor.

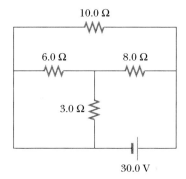

FIGURE P28.36

37. For the circuit shown in Figure P28.37, calculate (a) the current in the 2.0-Ω resistor and (b) the potential difference between points a and b.

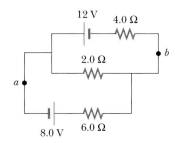

FIGURE P28.37

38. The resistor R in Figure P28.38 dissipates 20 W of power. Determine the value of R.
39. Calculate the power dissipated in each resistor in Figure P28.39.
40. Calculate the power dissipated in each resistor in Figure P28.40.

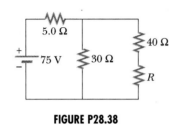

FIGURE P28.38

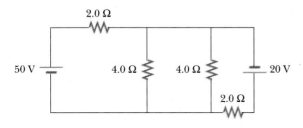

FIGURE P28.39

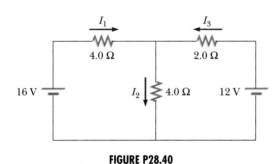

FIGURE P28.40

Section 28.4   *RC* Circuits

41. A fully charged capacitor stores 12 J of energy. How much energy remains when its charge has decreased to half its original value?

41A. A fully charged capacitor stores energy U_0. How much energy remains when its charge has decreased to half its original value?

42. Consider a series RC circuit (Fig. 28.15) for which $R = 1.00 \text{ M}\Omega$, $C = 5.00 \ \mu\text{F}$, and $\mathcal{E} = 30.0$ V. Find (a) the time constant of the circuit and (b) the maximum charge on the capacitor after the switch is closed. (c) If the switch is closed at $t = 0$, find the current in the resistor 10.0 s later.

43. In the circuit of Figure P28.43, the switch S has been open for a long time. It is then suddenly closed. Determine the time constant (a) before the switch is closed and (b) after the switch is closed. (c) If the switch is closed at $t = 0$ s, determine the current through it as a function of time.

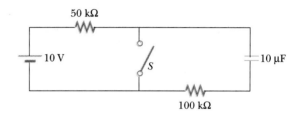

FIGURE P28.43

44. At $t = 0$, an uncharged capacitor of capacitance C is connected through a resistance R to a battery of constant emf $\mathcal{E}$ (Fig. P28.44). How long does it take the capacitor to (a) reach one-half its final charge and (b) to become fully charged?

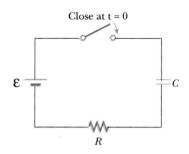

FIGURE P28.44

45. A 4.00-MΩ resistor and a 3.00-μF capacitor are connected in series with a 12.0-V power supply. (a) What is the time constant for the circuit? (b) Express the current in the circuit and the charge on the capacitor as functions of time.

46. A 750-pF capacitor has an initial charge of 6.00 μC. It is then connected to a 150-MΩ resistor and allowed to discharge through the resistor. (a) What is the time constant for the circuit? (b) Express the current in the circuit and the charge on the capacitor as functions of time.

47. The circuit in Figure P28.47 has been connected for a long time. (a) What is the voltage across the capacitor? (b) If the battery is disconnected, how long does it take the capacitor to discharge to 1/10 of its initial voltage?

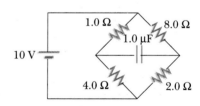

FIGURE P28.47

48. A 2.0×10^{-3}-μF capacitor with an initial charge of 5.1 μC is discharged through a 1.3-kΩ resistor. (a) Calculate the current through the resistor 9.0 μs after the resistor is connected across the terminals of the capacitor. (b) What charge remains on the capacitor after 8.0 μs? (c) What is the maximum current in the resistor?

49. Find the current through the ammeter 9.5 μs after the switch in Figure P28.49 is thrown from position *a* to position *b*.

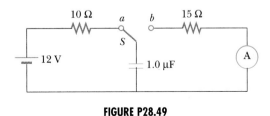

FIGURE P28.49

50. A capacitor in an RC circuit is charged to 60% of its maximum value in 0.90 s. What is the time constant of the circuit?

51. Dielectric materials used in the manufacture of capacitors are characterized by conductivities that are small but not zero. Therefore, a charged capacitor slowly loses its charge by "leaking" across the dielectric. If a certain 3.60-μF capacitor leaks charge such that the potential difference decreases to half its initial value in 4.00 s, what is the equivalent resistance of the dielectric?

51A. Dielectric materials used in the manufacture of capacitors are characterized by conductivities that are small but not zero. Therefore, a charged capacitor slowly loses its charge by "leaking" across the dielectric. If a capacitor having capacitance C leaks charge such that the potential difference decreases to half its initial value in a time t, what is the equivalent resistance of the dielectric?

*Section 28.5   Electrical Instruments

52. A typical galvanometer, which requires a current of 1.50 mA for full-scale deflection and has a resistance of 75.0 Ω, may be used to measure currents of much larger values. To enable an operator to measure large currents without damage to the galvanometer, a relatively small shunt resistor is wired in parallel with the galvanometer similar to Figure 28.23a. Most of the current then flows through the shunt resistor. Calculate the value of the shunt resistor that enables the galvanometer to be used to measure a current of 1.00 A at full-scale deflection. (*Hint:* Use Kirchhoff's laws.)

53. The same galvanometer described in the previous problem may be used to measure voltages. In this case a large resistor is wired in series with the galvanometer similar to Figure 28.22b, which in effect limits the current that flows through the galvanometer when large voltages are applied. Most of the potential drop occurs across the resistor placed in series. Calculate the value of the resistor that enables the galvanometer to measure an applied voltage of 25.0 V at full-scale deflection.

54. For each voltage setting, a galvanometer having an internal resistance of 100 Ω deflects full scale when the current is 1.0 mA. For the multiscale voltmeter in Figure P28.54, what are the values of R_1, R_2, and R_3?

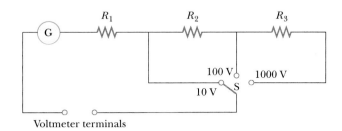

FIGURE P28.54

55. Assume that a galvanometer has an internal resistance of 60.0 Ω and requires a current of 0.500 mA to produce full-scale deflection. What resistance must be connected in parallel with the galvanometer if the combination is to serve as an ammeter that has a full-scale deflection for a current of 0.100 A?

56. An ammeter is constructed using a galvanometer that requires a potential difference of 50.0 mV across the galvanometer and a current of 1.00 mA through the galvanometer to cause a full-scale deflection. Find the shunt resistance R that produces a full-scale deflection when a current of 5.00 A enters the ammeter.

57. A galvanometer having a full-scale sensitivity of 1.00 mA requires a 900-Ω series resistor to make a voltmeter reading full scale when 1.00 V is measured across the terminals. What series resistor is required to make the same galvanometer into a 50.0-V (full-scale) voltmeter?

58. A current of 2.50 mA causes a given galvanometer to deflect full scale. The resistance of the galvanometer is 200 Ω. (a) Show by means of a circuit diagram, using two resistors and three external jacks, how the galvanometer may be made into a dual-range voltmeter. (b) Determine the values of the resistors needed to make the high range 0–200 V and the low range 0–20.0 V. Indicate these values on the diagram.

59. For the same galvanometer as in the previous problem, (a) show by means of a circuit diagram, using two resistors and three external jacks, how the galvanometer may be made into a dual-range ammeter.

(b) Determine the values of the resistors needed to make the high range 0–10.0 A and the low range 0–1.00 A. Indicate these values on the diagram.

60. A Wheatstone bridge of the type shown in Figure 28.24 is used to make a precise measurement of the resistance of a wire connector. If $R_3 = 1.00$ kΩ and the bridge is balanced by adjusting R_1 such that $R_1 = 2.50R_2$, what is R_x?

61. Consider the case when the Wheatstone bridge shown in Figure 28.24 is unbalanced. Calculate the current through the galvanometer when $R_x = R_3 = 7.00$ Ω, $R_2 = 21.0$ Ω, and $R_1 = 14.0$ Ω. Assume the voltage across the bridge is 70.0 V, and neglect the galvanometer's resistance.

62. When the Wheatstone bridge shown in Figure 28.24 is balanced, the voltage drop across R_x is 3.20 V and $I_1 = 200$ μA. If the total current drawn from the power supply is 500 μA, what is R_x?

63. The Wheatstone bridge in Figure 28.24 is balanced when $R_1 = 10.0$ Ω, $R_2 = 20.0$ Ω, and $R_3 = 30.0$ Ω. Calculate R_x.

64. Consider the potentiometer circuit shown in Figure 28.25. When a standard battery of emf 1.0186 V is used in the circuit and the resistance between a and d is 36.0 Ω, the galvanometer reads zero. When the standard battery is replaced by an unknown emf, the galvanometer reads zero when the resistance is adjusted to 48.0 Ω. What is the value of the unknown emf?

*Section 28.6   Household Wiring and Electrical Safety

65. An electric heater is rated at 1500 W, a toaster at 750 W, and an electric grill at 1000 W. The three appliances are connected to a common 120-V circuit. (a) How much current does each draw? (b) Is a 25-A circuit sufficient in this situation? Explain.

66. A 1000-W toaster, 800-W microwave oven, and 500-W coffee pot are all plugged into the same 120-V outlet. If the circuit is protected by a 20-A fuse, will the fuse blow if all these appliances are used at once?

67. An 8-foot extension cord has two 18-gauge copper wires, each having a diameter of 1.024 mm. How much power does this cord dissipate when carrying a current of (a) 1.0 A and (b) 10 A?

68. Sometimes aluminum wiring is used instead of copper for economic reasons. According to the National Electrical Code, the maximum allowable current for 12-gauge copper wire with rubber insulation is 20 A. What should be the maximum allowable current in a 12-gauge aluminum wire if it is to dissipate the same power per unit length as the copper wire?

69. A 4.0-kW heater is wired for 240-V operation with Nichrome wire having a total mass M. (a) How much current does the heater require? (b) How much current does a 120-V, 4.0-kW heater require? (c) If a 240-V, 4.0-kW heater and a 120-V, 4.0-kW heater have the same length of wires in them, how does the mass of the wire in the 120-V heater compare with the mass of the wire in the 240-V heater?

ADDITIONAL PROBLEMS

70. Calculate the potential difference between points a and b in Figure P28.70 and identify which point is at the higher potential.

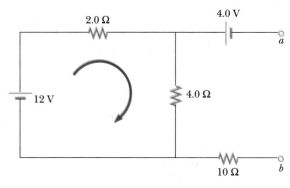

FIGURE P28.70

71. When two unknown resistors are connected in series with a battery, 225 W is dissipated with a total current of 5.00 A. For the same total current, 50.0 W is dissipated when the resistors are connected in parallel. Determine the values of the two resistors.

71A. When two unknown resistors are connected in series with a battery, a total power P_s is dissipated with a total current of I. For the same total current, a total power P_p is dissipated when the resistors are connected in parallel. Determine the values of the two resistors.

72. Before the switch is closed in Figure P28.72, there is no charge stored by the capacitor. Determine the currents in R_1, R_2, and C (a) at the instant the switch is closed (that is, at $t = 0$) and (b) after the switch is closed for a long time (that is, as $t \rightarrow \infty$).

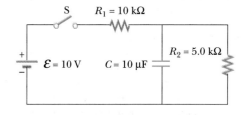

FIGURE P28.72

73. Three resistors, each of value 3.0 Ω, are connected in two arrangements as in Figure P28.73. If the maximum allowable power for each resistor is 48 W, cal-

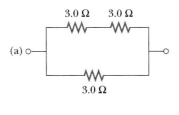

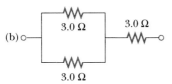

FIGURE P28.73

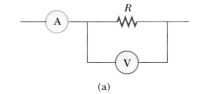

(a)

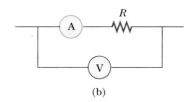

(b)

FIGURE P28.77

culate the maximum power that can be dissipated by (a) the circuit in Figure P28.73a and (b) the circuit in Figure P28.73b.

74. Arrange nine 100-Ω resistors in a series-parallel network so that the total resistance of the network is also 100 Ω. All nine resistors must be used.

75. Three 60-W, 120-V lightbulbs are connected across a 120-V power source, as shown in Figure P28.75. Find (a) the total power dissipated in the three bulbs and (b) the voltage across each. Assume that the resistance of each bulb conforms to Ohm's law (even though in reality the resistance increases markedly with current).

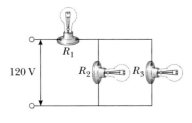

FIGURE P28.75

76. A series combination of a 12-kΩ resistor and an unknown capacitor is connected to a 12-V battery. One second after the circuit is completed, the voltage across the capacitor is 10 V. Determine the capacitance.

77. The value of a resistor R is to be determined using the ammeter-voltmeter setup shown in Figure P28.77. The ammeter has a resistance of 0.50 Ω, and the voltmeter has a resistance of 20 000.0 Ω. Within what range of actual values of R will the measured values be correct to within 5% if the measurement is made using the circuit shown in (a) Figure P28.77a and (b) Figure P28.77b?

78. A power supply has an open-circuit voltage of 40.0 V and an internal resistance of 2.0 Ω. It is used to charge two storage batteries connected in series, each having an emf of 6.0 V and internal resistance of 0.30 Ω. If the charging current is to be 4.0 A, (a) what additional resistance should be added in series? (b) Find the power lost in the supply, the batteries, and the added series resistance. (c) How much power is converted to chemical energy in the batteries?

79. A battery has an emf $\mathcal{E}$ and internal resistance r. A variable resistor R is connected across the terminals of the battery. Find the value of R such that (a) the potential difference across the terminals is a maximum, (b) the current in the circuit is a maximum, (c) the power delivered to the resistor is a maximum.

80. Consider the circuit shown in Figure P28.80. (a) Calculate the current in the 5.0-Ω resistor. (b) What power is dissipated by the circuit? (c) Determine the potential difference between points a and b. Which point is at the higher potential?

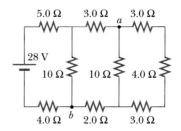

FIGURE P28.80

81. The values of the components in a simple series RC circuit containing a switch (Fig. 28.15) are $C =$

$1.00\ \mu F$, $R = 2.00 \times 10^6\ \Omega$, and $\mathcal{E} = 10.0$ V. At the instant 10.0 s after the switch is closed, calculate (a) the charge on the capacitor, (b) the current in the resistor, (c) the rate at which energy is being stored in the capacitor, and (d) the rate at which energy is being delivered by the battery.

82. A battery is used to charge a capacitor through a resistor, as in Figure 28.15. Show that half the energy supplied by the battery is dissipated as heat in the resistor and half is stored in the capacitor.

83. The switch in Figure P28.83a closes when $V_c \geq 2V/3$ and opens when $V_c \leq V/3$. The voltmeter reads a voltage as plotted in Figure P28.83b. What is the period, T, of the waveform in terms of R_A, R_B, and C?

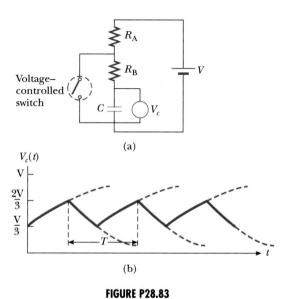

(a)

(b)

FIGURE P28.83

84. Design a multirange voltmeter capable of full-scale deflection for (a) 20.0 V, (b) 50.0 V, and (c) 100.0 V. Assume a meter that has a resistance of $60.0\ \Omega$ and gives a full-scale deflection for a current of 1.00 mA.

85. Design a multirange ammeter capable of full-scale deflection for (a) 25.0 mA, (b) 50.0 mA, and (c) 100.0 mA. Assume a meter that has a resistance of $25.0\ \Omega$ and gives a full-scale deflection for 1.00 mA.

86. A particular galvanometer serves as a 2.00-V full-scale voltmeter when a 2500-Ω resistor is connected in series with it. It serves as a 0.500-A full-scale ammeter when a 0.220-Ω resistor is connected in parallel with it. Determine the internal resistance of the galvanometer and the current required to produce full-scale deflection.

87. In Figure P28.87, suppose the switch has been closed sufficiently long for the capacitor to become fully charged. Find (a) the steady-state current through

each resistor and (b) the charge Q on the capacitor. (c) The switch is now opened at $t = 0$. Write an equation for the current i_{R_2} through R_2 as a function of time and (d) find the time that it takes for the charge on the capacitor to fall to one-fifth its initial value.

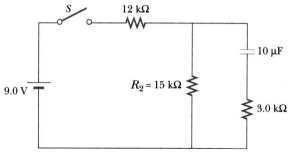

FIGURE P28.87

88. A 10.0-μF capacitor is charged by a 10.0-V battery through a resistance R. The capacitor reaches a potential difference of 4.00 V in a time 3.00 s after charging begins. Find R.

89. (a) Determine the charge on the capacitor in Figure P28.89 when $R = 10\ \Omega$. (b) For what value of R is the charge on the capacitor zero?

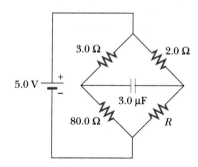

FIGURE P28.89

90. (a) Using symmetry arguments, show that the current through any resistor in the configuration of Figure P28.90 is either $I/3$ or $I/6$. All resistors have the same resistance r. (b) Show that the equivalent resistance between points a and b is $(5/6)r$.

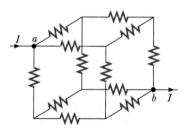

FIGURE P28.90

91. The circuit shown in Figure P28.91 is set up in the laboratory to measure an unknown capacitance C using a voltmeter of resistance $R = 10.0$ MΩ and a battery whose emf is 6.19 V. The data given in the table below are the measured voltages across the capacitor as a function of time, where $t = 0$ represents the time the switch is open. (a) Construct a graph of $\ln(\mathcal{E}/V)$ versus t, and do a linear least-squares fit on the data. (b) From the slope of your graph, obtain a value for the time constant of the circuit and a value for the capacitance.

V(V)	t(s)	$\ln(\mathcal{E}/V)$
6.19	0	
5.55	4.87	
4.93	11.1	
4.34	19.4	
3.72	30.8	
3.09	46.6	
2.47	67.3	
1.83	102.2	

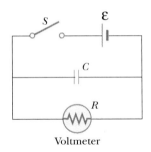

FIGURE P28.91

92. The student engineer of a campus radio station wishes to verify the effectiveness of the lightning rod on the antenna mast (Fig. P28.92). The unknown resistance R_x is between points C and E. Point E is a true ground but is inaccessible for direct measurement because it is several meters below the Earth's surface. Two identical rods are driven into the ground at A and B, introducing an unknown resistance, R_y. The procedure for determining the effectiveness of the rod is as follows: Measure resistance R_1 between A and B, then connect A and B with a heavy conducting wire and measure resistance R_2 between A and C. (a) Derive a formula for R_x in terms of the observable resistances, R_1 and R_2. (b) A satisfactory ground resistance would be $R_x < 2.0$ Ω. Is the grounding of the station adequate if measurements give $R_1 = 13$ Ω and $R_2 = 6.0$ Ω?

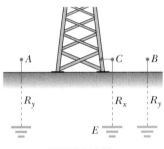

FIGURE P28.92

93. Three 2.0-Ω resistors are connected as in Figure P28.93. Each can dissipate a maximum power of 32 W without being excessively heated. Determine the maximum power the network can dissipate.

93A. Three resistors each having resistance R are connected as in Figure P28.93. Each can dissipate a maximum power P without being excessively heated. Determine the maximum power the network can dissipate.

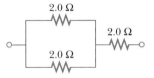

FIGURE P28.93

94. In Figure P28.94, $R_1 = 2.0$ kΩ, $R_2 = 3.0$ kΩ, $C_1 = 2.0$ μF, $C_2 = 3.0$ μF, and $\mathcal{E} = 120$ V. If there are no charges on the capacitors before switch S is closed, determine the charges q_1 and q_2 on capacitors C_1 and C_2, after the switch is closed. (*Hint:* First reconstruct the circuit so that it becomes a simple RC circuit containing a single resistor and single capacitor in series, in series with the battery, and then determine the total charge q stored in the circuit.)

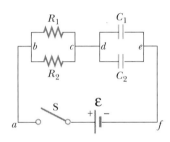

FIGURE P28.94

SPREADSHEET PROBLEM

S1. The application of Kirchhoff's rules to a dc circuit leads to a set of n linear equations in n unknowns. It is very tedious to solve these algebraically if $n > 3$. The purpose of this problem is to solve for the currents in a moderately complex circuit using matrix operations on a spreadsheet. You can solve equations very easily this way, and you can also readily explore the consequences of changing the values of the circuit parameters. (a) Consider the circuit in Figure S28.1. Assume the four unknown currents are in the directions shown.

- Apply Kirchhoff's rules to get four independent equations for the four unknown currents I_i, $i = 1$, 2, 3, and 4.
- Write these equations in matrix form $\mathbf{AI} = \mathbf{B}$, that is,

$$\sum_{j=1}^{4} A_{ij} I_j = B_i, \ i = 1, 2, 3, 4$$

The solution is $\mathbf{I} = \mathbf{A}^{-1}\mathbf{B}$, where $\mathbf{A}^{-1}$ is the inverse matrix of $\mathbf{A}$.

- Set $R_1 = 2\ \Omega$, $R_2 = 4\ \Omega$, $R_3 = 6\ \Omega$, $R_4 = 8\ \Omega$, $\mathcal{E}_1 = 3$ V, $\mathcal{E}_2 = 9$ V, and $\mathcal{E}_3 = 12$ V.
- Enter the matrix $\mathbf{A}$ into your spreadsheet, one value per cell. Use the matrix inversion operation of the spreadsheet to calculate $\mathbf{A}^{-1}$.

- Find the currents by using the matrix multiplication operation of the spreadsheet to calculate $\mathbf{I} = \mathbf{A}^{-1}\mathbf{B}$.

(b) Change the sign of $\mathcal{E}_3$, and repeat the calculations in part (a). This is equivalent to changing the polarity of $\mathcal{E}_3$. (c) Set $\mathcal{E}_1 = \mathcal{E}_2 = 0$ and repeat the calculations in part (a). For these values, the circuit can be solved using simple series-parallel rules. Compare your results using both methods. (d) Investigate any other cases of interest. For example, see how the currents change if you vary R_4.

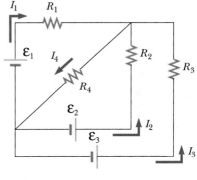

FIGURE S28.1

Magnetic Fields

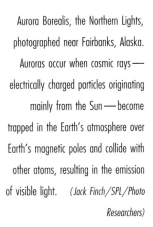

Aurora Borealis, the Northern Lights, photographed near Fairbanks, Alaska. Auroras occur when cosmic rays — electrically charged particles originating mainly from the Sun — become trapped in the Earth's atmosphere over Earth's magnetic poles and collide with other atoms, resulting in the emission of visible light. *(Jack Finch/SPL/Photo Researchers)*

M any historians of science believe that the compass, which uses a magnetic needle, was used in China as early as the 13th century B.C., its invention being of Arabic or Indian origin. The early Greeks knew about magnetism as early as 800 B.C. They discovered that certain stones, now called magnetite (Fe_3O_4), attract pieces of iron. Legend ascribes the name *magnetite* to the shepherd Magnes, the nails of whose shoes and the tip of whose staff stuck fast in a magnetic field while he pastured his flocks. In 1269 Pierre de Maricourt mapped out the directions taken by a needle when it was placed at various points on the surface of a spherical natural magnet. He found that the directions formed lines that encircled the sphere and passed through two points diametrically opposite each other, which he called the *poles* of the magnet. Subsequent experiments showed that every magnet, regardless of its shape, has two poles, called *north* and *south poles*, which exhibit forces on each other in a manner analogous to electric charges. That is, like poles repel each other and unlike poles attract each other. The poles received their names because of the behavior of a magnet in the presence of the Earth's magnetic field. If a bar magnet is suspended from its midpoint by a piece of string so that it can swing freely in a horizontal plane, it will rotate until its "north" pole points to the north of the Earth and its "south" pole points to the south. (The same idea is used to construct a simple compass.)

In 1600 William Gilbert extended these experiments to a variety of materials. Using the fact that a compass needle orients in preferred directions, he suggested that the Earth itself is a large permanent magnet. In 1750 John Michell used a torsion balance to show that magnetic poles exert attractive or repulsive forces on each other and that these forces vary as the inverse square of their separation. Although the force between two magnetic poles is similar to the force between two electric charges, there is an important difference. Electric charges can be isolated (witness the electron or proton), whereas *magnetic poles cannot be isolated.* That is, *magnetic poles are always found in pairs.* All attempts thus far to detect an isolated magnetic monopole have been unsuccessful. No matter how many times a permanent magnet is cut, each piece will always have a north and a south pole. (There is some theoretical basis for speculating that magnetic monopoles—isolated north or south poles—may exist in nature, and attempts to detect them currently make up an active experimental field of investigation. However, none of these attempts has proven successful.)

The relationship between magnetism and electricity was discovered in 1819 when, during a lecture demonstration, the Danish scientist Hans Christian Oersted (1777–1851) found that an electric current in a wire deflected a nearby compass needle.[1] Shortly thereafter, André Ampère (1775–1836) formulated quantitative laws for calculating the magnetic force between current-carrying conductors. He also suggested that electric current loops of molecular size are responsible for *all* magnetic phenomena.

In the 1820s, further connections between electricity and magnetism were demonstrated by Faraday and independently by Joseph Henry (1797–1878). They showed that an electric current can be produced in a circuit either by moving a magnet near the circuit or by changing the current in another nearby circuit. These observations demonstrate that a changing magnetic field produces an electric field. Years later, theoretical work by Maxwell showed that the reverse is also true: A changing electric field gives rise to a magnetic field.

There is a similarity between electric and magnetic effects that has provided methods of making permanent magnets. In Chapter 23 we learned that when rubber and wool are rubbed together, both become charged, one positively and the other negatively. In an analogous fashion, an unmagnetized piece of iron can be magnetized by stroking it with a magnet. Magnetism can also be induced in iron (and other materials) by other means. For example, if a piece of unmagnetized iron is placed near a strong magnet, the piece of iron eventually becomes magnetized. The process of magnetizing the piece of iron in the presence of a strong external field can be accelerated either by heating and cooling the iron or by hammering.

This chapter examines forces on moving charges and on current-carrying wires in the presence of a magnetic field. The source of the magnetic field itself is described in Chapter 30.

An electromagnet is used to move tons of scrap metal.   *(Ray Pfortner/Peter Arnold, Inc.)*

Hans Christian Oersted (1777–1851), Danish physicist.   *(The Bettmann Archive)*

29.1   THE MAGNETIC FIELD

In earlier chapters we found it convenient to describe the interaction between charged objects in terms of electric fields. Recall that an electric field surrounds any electric charge. The region of space surrounding a *moving* charge includes a

---

[1] It is interesting to note that the same discovery was reported in 1802 by an Italian jurist, Gian Dominico Romognosi, but was overlooked, probably because it was published in a newspaper, *Gazetta de Trentino,* rather than in a scholarly journal.

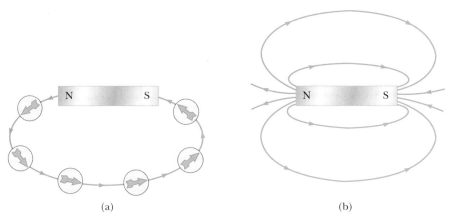

(a)   (b)

FIGURE 29.1 (a) Tracing the magnetic field lines of a bar magnet. (b) Several magnetic field lines of a bar magnet.

magnetic field in addition to the electric field. A magnetic field also surrounds any magnetic substance.

In order to describe any type of field, we must define its magnitude, or strength, and its direction. The direction of the magnetic field **B** at any location is in the direction in which the north pole of a compass needle points at that location. Figure 29.1a shows how the magnetic field of a bar magnet can be traced with the aid of a compass. Several magnetic field lines of a bar magnet traced out in this manner are shown in Figure 29.1b. Magnetic field patterns can be displayed by small iron filings, as in Figure 29.2.

We can define a magnetic field **B** at some point in space in terms of the magnetic force exerted on an appropriate test object. Our test object is a charged particle moving with a velocity **v**. For the time being, let us assume there are no electric or gravitational fields present in the region of the charge. Experiments on

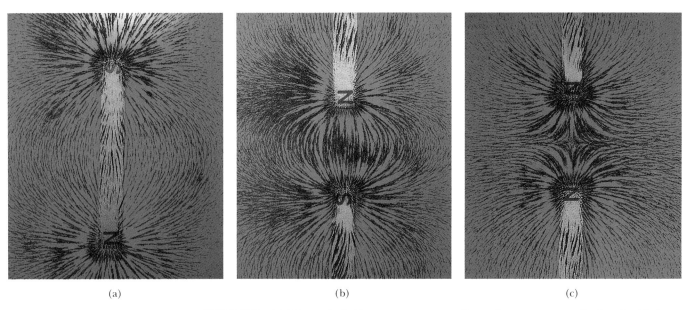

(a)   (b)   (c)

FIGURE 29.2 (a) Magnetic field patterns surrounding a bar magnet as displayed with iron filings. (b) Magnetic field patterns between *unlike* poles of two bar magnets. (c) Magnetic field pattern between *like* poles of two bar magnets. *(Courtesy of Henry Leap and Jim Lehman)*

the motion of various charged particles moving in a magnetic field give the following results:

- The magnitude of the magnetic force is proportional to the charge q and speed v of the particle.
- The magnitude and direction of the magnetic force depend on the velocity of the particle and on the magnitude and direction of the magnetic field.
- When a charged particle moves parallel to the magnetic field vector, the magnetic force on the charge is zero.
- When the velocity vector makes an angle θ with the magnetic field, the magnetic force acts in a direction perpendicular to both **v** and **B**; that is, **F** is perpendicular to the plane formed by **v** and **B** (Fig. 29.3a).
- The magnetic force on a positive charge is in the direction opposite the direction of the force on a negative charge moving in the same direction (Fig. 29.3b).
- If the velocity vector makes an angle θ with the magnetic field, the magnitude of the magnetic force is proportional to sin θ.

Properties of the magnetic force on a charge moving in a **B** field

These observations can be summarized by writing the magnetic force in the form

$$\mathbf{F} = q\mathbf{v} \times \mathbf{B} \tag{29.1}$$

where the direction of the magnetic force is in the direction of **v** × **B** if Q is positive, which, by definition of the cross product, is perpendicular to both **v** and **B**. We can regard this equation as an operational definition of the magnetic field at some point in space. That is, the magnetic field is defined in terms of a sideways force acting on a moving charged particle.

The white arc in this photograph indicates the circular path followed by an electron beam moving in a magnetic field. The vessel contains gas at very low pressure, and the beam is made visible as the electrons collide with the gas atoms, which in turn emit visible light. The magnetic field is produced by two coils (not shown). The apparatus can be used to measure the charge/mass ratio for the electron. *(Courtesy of Central Scientific Company)*

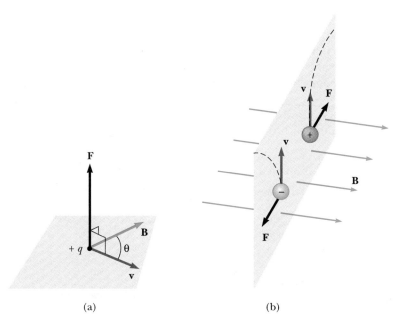

(a)   (b)

FIGURE 29.3   The direction of the magnetic force on a charged particle moving with a velocity **v** in the presence of a magnetic field **B**. (a) When **v** is at an angle θ to **B**, the magnetic force is perpendicular to both **v** and **B**. (b) In the presence of a magnetic field, the moving charged particles are deflected as indicated by the dotted lines.

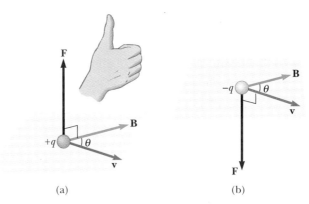

(a)   (b)

FIGURE 29.4   The right-hand rule for determining the direction of the magnetic force **F** acting on a charge *q* moving with a velocity **v** in a magnetic field **B**. If *q* is positive, **F** is upward in the direction of the thumb. If *q* is negative, **F** is downward.

Figure 29.4 reviews the right-hand rule for determining the direction of the cross product **v** × **B**. You point the four fingers of your right hand along the direction of **v**, and then turn them until they point along the direction of **B**. The thumb then points in the direction of **v** × **B**. Since **F** = *q***v** × **B**, **F** is in the direction of **v** × **B** if *q* is positive (Fig. 29.4a) and opposite the direction of **v** × **B** if *q* is negative (Fig. 29.4b). The magnitude of the magnetic force has the value

Magnetic force on a charged particle moving in a magnetic field

$$\mathbf{F} = qvB \sin \theta \qquad (29.2)$$

where θ is the smaller angle between **v** and **B**. From this expression, we see that *F* is zero when **v** is parallel to **B** ($\theta = 0$ or $180°$) and maximum ($F_{max} = qvB$) when **v** is perpendicular to **B** ($\theta = 90°$).

There are several important differences between electric and magnetic forces:

Differences between electric and magnetic fields

- The electric force is always in the direction of the electric field, whereas the magnetic force is perpendicular to the magnetic field.
- The electric force acts on a charged particle independent of the particle's velocity, whereas the magnetic force acts on a charged particle only when the particle is in motion.
- The electric force does work in displacing a charged particle, whereas the magnetic force associated with a steady magnetic field does no work when a particle is displaced.

This last statement is a consequence of the fact that when a charge moves in a steady magnetic field, the magnetic force is always *perpendicular* to the displacement. That is, $\mathbf{F} \cdot d\mathbf{s} = (\mathbf{F} \cdot \mathbf{v}) \, dt = 0$, because the magnetic force is a vector perpendicular to **v**. From this property and the work-energy theorem, we conclude that the kinetic energy of a charged particle cannot be altered by a magnetic field alone. In other words,

A steady magnetic field cannot change the speed of a particle

when a charge moves with a velocity **v**, an applied magnetic field can alter the direction of the velocity vector, but it cannot change the speed of the particle. That is, a static magnetic field changes the direction of the velocity but does not affect the speed or kinetic energy of the charged particle.

The SI unit of the magnetic field is the **weber per square meter** (Wb/m²), also called the **tesla** (T). This unit can be related to the fundamental units by using Equation 29.1: A 1-C charge moving through a field of 1 T with a velocity of 1 m/s perpendicular to the field experiences a force of 1 N:

$$[B] = \text{T} = \frac{\text{Wb}}{\text{m}^2} = \frac{\text{N}}{\text{C}\cdot\text{m/s}} = \frac{\text{N}}{\text{A}\cdot\text{m}}$$

Another non-SI unit in common use, called the gauss (G), is related to the tesla through the conversion $1\ \text{T} = 10^4\ \text{G}$.

Conventional laboratory magnets can produce magnetic fields as large as 2.5 T. Superconducting magnets that can generate magnetic fields as high as 25 T have been constructed. This value can be compared with the Earth's magnetic field near its surface, which is about 0.5×10^{-4} T.

EXAMPLE 29.1   A Proton Moving in a Magnetic Field

A proton moves with a speed of 8.0×10^6 m/s along the x axis. It enters a region where there is a magnetic field of magnitude 2.5 T, directed at an angle of 60° to the x axis and lying in the xy plane (Fig. 29.5). Calculate the initial magnetic force on and acceleration of the proton.

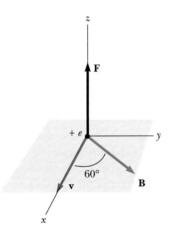

FIGURE 29.5   (Example 29.1) The magnetic force **F** on a proton is in the positive z direction when **v** and **B** lie in the xy plane.

Solution   From Equation 29.2, we get

$$F = qvB \sin \theta$$
$$= (1.60 \times 10^{-19}\ \text{C})(8.0 \times 10^6\ \text{m/s})(2.5\ \text{T})(\sin 60°)$$
$$= \boxed{2.8 \times 10^{-12}\ \text{N}}$$

Because $\mathbf{v} \times \mathbf{B}$ is in the positive z direction (the right-hand rule), and the charge is positive, **F** is in the positive z direction.

The mass of the proton is 1.67×10^{-27} kg, and so its initial acceleration is

$$a = \frac{F}{m} = \frac{2.8 \times 10^{-12}\ \text{N}}{1.67 \times 10^{-27}\ \text{kg}} = \boxed{1.7 \times 10^{-15}\ \text{m/s}^2}$$

in the positive z direction.

Exercise   Calculate the acceleration of an electron that moves through the same magnetic field at the same speed as the proton.

Answer 3.0×10^{18} m/s².

29.2   MAGNETIC FORCE ON A CURRENT-CARRYING CONDUCTOR

If a magnetic force is exerted on a single charged particle when it moves through a magnetic field, it should not surprise you that a current-carrying wire also experiences a force when placed in a magnetic field. This follows from the fact that the current represents a collection of many charged particles in motion; hence, the resultant force on the wire is due to the sum of the individual forces exerted on the charged particles. The force on the particles is transmitted to the "bulk" of the wire through collisions with the atoms making up the wire.

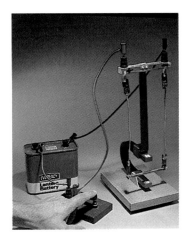

This apparatus demonstrates the force on a current-carrying conductor in an external magnetic field. Why does the bar swing *into* the magnet after the switch is closed? *(Henry Leap and Jim Lehman)*

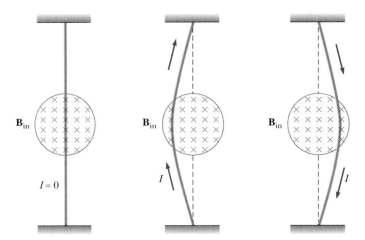

FIGURE 29.6 A segment of a flexible vertical wire is stretched between the poles of a magnet with the magnetic field (blue crosses) directed into the paper. (a) When there is no current in the wire, it remains vertical. (b) When the current is upward, the wire deflects to the left. (c) When the current is downward, the wire deflects to the right.

Before we continue our discussion, some explanation is in order concerning notation in many of our figures. To indicate the direction of **B**, we use the following convention. If **B** is directed into the page as in Figure 29.6a, we use a series of blue crosses, which represent the tails of arrows. If **B** is directed out of the page, we use a series of blue dots, which represent the tips of arrows. If **B** lies in the plane of the page, we use a series of blue field lines with arrowheads.

The force on a current-carrying conductor can be demonstrated by hanging a wire between the poles of a magnet as in Figure 29.6. In this figure (which shows only the farther pole face), the magnetic field is directed into the page and covers the region within the shaded circles. When the current in the wire is zero, the wire remains vertical as in Figure 29.6a. However, when a current is set up in the wire directed upwards as in Figure 29.6b, the wire deflects to the left. If we reverse the current, as in Figure 29.6c, the wire deflects to the right.

Let us quantify this discussion by considering a straight segment of wire of length L and cross-sectional area A, carrying a current I in a uniform magnetic field **B** as in Figure 29.7. The magnetic force on a charge q moving with a drift velocity $\mathbf{v}_d$ is $q\mathbf{v}_d \times \mathbf{B}$. To find the total force on the wire, we multiply the force on one charge, $q\mathbf{v}_d \times \mathbf{B}$, by the number of charges in the segment. Since the volume of the segment is AL the number of charges in the segment is nAL, where n is the number of charges per unit volume. Hence, the total magnetic force on the wire of length L is

$$\mathbf{F} = (q\mathbf{v}_d \times \mathbf{B})nAL$$

This can be written in a more convenient form by noting that, from Equation 27.4, the current in the wire is $I = nqv_dA$. Therefore,

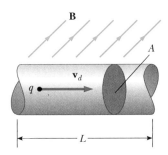

FIGURE 29.7 A section of a wire containing moving charges in a magnetic field **B**. The magnetic force on each charge is $q\mathbf{v}_d \times \mathbf{B}$, and the net force on the segment of length L is $I\mathbf{L} \times \mathbf{B}$.

$$\mathbf{F} = I\mathbf{L} \times \mathbf{B} \qquad (29.3)$$

where **L** is a vector in the direction of the current I; the magnitude of **L** equals the length L of the segment. Note that this expression applies only to a straight segment of wire in a uniform magnetic field.

Now consider an arbitrarily shaped wire segment of uniform cross-section in a magnetic field, as in Figure 29.8. It follows from Equation 29.3 that the magnetic force on a very small segment $d\mathbf{s}$ in the presence of a field $\mathbf{B}$ is

$$d\mathbf{F} = I \, d\mathbf{s} \times \mathbf{B} \tag{29.4}$$

where $d\mathbf{F}$ is directed out of the page for the directions assumed in Figure 29.8. We can consider Equation 29.4 as an alternative definition of $\mathbf{B}$. That is, the field $\mathbf{B}$ can be defined in terms of a measurable force on a current element, where the force is a maximum when $\mathbf{B}$ is perpendicular to the element and zero when $\mathbf{B}$ is parallel to the element.

To get the total force $\mathbf{F}$ on the wire, we integrate Equation 29.4 over the length of the wire:

$$\mathbf{F} = I \int_{a}^{b} d\mathbf{s} \times \mathbf{B} \tag{29.5}$$

where a and b represent the end points of the wire. When this integration is carried out, the magnitude of the magnetic field and the direction the field makes with the vector $d\mathbf{s}$ (that is, the element orientation) may differ at different points.

Now let us consider two special cases involving the application of Equation 29.5. In both cases, the magnetic field is taken to be constant in magnitude and direction.

Case I

Consider a curved wire carrying a current I; the wire is located in a uniform magnetic field $\mathbf{B}$ as in Figure 29.9a. Since the field is uniform, $\mathbf{B}$ can be taken outside the integral in Equation 29.5, and we get

$$\mathbf{F} = I \left(\int_{a}^{b} d\mathbf{s} \right) \times \mathbf{B} \tag{29.6}$$

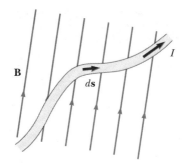

FIGURE 29.8 A wire segment of arbitrary shape carrying a current I in a magnetic field $\mathbf{B}$ experiences a magnetic force. The force on any segment $d\mathbf{s}$ is $I \, d\mathbf{s} \times \mathbf{B}$ and is directed *out* of the page. You should use the right-hand rule to confirm this direction.

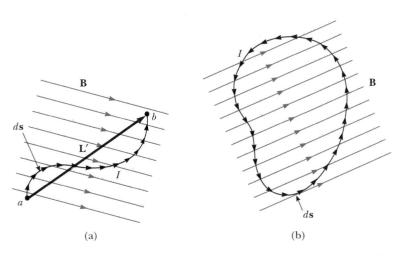

(a)   (b)

FIGURE 29.9 (a) A curved conductor carrying a current I in a uniform magnetic field. The magnetic force on the conductor is equivalent to the force on a straight segment of length L' running between the ends of the wire, a and b. (b) A current-carrying loop of arbitrary shape in a uniform magnetic field. The net magnetic force on the loop is 0.

But the quantity $\int_a^b d\mathbf{s}$ represents the *vector sum* of all the displacement elements from a to b. From the law of vector addition (Chapter 3), the sum equals the vector $\mathbf{L}'$, which is directed from a to b. Therefore, Equation 29.6 reduces to

$$\mathbf{F} = I\mathbf{L}' \times \mathbf{B} \qquad\qquad (29.7)$$

Case II

An arbitrarily shaped, closed loop carrying a current I is placed in a uniform magnetic field as in Figure 29.9b. Again, we can express the force in the form of Equation 29.6. In this case, the vector sum of the displacement vectors must be taken over the closed loop. That is,

$$\mathbf{F} = I\left(\oint d\mathbf{s}\right) \times \mathbf{B}$$

Since the set of displacement vectors forms a closed polygon (Fig. 29.9b), the vector sum must be zero. This follows from the graphical procedure of adding vectors by the polygon method (Chapter 3). Since $\oint d\mathbf{s} = 0$, we conclude that $\mathbf{F} = 0$. That is,

> the total magnetic force on any closed current loop in a uniform magnetic field is zero.

EXAMPLE 29.2   Force on a Semicircular Conductor

A wire bent into the shape of a semicircle of radius R forms a closed circuit and carries a current I. The circuit lies in the xy plane, and a uniform magnetic field is present along the positive y axis as in Figure 29.10. Find the magnetic force on the straight portion of the wire and on the curved portion.

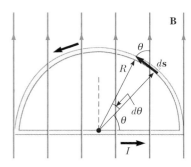

FIGURE 29.10   (Example 29.2) The net force on a closed-current loop in a uniform magnetic field is zero. In this case, the force on the straight portion is $2IRB$ and outward, while the force on the curved portion is also $2IRB$ and inward.

Reasoning and Solution   The force on the straight portion of the wire has a magnitude $F_1 = ILB = 2IRB$, since $L = 2R$ and the wire is perpendicular to $\mathbf{B}$. The direction of $\mathbf{F}_1$ is out of the paper since $\mathbf{L} \times \mathbf{B}$ is outward. (That is, $\mathbf{L}$ is to the right, in the direction of the current, and so by the rule of cross products, $\mathbf{L} \times \mathbf{B}$ is outward.)

To find the force on the curved part, we must first write an expression for the force $d\mathbf{F}_2$ on the element $d\mathbf{s}$. If θ is the angle between $\mathbf{B}$ and $d\mathbf{s}$ in Figure 29.10, then the magnitude of $d\mathbf{F}_2$ is

$$dF_2 = I|d\mathbf{s} \times \mathbf{B}| = IB \sin\theta\, ds$$

where ds is the length of the small element measured along the circular arc. In order to integrate this expression, we must express ds in terms of θ. Since $s = R\theta$, $ds = R\, d\theta$, and the expression for dF_2 can be written

$$dF_2 = IRB \sin\theta\, d\theta$$

To get the total force F_2 on the curved portion, we can integrate this expression to account for contributions from all elements. Note that the direction of the force on every element is the same: into the paper (since $d\mathbf{s} \times \mathbf{B}$ is inward). Therefore, the resultant force $\mathbf{F}_2$ on the curved wire must also be into the paper. Integrating dF_2 over the limits $\theta = 0$ to $\theta = \pi$ (that is, the entire semicircle) gives

$$F_2 = IRB \int_0^\pi \sin\theta \, d\theta = IRB[-\cos\theta]_0^\pi$$

$$= -IRB(\cos\pi - \cos 0) = -IRB(-1 - 1) = \boxed{2IRB}$$

Since $F_2 = 2IRB$ and is directed into the paper while the force on the straight wire $F_1 = 2IRB$ is out of the paper, we see that the net force on the closed loop is zero. This result is consistent with Case II as described above.

29.3   TORQUE ON A CURRENT LOOP IN A UNIFORM MAGNETIC FIELD

In the previous section we showed how a force is exerted on a current-carrying conductor when the conductor is placed in a magnetic field. With this as a starting point, we now show that a torque is exerted on a current loop placed in a magnetic field. The results of this analysis will be of great practical value when we discuss generators in a future chapter.

Consider a rectangular loop carrying a current I in the presence of a uniform magnetic field directed parallel to the plane of the loop, as in Figure 29.11a. The forces on the sides of length a are zero because these wires are parallel to the field; hence, $d\mathbf{s} \times \mathbf{B} = 0$ for these sides. The magnitude of the forces on the sides of length b, however, is

$$F_1 = F_2 = IbB$$

The direction of $\mathbf{F}_1$, the force on the left side of the loop, is out of the paper and that of $\mathbf{F}_2$, the force on the right side of the loop, is into the paper. If we were to view the loop by standing underneath the bottom and looking up, we would see the view shown in Figure 29.11b, and the forces would be as shown there. If we assume that the loop is pivoted so that it can rotate about point O, we see that these two forces produce a torque about O that rotates the loop clockwise. The magnitude of this torque, τ_{max}, is

$$\tau_{max} = F_1 \frac{a}{2} + F_2 \frac{a}{2} = (IbB) \frac{a}{2} + (IbB) \frac{a}{2} = IabB$$

where the moment arm about O is $a/2$ for each force. Since the area of the loop is $A = ab$, the maximum torque can be expressed as

$$\tau_{max} = IAB \tag{29.8}$$

Remember that this result is valid only when the magnetic field is parallel to the plane of the loop. The sense of the rotation is clockwise when viewed from the bottom end, as indicated in Figure 29.11b. If the current were reversed, the forces would reverse and the rotational tendency would be counterclockwise.

Now suppose the uniform magnetic field makes an angle θ with a line perpendicular to the plane of the loop, as in Figure 29.12a. For convenience, we assume that $\mathbf{B}$ is perpendicular to the sides of length b. (The end view of these sides is shown in Fig. 29.12b.) In this case, the magnetic forces $\mathbf{F}_3$ and $\mathbf{F}_4$ on the sides of length a cancel each other and produce no torque because they pass through a common origin. However, the forces acting on the sides of length b, $\mathbf{F}_1$ and $\mathbf{F}_2$, form a couple and hence produce a torque about *any point*. Referring to the end view in Figure 29.12b, we note that the moment arm of $\mathbf{F}_1$ about the point O is equal to $(a/2) \sin\theta$. Likewise, the moment arm of $\mathbf{F}_2$ about O is also $(a/2) \sin\theta$.

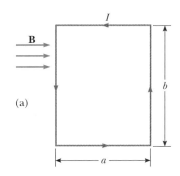

(a)

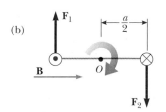

(b)

FIGURE 29.11   (a) Front view of a rectangular loop in a uniform magnetic field. There are no forces acting on the sides of width a parallel to $\mathbf{B}$, but there are forces acting on the sides of length b. (b) Bottom view of the rectangular loop shows that the forces $\mathbf{F}_1$ and $\mathbf{F}_2$ on the sides of length b create a torque that tends to twist the loop clockwise as shown.

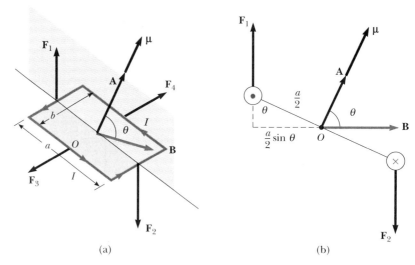

FIGURE 29.12   (a) A rectangular current loop whose normal makes an angle θ with a uniform magnetic field. The forces on the sides of length a cancel while the forces on the sides of width b create a torque on the loop. (b) An end view of the loop. The magnetic moment $\boldsymbol{\mu}$ is in the direction normal to the plane of the loop.

FIGURE 29.13   A right-hand rule for determining the direction of the vector **A**. The magnetic moment $\boldsymbol{\mu}$ is also in the direction of **A**.

Torque on a current loop

Since $F_1 = F_2 = IbB$, the net torque about O has the magnitude

$$\tau = F_1 \frac{a}{2} \sin \theta + F_2 \frac{a}{2} \sin \theta$$

$$= IbB \left(\frac{a}{2} \sin \theta \right) + IbB \left(\frac{a}{2} \sin \theta \right) = IabB \sin \theta$$

$$= IAB \sin \theta$$

where $A = ab$ is the area of the loop. This result shows that the torque has its maximum value IAB when the field is parallel to the plane of the loop ($\theta = 90°$), as we saw when discussing Figure 29.11, and is zero when the field is perpendicular to the plane of the loop ($\theta = 0$). As we see in Figure 29.12, the loop tends to rotate in the direction of decreasing values of θ (that is, so that the normal to the plane of the loop rotates toward the direction of the magnetic field).

A convenient expression for the torque is

$$\boldsymbol{\tau} = I\mathbf{A} \times \mathbf{B} \tag{29.9}$$

where **A**, a vector perpendicular to the plane of the loop, has a magnitude equal to the area of the loop. The sense of **A** is determined by the right-hand rule as described in Figure 29.13. By rotating the four fingers of the right hand in the direction of the current in the loop, the thumb points in the direction of **A**. The product $I\mathbf{A}$ is defined to be the **magnetic moment** $\boldsymbol{\mu}$ of the loop. That is,

---

Magnetic moment of a current loop

$$\boldsymbol{\mu} = I\mathbf{A} \tag{29.10}$$

The SI unit of magnetic moment is ampere-meter^2 ($\mathrm{A \cdot m^2}$). Using this definition, the torque can be expressed as

$$\boldsymbol{\tau} = \boldsymbol{\mu} \times \mathbf{B} \tag{29.11}$$

Note that this result is analogous to the torque acting on an electric dipole in the presence of an external electric field **E**, where $\tau = \mathbf{p} \times \mathbf{E}$, where **p** is the dipole moment defined by Equation 26.15.

Although we obtained the torque for a particular orientation of **B** with respect to the loop, the equation $\tau = \boldsymbol{\mu} \times \mathbf{B}$ is valid for any orientation. Furthermore, although we derived the torque expression for a rectangular loop, the result is valid for a loop of any shape.

If a coil consists of N turns of wire, each carrying the same current and having the same area, the total magnetic moment of the coil is the product of the number of turns and the magnetic moment for one turn. The torque on an N-turn coil is N times greater than that on a one-turn coil. That is, $\tau = N\boldsymbol{\mu} \times \mathbf{B}$.

EXAMPLE 29.3   The Magnetic Moment of a Coil

A rectangular coil of dimensions 5.40 cm × 8.50 cm consists of 25 turns of wire. The coil carries a current of 15.0 mA. (a) Calculate the magnitude of its magnetic moment.

Solution   The magnitude of the magnetic moment of a current loop is $\mu = IA$ (see Eq. 29.10). In this case, $A = (0.0540 \text{ m})(0.0850 \text{ m}) = 4.59 \times 10^{-3} \text{ m}^2$. Since the coil has 25 turns, and assuming that each turn has the same area A, we have

$$\mu_{coil} = NIA = (25)(15.0 \times 10^{-3} \text{ A})(4.59 \times 10^{-3} \text{ m}^2)$$

$$= 1.72 \times 10^{-3} \text{ A} \cdot \text{m}^2$$

(b) Suppose a magnetic field of magnitude 0.350 T is applied parallel to the plane of the loop. What is the magnitude of the torque acting on the loop?

Solution   The torque is given by Equation 29.11, $\tau = \boldsymbol{\mu} \times \mathbf{B}$. In this case, **B** is *perpendicular* to $\boldsymbol{\mu}_{coil}$, so that

$$\tau = \mu_{coil}B = (1.72 \times 10^{-3} \text{ A} \cdot \text{m}^2)(0.350 \text{ T})$$

$$= 6.02 \times 10^{-4} \text{ N} \cdot \text{m}$$

Note that this is the basic principle behind the operation of a galvanometer coil discussed in Chapter 28.

Exercise   Show that the units $\text{A} \cdot \text{m}^2 \cdot \text{T}$ reduce to $\text{N} \cdot \text{m}$.

Exercise   Calculate the magnitude of the torque on the coil when the 0.350-T magnetic field makes angles of (a) 60° and (b) 0° with $\boldsymbol{\mu}$.

Answer   (a) $5.21 \times 10^{-4} \text{ N} \cdot \text{m}$; (b) zero.

29.4   MOTION OF A CHARGED PARTICLE IN A MAGNETIC FIELD

In Section 29.1 we found that the magnetic force acting on a charged particle moving in a magnetic field is perpendicular to the velocity of the particle and that consequently the work done on the particle by the magnetic force is zero. Consider now the special case of a positively charged particle moving in a uniform magnetic field with its initial velocity vector perpendicular to the field. Let us assume that the magnetic field is into the page. Figure 29.14 shows that

the charged particle moves in a circle whose plane is perpendicular to the magnetic field.

The particle moves in this way because the magnetic force **F** is at right angles to **v** and **B** and has a constant magnitude equal to qvB. As the force deflects the particle, the directions of **v** and **F** change continuously, as in Figure 29.14. Therefore **F** acts like a central force, which changes only the direction of **v** and not its magnitude. The sense of the rotation, as shown in Figure 29.14, is counterclockwise for a positive charge. If q were negative, the sense of the rotation would be clockwise.

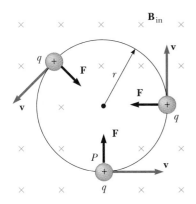

FIGURE 29.14 When the velocity of a charged particle is perpendicular to a uniform magnetic field, the particle moves in a circular path whose plane is perpendicular to **B**. In this case, **B** is directed into the page and the charge is positive. The magnetic force **F** on the charge is always directed toward the center of the circle.

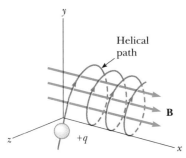

FIGURE 29.15 A charged particle having a velocity vector that has a component parallel to a uniform magnetic field moves in a helical path.

Since **F** (which is in the radial direction) has a magnitude qvB, we can equate this to the required central force, which is the mass m multiplied by the centripetal acceleration v^2/r. From Newton's second law, we find that

$$F = qvB = \frac{mv^2}{r}$$

$$r = \frac{mv}{qB} \tag{29.12}$$

That is, the radius of the path is proportional to the momentum mv of the particle and inversely proportional to the magnitude of the magnetic field. The angular frequency of the rotating charged particle is

$$\omega = \frac{v}{r} = \frac{qB}{m} \tag{29.13}$$

The period of its motion (the time for one revolution) is equal to the circumference of the circle divided by the speed of the particle:

$$T = \frac{2\pi r}{v} = \frac{2\pi}{\omega} = \frac{2\pi m}{qB} \tag{29.14}$$

These results show that the angular frequency and period of the circular motion do not depend on the speed of the particle or the radius of the orbit. The frequency, $\omega/2\pi$, is often referred to as the **cyclotron frequency** because charged particles circulate at this frequency in one type of accelerator called a *cyclotron*, discussed in Section 29.5.

If a charged particle moves in a uniform magnetic field with its velocity at some arbitrary angle to **B**, its path is a helix. For example, if the field is in the x direction as in Figure 29.15, there is no component of force in the x direction, and hence $a_x = 0$ and the x component of velocity remains constant. On the other hand, the magnetic force $q\mathbf{v} \times \mathbf{B}$ causes the components v_y and v_z to change in time, and the resulting motion is a helix having its axis parallel to the **B** field. The projection of the path onto the yz plane (viewed along the x axis) is a circle. (The projections of the path onto the xy and xz planes are sinusoids!) Equations 29.12 to 29.14 still apply, provided that v is replaced by $v_\perp = \sqrt{v_y^2 + v_z^2}$.

EXAMPLE 29.4   A Proton Moving Perpendicular to a Uniform Magnetic Field

A proton is moving in a circular orbit of radius 14 cm in a uniform magnetic field of magnitude 0.35 T directed perpendicular to the velocity of the proton. Find the orbital speed of the proton.

Solution   From Equation 29.12, we get

$$v = \frac{qBr}{m} = \frac{(1.60 \times 10^{-19}\ \text{C})(0.35\ \text{T})(14 \times 10^{-2}\ \text{m})}{1.67 \times 10^{-27}\ \text{kg}}$$

$$= 4.7 \times 10^6\ \text{m/s}$$

Exercise   If an electron moves perpendicular to the same magnetic field with this speed, what is the radius of its circular orbit?

Answer $7.6 \times 10^{-5}\ \text{m}$.

EXAMPLE 29.5   The Bending of an Electron Beam

In an experiment designed to measure the strength of a uniform magnetic field produced by a set of coils, the electrons are accelerated from rest through a potential difference of 350 V, and the beam associated with the electrons is measured to have a radius of 7.5 cm, shown in Figure 29.16. Assuming the magnetic field is perpendicular to the beam, (a) what is the magnitude of the magnetic field?

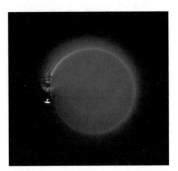

FIGURE 29.16   (Example 29.5) The bending of an electron beam in a magnetic field. The tube contains gas at very low pressure, and the beam is made visible as the electrons collide with the gas atoms, which in turn emit visible light. The apparatus used to take this photograph is part of a system designed to measure the ratio e/m. *(Henry Leap and Jim Lehman)*

Reasoning   First, we must calculate the speed of the electrons using the fact that the increase in their kinetic energy must equal the change in their potential energy, $|e|$ V (because of conservation of energy). Then we use Equation 29.12 to find the strength of the magnetic field.

Solution   Since $K_i = 0$ and $K_f = mv^2/2$, we have

$$\tfrac{1}{2}mv^2 = |e|\,V$$

$$v = \sqrt{\frac{2\,|e|\,V}{m}} = \sqrt{\frac{2(1.60 \times 10^{-19}\ \text{C})(350\ \text{V})}{9.11 \times 10^{-31}\ \text{kg}}}$$

$$= 1.11 \times 10^7\ \text{m/s}$$

We now use Equation 29.12 to find B:

$$B = \frac{mv}{|e|\,r} = \frac{(9.11 \times 10^{-31}\ \text{kg})(1.11 \times 10^7\ \text{m/s})}{(1.60 \times 10^{-19}\ \text{C})(0.075\ \text{m})}$$

$$= 8.4 \times 10^{-4}\ \text{T}$$

(b) What is the angular frequency of the electrons?

Solution   Using Equation 29.13, we find

$$\omega = \frac{v}{r} = \frac{1.11 \times 10^7\ \text{m/s}}{0.075\ \text{m}} = 1.5 \times 10^8\ \text{rad/s}$$

Exercise   What is the period of revolution of the electrons?

Answer $T = 43$ ns.

When charged particles move in a nonuniform magnetic field, the motion is complex. For example, in a magnetic field that is strong at the ends and weak in the middle, as in Figure 29.17, the particles can oscillate back and forth between the end points. Such a field can be produced by two current loops as in Figure 29.17. In this case, a charged particle starting at one end spirals along the field lines until it reaches the other end, where it reverses its path and spirals back. This configuration is known as a *magnetic bottle* because charged particles can be trapped in it. This setup has been used to confine plasmas, and such a plasma-confinement scheme could play a crucial role in controlling nuclear fusion, a process that could supply us with an almost endless source of energy. Unfortunately, the magnetic bottle has its problems. If a large number of particles are trapped, collisions between the particles cause them to eventually leak from the system.

The Van Allen radiation belts, discovered in 1958 by a team of researchers under the direction of James Van Allen, consist of charged particles (mostly electrons and protons) surrounding the Earth in doughnut-shaped regions (Fig. 29.18). The particles, trapped by the Earth's nonuniform magnetic field, spiral around the field lines from pole to pole. These particles originate mainly from the Sun, but some come from stars and other heavenly objects. For this reason, the particles are called *cosmic rays*. Most cosmic rays are deflected by the Earth's magnetic field and never reach the Earth. However, some become trapped, and these are the ones that make up the Van Allen belts. When the particles are in the Earth's atmosphere over the poles, they frequently collide with atoms, causing

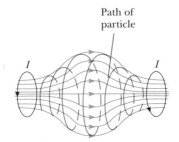

FIGURE 29.17   A charged particle moving in a nonuniform magnetic field represented by blue lines (a magnetic bottle) spirals about the field (red path) and oscillates between the end points.

FIGURE 29.18 The Van Allen belts are made up of charged particles (electrons and protons) trapped by the Earth's nonuniform magnetic field. The magnetic field lines are in blue and the particle paths in red.

This color-enhanced photograph, taken at CERN, the particle physics laboratory outside Geneva, Switzerland, shows a collection of tracks left by subatomic particles in a bubble chamber. A bubble chamber is a container filled with liquid hydrogen which is super-heated, that is, momentarily raised above its normal boiling point by a sudden drop in pressure in the container. Any charged particle passing through the liquid in this state leaves behind a trail of tiny bubbles as the liquid boils in its wake. These bubbles are seen as fine tracks, showing the characteristic paths of different types of particles. The paths are curved due to an intense applied magnetic field. The tightly wound spiral tracks are due to electrons and positrons. *(Patrice Loiez, CERN/SPL/Photo Researchers)*

them to emit visible light. This is the origin of the beautiful Aurora Borealis, or Northern Lights. A similar phenomenon seen in the southern hemisphere is called the Aurora Australis.

*29.5 APPLICATIONS OF THE MOTION OF CHARGED PARTICLES IN A MAGNETIC FIELD

In this section we describe some important devices that involve the motion of charged particles in uniform magnetic fields. For many situations, the charge moves with a velocity **v** in the presence of both an electric field **E** and a magnetic field **B**. Therefore, the charge experiences both an electric force $q\mathbf{E}$ and a magnetic force $q\mathbf{v} \times \mathbf{B}$, and so the total force, called the **Lorentz force**, is

$$\mathbf{F} = q\mathbf{E} + q\mathbf{v} \times \mathbf{B} \qquad (29.15)$$

Lorentz force

Velocity Selector

In many experiments involving the motion of charged particles, it is important to have particles that move with essentially the same velocity. This can be achieved by applying a combination of an electric field and a magnetic field oriented as shown in Figure 29.19. A uniform electric field vertically downward is provided by a pair of charged parallel plates, while a uniform magnetic field is applied perpendicular to the page. For q positive, the magnetic force $q\mathbf{v} \times \mathbf{B}$ is upward and the electric force $q\mathbf{E}$ is downward. If the fields are chosen so that the electric force balances the

The technology underlying many appliances such as television sets and computer monitors requires an understanding of the motion of charged particles in electric and/or magnetic fields. Some of the most fundamental properties of electrons and other subatomic particles have been determined in controlled experiments involving electric and magnetic fields. Using this simulator, you will be able to reproduce these famous experiments and observe the motion of a particle as you modify the magnetic field, the electric field, the charge on the particle, and its mass and velocity.

Motion of Charged Particles in Electric and Magnetic Fields

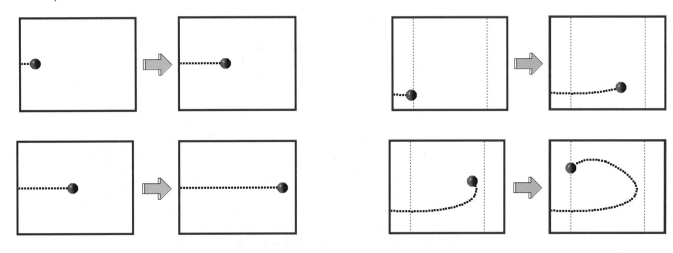

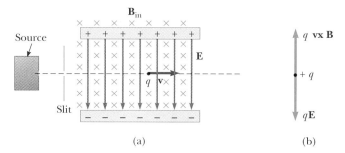

FIGURE 29.19 (a) A velocity selector. When a positively charged particle is in the presence of both an inward magnetic field and a downward electric field, it experiences both an electric force $q\mathbf{E}$ downward and a magnetic force $q\mathbf{v} \times \mathbf{B}$ upward. (b) When these forces balance each other, the particle moves in a horizontal line through the fields.

magnetic force, the particle moves in a straight horizontal line through the region of the fields. If we adjust the magnitudes of the two fields so that $qvB = qE$, we get

$$v = \frac{E}{B} \tag{29.16}$$

Only those particles having this speed pass undeflected through the perpendicular electric and magnetic fields. The magnetic force acting on particles with speeds greater than this is stronger than the electric force, and these particles are deflected upward. Those having speeds less than this are deflected downward.

The Mass Spectrometer

The **mass spectrometer** separates ions according to their mass-to-charge ratio. In one version, known as the *Bainbridge mass spectrometer,* a beam of ions first passes through a velocity selector and then enters a second uniform magnetic field $\mathbf{B}_0$ directed into the paper (Fig. 29.20). Upon entering the second magnetic field, the ions move in a semicircle of radius r before striking a photographic plate at P. From Equation 29.12, we can express the ratio m/q as

$$\frac{m}{q} = \frac{rB_0}{v}$$

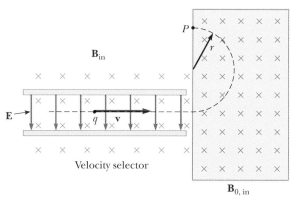

FIGURE 29.20 A mass spectrometer. Charged particles are first sent through a velocity selector. They then enter a region where the magnetic field $\mathbf{B}_0$ (inward) causes positive ions to move in a semicircular path and strike a photographic film at P.

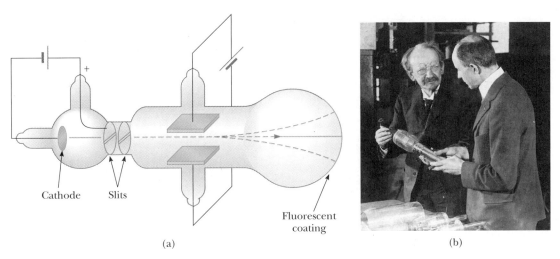

(a)   (b)

FIGURE 29.21   (a) Thomson's apparatus for measuring e/m. Electrons are accelerated from the cathode, pass through two slits, and are deflected by both an electric field and a magnetic field (not shown, but directed perpendicular to the electric field). The deflected beam then strikes a phosphorescent screen. (b) J. J. Thomson (*left*) with Frank Baldwin Jewett at Western Electric Company in 1923.   *(Bell Telephone Labs/Courtesy Emilio Segrè Visual Archives)*

Using Equation 29.16, we find that

$$\frac{m}{q} = \frac{rB_0 B}{E} \tag{29.17}$$

Therefore, m/q can be determined by measuring the radius of curvature and knowing the fields B, B_0, and E. In practice, one usually measures the masses of various isotopes of a given ion with the same charge q. Hence, the mass ratios can be determined even if q is unknown.

A variation of this technique was used by J. J. Thomson (1856–1940) in 1897 to measure the ratio e/m for electrons. Figure 29.21a shows the basic apparatus he used. Electrons are accelerated from the cathode to the anodes, collimated by slits in the anodes, and then allowed to drift into a region of crossed (perpendicular) electric and magnetic fields. The simultaneously applied **E** and **B** fields are first adjusted to produce an undeflected beam. If the **B** field is then turned off, the **E** field alone produces a measurable beam deflection on the phosphorescent screen. From the size of the deflection and the measured values of **E** and **B**, the charge to mass ratio may be determined. The results of this crucial experiment represent the discovery of the electron as a fundamental particle of nature.

The Cyclotron

The **cyclotron,** invented in 1934 by E. O. Lawrence and M. S. Livingston, can accelerate charged particles to very high speeds. Both electric and magnetic forces play a key role. The energetic particles produced are used to bombard other nuclei and thereby produce nuclear reactions of interest to researchers. A number of hospitals use cyclotron facilities to produce radioactive substances for diagnosis and treatment.

A schematic drawing of a cyclotron is shown in Figure 29.22. The charges move in two semicircular containers, D_1 and D_2, referred to as *dees*. The dees are evacuated in order to minimize energy losses resulting from collisions between the ions and air molecules. A high-frequency alternating voltage is applied to the dees, and

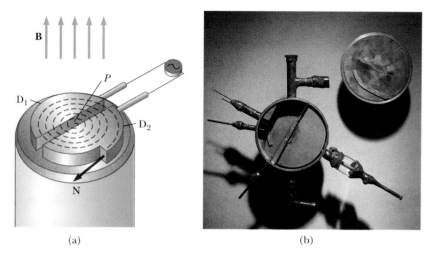

(a)   (b)

FIGURE 29.22   (a) The cyclotron consists of an ion source, two dees across which an alternating voltage is applied, and a uniform magnetic field provided by an electromagnet. (The south pole of the magnet is not shown.) (b) The first cyclotron, invented by E. O. Lawrence and M. S. Livingston in 1934.   *(Courtesy of Lawrence Berkeley Laboratory, University of California)*

a uniform magnetic field provided by an electromagnet is directed perpendicular to them. Positive ions released at P near the center of the magnet move in a semicircular path and arrive back at the gap in a time $T/2$, where T is the period of revolution, given by Equation 29.14. The frequency of the applied voltage is adjusted so that the polarity of the dees is reversed in the same time it takes the ions to complete one half of a revolution. If the phase of the applied voltage is adjusted such that D_2 is at a lower potential than D_1 by an amount V, the ion accelerates across the gap to D_2 and its kinetic energy increases by an amount qV. The ion then continues to move in D_2 in a semicircular path of larger radius (since its speed has increased). After a time $T/2$, it again arrives at the gap. By this time, the potential across the dees is reversed (so that D_1 is now negative) and the ion is given another "kick" across the gap. The motion continues so that for each half revolution, the ion gains additional kinetic energy equal to qV. When the radius of its orbit is nearly that of the dees, the energetic ion leaves the system through the exit slit.

It is important to note that the operation of the cyclotron is based on the fact that the time for one revolution is independent of the speed of the ion or the radius of its orbit.

We can obtain an expression for the kinetic energy of the ion when it exits from the cyclotron in terms of the radius R of the dees. From Equation 29.12 we know that $v = qBR/m$. Hence, the kinetic energy is

$$K = \tfrac{1}{2}mv^2 = \frac{q^2B^2R^2}{2m} \tag{29.18}$$

When the energy of the ions exceeds about 20 MeV, relativistic effects come into play and the ion masses are no longer constant. (Such effects are discussed in Chapter 39.) For this reason, the period of the orbit increases and the rotating ions do not remain in phase with the applied voltage. Some accelerators solve this problem by modifying the period of the applied voltage so that it remains in phase with the rotating ion. In 1977, protons were accelerated to 400 GeV (1 GeV = 10^9 eV) in an accelerator in Batavia, Illinois. The system incorporates 954 magnets and has a circumference of 6.3 km (4.1 miles)!

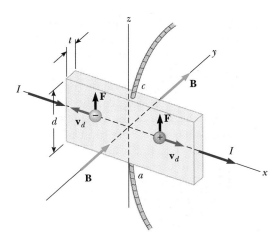

FIGURE 29.23 To observe the Hall effect, a magnetic field is applied to a current-carrying conductor. When I is in the x direction and **B** in the y direction as shown, both positive and negative charge carriers are deflected upward in the magnetic field. The Hall voltage is measured between points a and c.

*29.6 THE HALL EFFECT

In 1879 Edwin Hall discovered that, when a current-carrying conductor is placed in a magnetic field, a voltage is generated in a direction perpendicular to both the current and the magnetic field. This observation, known as the *Hall effect,* arises from the deflection of charge carriers to one side of the conductor as a result of the magnetic force they experience. It gives information regarding the sign of the charge carriers and their density and also provides a convenient technique for measuring magnetic fields.

The arrangement for observing the Hall effect consists of a conductor in the form of a flat strip carrying a current I in the x direction as in Figure 29.23. A uniform magnetic field **B** is applied in the y direction. If the charge carriers are electrons moving in the negative x direction with a velocity v_d, they experience an upward magnetic force **F**, are deflected upward, and accumulate at the upper edge leaving an excess positive charge at the lower edge (Fig. 29.24a). This accumulation of charge at the edges increases until the electrostatic field set up by the charge separation balances the magnetic force on the carriers. When this equilibrium condition is reached, the electrons are no longer deflected upward. A sensi-

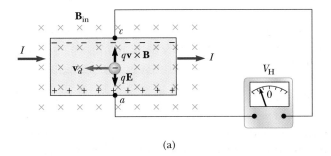

(a)

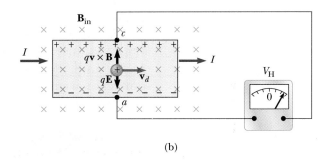

(b)

FIGURE 29.24 (a) When the charge carriers are negative, the upper edge becomes negatively charged, and c is at a lower potential than a. (b) When the charge carriers are positive, the upper edge becomes positively charged and c is at a higher potential than a. In either case, the charge carriers are no longer deflected when the edges become fully charged, that is, when there is a balance between the electrostatic force trying to combine the charges and the magnetic deflection force.

tive voltmeter or potentiometer connected across the sample as in Figure 29.24 can be used to measure the potential difference generated across the conductor, known as the **Hall voltage** V_H. If the charge carriers are positive and hence move in the positive x direction as in Figure 29.24b, they also experience an upward magnetic force $q\mathbf{v}_d \times \mathbf{B}$. This produces a buildup of positive charge on the upper edge and leaves an excess of negative charge on the lower edge. Hence, the sign of the Hall voltage generated in the sample is opposite the sign of the voltage resulting from the deflection of electrons. The sign of the charge carriers can therefore be determined from a measurement of the polarity of the Hall voltage.

To find an expression for the Hall voltage, first note that the magnetic force on the charge carriers has a magnitude $qv_d B$. In equilibrium, this force is balanced by the electrostatic force qE_H, where E_H is the electric field due to the charge separation (sometimes referred to as the *Hall field*). Therefore,

$$qv_d B = qE_H$$

$$E_H = v_d B$$

If d is the width of the conductor, the Hall voltage V_H is equal to $E_H d$, or

$$V_H = E_H d = v_d B d \tag{29.19}$$

Thus, we see that the measured Hall voltage gives a value for the drift speed of the charge carriers if d and B are known.

The number of charge carriers per unit volume (or charge density), n, can be obtained by measuring the current in the sample. From Equation 27.4, the drift speed can be expressed as

$$v_d = \frac{I}{nqA} \tag{29.20}$$

where A is the cross-sectional area of the conductor. Substituting Equation 29.20 into Equation 29.19, we obtain

$$V_H = \frac{IBd}{nqA} \tag{29.21}$$

Since $A = td$, where t is the thickness of the conductor, we can also express Equation 29.21 as

The Hall voltage

$$V_H = \frac{IB}{nqt} \tag{29.22}$$

The quantity $1/nq$ is referred to as the **Hall coefficient** R_H. Equation 29.22 shows that a properly calibrated conductor can be used to measure the strength of an unknown magnetic field.

Since all quantities appearing in Equation 29.22 other than nq can be measured, a value for the Hall coefficient is readily obtained. The sign and magnitude of R_H give the sign of the charge carriers and their density. In metals, the charge carriers are electrons and the charge density determined from Hall-effect measurements is in good agreement with calculated values for monovalent metals, such as Li, Na, Cu, and Ag, where n is approximately equal to the number of valence electrons per unit volume. However, this classical model is not valid for metals such as Fe, Bi, and Cd or for semiconductors. These discrepancies can be explained only by using a model based on the quantum nature of solids.

EXAMPLE 29.6 **The Hall Effect for Copper**

A rectangular copper strip 1.5 cm wide and 0.10 cm thick carries a current of 5.0 A. A 1.2-T magnetic field is applied perpendicular to the strip as in Figure 29.24. Find the resulting Hall voltage.

Solution If we assume there is one electron per atom available for conduction, then we can take the charge density to be $n = 8.48 \times 10^{28}$ electrons/m³ (Example 27.1). Substituting this value and the given data into Equation 29.22 gives

$$V_H = \frac{IB}{nqt}$$

$$= \frac{(5.0 \text{ A})(1.2 \text{ T})}{(8.48 \times 10^{28} \text{ m}^{-3})(1.6 \times 10^{-19} \text{ C})(0.10 \times 10^{-2} \text{ m})}$$

$$V_H = \boxed{0.44 \ \mu V}$$

Hence, the Hall voltage is quite small in good conductors. Note that the width of this sample is not needed in this calculation.

In semiconductors, where n is much smaller than in monovalent metals, one finds a larger Hall voltage since V_H varies as the inverse of n. Current levels of the order of 1 mA are generally used for such materials. Consider a piece of silicon with the same dimensions as the copper strip, with $n = 1.0 \times 10^{20}$ electrons/m³. Taking $B = 1.2$ T and $I = 0.10$ mA, we find that $V_H = 7.5$ mV. Such a voltage is readily measured with a potentiometer.

*29.7 THE QUANTUM HALL EFFECT

Although the Hall effect was discovered over 100 years ago, it continues to be one of the most valuable techniques for helping scientists understand the electronic properties of metals and semiconductors. For example, in 1980, scientists reported that at low temperatures and in very strong magnetic fields, a two-dimensional system of electrons in a semiconductor has a conductivity $\sigma = i(e^2/h)$, where i is a small integer, e is the electronic charge, and h is Planck's constant. This behavior manifests itself as a series of plateaus in the Hall voltage as the applied magnetic field is varied. The quantized nature of this two-dimensional conductivity was totally unanticipated. As its discoverer, Klaus von Klitzing stated, "It is quite astonishing that it is the total macroscopic conductance of the Hall device which is quantized rather than some idealized microscopic conductivity."

One of the important consequences of the quantum Hall effect is the ability to measure the ratio e^2/h to an accuracy of at least one part in 10^5. This provides a very accurate measure of the dimensionless fine-structure constant, given by $\alpha = e^2/hc \approx 1/137$, since c is an exactly defined quantity (the speed of light). In addition, the quantum Hall effect provides scientists with a new and convenient standard of resistance. The 1985 Nobel Prize in Physics was awarded to von Klitzing for this fundamental discovery.

Another great surprise occurred in 1982 when scientists announced that in some nearly ideal samples at very low temperatures, the Hall conductivity could take on both integer and fractional values of e^2/h. Undoubtedly, future discoveries in this and related areas of science will continue to improve our understanding of the nature of matter.

SUMMARY

The magnetic force that acts on a charge q moving with a velocity **v** in a magnetic field **B** is

$$\mathbf{F} = q\mathbf{v} \times \mathbf{B} \tag{29.1}$$

This magnetic force is in a direction perpendicular both to the velocity of the particle and to the field. The magnitude of this force is

$$F = qvB \sin \theta \qquad (29.2)$$

where θ is the smaller angle between **v** and **B**. The SI unit of **B** is the **weber per square meter** (Wb/m²), also called the **tesla** (T), where $[B] = T = Wb/m^2 = N/A \cdot m$.

When a charged particle moves in a magnetic field, the work done by the magnetic force on the particle is zero because the displacement is always perpendicular to the direction of the magnetic force. The magnetic field can alter the direction of the velocity vector, but it cannot change the speed of the particle.

If a straight conductor of length L carries a current I, the force on that conductor when placed in a uniform magnetic field **B** is

$$\mathbf{F} = I\mathbf{L} \times \mathbf{B} \qquad (29.3)$$

where the direction of **L** is in the direction of the current and $|\mathbf{L}| = L$.

If an arbitrarily shaped wire carrying a current I is placed in a magnetic field, the magnetic force on a very small segment $d\mathbf{s}$ is

$$d\mathbf{F} = I \, d\mathbf{s} \times \mathbf{B} \qquad (29.4)$$

To determine the total magnetic force on the wire, one has to integrate Equation 29.4, keeping in mind that both **B** and $d\mathbf{s}$ may vary at each point.

The force on a current-carrying conductor of arbitrary shape in a uniform magnetic field is

$$\mathbf{F} = I\mathbf{L'} \times \mathbf{B} \qquad (29.7)$$

where **L'** is a vector directed from one end of the conductor to the opposite end.

The net magnetic force on any closed loop carrying a current in a uniform magnetic field is zero.

The **magnetic moment** $\boldsymbol{\mu}$ of a current loop carrying a current I is

$$\boldsymbol{\mu} = I\mathbf{A} \qquad (29.10)$$

where **A** is perpendicular to the plane of the loop and $|\mathbf{A}|$ is equal to the area of the loop. The SI unit of $\boldsymbol{\mu}$ is $A \cdot m^2$.

The torque $\boldsymbol{\tau}$ on a current loop when the loop is placed in a uniform *external* magnetic field **B** is

$$\boldsymbol{\tau} = \boldsymbol{\mu} \times \mathbf{B} \qquad (29.11)$$

If a charged particle moves in a uniform magnetic field so that its initial velocity is perpendicular to the field, the particle moves in a circle whose plane is perpendicular to the magnetic field. The radius r of the circular path is

$$r = \frac{mv}{qB} \qquad (29.12)$$

where m is the mass of the particle and q is its charge. The angular frequency of the rotating charged particle is

$$\omega = \frac{qB}{m} \qquad (29.13)$$

QUESTIONS

1. At a given instant, a proton moves in the positive *x* direction in a region where there is a magnetic field in the negative *z* direction. What is the direction of the magnetic force? Does the proton continue to move in the positive *x* direction? Explain.

2. Two charged particles are projected into a region where there is a magnetic field perpendicular to their velocities. If the charges are deflected in opposite directions, what can you say about them?

3. If a charged particle moves in a straight line through some region of space, can you say that the magnetic field in that region is zero?

4. Suppose an electron is chasing a proton up this page when suddenly a magnetic field is formed perpendicular to the page. What happens to the particles?

5. Why does the picture on a TV screen become distorted when a magnet is brought near the screen?

6. How can the motion of a moving charged particle be used to distinguish between a magnetic field and an electric field? Give a specific example to justify your argument.

7. List several similarities and differences in electric and magnetic forces.

8. Justify the following statement: "It is impossible for a constant (in other words, a time independent) magnetic field to alter the speed of a charged particle."

9. In view of the above statement, what is the role of a magnetic field in a cyclotron?

10. A current-carrying conductor experiences no magnetic force when placed in a certain manner in a uniform magnetic field. Explain.

11. Is it possible to orient a current loop in a uniform magnetic field so that the loop does not tend to rotate? Explain.

12. How can a current loop be used to determine the presence of a magnetic field in a given region of space?

13. What is the net force on a compass needle in a uniform magnetic field?

14. What type of magnetic field is required to exert a resultant force on a magnetic dipole? What is the direction of the resultant force?

15. A proton moving horizontally enters a region where there is a uniform magnetic field perpendicular to the proton's velocity, as shown in Figure 29.25. Describe the subsequent motion of the proton. How would an electron behave under the same circumstances?

16. In a magnetic bottle, what reverses the direction of the velocity of the confined charged particles? (*Hint:* Find the direction of the magnetic force on these particles in a region where the field becomes stronger and the field lines converge.)

17. In the cyclotron, why do particles of different velocities take the same amount of time to complete one half of a revolution?

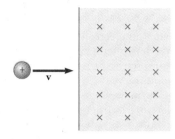

FIGURE 29.25   (Question 15).

18. The *bubble chamber* is a device used for observing tracks of particles that pass through the chamber, which is immersed in a magnetic field. If some of the tracks are spirals and others are straight lines, what can you say about the particles?

19. Can a magnetic field set a resting electron into motion? If so, how?

20. You are designing a magnetic probe that uses the Hall effect to measure magnetic fields. Assume that you are restricted to using a given material and that you have already made the probe as thin as possible. What, if anything, can be done to increase the Hall voltage produced for a given magnetic field strength?

21. The electron beam in Figure 29.26 is projected to the right. The beam deflects downward in the presence of a magnetic field produced by a pair of current-carrying coils. (a) What is the direction of the magnetic field? (b) What would happen to the beam if the current in the coils were reversed?

FIGURE 29.26   (Question 21).   *(Courtesy of Central Scientific Company)*

PROBLEMS

Section 29.1   The Magnetic Field

1. Consider an electron near the equator. In which direction does it tend to deflect if its velocity is directed (a) downward, (b) northward, (c) westward, or (d) southeastward?

2. An electron moving along the positive x axis perpendicular to a magnetic field experiences a magnetic deflection in the negative y direction. What is the direction of the magnetic field?

3. An electron in a uniform electric and magnetic field has a velocity of 1.2×10^4 m/s in the positive x direction and an acceleration of 2.0×10^{12} m/s² in the positive z direction. If the electric field has strength of 20 N/C (in the positive z direction), what is the magnetic field in the region?

4. What magnetic force is experienced by a proton moving north to south at 4.8×10^6 m/s at a location where the vertical component of the Earth's magnetic field is 75 μT directed downward? In what direction is the proton deflected?

5. A proton moving at 4.0×10^6 m/s through a magnetic field of 1.7 T experiences a magnetic force of magnitude 8.2×10^{-13} N. What is the angle between the proton's velocity and the field?

6. A metal ball having net charge $Q = 5.0$ μC is thrown out of a window horizontally at a speed $v = 20$ m/s. The window is at a height $h = 20$ m above the ground. A uniform horizontal magnetic field of magnitude $B = 0.010$ T is perpendicular to the plane of the ball's trajectory. Find the magnetic force acting on the ball just before it hits the ground.

6A. A metal ball having net charge Q is thrown out of a window horizontally at a speed v. The window is at a height h above the ground. A uniform horizontal magnetic field of magnitude B is perpendicular to the plane of the ball's trajectory. Find the magnetic force acting on the ball just before it hits the ground.

7. A duck flying due north at 15 m/s passes over Atlanta, where the Earth's magnetic field is 5.0×10^{-5} T in a direction 60° below the horizontal line running north and south. If the duck has a net positive charge of 0.040 μC, what is the magnetic force acting on it?

8. An electron is projected into a uniform magnetic field $\mathbf{B} = (1.4\mathbf{i} + 2.1\mathbf{j})$ T. Find the vector expression for the force on the electron when its velocity is $\mathbf{v} = 3.7 \times 10^5\mathbf{j}$ m/s.

9. A proton moves with a velocity of $\mathbf{v} = (2\mathbf{i} - 4\mathbf{j} + \mathbf{k})$ m/s in a region in which the magnetic field is $\mathbf{B} = (\mathbf{i} + 2\mathbf{j} - 3\mathbf{k})$ T. What is the magnitude of the magnetic force this charge experiences?

10. A proton moves perpendicular to a uniform magnetic field B at 1.00×10^7 m/s and experiences an acceleration of 2.00×10^{13} m/s² in the $+ x$ direction when its velocity is in the $+ z$ direction. Determine the magnitude and direction of the field.

11. Show that the work done by the magnetic force on a charged particle moving in a magnetic field is zero for any displacement of the particle.

Section 29.2   Magnetic Force on a Current-Carrying Conductor

12. A wire 40 cm long carries a current of 20 A. It is bent into a loop and placed with its plane perpendicular to a magnetic field having a flux density of 0.52 T. What is the torque on the loop if it is bent into (a) an equilateral triangle, (b) a square, (c) a circle. (d) Which torque is greatest?

13. A wire carries a steady current of 2.4 A. A straight section of the wire is 0.75 m long and lies along the x axis within a uniform magnetic field, $\mathbf{B} = (1.6\mathbf{k})$ T. If the current is in the $+ x$ direction, what is the magnetic force on the section of wire?

14. A conductor suspended by two flexible wires as in Figure P29.14 has a mass per unit length of 0.040 kg/m. What current must exist in the conductor in order for the tension in the supporting wires to be zero when the magnetic field is 3.6 T into the page? What is the required direction for the current?

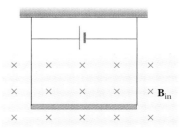

FIGURE P29.14

15. A wire having a mass per unit length of 0.50 g/cm carries a 2.0-A current horizontally to the south. What are the direction and magnitude of the minimum magnetic field needed to lift this wire vertically upward?

16. A rectangular loop with dimensions 10.0 cm × 20.0 cm is suspended by a string, and the lower hori-

zontal section of the loop is immersed in a magnetic field confined to a circular region (Fig. P29.16). If a current of 3.00 A is maintained in the loop in the direction shown, what are the direction and magnitude of the magnetic field required to produce a tension of 4.00×10^{-2} N in the supporting string? (Neglect the mass of the loop.)

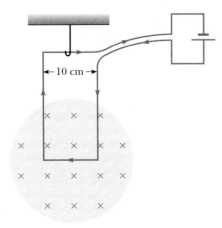

←10 cm→

FIGURE P29.16

17. A wire 2.8 m in length carries a current of 5.0 A in a region where a uniform magnetic field has a magnitude of 0.39 T. Calculate the magnitude of the magnetic force on the wire if the angle between the magnetic field and the current is (a) 60°, (b) 90°, (c) 120°.

18. In Figure P29.18, the cube is 40.0 cm on each edge. Four straight segments of wire— *ab*, *bc*, *cd*, and *da*— form a closed loop that carries a current $I = 5.0$ A in the direction shown. A uniform magnetic field $B = 0.020$ T is in the positive direction. Determine the magnitude and direction of the magnetic force on each segment.

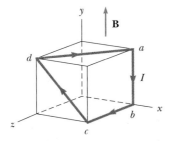

FIGURE P29.18

19. Imagine a very long, uniform wire that has a linear mass density of 1.0 g/m and that encircles the Earth at its magnetic equator. What are the magnitude and direction of the current in the wire that keep it levitated just above the ground?

20. A rod of mass 0.72 kg and radius 6.0 cm rests on two parallel rails (Fig. P29.20) that are $d = 12$ cm apart and $L = 45$ cm long. The rod carries a current $I = 48$ A in the direction shown and rolls along the rails without slipping. If the rod starts from rest, what is its speed as it leaves the rails if there is a uniform 0.24-T magnetic field directed perpendicular to the rod and the rails?

20A. A rod of mass m and radius R rests on two parallel rails (Fig. P29.20) that are a distance d apart and have a length L. The rod carries a current I in the direction shown and rolls along the rails without slipping. If the rod starts from rest, what is its speed as it leaves the rails if there is a uniform magnetic field **B** directed perpendicular to the rod and the rails?

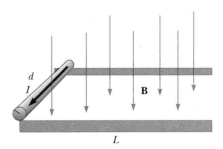

FIGURE P29.20

21. A strong magnet is placed under a horizontal conducting ring of radius r that carries a current I as in Figure P29.21. If the magnetic field **B** makes an angle θ with the vertical at the ring's location, what are the magnitude and direction of the resultant force on the ring?

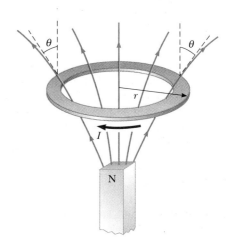

FIGURE P29.21

Section 29.3   Torque on a Current Loop in a Uniform Magnetic Field

22. A current of 17.0 mA is maintained in a single circular loop of 2.00 m circumference. A magnetic field of 0.800 T is directed parallel to the plane of the loop. (a) Calculate the magnetic moment of the loop. (b) What is the magnitude of the torque exerted on the loop by the magnetic field?

23. A rectangular loop consists of $N = 100$ closely wrapped turns and has dimensions $a = 0.40$ m and $b = 0.30$ m. The loop is hinged along the y axis, and its plane makes an angle $\theta = 30°$ with the x axis (Fig. P29.23). What is the magnitude of the torque exerted on the loop by a uniform magnetic field $B = 0.80$ T directed along the x axis when the current is $I = 1.2$ A in the direction shown? What is the expected direction of rotation of the loop?

23A. A rectangular loop consists of N closely wrapped turns and has dimensions a and b. The loop is hinged along the y axis, and its plane makes an angle θ with the x axis (Fig. P29.23). What is the magnitude of the torque exerted on the loop by a uniform magnetic field B directed along the x axis when the current is I in the direction shown? What is the expected direction of rotation of the loop?

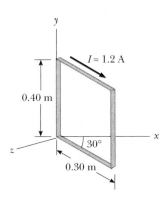

FIGURE P29.23

24. A square loop, hinged along one side, is made of a wire that has a mass per unit length of 0.10 kg/m and carries a current of 5.0 A. A 0.010-T uniform magnetic field directed perpendicular to the hinged side exists in the region. Determine the maximum linear acceleration of the side of the loop opposite the hinged side.

25. A circular coil of 225 turns and area 0.45 m² is in a uniform magnetic field of 0.21 T. The maximum torque exerted on the coil by the field is 8.0×10^{-3} N·m. (a) Calculate the current in the coil. (b) Would this value be different if the 225 turns of wire were used to form a single-turn coil with the same shape but much larger area? Explain.

26. A wire is formed into a circle having a diameter of 10.0 cm and placed in a uniform magnetic field of 3.00×10^{-3} T. A current of 5.00 A passes through the wire. Find (a) the maximum torque on the wire and (b) the range of potential energy the wire possesses for different orientations.

27. A long piece of wire of mass 0.10 kg and length 4.0 m is used to make a square coil 0.10 m on a side. The coil is hinged along a horizontal side, carries a 3.4-A current, and is placed in a vertical magnetic field of magnitude 0.010 T. (a) Determine the angle that the plane of the coil makes with the vertical when the coil is in equilibrium. (b) Find the torque acting on the coil due to the magnetic force at equilibrium.

27A. A long piece of wire of mass m and length L is used to make a square coil having side d. The coil is hinged along a horizontal side, carries a current I, and is placed in a vertical magnetic field of magnitude B. (a) Determine the angle that the plane of the coil makes with the vertical when the coil is in equilibrium. (b) Find the torque acting on the coil due to the magnetic force at equilibrium.

Section 29.4   Motion of a Charged Particle in a Magnetic Field

28. The magnetic field of the Earth at a certain location is directed vertically downward and has a magnitude of 0.5×10^{-4} T. A proton is moving horizontally towards the west in this field with a speed of 6.2×10^6 m/s. (a) What are the direction and magnitude of the magnetic force the field exerts on this charge? (b) What is the radius of the circular arc followed by this proton?

29. A singly charged positive ion has a mass of 3.20×10^{-26} kg. After being accelerated through a potential difference of 833 V, the ion enters a magnetic field of 0.920 T along a direction perpendicular to the direction of the field. Calculate the radius of the path of the ion in the field.

30. One electron collides with a second electron initially at rest. After the collision, the radii of their trajectories are 1.0 cm and 2.4 cm. The trajectories are perpendicular to a uniform magnetic field of magnitude 0.044 T. Determine the energy (in keV) of the incident electron.

30A. One electron collides with a second electron initially at rest. After the collision, the radii of their trajectories are R_1 and R_2. The trajectories are perpendicular to a uniform magnetic field of magnitude B. Determine the energy (in keV) of the incident electron.

31. A proton moving in a circular path perpendicular to a constant magnetic field takes 1.00 μs to complete one revolution. Determine the magnitude of the field.

32. An electron moves in a circular path perpendicular to a constant magnetic field of magnitude 1.00 mT. If the angular momentum of the electron about the center of the circle is 4.00×10^{-25} J·s, determine (a) the radius of the path and (b) the speed of the electron.

33. A proton (charge $+ e$, mass m_p), a deuteron (charge $+ e$, mass $2m_p$), and an alpha particle, (charge $+ 2e$, mass $4m_p$) are accelerated through a common potential difference, V. The particles enter a uniform magnetic field, **B**, in a direction perpendicular to **B**. The proton moves in a circular path of radius r_p. Determine the values of the radii of the circular orbits for the deuteron, r_d, and the alpha particle, r_α, in terms of r_p.

34. Calculate the cyclotron frequency of a proton in a magnetic field of magnitude 5.2 T.

35. A cosmic-ray proton in interstellar space has an energy of 10 MeV and executes a circular orbit having a radius equal to that of Mercury's orbit around the Sun (5.8×10^{10} m). What is the magnetic field in that region of space?

36. A singly charged ion of mass m is accelerated from rest by a potential difference V. It is then deflected by a uniform magnetic field (perpendicular to the ion's velocity) into a semicircle of radius R. Now a doubly charged ion of mass m' is accelerated through the same potential difference and deflected by the same magnetic field into a semicircle of radius $R' = 2R$. What is the ratio of the ions' masses?

37. A singly charged positive ion moving at 4.60×10^5 m/s leaves a circular track of radius 7.94 mm along a direction perpendicular to the 1.80-T magnetic field of a bubble chamber. Compute the mass (in atomic mass units) of this ion, and, from that value, identify it.

38. The accelerating voltage that is applied to an electron gun is 15 kV, and the horizontal distance from the gun to a viewing screen is 35 cm. What is the deflection caused by the vertical component of the Earth's magnetic field (4.0×10^{-5} T), assuming that any change in the horizontal component of the beam velocity is negligible.

*Section 29.5   Applications of the Motion of Charged Particles in a Magnetic Field

39. A crossed-field velocity selector has a magnetic field of magnitude 1.00×10^{-2} T. What electric field strength is required if 10.0-keV electrons are to pass through undeflected?

40. A velocity selector consists of magnetic and electric fields described by $\mathbf{E} = E\mathbf{k}$ and $\mathbf{B} = B\mathbf{j}$. If $B = 0.015$ T, find the value of E such that a 750-eV electron moving along the positive x axis is undeflected.

41. At the equator, near the surface of the Earth, the magnetic field is approximately 50 μT northward

and the electric field is about 100 N/C downward (in other words, toward the ground). Find the gravitational, electric, and magnetic forces on a 100-eV electron moving eastward in a straight line in this environment.

42. (a) Singly charged uranium-238 ions are accelerated through a potential difference of 2.00 kV and enter a uniform magnetic field of 1.20 T directed perpendicular to their velocities. Determine the radius of their circular path. (b) Repeat for uranium-235 ions. How does the ratio of these path radii depend on the accelerating voltage and the magnetic field strength?

43. Consider the mass spectrometer shown schematically in Figure 29.20. The electric field between the plates of the velocity selector is 2500 V/m, and the magnetic field in both the velocity selector and the deflection chamber has a magnitude of 0.0350 T. Calculate the radius of the path for a singly charged ion having a mass $m = 2.18 \times 10^{-26}$ kg.

44. What is the required radius of a cyclotron designed to accelerate protons to energies of 34 MeV using a magnetic field of 5.2 T?

45. What is the minimum size of a cyclotron designed to accelerate protons to an energy of 18.0 MeV with a cyclotron frequency of 30.0 MHz?

46. At the Fermilab accelerator in Batavia, Illinois, protons having momentum 4.8×10^{-16} kg·m/s are held in a circular orbit of radius 1.0 km by an upward magnetic field. What is the magnitude of this field?

47. A cyclotron designed to accelerate protons has a magnetic field of magnitude 0.45 T over a region of radius 1.2 m. What are (a) the cyclotron frequency and (b) the maximum speed acquired by the protons?

48. Deuterium ions are accelerated through a potential difference of 45 kV. The ions enter a velocity selector in which the electric field intensity is 2.5 kV/m. They then continue into a uniform magnetic field that has the same flux density and direction as the magnetic field in the velocity selector. What are (a) the radius of the deuterons' orbit and (b) their speed? (c) What is the strength of the magnetic field?

49. The picture tube in a television uses magnetic deflection coils rather than electric deflection plates. Suppose an electron beam is accelerated through a 50.0-kV potential difference and then travels through a region of uniform magnetic field 1.00 cm wide. The screen is located 10.0 cm from the center of the coils and is 50.0 cm wide. When the field is turned off, the electron beam hits the center of the screen. What field strength is necessary to deflect the beam to the side of the screen?

*Section 29.6   The Hall Effect

50. A flat ribbon of silver having a thickness $t = 0.20$ mm is used in a Hall-effect measurement of a uniform

magnetic field perpendicular to the ribbon, as in Figure P29.50. The Hall coefficient for silver is $R_H = 0.84 \times 10^{-10}$ m^3/C. (a) What is the density of charge carriers in silver? (b) If a current $I = 20$ A produces a Hall voltage $V_H = 15$ μV, what is the magnitude of the applied magnetic field?

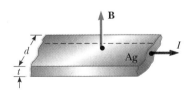

FIGURE P29.50

51. A section of conductor 0.40 cm thick is used in a Hall-effect measurement. If a Hall voltage of 35 μV is measured for a current of 21 A in a magnetic field of 1.8 T, calculate the Hall coefficient for the conductor.

52. The thickness of a thin film of copper is to be determined using the Hall effect. In the experiment, a Hall voltage of 27.0 μV is measured for a current of 17.0 A in a 2.10-T magnetic field. Calculate the thickness of the film.

53. In an experiment designed to measure the Earth's magnetic field using the Hall effect, a copper bar 0.50 cm thick is positioned along an east-west direction. If a current of 8.0 A in the conductor results in a Hall voltage of 5.1×10^{-12} V, what is the magnitude of the Earth's magnetic field? (Assume that $n = 8.48 \times 10^{28}$ electrons/m^3 and that the plane of the bar is rotated to be perpendicular to the direction of **B**.)

54. A flat copper ribbon 0.33 mm thick carries a steady current of 50 A and is located in a uniform 1.3-T magnetic field directed perpendicular to the plane of the ribbon. If a Hall voltage of 9.6 μV is measured across the ribbon, what is the charge density of the free electrons? What effective number of free electrons per atom does this result indicate?

54A. A flat copper ribbon of thickness t carries a steady current I and is located in a uniform magnetic field B directed perpendicular to the plane of the ribbon. If a Hall voltage V_H is measured across the ribbon, what is the charge density of the free electrons? What effective number of free electrons per atom does this result indicate?

55. The Hall effect can be used to measure n, the number of conduction electrons per unit volume for an unknown sample. The sample is 15 mm thick and when placed in a 1.8-T magnetic field produces a Hall voltage of 0.122 μV while carrying a 12-A current. What is the value of n?

56. A Hall-effect probe operates with a 120-mA current. When the probe is placed in a uniform magnetic field of magnitude 0.080 T, it produces a Hall voltage of 0.70 μV. (a) When it is measuring an unknown magnetic field, the Hall voltage is 0.33 μV. What is the unknown field strength? (b) If the thickness of the probe in the direction of **B** is 2.0 mm, find the charge-carrier density (each of charge e).

ADDITIONAL PROBLEMS

57. A wire having a linear mass density of 1.0 g/cm is placed on a horizontal surface that has a coefficient of friction of 0.20. The wire carries a current of 1.5 A toward the east and moves horizontally to the north. What are the magnitude and direction of the smallest magnetic field that enables the wire to move in this fashion?

58. Indicate the initial direction of the deflection of the charged particles as they enter the magnetic fields shown in Figure P29.58.

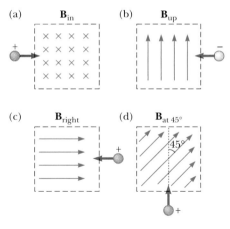

FIGURE P29.58

59. A positive charge $q = 3.2 \times 10^{-19}$ C moves with a velocity $\mathbf{v} = (2\mathbf{i} + 3\mathbf{j} - \mathbf{k})$ m/s through a region where both a uniform magnetic field and a uniform electric field exist. (a) Calculate the total force on the moving charge (in unit-vector notation) if $\mathbf{B} = (2\mathbf{i} + 4\mathbf{j} + \mathbf{k})$ T and $\mathbf{E} = (4\mathbf{i} - \mathbf{j} - 2\mathbf{k})$ V/m. (b) What angle does the force vector make with the positive x axis?

60. A cosmic-ray proton traveling at half the speed of light is heading directly toward the center of the Earth in the plane of the Earth's equator. Will it hit the Earth? Assume that the magnitude of the Earth's magnetic field is 5.0×10^{-5} T and extends out one Earth diameter, or 1.3×10^7 m. Calculate the radius of curvature of the proton in this magnetic field.

61. The circuit in Figure P29.61 consists of wires at the top and bottom and identical metal springs as the left and right sides. The wire at the bottom has a mass of 10 g and is 5.0 cm long. The springs stretch 0.50 cm under the weight of the wire and the circuit has a total resistance of 12 Ω. When a magnetic field is turned on, directed out of the page, the springs stretch an additional 0.30 cm. What is the strength of the magnetic field? (The upper portion of the circuit is fixed.)

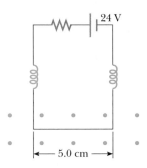

FIGURE P29.61

62. An electron enters a region traveling perpendicular to the linear boundary of a 0.10-T magnetic field. The direction of the field is perpendicular to the velocity of the electron. (a) Determine the time it takes for the electron to leave the "field-filled" region, given that it travels a semicircular path. (b) Find the kinetic energy of the electron if the maximum depth of penetration in the field is 2.0 cm.

63. Sodium melts at 99°C. Liquid sodium, an excellent thermal conductor, is used in some nuclear reactors to remove thermal energy from the reactor core. The liquid sodium is moved through pipes by pumps that exploit the force on a moving charge in a magnetic field. The principle is as follows: Imagine the liquid metal to be in a pipe having a rectangular cross-section of width w and height h. A uniform magnetic field perpendicular to the pipe affects a section of length L (Fig. P29.63). An electric current directed perpendicular to the pipe and to the magnetic field produces a current density J. (a) Explain why this

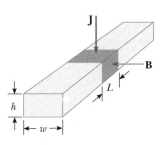

FIGURE P29.63

arrangement produces on the liquid a force that is directed along the length of the pipe. (b) Show that the section of liquid in the magnetic field experiences a pressure increase JLB.

64. A metal rod having a mass per unit length of 0.010 kg/m carries a current of $I = 5.0$ A. The rod hangs from two vertical wires in a uniform vertical magnetic field as in Figure P29.64. If the wires make an angle $\theta = 45°$ with the vertical when in equilibrium, determine the strength of the magnetic field.

64A. A metal rod having a mass per unit length μ carries a current I. The rod hangs from two vertical wires in a uniform vertical magnetic field as in Figure P29.64. If the wires make an angle θ with the vertical when in equilibrium, determine the strength of the magnetic field.

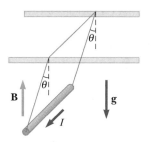

FIGURE P29.64

65. Cyclotrons are sometimes used for carbon-dating by accelerating C^{14} and C^{12} ions from a sample of material. If the cyclotron has a 2.4-T magnetic field, what is the difference in cyclotron frequencies for the two ions?

66. A 0.20-kg metal rod carrying a current of 10 A glides on two horizontal rails 0.50 m apart. What vertical magnetic field is required to keep the rod moving at a constant speed if the coefficient of kinetic friction between rod and rails is 0.10?

66A. A metal rod of mass m and carrying a current I glides on two horizontal rails separated by a distance d. What vertical magnetic field is required to keep the rod moving at a constant speed if the coefficient of kinetic friction between rod and rails is μ?

67. A singly charged ion completes five revolutions in a uniform magnetic field of magnitude 5.00×10^{-2} T in 1.50 ms. Calculate the approximate mass of the ion in kilograms.

68. A uniform magnetic field of magnitude 0.15 T is directed along the positive x axis. A positron moving at 5.0×10^6 m/s enters the field along a direction that makes an angle of 85° with the x axis (Fig. P29.68). The motion of the particle is expected to be a helix, as described in Section 29.4. Calculate (a) the pitch p and (b) the radius r of the trajectory.

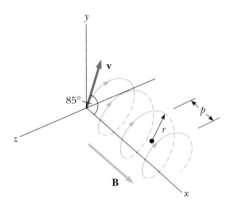

FIGURE P29.68

69. Consider an electron orbiting a proton and maintained in a fixed circular path of radius $R = 5.29 \times 10^{-11}$ m by the Coulomb force. Treating the orbiting charge as a current loop, calculate the resulting torque when the system is in a magnetic field of 0.400 T directed perpendicular to the magnetic moment of the electron.

70. A proton moving in the plane of the page has a kinetic energy of 6.0 MeV. It enters a magnetic field of magnitude $B = 1.0$ T directed into the page at an angle $\theta = 45°$ to the linear boundary of the field as shown in Figure P29.70. (a) Find x, the distance from the point of entry to where the proton will leave the field. (b) Determine θ', the angle between the boundary and the proton's velocity vector as it leaves the field.

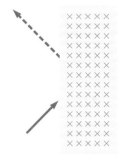

FIGURE P29.70

71. Protons having a kinetic energy of 5.00 MeV are moving in the positive x direction and enter a magnetic field $\mathbf{B} = (0.0500 \text{ T})\mathbf{k}$ directed out of the plane of the page and extending from $x = 0$ to $x = 1.00$ m as in Figure P29.71. (a) Calculate the y component of the protons' momentum as they leave the magnetic field. (b) Find the angle α between the initial velocity vector of the proton beam and the velocity vector after the beam emerges from the field. (*Hint:* Ne-

glect relativistic effects and note that 1 eV $= 1.60 \times 10^{-19}$ J.)

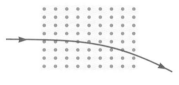

FIGURE P29.71

72. Table 29.1 shows measurements of a Hall voltage and corresponding magnetic field for a probe used to measure magnetic fields. (a) Plot these data, and deduce a relationship between the two variables. (b) If the measurements were taken with a current of 0.20 A and the sample is made from a material having a charge-carrier density of $1.0 \times 10^{26}/\text{m}^3$, what is the thickness of the sample?

TABLE 29.1

V_H (μV)	B (T)
0	0.00
11	0.10
19	0.20
28	0.30
42	0.40
50	0.50
61	0.60
68	0.70
79	0.80
90	0.90
102	1.00

SPREADSHEET PROBLEMS

S1. A galvanometer consists of a coil of wire suspended in a radial magnetic field by a thin, flexible fiber. When a current I passes through the coil, a torque is produced that causes the coil to rotate. The fiber, in turn, supplies a restoring torque τ that is proportional to the angle θ through which it has been twisted. That is, $\tau = \kappa\theta$, where κ is the torsion constant of the supporting fiber. The current I through the coil is

$$I = \frac{\kappa\theta}{NAB}$$

where N is the number of turns in the coil, A is the coil's area, and B is magnitude of the magnetic field.

A student passes small currents through a coil and measures its angular deflections for each current. The following data are obtained for a coil of area 2.0 cm² with 100 turns of wire and $B = 0.015$ T:

$I(\mu A)$	$\theta(\text{deg})$
0.10	3
0.15	6
0.20	7
0.30	11
0.50	18
0.75	27

Using a spreadsheet, plot these data points on a graph of current versus angular deflection. (Plot the data as *points*, not as a connected line.) Use the spreadsheet's regression (least-squares) routine to determine the straight line that best fits the data. Add the best-fit line to the plot, and obtain the torsion constant κ from the slope of this line.

S2. An electron has an initial velocity v_0 at the origin of a coordinate system at $t = 0$. A uniform electric field $\mathbf{E} = (1.00 \times 10^3 \text{ V/m})\mathbf{i}$ and a uniform magnetic field $\mathbf{B} = (0.500 \times 10^{-4} \text{ T})\mathbf{j}$ are turned on at $t = 0$. Write a spreadsheet or computer program to integrate the equations of motion. Since v_0 can be in any direction, you must consider the motion along x, y, and z directions. Describe the general motion of the electron for various values of v_0.

CHAPTER 30

Sources of the
Magnetic Field

Oxygen, a paramagnetic substance, is attracted to a magnetic field. The liquid oxygen in this photograph is suspended between the poles of a permanent magnet. Paramagnetic substances contain atoms (or ions) that have permanent magnetic dipole moments. These dipoles interact weakly with each other and are randomly oriented in the absence of an external magnetic field. When the substance is placed in an external magnetic field, its atomic dipoles tend to line up with the field. *(Courtesy of Leon Lewandowski)*

The preceding chapter treated a class of problems involving the magnetic force on a charged particle moving in a magnetic field. To complete the description of the magnetic interaction, this chapter deals with the origin of the magnetic field, namely, moving charges or electric currents. We begin by showing how to use the law of Biot and Savart to calculate the magnetic field produced at a point by a current element. Using this formalism and the superposition principle, we then calculate the total magnetic field due to a distribution of currents for several geometries. Next, we show how to determine the force between two current-carrying conductors, a calculation that leads to the definition of the ampere. We also introduce Ampère's law, which is very useful for calculating the magnetic field of highly symmetric configurations carrying steady currents. We apply Ampère's law to determine the magnetic field for several current configurations.

This chapter is also concerned with some aspects of the complex processes that occur in magnetic materials. All magnetic effects in matter can be explained on the basis of magnetic dipole moments similar to those associated with current loops. These atomic magnetic moments arise both from the orbital motion of the electrons and from an intrinsic property of the electrons known as spin. Our description of magnetism in matter is based in part on the experimental fact that the presence of bulk matter generally modifies the magnetic field produced by currents. For example, when a material is placed inside a current-carrying solenoid, the material sets up its own magnetic field, which adds vectorially to the field previously present.

30.1 THE BIOT-SAVART LAW

Shortly after Oersted's discovery in 1819 that a compass needle is deflected by a current-carrying conductor, Jean Baptiste Biot and Felix Savart reported that a conductor carrying a steady current exerts a force on a magnet. From their experimental results, Biot and Savart arrived at an expression that gives the magnetic field at some point in space in terms of the current that produces the field. The Biot-Savart law says that if a wire carries a steady current I, the magnetic field $d\mathbf{B}$ at a point P associated with an element of the wire $d\mathbf{s}$ (Fig. 30.1) has the following properties:

- The vector $d\mathbf{B}$ is perpendicular both to $d\mathbf{s}$ (which is a vector having units of length and in the direction of the current) and to the unit vector $\hat{\mathbf{r}}$ directed from the element to P.
- The magnitude of $d\mathbf{B}$ is inversely proportional to r^2, where r is the distance from the element to P.
- The magnitude of $d\mathbf{B}$ is proportional to the current and to the length ds of the element.
- The magnitude of $d\mathbf{B}$ is proportional to $\sin\theta$, where θ is the angle between the vectors $d\mathbf{s}$ and $\hat{\mathbf{r}}$.

Properties of the magnetic field created by an electric current

The **Biot-Savart law** can be summarized

$$d\mathbf{B} = k_m \frac{I\,d\mathbf{s} \times \hat{\mathbf{r}}}{r^2} \tag{30.1}$$

Biot-Savart law

where k_m is a constant that in SI units is exactly 10^{-7} T·m/A. This constant is usually written $\mu_0/4\pi$, where μ_0 is another constant, called the **permeability of free space**:

$$\frac{\mu_0}{4\pi} = k_m = 10^{-7} \text{ T·m/A} \tag{30.2}$$

$$\mu_0 = 4\pi k_m = 4\pi \times 10^{-7} \text{ T·m/A} \tag{30.3}$$

Permeability of free space

Hence, Equation 30.1 can also be written

$$d\mathbf{B} = \frac{\mu_0}{4\pi}\frac{I\,d\mathbf{s} \times \hat{\mathbf{r}}}{r^2} \tag{30.4}$$

Biot-Savart law

It is important to note that the Biot-Savart law gives the magnetic field at a point only for a small element of the conductor. To find the total magnetic field **B** created at some point by a conductor of finite size, we must sum up contributions from all current elements making up the conductor. That is, we must evaluate **B** by integrating Equation 30.4:

$$\mathbf{B} = \frac{\mu_0 I}{4\pi} \int \frac{d\mathbf{s} \times \hat{\mathbf{r}}}{r^2} \tag{30.5}$$

where the integral is taken over the entire conductor. This expression must be handled with special care because the integrand is a vector quantity.

There are interesting similarities between the Biot-Savart law of magnetism and Coulomb's law of electrostatics. The current element produces a magnetic field, whereas a point charge produces an electric field. Furthermore, *the magnitude of the magnetic field varies as the inverse square of the distance from the current element,* as does the electric field due to a point charge. However, the directions of the two fields are quite different. The electric field created by a point charge is radial. In the case of a positive point charge, **E** is directed from the charge to any point. The magnetic field created by a current element is perpendicular to both the element and the radius vector. Hence, if the conductor lies in the plane of the paper, as in Figure 30.1, *d***B** points out of the paper at *P* and into the paper at *P'*.

The examples that follow illustrate how to use the Biot-Savart law for calculating the magnetic field of several important geometric arrangements. It is important that you recognize that the magnetic field described in these calculations is *the field created by a current-carrying conductor.* This is not to be confused with any external field that may be applied to the conductor.

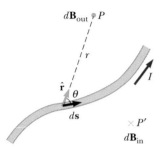

FIGURE 30.1 The magnetic field *d***B** at a point *P* due to a current element *d***s** is given by the Biot-Savart law. The field is out of the page at *P* and into the page at *P'*.

EXAMPLE 30.1 Magnetic Field Surrounding a Thin, Straight Conductor

Consider a thin, straight wire carrying a constant current *I* and placed along the *x* axis as in Figure 30.2. Calculate the total magnetic field at *P*.

Solution An element *d***s** is a distance *r* from *P*. The direction of the field at *P* due to this element is out of the paper because *d***s** × **r̂** is out of the paper. In fact, *all* elements produce a magnetic field directed out of the paper at *P*. Therefore, we have only to determine the magnitude of the field at *P*. Taking the origin at *O* and letting *P* be along the positive *y* axis, with **k** being a unit vector pointing out of the paper, we see that

$$d\mathbf{s} \times \hat{\mathbf{r}} = \mathbf{k} \, | \, d\mathbf{s} \times \hat{\mathbf{r}} \, | = \mathbf{k}(dx \sin \theta)$$

Substitution into Equation 30.4 gives *d***B** = **k** *dB*, with

$$(1) \qquad dB = \frac{\mu_0 I}{4\pi} \frac{dx \sin \theta}{r^2}$$

In order to integrate this expression, we must relate the variables *θ*, *x*, and *r*. One approach is to express *x* and *r* in terms of *θ*. From the geometry in Figure 30.2a and some simple differentiation, we obtain the following relationship:

$$(2) \qquad r = \frac{a}{\sin \theta} = a \csc \theta$$

Since tan *θ* = −*a*/*x* from the right triangle in Figure 30.2a, we have

$$x = -a \cot \theta$$

$$(3) \qquad dx = a \csc^2 \theta \, d\theta$$

Substitution of (2) and (3) into (1) gives

$$(4) \qquad dB = \frac{\mu_0 I}{4\pi} \frac{a \csc^2 \theta \sin \theta \, d\theta}{a^2 \csc^2 \theta}$$

$$= \frac{\mu_0 I}{4\pi a} \sin \theta \, d\theta$$

Thus, we have reduced the expression to one involving only the variable *θ*. We can now obtain the total field at *P* by integrating (4) over all elements subtending angles ranging from *θ₁* to *θ₂* as defined in Figure 30.2b:

$$B = \frac{\mu_0 I}{4\pi a} \int_{\theta_1}^{\theta_2} \sin \theta \, d\theta = \frac{\mu_0 I}{4\pi a} (\cos \theta_1 - \cos \theta_2) \tag{30.6}$$

We can apply this result to find the magnetic field of any straight wire if we know the geometry and hence the angles *θ₁* and *θ₂*.

Consider the special case of an infinitely long, straight wire. In this case, *θ₁* = 0 and *θ₂* = *π*, as can be seen from

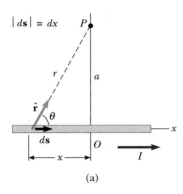

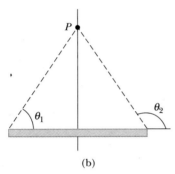

FIGURE 30.2   (Example 30.1) (a) A straight wire segment carrying a current *I*. The magnetic field at *P* due to each element *d***s** is out of the paper, and so the net field is also out of the paper. (b) The limiting angles θ_1 and θ_2 for this geometry.

Figure 30.2b, for segments ranging from $x = -\infty$ to $x = +\infty$. Since $(\cos \theta_1 - \cos \theta_2) = (\cos 0 - \cos \pi) = 2$, Equation 30.6 becomes

$$B = \frac{\mu_0 I}{2 \pi a} \qquad (30.7)$$

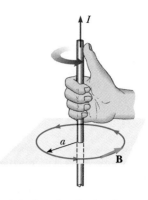

FIGURE 30.3   The right-hand rule for determining the direction of the magnetic field surrounding a long, straight wire carrying a current. Note that the magnetic field lines form circles around the wire.

A three-dimensional view of the direction of **B** for a long, straight wire is shown in Figure 30.3. The field lines are circles concentric with the wire and are in a plane perpendicular to the wire. The magnitude of **B** is constant on any circle of radius *a* and is given by Equation 30.7. A convenient rule for determining the direction of **B** is to grasp the wire with the right hand, with the thumb along the direction of the current. The four fingers wrap in the direction of the magnetic field.

Our result shows that the magnitude of the magnetic field is proportional to the current and decreases as the distance from the wire increases, as one might intuitively expect. Notice that Equation 30.7 has the same mathematical form as the expression for the magnitude of the electric field due to a long charged wire (Eq. 24.7).

Exercise   Calculate the magnitude of the magnetic field 4.0 cm from a long, straight wire carrying a current of 5.0 A.

Answer 2.5×10^{-5} T.

EXAMPLE 30.2   Magnetic Field Due to a Wire Segment

Calculate the magnetic field at the point *O* for the wire segment shown in Figure 30.4. The wire consists of two straight portions and a circular arc of radius *R*, which subtends an angle θ.

Reasoning   First, note that the magnetic field at *O* due to the straight segments *AA'* and *CC'* is identically zero, because *d***s** is parallel to $\hat{\mathbf{r}}$ along these paths so that $d\mathbf{s} \times \hat{\mathbf{r}} = 0$.

Note that each element along the path *AC* is at the same distance *R* from *O*, and each gives a contribution *d***B**, which is directed into the paper at *O*. Furthermore, at every point on the path *AC*, *d***s** is perpendicular to $\hat{\mathbf{r}}$, so that $|d\mathbf{s} \times \hat{\mathbf{r}}| = ds$.

Solution   Using this information and Equation 30.4, we get for the field at *O* due to the segment *d***s**

$$dB = \frac{\mu_0 I}{4\pi} \frac{ds}{R^2}$$

Since *I* and *R* are constants, we can easily integrate this expression:

$$B = \frac{\mu_0 I}{4\pi R^2} \int ds = \frac{\mu_0 I}{4\pi R^2} s = \frac{\mu_0 I}{4\pi R} \theta \qquad (30.8)$$

where we have used the fact that $s = R\theta$, where θ is measured in radians. The direction of **B** is into the paper at O because $d\mathbf{s} \times \hat{\mathbf{r}}$ is into the paper for every segment.

Exercise   A loop in the form of a full circle of radius R carries a current I. What is the magnitude of the magnetic field at its center?

Answer $\mu_0 I/2R$.

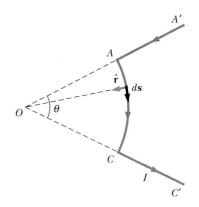

FIGURE 30.4   (Example 30.2) The magnetic field at O due to the curved segment AC is into the paper. The contribution to the field at O due to the straight segments is zero.

EXAMPLE 30.3   Magnetic Field on the Axis of a Circular Current Loop

Consider a circular loop of wire of radius R located in the yz plane and carrying a steady current I, as in Figure 30.5. Calculate the magnetic field at an axial point P a distance x from the center of the loop.

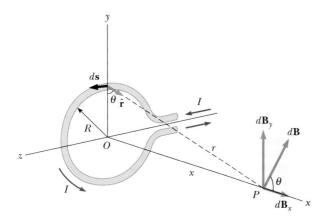

FIGURE 30.5   (Example 30.3) The geometry for calculating the magnetic field at an axial point P for a current loop. Note that by symmetry the total field **B** is along the x axis.

Reasoning   In this situation, note that any element $d\mathbf{s}$ is perpendicular to $\hat{\mathbf{r}}$. Furthermore, all elements around the loop are at the same distance r from P, where $r^2 = x^2 + R^2$. Hence, the magnitude of $d\mathbf{B}$ due to the element $d\mathbf{s}$ is

$$dB = \frac{\mu_0 I}{4\pi} \frac{|d\mathbf{s} \times \hat{\mathbf{r}}|}{r^2} = \frac{\mu_0 I}{4\pi} \frac{ds}{(x^2 + R^2)}$$

The direction of the magnetic field $d\mathbf{B}$ due to the element $d\mathbf{s}$ is perpendicular to the plane formed by $\hat{\mathbf{r}}$ and $d\mathbf{s}$, as in Figure 30.5. The vector $d\mathbf{B}$ can be resolved into a component dB_x, along the x axis, and a component dB_y, which is perpen-

dicular to the x axis. When the components perpendicular to the x axis are summed over the whole loop, the result is zero. That is, by symmetry any element on one side of the loop sets up a perpendicular component that cancels the component set up by an element diametrically opposite it.

Solution   For the reasons given above, *the resultant field at P must be along the x axis* and can be found by integrating the components $dB_x = dB\cos\theta$, where this expression is obtained from resolving the vector $d\mathbf{B}$ into its components as shown in Figure 30.5. That is, $\mathbf{B} = \mathbf{i}B_x$, where

$$B_x = \oint dB\cos\theta = \frac{\mu_0 I}{4\pi} \oint \frac{ds\cos\theta}{x^2 + R^2}$$

and the integral must be taken over the entire loop. Because θ, x, and R are constants for all elements of the loop and since $\cos\theta = R/(x^2 + R^2)^{1/2}$, we get

$$B_x = \frac{\mu_0 IR}{4\pi(x^2 + R^2)^{3/2}} \oint ds = \frac{\mu_0 IR^2}{2(x^2 + R^2)^{3/2}} \quad (30.9)$$

where we have used the fact that $\oint ds = 2\pi R$ (the circumference of the loop).

To find the magnetic field at the center of the loop, we set $x = 0$ in Equation 30.9. At this special point, this gives

$$B = \frac{\mu_0 I}{2R} \quad \text{(at } x = 0\text{)} \quad (30.10)$$

It is also interesting to determine the behavior of the magnetic field far from the loop, that is, when x is large compared with R. In this case, we can neglect the term R^2 in the denominator of Equation 30.9 and get

$$B \approx \frac{\mu_0 IR^2}{2x^3} \quad \text{(for } x \gg R\text{)} \quad (30.11)$$

Since the magnitude of the magnetic dipole moment μ of the loop is defined as the product of the current and the area (Eq. 29.10), $\mu = I(\pi R^2)$ and we can express Equation 30.11 in the form

$$B = \frac{\mu_0}{2\pi}\frac{\mu}{x^3} \qquad (30.12)$$

This result is similar in form to the expression for the electric field due to an electric dipole, $E = k_e p/y^3$ (Example 23.9), where p is the electric dipole moment. The pattern of the magnetic field lines for a circular loop is shown in Figure 30.6. For clarity, the lines are drawn only for one plane that contains the axis of the loop. The field pattern is axially symmetric.

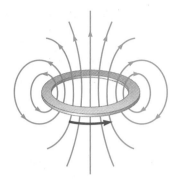

FIGURE 30.6 Magnetic field lines for a current loop. Far from the loop, the field lines are identical in form to those of an electric dipole.

30.2 THE MAGNETIC FORCE BETWEEN TWO PARALLEL CONDUCTORS

In the previous chapter we described the magnetic force that acts on a current-carrying conductor when the conductor is placed in an external magnetic field. Since a current in a conductor sets up its own magnetic field, it is easy to understand that two current-carrying conductors exert magnetic forces on each other. As we shall see, such forces can be used as the basis for defining the ampere and the coulomb.

Consider two long, straight, parallel wires separated by a distance a and carrying currents I_1 and I_2 in the same direction, as in Figure 30.7. We can easily determine the force on one wire due to a magnetic field set up by the other wire. Wire 2, which carries a current I_2, creates a magnetic field $\mathbf{B}_2$ at the position of wire 1. The direction of $\mathbf{B}_2$ is perpendicular to wire 1, as shown in Figure 30.7. According to Equation 29.3, the magnetic force on a length ℓ of wire 1 is $\mathbf{F}_1 = I_1\boldsymbol{\ell} \times \mathbf{B}_2$. Since $\boldsymbol{\ell}$ is perpendicular to $\mathbf{B}_2$, the magnitude of $\mathbf{F}_1$ is $F_1 = I_1\ell B_2$. Since the field created by wire 2 is given by Equation 30.7, we see that

$$F_1 = I_1\ell B_2 = I_1\ell\left(\frac{\mu_0 I_2}{2\pi a}\right) = \frac{\mu_0 I_1 I_2}{2\pi a}\ell$$

We can rewrite this in terms of the force per unit length as

$$\frac{F_1}{\ell} = \frac{\mu_0 I_1 I_2}{2\pi a} \qquad (30.13)$$

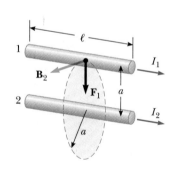

FIGURE 30.7 Two parallel wires each carrying a steady current exert a force on each other. The field $\mathbf{B}_2$ at wire 1 due to the current in wire 2 produces a force on wire 1 given by $F_1 = I_1\ell B_2$. The force is attractive if the currents are parallel as shown and repulsive if the currents are antiparallel.

The direction of $\mathbf{F}_1$ is downward, toward wire 2, because $\boldsymbol{\ell} \times \mathbf{B}_2$ is downward. If the field set up at wire 2 by wire 1 is considered, the force $\mathbf{F}_2$ on wire 2 is found to be equal to and opposite $\mathbf{F}_1$. This is what would be expected, if Newton's third law of action-reaction is to be obeyed.[1]

---

[1] Although the total force on wire 1 is equal to and opposite the total force on wire 2, Newton's third law does not apply when two small elements of the wires that are not opposite each other are considered in isolation. Resolution of this discrepancy for interacting current loops is described in more advanced treatments on electricity and magnetism.

When the currents are in opposite directions, the forces are reversed and the wires repel each other. Hence, we find that

parallel conductors carrying currents in the same direction attract each other, whereas parallel conductors carrying currents in opposite directions repel each other.

The force between two parallel wires each carrying a current is used to define the **ampere** as follows:

If two long, parallel wires 1 m apart carry the same current and the force per unit length on each wire is 2×10^{-7} N/m, then the current is defined to be 1 A.

The numerical value of 2×10^{-7} N/m is obtained from Equation 30.13, with $I_1 = I_2 = 1$ A and $a = 1$ m. Therefore, a mechanical measurement can be used to standardize the ampere. For instance, the National Institute of Standards and Technology uses an instrument called a current balance for primary current measurements. These results are then used to standardize other, more conventional instruments, such as ammeters.

The SI unit of charge, the **coulomb**, is defined in terms of the ampere as follows:

If a conductor carries a steady current of 1 A, then the quantity of charge that flows through a cross-section of the conductor in 1 s is 1 C.

30.3 AMPÈRE'S LAW

An experiment first carried out by Oersted in 1820 demonstrates that a current-carrying conductor produces a magnetic field. Several compass needles are placed in a horizontal plane near a long vertical wire, as in Figure 30.8a. When there is no

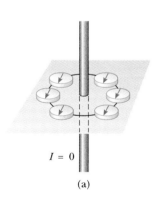

(a)

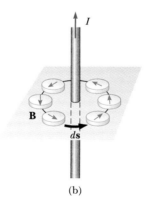

(b)

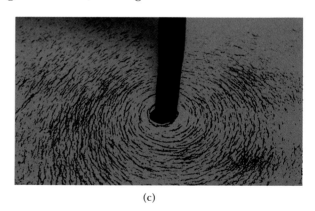

(c)

FIGURE 30.8 (a) When there is no current in the vertical wire, all compass needles point in the same direction. (b) When the wire carries a strong current, the compass needles deflect in a direction tangent to the circle, which is the direction of **B** due to the current. (c) Circular magnetic field lines surrounding a current-carrying conductor as displayed with iron filings. The photograph was taken using 30 parallel wires each carrying a current of 0.50 A. *(Henry Leap and Jim Lehman)*

André-Marie Ampère was a French mathematician, chemist, and philosopher who founded the science of electrodynamics. The unit of measure for electric current was named in his honor.

Ampère's genius, particularly in mathematics, became evident early in his life: He had mastered advanced mathematics by the age of 12. In his first publication, *Considerations on the Mathematical Theory of Games,* an early contribution to the theory of probability, he proposed the inevitability of a player losing a game of chance to a player with greater financial resources.

Ampère is credited with the discovery of electromagnetism—the relationship between electric current and magnetic fields. His work in this field was influenced by the findings of Danish physicist Hans Christian Oersted. Ampère presented a series of papers expounding the theory and basic laws of electromagnetism, which

Andre-Marie Ampère.

André-Marie Ampère

| 1 7 7 5 – 1 8 3 6 |

he called electrodynamics, to differentiate it from the study of stationary electric forces, which he called electrostatics.

The culmination of Ampère's studies came in 1827 when he published his *Mathematical Theory of Electrodynamic Phenomena Deduced Solely from Experiment,* in which he derived precise mathematical formulations of electromagnetism, notably Ampère's law.

Many stories are told of Ampère's absentmindedness, a trait he shared with Newton. In one instance, he forgot to honor an invitation to dine with the Emperor Napoleon.

Ampère's personal life was filled with tragedy. His father, a wealthy city official, was guillotined during the French Revolution, and his wife's death in 1803 was a major blow. Ampère died at the age of 61 of pneumonia. His judgment of his life is clear from the epitaph he chose for his gravestone: *Tandem felix* (Happy at last).

(Photo courtesy of AIP Niels Bohr Library)

current in the wire, all the needles point in the same direction (that of the Earth's magnetic field), as would be expected. When the wire carries a strong, steady current, the needles all deflect in a direction tangent to the circle, as in Figure 30.8b. These observations show that the direction of **B** is consistent with the right-hand rule described in Figure 30.3.

If the wire is grasped in the right hand with the thumb in the direction of the current, the fingers curl in the direction of **B**.

When the current is reversed, the needles in Figure 30.8b also reverse.

Because the compass needles point in the direction of **B**, we conclude that the lines of **B** form circles around the wire, as we discussed in the previous section. By symmetry, the magnitude of **B** is the same everywhere on a circular path centered on the wire and lying in a plane that is perpendicular to the wire. By varying the current and distance r from the wire, it is found that B is proportional to the current and inversely proportional to distance from the wire.

Now let us evaluate the product $\mathbf{B} \cdot d\mathbf{s}$ and sum these products over the closed circular path centered on the wire. Along this path, the vectors $d\mathbf{s}$ and **B** are parallel at each point (Fig. 30.8b), so that $\mathbf{B} \cdot d\mathbf{s} = B\,ds$. Furthermore, **B** is constant in magnitude on this circle and given by Equation 30.7. Therefore, the sum of the products $B\,ds$ over the closed path, which is equivalent to the line integral of

$\mathbf{B} \cdot d\mathbf{s}$, is

$$\oint \mathbf{B} \cdot d\mathbf{s} = B \oint ds = \frac{\mu_0 I}{2\pi r}(2\pi r) = \mu_0 I \qquad (30.14)$$

where $\oint ds = 2\pi r$ is the circumference of the circle.

This result was calculated for the special case of a circular path surrounding a wire. However, it holds when an arbitrary closed path is threaded by a *steady current*. This general case, known as **Ampère's law,** can be stated as follows:

The line integral of $\mathbf{B} \cdot d\mathbf{s}$ around any closed path equals $\mu_0 I$, where I is the total steady current passing through any surface bounded by the closed path.

Ampère's law

$$\oint \mathbf{B} \cdot d\mathbf{s} = \mu_0 I \qquad (30.15)$$

Ampère's law is valid only for steady currents and is useful only for calculating the magnetic field of current configurations having a high degree of symmetry.

EXAMPLE 30.4   The Magnetic Field Created by a Long, Current-Carrying Wire

A long, straight wire of radius R carries a steady current I_0 that is uniformly distributed through the cross-section of the wire (Fig. 30.9). Calculate the magnetic field a distance r from the center of the wire in the regions $r \geqslant R$ and $r < R$.

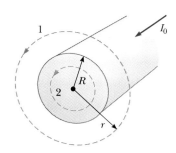

FIGURE 30.9 (Example 30.4) A long, straight wire of radius R carrying a steady current I_0 uniformly distributed across the wire. The magnetic field at any point can be calculated from Ampère's law using a circular path of radius r, concentric with the wire.

Solution In region 1, where $r \geqslant R$, let us choose for our path of integration a circle of radius r centered at the wire. From symmetry, we see that $\mathbf{B}$ must be constant in magnitude and parallel to $d\mathbf{s}$ at every point on this circle. Since the total

current passing through the plane of the circle is I_0, Ampère's law applied to the circle gives

$$\oint \mathbf{B} \cdot d\mathbf{s} = B \oint ds = B(2\pi r) = \mu_0 I_0$$

$$B = \frac{\mu_0 I_0}{2\pi r} \qquad \text{(for } r \geqslant R) \qquad (30.16)$$

which is identical in meaning to Equation 30.7.

Now consider the interior of the wire, that is, region 2, where $r < R$. Here the current I passing through the plane of the circle of radius $r < R$ is less than the total current I_0. Since the current is uniform over the cross-section of the wire, the fraction of the current enclosed by the circle of radius $r < R$ must equal the ratio of the area πr^2 enclosed by circle 2 and the cross-sectional area πR^2 of the wire[2]:

$$\frac{I}{I_0} = \frac{\pi r^2}{\pi R^2}$$

$$I = \frac{r^2}{R^2} I_0$$

---

[2] Alternatively, the current linked by path 2 must equal the product of the current density, $J = I_0 / \pi R^2$, and the area πr^2 enclosed by path 2.

Following the same procedure as for circle 1, we apply Ampère's law to circle 2:

$$\oint \mathbf{B} \cdot d\mathbf{s} = B(2\pi r) = \mu_0 I = \mu_0 \left(\frac{r^2}{R^2} I_0 \right)$$

$$B = \left(\frac{\mu_0 I_0}{2\pi R^2} \right) r \qquad \text{(for } r < R\text{)} \qquad (30.17)$$

The magnetic field strength versus r for this configuration is sketched in Figure 30.10. Note that inside the wire, $B \to 0$ as $r \to 0$. This result is similar in form to that of the electric field inside a uniformly charged rod.

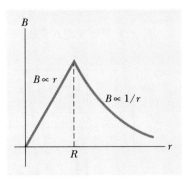

FIGURE 30.10 A sketch of the magnetic field versus r for the wire described in Example 30.4. The field is proportional to r inside the wire and varies as $1/r$ outside the wire.

EXAMPLE 30.5 The Magnetic Field Created by a Toroid

A toroid consists of N turns of wire wrapped around a ring-shaped structure as in Figure 30.11. You can think of a toroid as a solenoid bent into the shape of a doughnut. Assuming that the turns are closely spaced, calculate the magnetic field inside the toroid, a distance r from the center.

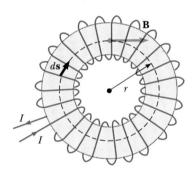

FIGURE 30.11 (Example 30.5) A toroid consists of many turns of wire wrapped around a doughnut-shaped structure (called a torus). If the coils are closely spaced, the field in the interior of the toroid is tangent to the dashed circle and varies as $1/r$, and the exterior field is zero.

Reasoning To calculate the field inside the toroid, we evaluate the line integral of $\mathbf{B} \cdot d\mathbf{s}$ over a circle of radius r. By

symmetry, we see that the magnetic field is constant in magnitude on this circle and tangent to it, so that $\mathbf{B} \cdot d\mathbf{s} = B\, ds$. Furthermore, note that the closed path threads N loops of wire, each of which carries a current I. Therefore, the right side of Equation 30.15 is $\mu_0 NI$ in this case.

Solution Ampère's law applied to the circle gives

$$\oint \mathbf{B} \cdot d\mathbf{s} = B \oint ds = B(2\pi r) = \mu_0 NI$$

$$B = \frac{\mu_0 NI}{2\pi r} \qquad (30.18)$$

This result shows that B varies as $1/r$ and hence is nonuniform within the coil. However, if r is large compared with the cross-sectional radius of the toroid, then the field is approximately uniform inside the coil.

Furthermore, for an ideal toroid, where the turns are closely spaced, the external magnitude field is zero. This can be seen by noting that the net current threaded by any circular path lying outside the toroid is zero (including the region of the "hole in the doughnut"). Therefore, from Ampère's law we find that $B = 0$ in the regions exterior to the coil. In reality, the turns of a toroid form a helix rather than circular loops. As a result, there is always a small field external to the coil.

EXAMPLE 30.6 Magnetic Field Created by an Infinite Current Sheet

An infinite sheet lying in the yz plane carries a surface current of density $\mathbf{J}_s$. The current is in the y direction, and J_s represents the current per unit length measured along the z axis. Find the magnetic field near the sheet.

Reasoning and Solution To evaluate the line integral in Ampère's law, let us take a rectangular path through the sheet as in Figure 30.12. The rectangle has dimensions ℓ and w, where the sides of length ℓ are parallel to the surface of the

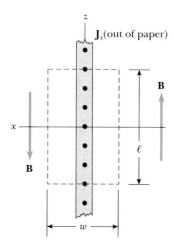

FIGURE 30.12 (Example 30.6) A top view of an infinite current sheet lying in the *yz* plane, where the current is in the *y* direction (out of the paper). This view shows the direction of **B** on both sides of the sheet.

sheet. The net current passing through the plane of the rectangle is $J_s\ell$. Hence, applying Ampère's law over the rectangle and noting that the two sides of length w do not contribute to the line integral (because the component of **B** along the direction of these paths is zero), we get

$$\oint \mathbf{B} \cdot d\mathbf{s} = \mu_0 I = \mu_0 J_s \ell$$

$$2B\ell = \mu_0 J_s \ell$$

$$B = \mu_0 \frac{J_s}{2} \qquad (30.19)$$

The result shows that *the magnetic field is independent of distance from the current sheet.* In fact, the magnetic field is uniform and is everywhere parallel to the plane of the sheet. This is reasonable since we are dealing with an infinite sheet of current. The result is analogous to the uniform electric field associated with an infinite sheet of charge. (See Example 24.8.)

EXAMPLE 30.7 The Magnetic Force on a Current Segment

Wire 1 in Figure 30.13 is oriented along the *y* axis and carries a steady current I_1. A rectangular circuit located to the right of the wire carries a current I_2. Find the magnetic force exerted on the top horizontal wire (wire 2) of the rectangular circuit.

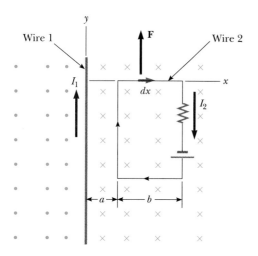

FIGURE 30.13 (Example 30.7).

Reasoning and Solution In this problem, you may be tempted to use Equation 30.13 to obtain the force exerted on a small segment of the horizontal wire. However, this result

applies only to two parallel wires, and cannot be used here. The correct approach is to consider the force on a small segment $d\mathbf{s}$ of the conductor. This force is given by $d\mathbf{F} = I\,d\mathbf{s} \times \mathbf{B}$ (Eq. 29.4), where $I = I_2$ and **B** is the magnetic field created by the current in wire 1 at the position of $d\mathbf{s}$. From Ampère's law, the field at a distance x from wire 1 is

$$\mathbf{B} = \frac{\mu_0 I_1}{2\pi x}(-\mathbf{k})$$

where the field points into the page as indicated by the unit vector notation $(-\mathbf{k})$. Because wire 2 is along the *x* axis, $d\mathbf{s} = dx\,\mathbf{i}$, and we find

$$d\mathbf{F} = \frac{\mu_0 I_1 I_2}{2\pi x}[\mathbf{i} \times (-\mathbf{k})]\,dx = \frac{\mu_0 I_1 I_2}{2\pi}\frac{dx}{x}\mathbf{j}$$

Integrating this equation over the limits $x = a$ to $x = a + b$ gives

$$\mathbf{F} = \frac{\mu_0 I_1 I_2}{2\pi} \ln x \Big]_a^{a+b} \mathbf{j} = \frac{\mu_0 I_1 I_2}{2\pi} \ln\left(1 + \frac{b}{a}\right)\mathbf{j}$$

The force points upward as indicated by the notation **j**, and as shown in Figure 30.13.

Exercise What is the force on wire 3?

Answer The force has the same magnitude as the force on wire 2, but is directed downward.

30.4 THE MAGNETIC FIELD OF A SOLENOID

A **solenoid** is a long wire wound in the form of a helix. With this configuration, a reasonably uniform magnetic field can be produced in the space surrounded by the turns of wire. When the turns are closely spaced, each can be regarded as a circular loop, and the net magnetic field is the vector sum of the fields due to all the turns.

Figure 30.14 shows the magnetic field lines of a loosely wound solenoid. Note that the field lines in the space surrounded by the coil are nearly parallel, uniformly distributed, and close together, indicating that the field in this space is uniform. The field lines between the turns tend to cancel each other. The field at exterior points, such as *P*, is weak because the field due to current elements on the upper portions tends to cancel the field due to current elements on the lower portions.

If the turns are closely spaced and the solenoid is of finite length, the field lines are as shown in Figure 30.15. In this case, the field lines diverge from one end and converge at the opposite end. An inspection of this field distribution shows a similarity with the field of a bar magnet. Hence, one end of the solenoid behaves like the north pole of a magnet while the opposite end behaves like the south pole. As the length of the solenoid increases, the field in the space enclosed by the coils becomes more and more uniform. The case of an *ideal solenoid* is approached when the turns are closely spaced and the length is long compared with the radius. In this case, the field outside the solenoid is weak compared with the field in the space enclosed by the coils and the field there is uniform over a large volume.

We can use Ampère's law to obtain an expression for the magnetic field in the space surrounded by an ideal solenoid. A longitudinal cross-section of part of our ideal solenoid (Fig. 30.16) carries a current *I*. For the ideal solenoid, **B** in the interior space (blue area) is uniform and parallel to the axis and **B** in the space

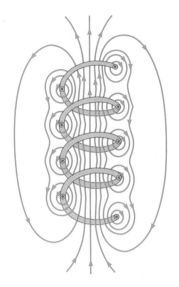

FIGURE 30.14 The magnetic field lines for a loosely wound solenoid. *(Adapted from D. Halliday and R. Resnick, Physics, New York, Wiley, 1978)*

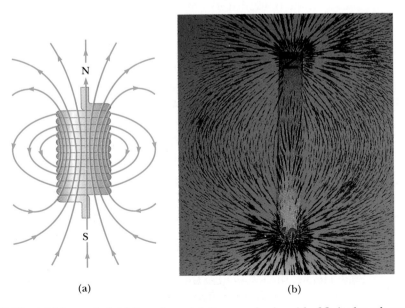

(a)   (b)

FIGURE 30.15 (a) Magnetic field lines for a tightly wound solenoid of finite length carrying a steady current. The field in the space enclosed by the solenoid is nearly uniform and strong. Note that the field lines resemble those of a bar magnet, so that the solenoid effectively has north and south poles. (b) Magnetic field pattern of a bar magnet, as displayed by small iron filings on a sheet of paper. *(Henry Leap and Jim Lehman)*

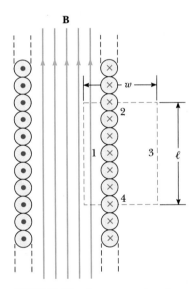

FIGURE 30.16 A cross-sectional view of a tightly wound solenoid. If the solenoid is long relative to its radius, we can assume that the magnetic field inside is uniform and the field outside is zero. Ampère's law applied to the red dashed rectangular path can then be used to calculate the field inside the solenoid.

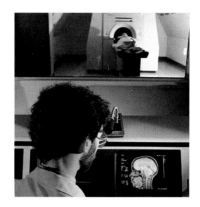

A technician studies the scan of a head. The scan was obtained using a medical diagnostic technique known as magnetic resonance imaging (MRI). This instrument makes use of strong magnetic fields produced by superconducting solenoids. *(Hank Morgan, Science Source)*

surrounding the coil (yellow area) is zero. Consider a rectangular path of length ℓ and width w as shown in Figure 30.16. We can apply Ampère's law to this path by evaluating the integral of $\mathbf{B} \cdot d\mathbf{s}$ over each side of the rectangle. The contribution along side 3 is clearly zero, because $\mathbf{B} = 0$ in this region. The contributions from sides 2 and 4 are both zero because $\mathbf{B}$ is perpendicular to $d\mathbf{s}$ along these paths. Side 1 gives a contribution $B\ell$ to the integral because $\mathbf{B}$ is uniform and parallel to $d\mathbf{s}$ along this path. Therefore, the integral over the closed rectangular path is

$$\oint \mathbf{B} \cdot d\mathbf{s} = \int_{\text{path 1}} \mathbf{B} \cdot d\mathbf{s} = B \int_{\text{path 1}} ds = B\ell$$

The right side of Ampère's law involves the total current that passes through the area bound by the path of integration. In our case, the total current through the rectangular path equals the current through each turn multiplied by the number of turns. If N is the number of turns in the length ℓ, then the total current through the rectangle equals NI. Therefore, Ampère's law applied to this path gives

$$\oint \mathbf{B} \cdot d\mathbf{s} = B\ell = \mu_0 NI$$

$$B = \mu_0 \frac{N}{\ell} I = \mu_0 n I \qquad (30.20)$$

where $n = N/\ell$ is the number of turns per unit length.

We also could obtain this result in a simpler manner by reconsidering the magnetic field of a toroid (Example 30.5). If the radius r of the toroid containing N turns is large compared with its cross-sectional radius a, then a short section of the toroid approximates a solenoid with $n = N/2\pi r$. In this limit, we see that Equation 30.18 derived for the toroid agrees with Equation 30.20.

Equation 30.20 is valid only for points near the center (that is, far from the ends) of a very long solenoid. As you might expect, the field near each end is smaller than the value given by Equation 30.20. At the very end of a long solenoid, the magnitude of the field is about one-half that of the field at the center. The field at arbitrary axial points of the solenoid is derived in Section 30.5.

*30.5 THE MAGNETIC FIELD ALONG THE AXIS OF A SOLENOID

Consider a solenoid of length ℓ and radius R containing N closely spaced turns and carrying a steady current I. Let us determine an expression for the magnetic field at an axial point P lying in the space enclosed by the solenoid, as indicated in Figure 30.17.

Perhaps the simplest way to obtain the desired result is to consider the solenoid as a distribution of current loops. The field of any one loop along the axis is given by Equation 30.9. Hence, the net field in the solenoid is the superposition of fields from all loops. The number of turns in a length dx of the solenoid is $(N/\ell) \, dx$; therefore the total current in a width dx is given by $I(N/\ell) \, dx$. Then, using Equation 30.9, we find that the field at P due to the section dx is

$$dB = \frac{\mu_0 R^2}{2(x^2 + R^2)^{3/2}} I \left(\frac{N}{\ell} \right) dx \qquad (30.21)$$

FIGURE 30.17 The geometry for calculating the magnetic field at an axial point P lying in the space enclosed by a tightly wound solenoid.

This expression contains the variable x, which can be expressed in terms of the variable ϕ, defined in Figure 30.17. That is, $x = R \tan \phi$, so that we have $dx = R \sec^2 \phi \, d\phi$. Substituting these expressions into Equation 30.21 and integrating from ϕ_1 to ϕ_2, we get

$$B = \frac{\mu_0 NI}{2\ell} \int_{\phi_1}^{\phi_2} \cos \phi \, d\phi = \frac{\mu_0 NI}{2\ell} (\sin \phi_2 - \sin \phi_1) \qquad (30.22)$$

If P is at the midpoint of the solenoid and if we assume that the solenoid is long compared with R, then $\phi_2 \approx 90°$ and $\phi_1 \approx -90°$; therefore,

$$B \approx \frac{\mu_0 NI}{2\ell} (1 + 1) = \frac{\mu_0 NI}{\ell} = \mu_0 nI \qquad \text{(at the center)}$$

which is in agreement with our previous result, Equation 30.20.

If P is a point at the end of a long solenoid (say, the bottom), then $\phi_1 \approx 0°$, $\phi_2 \approx 90°$, and

$$B \approx \frac{\mu_0 NI}{2\ell} (1 + 0) = \tfrac{1}{2}\mu_0 nI \qquad \text{(at the ends)}$$

This shows that the field at each end of a solenoid approaches one-half the value at the solenoid's center as the length ℓ approaches infinity.

A sketch of the field at axial points versus x for a solenoid is shown in Figure 30.18. If the length ℓ is large compared with R, the axial field is uniform over most of the solenoid and the curve is flat except at points near the ends. If ℓ is comparable to R, then the field has a value somewhat less than $\mu_0 nI$ at the middle and is uniform only over a small region.

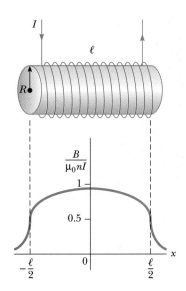

FIGURE 30.18   A sketch of the magnetic field along the axis versus x for a tightly wound solenoid. Note that the magnitude of the field at the ends is about one-half the value of the center.

30.6   MAGNETIC FLUX

The flux associated with a magnetic field is defined in a manner similar to that used to define the electric flux. Consider an element of area dA on an arbitrarily shaped surface, as in Figure 30.19. If the magnetic field at this element is $\mathbf{B}$, then the magnetic flux through the element is $\mathbf{B} \cdot d\mathbf{A}$, where $d\mathbf{A}$ is a vector perpendicular to the surface whose magnitude equals the area dA. Hence, the total magnetic flux Φ_B through the surface is

$$\Phi_B = \int \mathbf{B} \cdot d\mathbf{A} \qquad (30.23)$$

Consider the special case of a plane of area A and a uniform field $\mathbf{B}$ that makes an angle θ with the vector $d\mathbf{A}$. The magnetic flux through the plane in this case is

$$\Phi_B = BA \cos \theta \qquad (30.24)$$

If the magnetic field lies in the plane as in Figure 30.20a, then $\theta = 90°$ and the flux is zero. If the field is perpendicular to the plane as in Figure 30.20b, then $\theta = 0°$ and the flux is BA (the maximum value).

The unit of flux is the weber (Wb), where 1 Wb = 1 T·m².

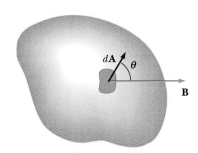

FIGURE 30.19   The magnetic flux through an area element dA is $\mathbf{B} \cdot d\mathbf{A} = BdA \cos \theta$. Note that $d\mathbf{A}$ is perpendicular to the surface.

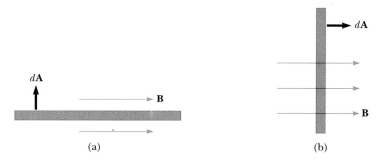

FIGURE 30.20   Edge view of a plane lying in a magnetic field. (a) The flux through the plane is zero when the magnetic field is parallel to the surface of the plane. (b) The flux through the plane is a maximum when the magnetic field is perpendicular to the plane.

EXAMPLE 30.8   Magnetic Flux Through a Rectangular Loop

A rectangular loop of width a and length b is located a distance c from a long wire carrying a current I (Fig. 30.21). The wire is parallel to the long side of the loop. Find the total magnetic flux through the loop.

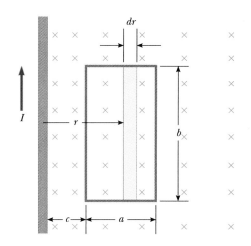

FIGURE 30.21   (Example 30.8) The magnetic field due to the wire carrying a current I is not uniform over the rectangular loop.

Reasoning   From Ampère's law, we know that the strength of the magnetic field created by the long current-carrying wire at a distance r from the wire is

$$B = \frac{\mu_0 I}{2\pi r}$$

That is, the field varies over the loop and is directed into the page as shown in Figure 30.21. Since **B** is parallel to $d\mathbf{A}$, we can express the magnetic flux through an area element dA as

$$\Phi_B = \int B \, dA = \int \frac{\mu_0 I}{2\pi r} \, dA$$

Note that because **B** is not uniform but rather depends on r, it cannot be removed from the integral.

Solution   In order to integrate, we first express the area element (the blue region in Fig. 30.21) as $dA = b \, dr$. Snce r is the only variable that now appears in the integral, the expression for Φ_B becomes

$$\Phi_B = \frac{\mu_0 I}{2\pi} b \int_c^{a+c} \frac{dr}{r} = \frac{\mu_0 Ib}{2\pi} \ln r \Big]_c^{a+c}$$

$$= \frac{\mu_0 Ib}{2\pi} \ln\left(\frac{a+c}{c}\right)$$

30.7   GAUSS'S LAW IN MAGNETISM

In Chapter 24 we found that the flux of the electric field through a closed surface surrounding a net charge is proportional to that charge (Gauss's law). In other words, the number of electric field lines leaving the surface depends only on the net charge within it. This property is based in part on the fact that electric field lines originate on electric charges.

   The situation is quite different for magnetic fields, which are continuous and form closed loops. Magnetic field lines created by currents do not begin or end at any point. The magnetic field lines of the bar magnet in Figure 30.22 illustrate this point. Note that for any closed surface, the number of lines entering that surface equals the number leaving that surface, and so the net magnetic flux is zero. This is in contrast to the case of a surface surrounding one charge of an electric dipole (Fig. 30.23), where the net electric flux is not zero.

> **Gauss's law for magnetism** states that the net magnetic flux through any closed surface is always zero:
>
> $$\oint \mathbf{B} \cdot d\mathbf{A} = 0 \tag{30.25}$$

This statement is based on the experimental fact that *isolated magnetic poles (or monopoles) have never been detected and perhaps do not even exist.*

30.8   DISPLACEMENT CURRENT AND THE GENERALIZED AMPÈRE'S LAW

We have seen that charges in motion, or currents, produce magnetic fields. When a current-carrying conductor has high symmetry, we can calculate the magnetic field using Ampère's law, given by Equation 30.15:

$$\oint \mathbf{B} \cdot d\mathbf{s} = \mu_0 I$$

where the line integral is over *any closed path through which the conduction current passes,* and the conduction current is defined by $I = dQ/dt$. (In this section, we use

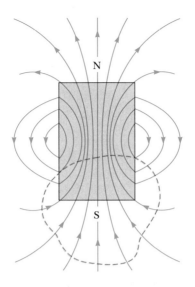

FIGURE 30.22   The magnetic field lines of a bar magnet form closed loops. Note that the net flux through the closed surface surrounding one of the poles (or any other closed surface) is zero.

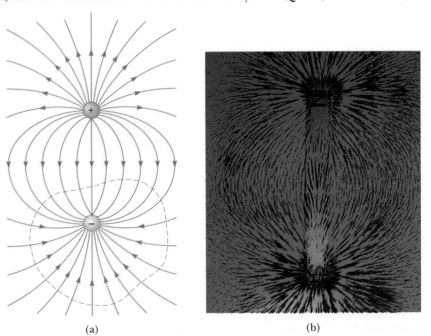

(a)   (b)

FIGURE 30.23   (a) The electric field lines of an electric dipole begin on the positive charge and terminate on the negative charge. The electric flux through a closed surface surrounding one of the charges is not zero. (b) Magnetic field pattern of a bar magnet.   *(Henry Leap and Jim Lehman)*

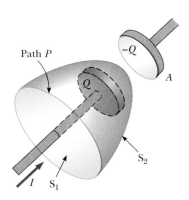

FIGURE 30.24   The surfaces S_1 and S_2 are bounded by the same path P. The conduction current in the wire passes only through S_1. This leads to a contradiction in Ampère's law that is resolved only if one postulates a displacement current through S_2.

the term *conduction current* to refer to the current carried by the wire.) We now show that *Ampère's law in this form is valid only if the conduction current is constant in time.* Maxwell recognized this limitation and modified Ampère's law to include all possible situations.

We can understand this problem by considering a capacitor being charged as in Figure 30.24. When the conduction current changes with time, the charge on the plate changes, but *no conduction current passes between the plates.* Now consider the two surfaces S_1 and S_2 in Figure 30.24 bounded by the same path P. Ampère's law says that the line integral of $\mathbf{B} \cdot d\mathbf{s}$ around this path must equal $\mu_0 I$, where I is the total current through any surface bounded by the path P.

When the path P is considered as bounding S_1, the result of the integral is $\mu_0 I$ because the current passes through S_1. When the path bounds S_2, however, the result is zero since no current passes through S_2. Thus, we have a contradictory situation that arises from the discontinuity of the current! Maxwell solved this problem by postulating an additional term on the right side of Equation 30.15, called the **displacement current,** I_d, defined as

$$I_d \equiv \epsilon_0 \frac{d\Phi_E}{dt} \tag{30.26}$$

Recall that Φ_E is the flux of the electric field, defined as $\Phi_E = \int \mathbf{E} \cdot d\mathbf{A}$.

As the capacitor is being charged (or discharged), the changing electric field between the plates may be thought of as a sort of current that bridges the discontinuity in the conduction current in the wire. When the expression for the displacement current given by Equation 30.26 is added to the right side of Ampère's law, the difficulty represented by Figure 30.24 is resolved. No matter what surface bounded by the path P is chosen, some combination of conduction and displacement current will pass through it. With this new term I_d, we can express the generalized form of Ampère's law (sometimes called the **Ampère-Maxwell law**) as[3]

Ampère-Maxwell law

$$\oint \mathbf{B} \cdot d\mathbf{s} = \mu_0(I + I_d) = \mu_0 I + \mu_0 \epsilon_0 \frac{d\Phi_E}{dt} \tag{30.27}$$

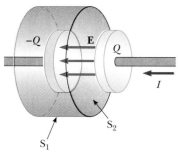

FIGURE 30.25   The conduction current $I = 0dQ/dt$ passes through S_1. The displacement current $I_d = \epsilon_0 d\Phi_E/dt$ passes through S_2. The two currents must be equal for continuity. In general, the total current through any surface bounded by some path is $I + I_d$.

The meaning of this expression can be understood by referring to Figure 30.25. The electric flux through S_2 is $\Phi_E = \int \mathbf{E} \cdot d\mathbf{A} = EA$, where A is the area of the capacitor plates and E is the uniform electric field strength between the plates. If Q is the charge on the plates at any instant, then $E = Q/\epsilon_0 A$ (Section 26.2). Therefore, the electric flux through S_2 is simply

$$\Phi_E = EA = \frac{Q}{\epsilon_0}$$

Hence, the displacement current I_d through S_2 is

$$I_d = \epsilon_0 \frac{d\Phi_E}{dt} = \frac{dQ}{dt} \tag{30.28}$$

That is, the displacement current is precisely equal to the conduction current I through S_1!

---

[3] Strictly speaking, this expression is valid only in a vacuum. If a magnetic material is present, a magnetizing current I_m must also be included on the right side of Equation 30.27 to make Ampère's law fully general.

The central point of this formalism is the fact that

magnetic fields are produced both by conduction currents and by changing electric fields.

EXAMPLE 30.9 Displacement Current in a Capacitor

A sinusoidal voltage is applied directly across an 8.00-μF capacitor. The frequency of the source is 3.00 kHz, and the voltage amplitude is 30.0 V. Find the displacement current between the plates of the capacitor.

Solution The angular frequency of the source is given by $\omega = 2\pi f = 2\pi(3.00 \times 10^3 \text{ Hz}) = 6\pi \times 10^3 \text{ s}^{-1}$. Hence, the voltage across the capacitor in terms of t is

$$V = V_{max} \sin \omega t = (30.0 \text{ V}) \sin(6\pi \times 10^3 t)$$

We can use Equation 30.28 and the fact that the charge on the capacitor is $Q = CV$ to find the displacement current:

$$I_d = \frac{dQ}{dt} = \frac{d}{dt}(CV) = C\frac{dV}{dt}$$

$$= (8.00 \times 10^{-6})\frac{d}{dt}[30.0 \sin(6\pi \times 10^3 t)]$$

$$= (4.52 \text{ A}) \cos(6\pi \times 10^3 t)$$

Hence, the displacement current varies sinusoidally with time and has a maximum value of 4.52 A.

---

*30.9 MAGNETISM IN MATTER

The magnetic field produced by a current in a coil gives us a hint as to what might cause certain materials to exhibit strong magnetic properties. Earlier we found that a coil like that shown in Figure 30.15 has a north and a south pole. In general, any current loop has a magnetic field and a corresponding magnetic moment. Similarly, the magnetic moments in a magnetized substance may be described as arising from internal currents on the atomic level. For electrons moving about the nucleus, this is consistent with the Bohr model (after modifying quantum numbers). There is also an intrinsic magnetic moment for electrons, protons, neutrons, and other particles that can only be roughly modeled as arising from rotating charges.

We begin with a brief discussion of the magnetic moments due to electrons. The mutual forces between these magnetic dipole moments and their interaction with an external magnetic field are of fundamental importance in understanding the behavior of magnetic materials. We shall describe three categories of materials as paramagnetic, ferromagnetic, and diamagnetic. **Paramagnetic** and **ferromagnetic** materials are those that have atoms with permanent magnetic dipole moments. **Diamagnetic** materials are those whose atoms have no permanent magnetic dipole moments.

The Magnetic Moments of Atoms

It is instructive to begin our discussion with a classical model of the atom in which electrons move in circular orbits around the much more massive nucleus. In this model, an orbiting electron constitutes a tiny current loop (because it is a moving charge) and the atomic magnetic moment is associated with this orbital motion. Although this model has many deficiencies, its predictions are in good agreement with the correct theory from quantum physics.

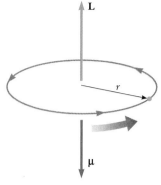

FIGURE 30.26 An electron moving in a circular orbit of radius r has an angular momentum L in one direction and a magnetic moment $\boldsymbol{\mu}$ in the opposite direction.

Orbital magnetic moment

Angular momentum is quantized

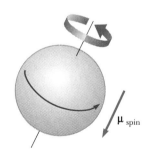

FIGURE 30.27 Classical model of a spinning electron. This model gives an incorrect magnitude, incorrect quantum numbers, and too many degrees of freedom.

Spin angular momentum

Consider an electron moving with constant speed v in a circular orbit of radius r about the nucleus, as in Figure 30.26. Because the electron travels a distance of $2\pi r$ (the circumference of the circle) in a time T, where T is the time for one revolution, its orbital speed is $v = 2\pi r / T$. The effective current associated with this orbiting electron equals its charge divided by the time for one revolution. Using $T = 2\pi / \omega$ and $\omega = v/r$, we have

$$I = \frac{e}{T} = \frac{e\omega}{2\pi} = \frac{ev}{2\pi r}$$

The magnetic moment associated with this effective current loop is $\mu = IA$, where $A = \pi r^2$ is the area of the orbit. Therefore,

$$\mu = IA = \left(\frac{ev}{2\pi r}\right)\pi r^2 = \tfrac{1}{2}evr \tag{30.29}$$

Since the magnitude of the orbital angular momentum of the electron is $L = mvr$, the magnetic moment can be written as

$$\mu = \left(\frac{e}{2m}\right)L \tag{30.30}$$

This result says that *the magnetic moment of the electron is proportional to its orbital angular momentum.* Note that because the electron is negatively charged, the vectors μ and L point in opposite directions. Both vectors are perpendicular to the plane of the orbit, as indicated in Figure 30.26.

A fundamental outcome of quantum physics is that orbital angular momentum is quantized, and always some integer multiple of $\hbar = h/2\pi = 1.06 \times 10^{-34}\,\mathrm{J \cdot s}$, where h is Planck's constant. That is

$$L = 0,\ \hbar,\ 2\hbar,\ 3\hbar,\ \ldots$$

Hence, the smallest nonzero value of the magnetic moment is

$$\mu = \frac{e}{2m}\hbar \tag{30.31}$$

Since all substances contain electrons, you may wonder why all substances are not magnetic. The main reason is that in most substances, the magnetic moment of one electron in an atom is canceled by the magnetic moment of another electron in the atom orbiting in the opposite direction. The net result is that, for most materials, *the magnetic effect produced by the orbital motion of the electrons is either zero or very small.*

So far we considered only the contribution an orbiting electron makes to the magnetic moment of an atom. However, an electron has another intrinsic property, called *spin*, that also contributes to the magnetic moment. In this regard, the electron can be viewed as a charged sphere spinning about its axis as it orbits the nucleus, as in Figure 30.27, but this classical description should not be taken literally. The property of spin arises from relativistic dynamics, which may be incorporated into quantum mechanics. The magnitude of this so-called spin magnetic moment is of the same order of magnitude as the magnetic moment due to the first effect current loop, the orbital motion. The magnitude of the spin angular momentum predicted by quantum theory is

$$S = \frac{\hbar}{2} = 5.2729 \times 10^{-35}\,\mathrm{J \cdot s}$$

The intrinsic magnetic moment associated with the spin of an electron has the value

$$\mu_B = \frac{e}{2m}\hbar = 9.27 \times 10^{-24} \, \text{J/T} \qquad (30.32)$$

Bohr magneton

which is called the **Bohr magneton.**

In atoms or ions containing many electrons, the electrons usually pair up with their spins opposite each other, a situation that results in a cancellation of the spin magnetic moments. However, atoms with an odd number of electrons must have at least one "unpaired" electron and a corresponding spin magnetic moment. The total magnetic moment of an atom is the vector sum of the orbital and spin magnetic moments, and a few examples are given in Table 30.1. Note that helium and neon have zero moments because their individual moments cancel.

The nucleus of an atom also has a magnetic moment associated with its constituent protons and neutrons. However, the magnetic moment of a proton or neutron is small compared with the magnetic moment of an electron and can usually be neglected. This can be understood by inspecting Equation 30.32. Since the masses of the proton and neutron are much greater than that of the electron, their magnetic moments are smaller than that of the electron by a factor of approximately 10^3.

TABLE 30.1	Magnetic Moments of Some Atoms and Ions
Atom (or Ion)	**Magnetic Moment (10^{-24} J/T)**
H	9.27
He	0
Ne	0
Ce^{3+}	19.8
Yb^{3+}	37.1

Magnetization and Magnetic Field Strength

The magnetic state of a substance is described by a quantity called the **magnetization vector, M.** *The magnitude of the magnetization vector is equal to the magnetic moment per unit volume of the substance.* As you might expect, the total magnetic field in a substance depends on both the applied (external) field and the magnetization of the substance.

Magnetization

Consider a region where there exists a magnetic field $\mathbf{B}_0$ produced by a current-carrying conductor. If we now fill that region with a magnetic substance, the total magnetic field $\mathbf{B}$ in that region is $\mathbf{B} = \mathbf{B}_0 + \mathbf{B}_m$ where $\mathbf{B}_m$ is the field produced by the magnetic substance. This contribution can be expressed in terms of the magnetization vector as $\mathbf{B}_m = \mu_0\mathbf{M}$; hence, the total magnetic field in the region becomes

$$\mathbf{B} = \mathbf{B}_0 + \mu_0\mathbf{M} \qquad (30.33)$$

It is convenient to introduce a field quantity $\mathbf{H}$, called the **magnetic field strength.** This vector quantity is defined by the relationship $\mathbf{H} = (\mathbf{B}/\mu_0) - \mathbf{M}$, or

Magnetic field strength

$$\mathbf{B} = \mu_0(\mathbf{H} + \mathbf{M}) \qquad (30.34)$$

In SI units, the dimensions of both $\mathbf{H}$ and $\mathbf{M}$ are amperes per meter.

To better understand these expressions, consider the region inside the space enclosed by a toroid that carries a current I. (We call this space the *core* of the toroid.) If this space is a vacuum, then $\mathbf{M} = 0$ and $\mathbf{B} = \mathbf{B}_0 = \mu_0\mathbf{H}$. Since $B_0 = \mu_0 nI$ in the core, where n is the number of turns per unit length of the toroid, then $H = B_0/\mu_0 = \mu_0 nI/\mu_0$ or

$$H = nI \qquad (30.35)$$

That is, the magnetic field strength in the core of the toroid is due to the current in its windings.

If the toroid core is now filled with some substance and the current I is kept constant, then $\mathbf{H}$ inside the substance remains unchanged and has magnitude nI.

This is because the magnetic field strength H is due solely to the current in the toroid. The total field **B**, however, changes when the substance is introduced. From Equation 30.34, we see that part of **B** arises from the term μ_0**H** associated with the current in the toroid; the second contribution to **B** is the term μ_0**M** due to the magnetization of the substance filling the core.

Classification of Magnetic Substances

For a large class of substances, specifically paramagnetic and diamagnetic substances, the magnetization vector **M** is proportional to the magnetic field strength **H**. In these substances, we can write

$$\mathbf{M} = \chi \mathbf{H} \tag{30.36}$$

Magnetic susceptibility

where χ (Greek letter chi) is a dimensionless factor called the **magnetic susceptibility**. If the sample is paramagnetic, χ is positive, in which case **M** is in the same direction as **H**. If the substance is diamagnetic, χ is negative, and **M** is opposite **H**. It is important to note that this linear relationship between **M** and **H** does not apply to ferromagnetic substances. The susceptibilities of some substances are given in Table 30.2. Substituting Equation 30.36 for **M** into Equation 30.34 gives

$$\mathbf{B} = \mu_0(\mathbf{H} + \mathbf{M}) = \mu_0(\mathbf{H} + \chi\mathbf{H}) = \mu_0(1 + \chi)\mathbf{H}$$

or

$$\mathbf{B} = \mu_m \mathbf{H} \tag{30.37}$$

where the constant μ_m is called the **magnetic permeability** of the substance and has the value

Magnetic permeability

$$\mu_m = \mu_0(1 + \chi) \tag{30.38}$$

Substances may also be classified in terms of how their magnetic permeability μ_m compares with μ_0 (the permeability of free space) as follows:

$$\text{Paramagnetic} \qquad \mu_m > \mu_0$$

$$\text{Diamagnetic} \qquad \mu_m < \mu_0$$

$$\text{Ferromagnetic} \qquad \mu_m \gg \mu_0$$

Since χ is very small for paramagnetic and diamagnetic substances (Table 30.2), μ_m is nearly equal to μ_0 in these cases. For ferromagnetic substances, however, μ_m

TABLE 30.2   Magnetic Susceptibilities of Some Paramagnetic and Diamagnetic Substances at 300 K

Paramagnetic Substance	χ	Diamagnetic Substance	χ
Aluminum	2.3×10^{-5}	Bismuth	-1.66×10^{-5}
Calcium	1.9×10^{-5}	Copper	-9.8×10^{-6}
Chromium	2.7×10^{-4}	Diamond	-2.2×10^{-5}
Lithium	2.1×10^{-5}	Gold	-3.6×10^{-5}
Magnesium	1.2×10^{-5}	Lead	-1.7×10^{-5}
Niobium	2.6×10^{-4}	Mercury	-2.9×10^{-5}
Oxygen (STP)	2.1×10^{-6}	Nitrogen (STP)	-5.0×10^{-9}
Platinum	2.9×10^{-4}	Silver	-2.6×10^{-5}
Tungsten	6.8×10^{-5}	Silicon	-4.2×10^{-6}

is typically several thousand times larger than μ_0. Although Equation 30.37 provides a simple relationship between **B** and **H**, it must be interpreted with care when dealing with ferromagnetic substances. As mentioned earlier, **M** is not a linear function of **H** for ferromagnetic substances. This is because the value of μ_m *is not a characteristic of the substance,* but rather depends on the previous state and treatment of the sample.

EXAMPLE 30.10   An Iron-Filled Toroid

A toroid wound with 60.0 turns/m of wire carries 5.00 A. The core is iron, which has a magnetic permeability of $5000\mu_0$ under the given conditions. Find H and B inside the iron.

Solution   Using Equations 30.35 and 30.37, we get

$$H = nI = \left(60.0\,\frac{\text{turns}}{\text{m}}\right)(5.00\text{ A}) = \boxed{300\,\frac{\text{A}\cdot\text{turns}}{\text{m}}}$$

$$B = \mu_m H = 5000\,\mu_0 H$$

$$= 5000\left(4\pi\times10^{-7}\,\frac{\text{Wb}}{\text{A}\cdot\text{m}}\right)\left(300\,\frac{\text{A}\cdot\text{turns}}{\text{m}}\right) = \boxed{1.88\text{ T}}$$

This value of B is 5000 times larger than the value in the absence of iron!

Exercise   Determine the magnitude and direction of the magnetization inside the iron core.

Answer $M = 1.5\times10^6$ A/m; **M** is in the direction of **H**.

Ferromagnetism

Certain crystalline substances, whose atomic constituents have permanent magnetic dipole moments, exhibit strong magnetic effects called **ferromagnetism**. Examples of ferromagnetic substances include iron, cobalt, nickel, gadolinium, and dysprosium. Such substances contain atomic magnetic moments that tend to align parallel to each other even in a weak external magnetic field. Once the moments are aligned, the substance remains magnetized after the external field is removed. This permanent alignment is due to a strong coupling between neighboring moments, which can be understood only in quantum mechanical terms.

All ferromagnetic materials contain microscopic regions called **domains,** within which all magnetic moments are aligned. These domains have volumes of about 10^{-12} to 10^{-8} m^3 and contain 10^{17} to 10^{21} atoms. The boundaries between the various domains having different orientations are called **domain walls.** In an unmagnetized sample, the domains are randomly oriented so that the net magnetic moment is zero as shown in Figure 30.28a. When the sample is placed in an external magnetic field, the magnetic moments of some domains may tend to align with the field, which results in a magnetized sample, as in Figure 30.28b. Observations show that domains initially oriented along the external field will grow in size at the expense of the less favorably oriented domains. When the external field is removed, the sample may retain a net magnetization in the direction of the original field. At ordinary temperatures, thermal agitation is not sufficiently high to disrupt this preferred orientation of magnetic moments.

A typical experimental arrangement used to measure the magnetic properties of a ferromagnetic material consists of a toroid-shaped sample wound with N turns of wire, as in Figure 30.29. This configuration is sometimes referred to as the **Rowland ring.** A secondary coil connected to a galvanometer is used to measure the magnetic flux. The magnetic field **B** within the core of the toroid is measured by increasing the current in the toroid coil from zero to I. As the current changes, the magnetic flux through the secondary coil changes by BA, where A is the cross-sectional area of the toroid. Because of this changing flux, an emf is induced in the secondary coil that is proportional to the rate of change in magnetic flux. If the

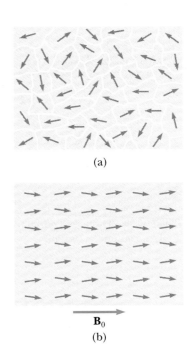

(a)

$\mathbf{B}_0$

(b)

FIGURE 30.28   (a) Random orientation of atomic magnetic dipoles in an unmagnetized substance. (b) When an external field $\mathbf{B}_{ext}$ is applied, the atomic magnetic dipoles tend to align with the field, giving the sample a net magnetization **M**.

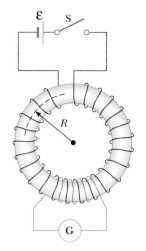

FIGURE 30.29 A toroidal winding arrangement used to measure the magnetic properties of a substance. The material under study fills the core of the toroid, and the circuit containing the galvanometer measures the magnetic flux.

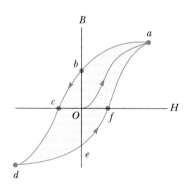

FIGURE 30.30 Hysteresis curve for a ferromagnetic material.

galvanometer in the secondary circuit is properly calibrated, a value for **B** corresponding to any value of the current in the toroid can be obtained. The magnetic field **B** is measured first in the empty coil and then with the same coil filled with the magnetic substance. The magnetic properties of the substance are then obtained from a comparison of the two measurements.

Now consider a toroid whose core consists of unmagnetized iron. If the current in the windings is increased from zero to some value I, the field intensity H increases linearly with I according to the expression $H = nI$. Furthermore, the total field B also increases with increasing current as shown in Figure 30.30. At point O, the domains are randomly oriented, corresponding to $B_m = 0$. As the external field increases, the domains become more aligned until all are nearly aligned at point a. At this point, the iron core is approaching saturation. (The condition of saturation corresponds to the case where all domains are aligned in the same direction.) Next, suppose the current is reduced to zero, thereby eliminating the external field. The B versus H curve, called a **magnetization curve,** now follows the path ab shown in Figure 30.30. Note that at point b, the field **B** is not zero, although the external field is $B_0 = 0$. This is explained by the fact that the iron core is now magnetized due to the alignment of a large number of domains (that is, $B = B_m$). At this point, the iron is said to have a remanent magnetization. If the external field is reversed in direction and increased in strength by reversing the current, the domains reorient until the sample is again unmagnetized at point c, where $\mathbf{B} = 0$. A further increase in the reverse current causes the iron to be magnetized in the opposite direction, approaching saturation at point d. A similar sequence of events occurs as the current is reduced to zero and then increased in the original (positive) direction. In this case, the magnetization curve follows the path def. If the current is increased sufficiently, the magnetization curve returns to point a, where the sample again has its maximum magnetization.

The effect just described, called **magnetic hysteresis,** shows that the magnetization of a ferromagnetic substance depends on the history of the substance as well as the strength of the applied field. (The word hysteresis literally means to "lag behind.") It is often said that a ferromagnetic substance has a "memory" since it remains magnetized after the external field is removed. The closed loop in Figure 30.30 is referred to as a hysteresis loop. Its shape and size depend on the properties of the ferromagnetic substance and on the strength of the maximum applied field. The hysteresis loop for "hard" ferromagnetic materials (used in permanent magnets) is characteristically wide as in Figure 30.31a, corresponding to a large remanent magnetization. Such materials cannot be easily demagnetized by an external field. This is in contrast to "soft" ferromagnetic materials, such as iron, that have a

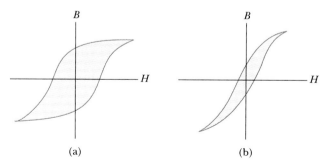

FIGURE 30.31 Hysteresis curves for (a) a hard ferromagnetic material and (b) a soft ferromagnetic material.

very narrow hysteresis loop and a small remanent magnetization (Fig. 30.31b). Such materials are easily magnetized and demagnetized. An ideal soft ferromagnet would exhibit no hysteresis and, hence, would have no remanent magnetization. A ferromagnetic substance can be demagnetized by carrying the substance through successive hysteresis loops, gradually decreasing the applied field as in Figure 30.32.

The magnetization curve is useful for another reason. *The area enclosed by the magnetization curve represents the work required to take the material through the hysteresis cycle.* The energy acquired by the sample in the magnetization process originates from the source of the external field, that is, the emf in the circuit of the toroidal coil. When the magnetization cycle is repeated, dissipative processes within the material due to realignment of the domains result in a transformation of magnetic energy into internal thermal energy, which raises the temperature of the substance. For this reason, devices subjected to alternating fields (such as transformers) use cores made of soft ferromagnetic substances, which have narrow hysteresis loops and a correspondingly small energy loss per cycle.

Paramagnetism

Paramagnetic substances have a positive but small susceptibility ($0 < \chi \ll 1$), which is due to the presence of atoms (or ions) with permanent magnetic dipole moments. These dipoles interact only weakly with each other and are randomly oriented in the absence of an external magnetic field. When the substance is placed in an external magnetic field, its atomic dipoles tend to line up with the field. However, this alignment process must compete with the effects of thermal motion, which tends to randomize the dipole orientations.

Experimentally, it is found that the magnetization of a paramagnetic substance is proportional to the applied magnetic field and inversely proportional to the absolute temperature under a wide range of conditions. That is,

$$M = C\frac{B}{T} \tag{30.39}$$

This is known as **Curie's law** after its discoverer Pierre Curie (1859–1906), and the constant C is called **Curie's constant**. This shows that the magnetization increases with increasing applied field and with decreasing temperature. When $B = 0$, the magnetization is zero, corresponding to a random orientation of dipoles. At very high fields or very low temperatures, the magnetization approaches its maximum, or saturation, value corresponding to a complete alignment of its dipoles and Equation 30.39 is no longer valid.

It is interesting to note when the temperature of a ferromagnetic substance reaches or exceeds a critical temperature, called the **Curie temperature,** the substance loses its spontaneous magnetization and becomes paramagnetic (see Fig. 30.33). Below the Curie temperature, the magnetic moments are aligned and the substance is ferromagnetic. Above the Curie temperature, the thermal energy is large enough to cause a random orientation of dipoles, hence the substance becomes paramagnetic. For example, the Curie temperature for iron is 1043 K. A list of Curie temperatures for several ferromagnetic substances is given in Table 30.3.

Diamagnetism

A diamagnetic substance is one whose atoms have no permanent magnetic dipole moment. When an external magnetic field is applied to a diamagnetic substance such as bismuth or silver, a weak magnetic dipole moment is induced in the direc-

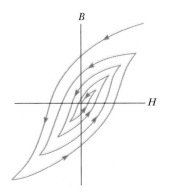

FIGURE 30.32 Demagnetizing a ferromagnetic material by carrying it through successive hysteresis loops.

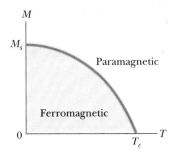

FIGURE 30.33 Plot of the magnetization versus absolute temperature for a ferromagnetic substance. The magnetic moments are aligned (ordered) below the Curie temperature T_c, where the substance is ferromagnetic. The substance becomes paramagnetic (disordered) above T_c.

TABLE 30.3	Curie Temperature for Several Ferromagnetic Substances
Substance	T_c **(K)**
Iron	1043
Cobalt	1394
Nickel	631
Gadolinium	317
Fe_2O_3	893

A small permanent magnet floats freely above a ceramic disk of the superconductor $YBa_2Cu_3O_7$ cooled by liquid nitrogen at 77 K. The superconductor has zero electric resistance at temperatures below 92 K and expels any applied magnetic field. *(D.O.E./Science Source/Photo Researchers)*

tion opposite the applied field. Although the effect of diamagnetism is present in all matter, it is weak compared to paramagnetism or ferromagnetism.

We can obtain some understanding of diamagnetism by considering two electrons of an atom orbiting the nucleus in opposite directions but with the same speed. The electrons remain in these circular orbits because of the attractive electrostatic force (the centripetal force) of the positively charged nucleus. Because the magnetic moments of the two electrons are equal in magnitude and opposite in direction, they cancel each other and the dipole moment of the atom is zero. When an external magnetic field is applied, the electrons experience an additional force $q\mathbf{v} \times \mathbf{B}$. This added force modifies the centripetal force so as to increase the orbital speed of the electron whose magnetic moment is antiparallel to the field and decreases the speed of the electron whose magnetic moment is parallel to the field. As a result, the magnetic moments of the electrons no longer cancel, and the substance acquires a net dipole moment that opposes the applied field.

As you recall from Chapter 27, superconductors are substances whose dc resistance is zero below some critical temperature characteristic of the substance. Certain types of superconductors also exhibit perfect diamagnetism in the superconducting state. As a result, an applied magnetic field is expelled by the superconductor so that the field is zero in its interior. This phenomenon of flux expulsion is known as the **Meissner effect.** If a permanent magnet is brought near a superconductor, the two substances will repel each other. This is illustrated in the photograph, which shows a small permanent magnet levitated above a superconductor maintained at 77 K. A more detailed description of the unusual properties of superconductors is presented in Chapter 44 of the extended version of this text.

EXAMPLE 30.11   Saturation Magnetization

Estimate the maximum magnetization in a long cylinder of iron, assuming there is one unpaired electron spin per atom.

Solution   The maximum magnetization, called the saturation magnetization, is obtained when all the magnetic moments in the sample are aligned. If the sample contains n atoms per unit volume, then the saturation magnetization M_s has the value

$$M_s = n\mu$$

where μ is the magnetic moment per atom. Since the molecular weight of iron is 55 g/mol and its density is 7.9 g/cm^3,

the value of n is 8.5×10^{28} atoms/m^3. Assuming each atom contributes one Bohr magneton (due to one unpaired spin) to the magnetic moment, we get

$$M_s = \left(8.5 \times 10^{28} \, \frac{\text{atoms}}{\text{m}^3}\right)\left(9.27 \times 10^{-24} \, \frac{\text{A} \cdot \text{m}^2}{\text{atom}}\right)$$

$$= 7.9 \times 10^5 \, \text{A/m}$$

This is about one-half the experimentally determined saturation magnetization for annealed iron, which indicates that there are actually two unpaired electron spins per atom.

---

*30.10   MAGNETIC FIELD OF THE EARTH

When we speak of a small bar magnet's having a north and a south pole, we should more properly say that it has a "north-seeking" and a "south-seeking" pole. By this we mean that if such a magnet is used as a compass, one end will seek, or point to, the north geographic pole of the Earth. Thus, we conclude that *a north magnetic pole is located near the south geographic pole, and a south magnetic pole is located near the north geographic pole.* In fact, the configuration of the Earth's magnetic field, pictured in

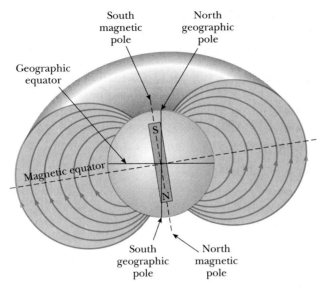

FIGURE 30.34   The Earth's magnetic field lines. Note that a south magnetic pole is at the north geographic pole and a north magnetic pole is at the south geographic pole.

Figure 30.34, is very much like that which would be achieved by burying a bar magnet deep in the interior of the Earth.

If a compass needle is suspended in bearings that allow it to rotate in the vertical plane as well as in the horizontal plane, the needle is horizontal with respect to the Earth's surface only near the equator. As the device is moved northward, the needle rotates so that it points more and more toward the surface of the Earth. Finally, at a point just north of Hudson Bay in Canada, the north pole of the needle would point directly downward. This location, first found in 1832, is considered to be the location of the south-seeking magnetic pole of the Earth. This site is approximately 1300 mi from the Earth's geographic North Pole and varies with time. Similarly, the north-seeking magnetic pole of the Earth is about 1200 miles away from the Earth's geographic South Pole. Thus, it is only approximately correct to say that a compass needle points north. The difference between true north, defined as the geographic North Pole, and north indicated by a compass varies from point to point on the Earth, and the difference is referred to as magnetic declination. For example, along a line through Florida and the Great Lakes, a compass indicates true north, whereas in Washington state, it aligns 25° east of true north.

Although the magnetic field pattern of the Earth is similar to that which would be set up by a bar magnet deep within the Earth, it is easy to understand why the source of the Earth's magnetic field cannot be large masses of permanently magnetized material. The Earth does have large deposits of iron ore deep beneath its surface, but the high temperatures in the Earth's core prevent the iron from retaining any permanent magnetization. It is considered more likely that the true source is charge-carrying convection currents in the Earth's core. Charged ions or electrons circling in the liquid interior could produce a magnetic field, just as a current in a loop of wire produces a magnetic field. There is also strong evidence to indicate that the strength of a planet's field is related to the planet's rate of rotation. For example, Jupiter rotates faster than the Earth, and recent space probes indicate that Jupiter's magnetic field is stronger than ours. Venus, on the other hand, rotates more slowly than the Earth, and its magnetic field is found to be weaker. Investigation into the cause of the Earth's magnetism remains open.

There is an interesting sidelight concerning the Earth's magnetic field. It has been found that the direction of the field has been reversed several times during the last million years. Evidence for this is provided by basalt (a type of rock that contains iron) that is spewed forth by volcanic activity on the ocean floor. As the lava cools, it solidifies and retains a picture of the Earth's magnetic field direction. The rocks can be dated by other means to provide the evidence for these periodic reversals of the magnetic field.

SUMMARY

The **Biot-Savart law** says that the magnetic field $d\mathbf{B}$ at a point P due to a current element $d\mathbf{s}$ carrying a steady current I is

$$d\mathbf{B} = k_m \frac{I\, d\mathbf{s} \times \hat{\mathbf{r}}}{r^2} \tag{30.1}$$

where $k_m = 10^{-7}\,\text{Wb/A}\cdot\text{m}$ and r is the distance from the element to the point P. To find the total field at P due to a current-carrying conductor, we must integrate this vector expression over the entire conductor.

The **magnetic field** at a distance a from a long, straight wire carrying a current I is given by

$$B = \frac{\mu_0 I}{2\pi a} \tag{30.7}$$

where $\mu_0 = 4\pi \times 10^{-7}\,\text{Wb/A}\cdot\text{m}$ is the **permeability of free space**. The field lines are circles concentric with the wire.

The force per unit length between two parallel wires separated by a distance a and carrying currents I_1 and I_2 has a magnitude given by

$$\frac{F}{\ell} = \frac{\mu_0 I_1 I_2}{2\pi a} \tag{30.13}$$

The force is attractive if the currents are in the same direction and repulsive if they are in opposite directions.

Ampère's law says that the line integral of $\mathbf{B}\cdot d\mathbf{s}$ around any closed path equals $\mu_0 I$, where I is the total steady current passing through any surface bounded by the closed path. That is,

$$\oint \mathbf{B}\cdot d\mathbf{s} = \mu_0 I \tag{30.15}$$

Using Ampère's law, it is found that the fields inside a toroid and solenoid are

$$B = \frac{\mu_0 N I}{2\pi r} \quad \text{(toroid)} \tag{30.18}$$

$$B = \mu_0 \frac{N}{\ell} I = \mu_0 n I \quad \text{(solenoid)} \tag{30.20}$$

where N is the total number of turns.

The **magnetic flux** Φ_B through a surface is defined by the surface integral

$$\Phi_B = \int \mathbf{B} \cdot d\mathbf{A} \qquad (30.23)$$

Gauss's law of magnetism states that the net magnetic flux through any closed surface is zero. That is, isolated magnetic poles (or magnetic monopoles) do not exist.

A **displacement current** I_d arises from a time-varying electric flux Φ_E and is defined by

$$I_d \equiv \epsilon_0 \frac{d\Phi_E}{dt} \qquad (30.26)$$

The **generalized form of Ampère's law,** which includes the displacement current, is

$$\oint \mathbf{B} \cdot d\mathbf{s} = \mu_0 I + \mu_0 \epsilon_0 \frac{d\Phi_E}{dt} \qquad (30.27)$$

This law describes the fact that magnetic fields are produced both by conduction currents and by changing electric fields.

QUESTIONS

1. Is the magnetic field created by a current loop uniform? Explain.
2. A current in a conductor produces a magnetic field that can be calculated using the Biot-Savart law. Since current is defined as the rate of flow of charge, what can you conclude about the magnetic field produced by stationary charges? What about moving charges?
3. Two parallel wires carry currents in opposite directions. Describe the nature of the resultant magnetic field created by the two wires at points (a) between the wires and (b) outside the wires in a plane containing them.
4. Explain why two parallel wires carrying currents in opposite directions repel each other.
5. When an electric circuit is being assembled, a common practice is to twist together two wires carrying equal and opposite currents. Why does this technique reduce stray magnetic fields?
6. Is Ampère's law valid for all closed paths surrounding a conductor? Why is it not useful for calculating **B** for all such paths?
7. Compare Ampère's law with the Biot-Savart law. Which is the more general method for calculating **B** for a current-carrying conductor?
8. Is the magnetic field inside a toroid uniform? Explain.
9. Describe the similarities between Ampère's law in magnetism and Gauss's law in electrostatics.
10. A hollow copper tube carries a current. Why is **B** = 0 inside the tube? Is **B** nonzero outside the tube?
11. Why is **B** nonzero outside a solenoid? Why is **B** = 0 outside a toroid? (The lines of **B** must form closed paths.)
12. Describe the change in the magnetic field in the space enclosed by a solenoid carrying a steady current I if (a) the length of the solenoid is doubled but the number of turns remains the same and (b) the number of turns is doubled but the length remains the same.
13. A flat conducting loop is located in a uniform magnetic field directed along the x axis. For what orientation of the loop is the flux through it a maximum? A minimum?
14. What new concept did Maxwell's generalized form of Ampère's circuital law include?
15. A magnet attracts a piece of iron. The iron can then attract another piece of iron. On the basis of domain alignment, explain what happens in each piece of iron.
16. You are an astronaut stranded on a planet with no test equipment for minerals around. The planet does not even have a magnetic field. You have two bars of iron in your possession: one is magnetized, one is not. How could you determine which is which?
17. Why does hitting a magnet with a hammer cause the magnetism to be reduced?
18. Will a nail be attracted to either pole of a magnet? Explain what is happening inside the nail when placed near the magnet.
19. The north-seeking pole of a magnet is attracted toward the geographic North Pole of the Earth. Yet, like poles repel. What is the way out of this dilemma?
20. A Hindu ruler once suggested that he be entombed in a magnetic coffin with the polarity arranged so that he would be forever suspended between Heaven and Earth. Is such magnetic levitation possible? Discuss.

21. Why is **M** = 0 in a vacuum? What is the relationship between **B** and **H** in a vacuum?

22. Explain why some atoms have permanent magnetic dipole moments and others do not.

23. What factors contribute to the total magnetic dipole moment of an atom?

24. Why is the susceptibility of a diamagnetic substance negative?

25. Why can the effect of diamagnetism be neglected in a paramagnetic substance?

26. Explain the significance of the Curie temperature for a ferromagnetic substance.

27. Discuss the difference between ferromagnetic, paramagnetic, and diamagnetic substances.

28. What is the difference between hard and soft ferromagnetic materials?

29. Should the surface of a computer disc be made from a hard or a soft ferromagnetic substance?

30. Explain why it is desirable to use hard ferromagnetic materials to make permanent magnets.

31. Why is an unmagnetized steel nail attracted to a permanent magnet?

32. Would you expect the tape from a tape recorder to be attracted to a magnet? (Try it, but not with a recording you wish to save.)

33. Given only a strong magnet and a screwdriver, how would you first magnetize and then demagnetize the screwdriver?

34. Figure 30.35 shows two permanent magnets, each having a hole through its center. Note that the upper magnet is levitated above the lower one. (a) How does this occur? (b) What purpose does the pencil serve? (c) What can you say about the poles of the magnets from this observation? (d) If the upper magnet were inverted, what do you suppose would happen?

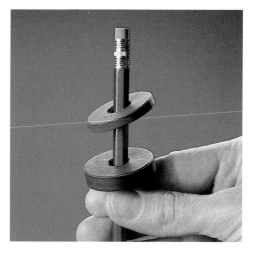

FIGURE 30.35   (Question 34) Magnetic levitation using two ceramic magnets. *(Courtesy of Central Scientific Co.)*

PROBLEMS

Review Problem

The square loop *abcd* shown in the figure has a total resistance 4*R*. Each side of the loop has a length *d* and the wire has a radius *r*. If a battery of voltage *V* is connected as shown, find
(a) the currents in each branch of the loop,
(b) the magnetic field at the center of the loop,
(c) the magnetic force between wires *ab* and *cd*,
(d) the magnetic force between wires *bc* and *ad*, and
(e) the equilibrium position (in the plane of the page) of a current-carrying wire that is parallel to wires *bc* and *ad*.

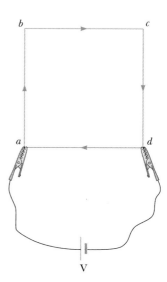

FIGURE RP30

☐ indicates problems that have full solutions available in the Student Solutions Manual and Study Guide.

Section 30.1 The Biot-Savart Law

1. Calculate the magnitude of the magnetic field at a point 100 cm from a long, thin conductor carrying a current of 1.0 A.

2. A long, thin conductor carries a current of 10.0 A. At what distance from the conductor is the magnitude of the resulting magnetic field 1.00×10^{-4} T?

3. A wire in which there is a current of 5.00 A is to be formed into a circular loop of one turn. If the required value of the magnetic field at the center of the loop is 10.0 μT, what is the required radius?

4. In Niels Bohr's 1913 model of the hydrogen atom, an electron circles the proton at a distance of 5.3×10^{-11} m with a speed of 2.2×10^{6} m/s. Compute the magnetic field strength that this motion produces at the location of the proton.

5. (a) A conductor in the shape of a square of edge length $\ell = 0.4$ m carries a current $I = 10$ A (Fig. P30.5). Calculate the magnitude and direction of the magnetic field at the center of the square. (b) If this conductor is formed into a single circular turn and carries the same current, what is the value of the magnetic field at the center?

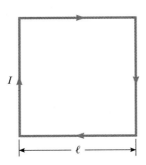

FIGURE P30.5

6. A 12-cm $\times$ 16-cm rectangular loop of superconducting wire carries a current of 30 A. What is the magnetic field at the center of the loop?

7. A long, straight wire lies on a horizontal table and carries a current of 1.2 μA. A proton moves parallel to the wire (opposite the current) with a constant speed of 2.3×10^{4} m/s at a distance d above the wire. Determine the value of d. You may ignore the magnetic field due to the Earth.

8. A conductor consists of a circular loop of radius $R = 0.100$ m and two straight, long sections, as in Figure P30.8. The wire lies in the plane of the paper and carries a current of $I = 7.00$ A. Determine the magnitude and direction of the magnetic field at the center of the loop.

8A. A conductor consists of a circular loop of radius R and two straight, long sections, as in Figure P30.8.

The wire lies in the plane of the paper and carries a current I. Determine the magnitude and direction of the magnetic field at the center of the loop.

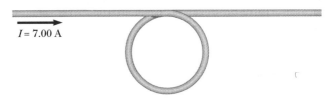

$I = 7.00$ A

FIGURE P30.8

9. Determine the magnetic field at a point P located a distance x from the corner of an infinitely long wire bent at a right angle, as in Figure P30.9. The wire carries a steady current I.

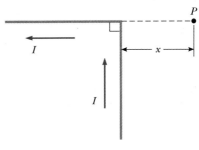

FIGURE P30.9

10. A segment of wire of total length $4r$ is formed into the shape shown in Figure P30.10 and carries a current $I = 6.00$ A. Find the magnitude and direction of the magnetic field at P when $r = 2\pi$ cm.

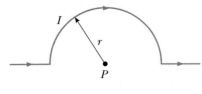

FIGURE P30.10

11. The segment of wire in Figure P30.11 carries a current of $I = 5.00$ A, and the radius of the circular arc is $R = 3.00$ cm. Determine the magnitude and direction of the magnetic field at the origin.

11A. The segment of wire in Figure P30.11 carries a current I, and the radius of the circular arc is R. Determine the magnitude and direction of the magnetic field at the origin.

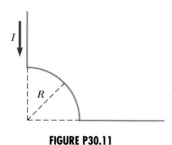

FIGURE P30.11

12. Consider the current-carrying loop shown in Figure P30.12, formed of radial lines and segments of circles whose centers are at point P. Find the magnitude and direction of **B** at P.

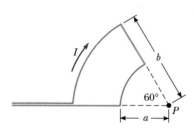

FIGURE P30.12

13. Determine the magnetic field (in terms of I, a, and d) at the origin due to the current loop in Figure P30.13.

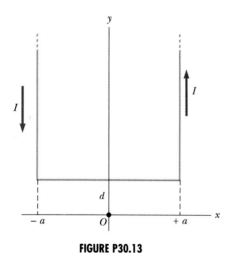

FIGURE P30.13

14. The loop in Figure P30.14 carries a current $I = 2.50$ A. The semicircular portion has a radius $R = 5.00$ cm and $L = 10.0$ cm. Determine the magnitude and direction of the magnetic field at point A.

14A. The loop in Figure P30.14 carries a current I. Determine the magnetic field at point A in terms of I, R, and L.

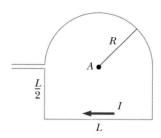

FIGURE P30.14

Section 30.2   The Magnetic Force Between Two Parallel Conductors

15. Two long, parallel conductors separated by 10.0 cm carry currents in the same direction. If $I_1 = 5.00$ A and $I_2 = 8.00$ A, what is the force per unit length exerted on each conductor by the other?

16. Two long, parallel wires, each having a mass per unit length of 40 g/m, are supported in a horizontal plane by strings 6.0 cm long, as in Figure P30.16. Each wire carries the same current I, causing the wires to repel each other so that the angle θ between the supporting strings is 16°. (a) Are the currents in the same or opposite directions? (b) Find the magnitude of each current.

16A. Two long, parallel wires, each having a mass per unit length μ, are supported in a horizontal plane by strings of length L, as in Figure P30.16. Each wire carries the same current I, causing the wires to repel each other so that the angle between the supporting strings is θ. (a) Are the currents in the same or opposite directions? (b) Find the magnitude of each current.

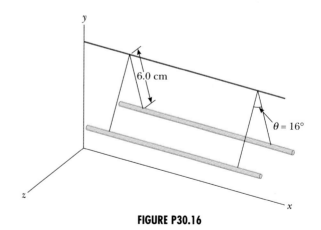

FIGURE P30.16

17. Two parallel copper rods are 1.00 cm apart. Lightning sends a 10.0-kA pulse of current along each conductor. Calculate the force per unit length on one conductor. Is the force attractive or repulsive?

18. Compute the magnetic force per unit length between two adjacent windings of a solenoid if each carries a current $I = 100$ A and the center-to-center distance between the wires is 4 mm.

19. In Figure P30.19, the current in the long, straight wire is $I_1 = 5.00$ A and the wire lies in the plane of the rectangular loop, which carries 10.0 A. The dimensions are $c = 0.100$ m, $a = 0.150$ m, and $\ell = 0.450$ m. Find the magnitude and direction of the net force exerted on the loop by the magnetic field created by the wire.

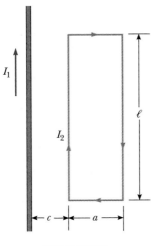

FIGURE P30.19

20. Three long, parallel conductors each carry a 2.0 A-current. Figure P30.20 is an end view of the conductors, with each current coming out of the page. If $a = 1.0$ cm, determine the magnitude and direction of the magnetic field at points A, B, and C.

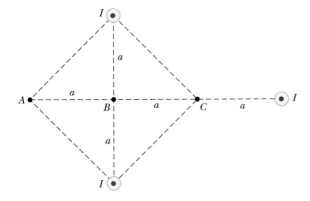

FIGURE P30.20

21. Two long, parallel conductors carry currents $I_1 = 3.00$ A and $I_2 = 3.00$ A, both directed into the page in Figure P30.21. Determine the magnitude and direction of the resultant magnetic field at P.

21A. Two long, parallel conductors carry currents I_1 and I_2, both directed into the page in Figure P30.21. Determine the magnitude and direction of the resultant magnetic field at P.

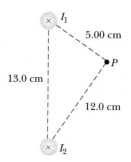

FIGURE P30.21

Section 30.3 Ampère's Law and
Section 30.4 The Magnetic Field of a Solenoid

22. A closely wound, long solenoid of overall length 30.0 cm has a magnetic field of 5.00×10^{-4} T at its center produced by a current of 1.00 A through its windings. How many turns of wire are on the solenoid?

23. A superconducting solenoid is to generate a magnetic field of 10.0 T. (a) If the solenoid winding has 2000 turns/m, what is the required current? (b) What force per unit length is exerted on the windings by this magnetic field?

24. What current is required in the windings of a long solenoid that has 1000 turns uniformly distributed over a length of 0.40 m in order to produce at the center of the solenoid a magnetic field of magnitude 1.0×10^{-4} T?

25. Some superconducting alloys at very low temperatures can carry very high currents. For example, Nb_3Sn wire at 10 K can carry 1.0×10^3 A and maintain its superconductivity. Determine the maximum value of B achievable in a solenoid of length 25 cm if 1000 turns of Nb_3Sn wire are wrapped on the outside surface.

26. Imagine a long cylindrical wire of radius R that has a current density $J(r) = J_0(1 - r^2/R^2)$ for $r \leqslant R$ and $J(r) = 0$, for $r > R$, where r is the distance from a point of interest to the central axis running along the length of the wire. (a) Find the resulting magnetic field inside ($r \leqslant R$) and outside ($r > R$) the wire. (b) Plot the magnitude of the magnetic field as a function of r. (c) Find the location where the magnetic field strength is a maximum, and the value of that maximum field.

27. The magnetic coils of a tokamak fusion reactor are in the shape of a toroid having an inner radius of 0.70 m and outer radius of 1.30 m. If the toroid has 900 turns of large-diameter wire, each of which carries a current of 14 kA, find the magnetic field strength along (a) the inner radius and (b) the outer radius.

28. A charged-particle beam that is shot horizontally moves into a region where there is a constant magnetic field of magnitude 2.45×10^{-3} T that points straight down. The particles then move in a circular path of radius 2.00 cm. If they accelerated through a potential difference of 211 V, determine their charge-to-mass ratio.

29. You are given a certain volume of copper from which you can make copper wires. The wires are then used to produce a tightly wound solenoid of maximum magnetic field at the center. (a) Should you make the wires long and thin or short and thick? (b) Should you make the solenoid radius small or large? Explain.

30. Niobium metal becomes a superconductor when cooled below 9 K. If superconductivity is destroyed when the surface magnetic field exceeds 0.10 T, determine the maximum current a 2.0-mm-diameter niobium wire can carry and remain superconducting.

31. A packed bundle of 100 long, straight, insulated wires forms a cylinder of radius $R = 0.50$ cm. (a) If each wire carries 2.0 A, what are the magnitude and direction of the magnetic force per unit length acting on a wire located 0.2 cm from the center of the bundle? (b) Would a wire on the outer edge of the bundle experience a force greater or smaller than the value calculated in part (a)?

32. In Figure P30.32, both currents are in the negative x direction. (a) Sketch the magnetic field pattern in the yz plane. (b) At what distance d along the z axis is the magnetic field a maximum?

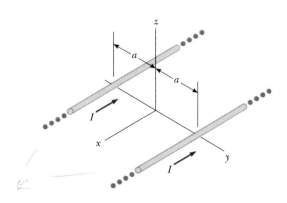

FIGURE P30.32

*Section 30.5   The Magnetic Field Along the Axis of a Solenoid

33. A solenoid of radius $R = 5.00$ cm is made of a long piece of wire of radius $r = 2.00$ mm, length $\ell = 10.0$ m $(\ell \gg R)$, and resistivity $\rho = 1.7 \times 10^{-8}$ $\Omega \cdot$m. Find the magnetic field at the center of the solenoid if the wire is connected to a battery having an emf $\mathcal{E} = 20.0$ V.

33A. A solenoid of radius R is made of a long piece of wire of radius r, length ℓ $(\ell \gg R)$, and resistivity ρ. Find the magnetic field at the center of the solenoid if the wire is connected to a battery having an emf $\mathcal{E}$.

34. A solenoid 80 cm long has 900 turns and a radius of 2.5 cm. If it carries a current of 3.0 A, calculate the magnetic field along its axis at (a) its center and (b) a point near one end.

35. A solenoid has 500 turns, a length of 50.0 cm, and a radius of 5.0 cm. If it carries 4.0 A, calculate the magnetic field at an axial point located 15 cm from the center (that is, 10 cm from one end).

Section 30.6   Magnetic Flux

36. A toroid is constructed from N rectangular turns of wire. Each turn has height h. The toroid has an inner radius a and outer radius b. (a) If the toroid carries a current I, show that the total magnetic flux through the turns of the toroid is proportional to $\ln(b/a)$. (b) Evaluate this flux if $N = 200$ turns, $h = 1.5$ cm, $a = 2.0$ cm, $b = 5.0$ cm, and $I = 2.0$ A.

37. A cube of edge length $\ell = 2.5$ cm is positioned as shown in Figure P30.37. There is throughout the region a uniform magnetic field given by $\mathbf{B} = (5.0\mathbf{i} + 4.0\mathbf{j} + 3.0\mathbf{k})$ T. (a) Calculate the flux through the shaded face. (b) What is the total flux through the six faces?

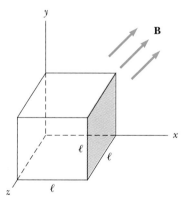

FIGURE P30.37

38. A solenoid 2.5 cm in diameter and 30 cm long has 300 turns and carries 12 A. (a) Calculate the flux

through the surface of a disk of radius 5.0 cm that is positioned perpendicular to and centered on the axis of the solenoid, as in Figure P30.38a. (b) Figure P30.38b shows an enlarged end view of the solenoid described above. Calculate the flux through the blue area, which is defined by an annulus that has an inner radius of 0.40 cm and outer radius of 0.80 cm.

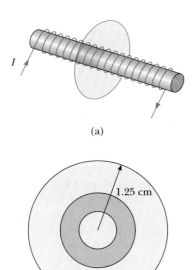

(a)

(b)

FIGURE P30.38

39. Consider the cube in Figure P30.39 having side L. A uniform magnetic field **B** is directed perpendicular to face *abfe*. Find the magnetic flux through the imaginary planar loops (a) *dfhd* and (b) *acfa*.

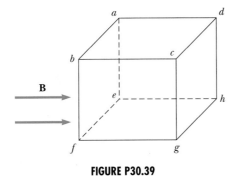

FIGURE P30.39

40. Consider the hemispherical closed surface in Figure P30.40. If the hemisphere is in a uniform magnetic field that makes an angle θ with the vertical, calculate the magnetic flux through (a) the flat surface S_1 and (b) the hemispherical surface S_2.

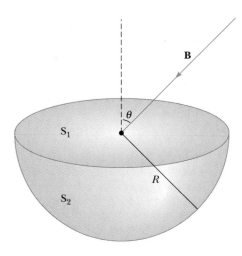

FIGURE P30.40

Section 30.8 Displacement Current and the Generalized Ampère's Law

41. The applied voltage across the plates of a 4.00-μF capacitor varies in time according to the expression

$$V_{app} = (8.00 \text{ V})(1 - e^{-t/4})$$

where t is in seconds. Calculate (a) the displacement current as a function of time and (b) the value of the current at $t = 4.00$ s.

42. A capacitor of capacitance C has a charge Q at $t = 0$. At that time, a resistor of resistance R is connected to the capacitor plates. (a) Find the displacement current in the dielectric between the plates as a function of time. (b) Evaluate this displacement current at time $t = 0.10$ s if $C = 2.0$ μF, $Q = 20$ μC, and $R = 500$ kΩ. (c) At what rate is the electric flux between the plates changing at $t = 0.10$ s?

43. A 0.10 A current is charging a capacitor that has square plates, 5.0 cm on a side. If the plate separation is 4.0 mm, find (a) the time rate of change of electric flux between the plates and (b) the displacement current between the plates.

44. A 0.20-A current is charging a capacitor that has circular plates, 10 cm in radius. If the plate separation is 4.0 mm, (a) what is the time rate of increase of electric field between the plates? (b) What is the magnetic field between the plates 5.0 cm from the center?

*Section 30.9 Magnetism in Matter

45. What is the relative permeability of a material that has a magnetic susceptibility of 10^{-4}?

46. An iron-core toroid is wrapped with 250 turns of wire per meter of its length. The current in the winding is 8.00 A. Taking the magnetic permeability of iron to

be $\mu_m = 5000\mu_0$, calculate (a) the magnetic field strength, **H**, and (b) the field, **B**.

47. A toroid with a mean radius of 20 cm and 630 turns (Fig. 30.29) is filled with powdered steel whose magnetic susceptibility χ is 100. If the current in the windings is 3.00 A, find B (assumed uniform) inside the toroid.

48. A toroid has an average radius of 9.0 cm. The current in the coil is 0.50 A. How many turns are required to produce a magnetic field strength of $700 \text{ A} \cdot \text{turns}/\text{m}$ within the toroid?

49. A magnetic field of magnitude 1.3 T is to be set up in an iron-core toroid. The toroid has a mean radius of 10 cm, and magnetic permeability of $5000\mu_0$. What current is required if there are 470 turns of wire in the winding?

50. A toroidal solenoid has an average radius of 10 cm and a cross-sectional area of 1.0 cm^2. There are 400 turns of wire on the soft iron core, which has a permeability of $800\mu_0$. Calculate the current necessary to produce a magnetic flux of $5.0 \times 10^{-4} \text{ Wb}$ through a cross-section of the core.

51. A coil of 500 turns is wound on an iron ring ($\mu_m = 750\mu_0$) of 20-cm mean radius and 8.0-cm^2 cross-sectional area. Calculate the magnetic flux Φ in this Rowland ring when the current in the coil is 0.50 A.

52. A uniform ring of radius 2.0 cm and total charge 6.0 μC rotates with a constant angular speed of 4.0 rad/s around an axis perpendicular to the plane of the ring and passing through its center. What is the magnetic moment of the rotating ring?

52A. A uniform ring of radius R and total charge Q rotates with constant angular speed ω around an axis perpendicular to the plane of the ring and passing through its center. What is the magnetic moment of the rotating ring?

53. In the text, we found that an alternative description for magnetic field **B** in terms of magnetic field strength **H** and magnetization **M** is $\mathbf{B} = \mu_0\mathbf{H} + \mu_0\mathbf{M}$. Relate the magnetic susceptibility χ to $|\mathbf{H}|$ and $|\mathbf{M}|$ for paramagnetic or diamagnetic materials.

54. Calculate the magnetic field strength H of a magnetized substance characterized by a magnetization of $0.88 \times 10^6 \text{ A} \cdot \text{turns}/\text{m}$ and a magnetic field of magnitude 4.4 T. (*Hint:* See Problem 53.)

55. A magnetized cylinder of iron has a magnetic field $B = 0.040$ T in its interior. The magnet is 3.0 cm in diameter and 20 cm long. If the same magnetic field is to be produced by a 5.0-A current carried by an air-core solenoid having the same dimensions as the cylindrical magnet, how many turns of wire must be on the solenoid?

56. In Bohr's 1913 model of the hydrogen atom, the electron is in a circular orbit of radius 5.3×10^{-11} m

and its speed is 2.2×10^6 m/s. (a) What is the magnitude of the magnetic moment due to the electron's motion? (b) If the electron orbits counterclockwise in a horizontal circle, what is the direction of this magnetic moment vector?

57. At saturation, the alignment of spins in iron can contribute as much as 2.0 T to the total magnetic field B. If each electron contributes a magnetic moment of $9.27 \times 10^{-24} \text{ A} \cdot \text{m}^2$ (one Bohr magneton), how many electrons per atom contribute to the saturated field of iron? (*Hint:* There are 8.5×10^{28} iron atoms/m^3.)

*Section 30.10   Magnetic Field of the Earth

58. A circular coil of five turns and a diameter of 30 cm is oriented in a vertical plane with its axis perpendicular to the horizontal component of the Earth's magnetic field. A horizontal compass placed at the center of the coil is made to deflect 45° from magnetic north by a current of 0.60 A in the coil. (a) What is the horizontal component of the Earth's magnetic field? (b) If a compass "dip" needle oriented in a vertical north-south plane makes an angle of 13° from the vertical, what is the total strength of the Earth's magnetic field at this location?

59. The magnetic moment of the Earth is approximately $8.7 \times 10^{22} \text{ A} \cdot \text{m}^2$. (a) If this were caused by the complete magnetization of a huge iron deposit, how many unpaired electrons would this correspond to? (b) At two unpaired electrons per iron atom, how many kilograms of iron would this correspond to? (The density of iron is 7900 kg/m^3, and there are approximately 8.5×10^{28} iron atoms/m^3.)

ADDITIONAL PROBLEMS

60. A lightning bolt may carry a current of 1.0×10^4 A for a short period of time. What is the resulting magnetic field 100 m from the bolt?

61. Measurements of the magnetic field of a large tornado were made at the Geophysical Observatory in Tulsa, Oklahoma, in 1962. If the tornado's field was $B = 1.5 \times 10^{-8}$ T pointing north when the tornado was 9.0 km east of the observatory, what current was carried up/down the funnel of the tornado?

62. Figure P30.62 is a cross-sectional view of a coaxial cable. The center conductor is surrounded by a rubber layer, which is surrounded by an outer conductor, which is surrounded by another rubber layer. The current in the inner conductor is 1.00 A out of the page and the current in the outer conductor is 3.00 A into the page. Determine the magnitude and direction of the magnetic field at points a and b.

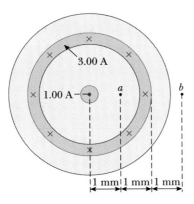

FIGURE P30.62

63. Two long, parallel conductors carry currents in the same direction as in Figure P30.63. Conductor A carries a current of 150 A and is held firmly in position. Conductor B carries a current I_B and is allowed to slide freely up and down (parallel to A) between a set of nonconducting guides. If the mass per unit length of conductor B is 0.10 g/cm, what value of current I_B will result in equilibrium when the distance between the two conductors is 2.5 cm?

63A. Two long, parallel conductors carry currents in the same direction as in Figure P30.63. Conductor A carries a current of I_A and is held firmly in position. Conductor B carries a current I_B and is allowed to slide freely up and down (parallel to A) between a set of nonconducting guides. If the mass per unit length of conductor B is μ, what value of current I_B will result in equilibrium when the distance between the two conductors is d?

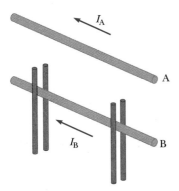

FIGURE P30.63

64. Two parallel conductors carry current in opposite directions as shown in Figure P30.64. One conductor carries a current of 10 A. Point A is at the midpoint between the wires and point C is a distance $d/2$ to the right of the 10-A current. If $d = 18$ cm and I is adjusted so that the magnetic field at C is zero, find

(a) the value of the current I and (b) the value of the magnetic field at A.

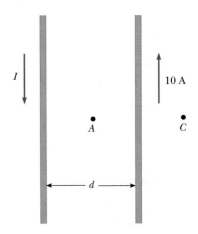

FIGURE P30.64

65. A very long, thin strip of metal of width w carries a current I along its length as in Figure P30.65. Find the magnetic field in the plane of the strip (at an external point P) a distance b from one edge.

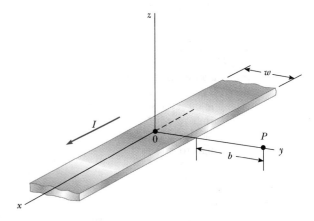

FIGURE P30.65

66. A large nonconducting belt with a uniform surface charge density σ moves with a speed v on a set of rollers as shown in Figure P30.66. Consider a point

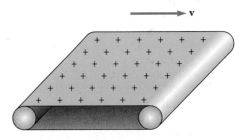

FIGURE P30.66

just above the surface of the moving belt. (a) Find an expression for the magnitude of the magnetic field **B** at this point. (b) If the belt is positively charged, what is the direction of **B**? (Note that the belt may be considered as an infinite sheet.)

67. A straight wire located at the equator is oriented parallel to the Earth along the east-west direction. The Earth's magnetic field at this point is horizontal and has a magnitude of 3.3×10^{-5} T. If the mass per unit length of the wire is 2.0×10^{-3} kg/m, what current must the wire carry in order that the magnetic force balance the weight of the wire?

68. The magnitude of the Earth's magnetic field at either pole is approximately 7.0×10^{-5} T. Using a model in which you assume that this field is produced by a current loop around the equator, determine the current that would generate such a field. (The radius of the Earth is $R_E = 6.37 \times 10^6$ m.)

69. A nonconducting ring of radius R is uniformly charged with a total positive charge q. The ring rotates at a constant angular speed ω about an axis through its center, perpendicular to the plane of the ring. If $R = 0.10$ m, $q = 10$ μC, and $\omega = 20$ rad/s, what is the magnitude of the magnetic field on the axis of the ring 0.050 m from its center?

69A. A nonconducting ring of radius R is uniformly charged with a total positive charge q. The ring rotates at a constant angular speed ω about an axis through its center, perpendicular to the plane of the ring. What is the magnitude of the magnetic field on the axis of the ring a distance $R/2$ from its center?

70. Consider a thin disk of radius R mounted to rotate about the x axis in the yz plane. The disk has a positive uniform surface charge density σ and angular velocity ω. Show that the magnetic field at the center of the disk is $B = \frac{1}{2}\mu_0\sigma\omega R$.

71. Two circular coils of radius R are each perpendicular to a common axis. The coil centers are a distance R apart and a steady current I flows in the same direction around each coil as shown in Figure P30.71. (a) Show that the magnetic field on the axis at a distance x from the center of one coil is

$$B = \frac{\mu_0 I R^2}{2}\left[\frac{1}{(R^2 + x^2)^{3/2}}\right.$$

$$\left. + \frac{1}{(2R^2 + x^2 - 2Rx)^{3/2}}\right]$$

(b) Show that $\dfrac{dB}{dx}$ and $\dfrac{d^2B}{dx^2}$ are both zero at a point midway between the coils. This means the magnetic field in the region midway between the coils is uniform. Coils in this configuration are called **Helmholtz coils.**

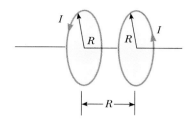

FIGURE P30.71

72. Two identical, flat, circular coils of wire each have 100 turns and a radius of 0.50 m. If these coils are arranged as a set of Helmholtz coils and each coil carries a current of 10 A, determine the magnitude of the magnetic field at a point halfway between the coils and on the axis of the coils. (See Problem 71.)

73. A long cylindrical conductor of radius R carries a current I as in Figure P30.73. The current density J, however, is not uniform over the cross-section of the conductor but is a function of the radius according to $J = br$, where b is a constant. Find an expression for the magnetic field B (a) at a distance $r_1 < R$ and (b) at a distance $r_2 > R$, measured from the axis.

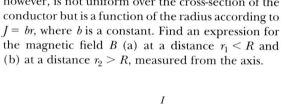
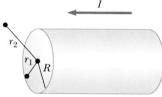

FIGURE P30.73

74. A bar magnet (mass = 39.4 g, magnetic moment = 7.65 J/T, length = 10 cm) is connected to the ceiling by a string. A uniform external magnetic field is applied horizontally, as shown in Figure P30.74. The magnet is in equilibrium, making an angle θ with the horizontal. If $\theta = 5.0°$, determine the strength of the applied magnetic field.

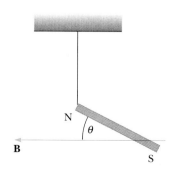

FIGURE P30.74

75. Two circular loops are parallel, coaxial, and almost in contact, 1.0 mm apart (Fig. P30.75). Each loop is 10 cm in radius. The top loop carries a clockwise current of 140 A. The bottom loop carries a counterclockwise current of 140 A. (a) Calculate the magnetic force that the bottom loop exerts on the top loop. (b) The upper loop has a mass of 0.021 kg. Calculate its acceleration, assuming that the only forces acting on it are the force in part (a) and its weight.

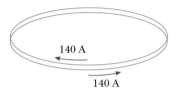

140 A

140 A

FIGURE P30.75

76. For a research project, a student needs a solenoid that produces an interior magnetic field of 0.030 T. She decides to use a current of 1.0 A and a wire 0.50 mm in diameter. She winds the solenoid as layers on an insulating form 1.0 cm in diameter and 10.0 cm long. Determine the number of layers of wire needed and the total length of the wire.

77. A toroid filled with a magnetic substance carries a steady current of 2.00 A. The coil contains 1505 turns, has an average radius of 4.00 cm, and its core has a cross-sectional area of 1.21 cm². The total magnetic flux through a cross-section of the toroid is 3.00×10^{-5} Wb. Assume the flux density is constant. (a) What is the magnetic field strength H within the core? (b) Determine the permeability of the core material if its susceptibility is 3.38×10^{-4}.

78. A paramagnetic substance achieves 10% of its saturation magnetization when placed in a magnetic field of 5.0 T at a temperature of 4.0 K. The density of magnetic atoms in the sample is 8.0×10^{27} atoms/m³, and the magnetic moment per atom is 5.0 Bohr magnetons. Calculate the Curie constant for this substance.

79. An infinitely long, straight wire carrying a current $I_1 = 50.0$ A is partially surrounded by a loop as in Figure P30.79. The loop has a length $L = 35.0$ cm, and a radius $R = 15.0$ cm, and carries a current $I_2 = 20.0$ A. The central perpendicular axis of the loop coincides with the wire. Calculate the force exerted on the loop.

79A. An infinitely long, straight wire carrying a current I_1 is partially surrounded by a loop as in Figure P30.79. The loop has length L, and radius R, and carries a current I_2. The axis of the loop coincides with the wire. Calculate the force exerted on the loop.

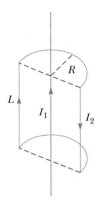

FIGURE P30.79

80. The force on a magnetic dipole M aligned with a nonuniform magnetic field in the x direction is given by $F_x = M \, dB/dx$. Suppose that two flat loops of wire each have radius R and carry current I. (a) If the loops are arranged coaxially and separated by a large variable distance x, show that the magnetic force between them varies as $1/x^4$. (b) Evaluate the magnitude of this force if $I = 10$ A, $R = 0.5$ cm, and $x = 5.0$ cm.

81. A wire is formed into the shape of a square of edge length L (Fig. P30.81). Show that when the current in the loop is I, the magnetic field at point P a distance x from the center of the square along its axis is

$$B = \frac{\mu_0 I L^2}{2\pi \left(x^2 + \dfrac{L^2}{4} \right) \sqrt{x^2 + \dfrac{L^2}{2}}}$$

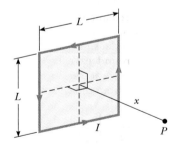

FIGURE P30.81

82. A wire is bent into the shape shown in Figure P30.82a, and the magnetic field is measured at P_1 when the current in the wire is I. The same wire is then formed into the shape shown in Figure P30.82b, and the magnetic field measured at point P_2 when the current is again I. If the total length of wire is the same in each case, what is the ratio of B_1/B_2?

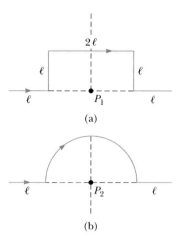

(a)

(b)

FIGURE P30.82

83. A wire carrying a current I is bent into the shape of an exponential spiral, $r = e^\theta$, from $\theta = 0$ to $\theta = 2\pi$ as in Figure P30.83. To complete a loop, the ends of the spiral are connected by a straight wire along the x axis. Find the magnitude and direction of **B** at the origin. *Hints:* Use the Biot-Savart law. The angle β between a radial line and its tangent line at any point on the curve $r = f(\theta)$ is related to the function in the following way:

$$\tan \beta = \frac{r}{dr/d\theta}$$

Thus in this case $r = e^\theta$, $\tan \beta = 1$, and $\beta = \pi/4$. Therefore, the angle between $d\mathbf{s}$ and $\hat{\mathbf{r}}$ is $\pi - \beta = 3\pi/4$. Also

$$d\mathbf{s} = \frac{dr}{\sin \pi/4} = \sqrt{2}\, dr$$

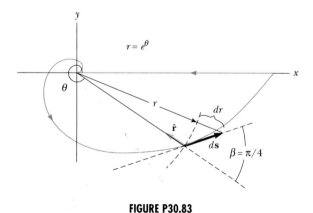

FIGURE P30.83

84. A long cylindrical conductor of radius a has two cylindrical cavities of diameter a through its entire length, as shown in Figure P30.84. A current, I, is directed out of the page and is uniform through a cross-section of the conductor. Find the magnitude and direction of the magnetic field at (a) point P_1 and (b) point P_2 in terms of μ_0, I, r, and a.

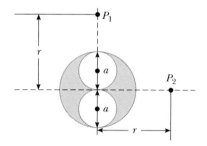

FIGURE P30.84

85. Four long, parallel conductors all carry 5.00 A. An end view of the conductors is shown in Figure P30.85. The current direction is out of the page at points A and B (indicated by the dots) and into the page at points C and D (indicated by the crosses). Calculate the magnitude and direction of the magnetic field at point P, located at the center of the square.

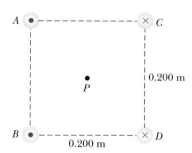

FIGURE P30.85

86. Consider a flat circular current loop of radius R carrying current I. Choose the x axis to be along the axis of the loop with the origin at the center of the loop. Plot a graph of the ratio of the magnitude of the magnetic field at coordinate x to that at the origin for $x = 0$ to $x = 5R$. It may be useful to use a programmable calculator or small computer to solve this problem.

87. A sphere of radius R has a constant volume charge density ρ. Determine the magnetic field at the center of the sphere when it rotates as a rigid body with angular velocity ω about an axis through its center (Fig. P30.87).

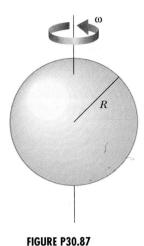

FIGURE P30.87

88. Table 30.4 is data taken on a ferromagnetic material. (a) Construct a magnetization curve from the data. Remember that $\mathbf{B} = \mathbf{B}_0 + \mu_0\mathbf{M}$. (b) Determine the ratio B/B_0 for each pair of values of B and B_0, and construct a graph of B/B_0 versus B_0. (B/B_0 is called the relative permeability, and it is a measure of the induced magnetic field.)

TABLE 30.4

B (T)	B_0 (T)
0.2	4.8×10^{-5}
0.4	7.0×10^{-5}
0.6	8.8×10^{-5}
0.8	1.2×10^{-4}
1.0	1.8×10^{-4}
1.2	3.1×10^{-4}
1.4	8.7×10^{-4}
1.6	3.4×10^{-3}
1.8	1.2×10^{-1}

89. A sphere of radius R has a constant volume charge density ρ. Determine the magnetic dipole moment of the sphere when it rotates as a rigid body with angular velocity ω about an axis through its center (Fig. P30.87).

SPREADSHEET PROBLEMS

S1. Spreadsheet 30.1 calculates the magnetic field along the x axis of a solenoid of length l, radius R, and n turns per unit length carrying a current I. The solenoid is centered at the origin with its axis along the x axis. The field at any point x is

$$B = \frac{1}{2}\mu_0 nI[\,f_1(x) - f_2(x)\,]$$

where

$$f_1(x) = \frac{x + \frac{1}{2}l}{\left[R^2 + \left(x + \frac{1}{2}l\right)^2\right]^{1/2}}$$

$$f_2(x) = \frac{x - \frac{1}{2}l}{\left[R^2 + \left(x - \frac{1}{2}l\right)^2\right]^{1/2}}$$

(a) Let $l = 10$ cm, $R = 0.50$ cm, $I = 4.0$ A, and $n = 1500$ turns/m. Plot B versus x for positive values of x ranging from $x = 0$ to $x = 20$ cm. (b) Change R to the following values, and observe the effects on the graph in each case: $R = 0.10$ cm, 1.0 cm, 2.0 cm, 5.0 cm, and 10.0 cm. For small values of R (small compared to l), the field inside the solenoid should look like that of an ideal solenoid; for large values of R, the field should look like that of a loop. Does it?

S2. If $x \gg l$ (where x is measured from the center of the solenoid), the magnetic field of a finite solenoid along the x axis approaches

$$\frac{\mu_0}{4\pi}\frac{2\mu}{x^3}$$

where $\mu = NI(\pi R^2)$ is the magnetic dipole moment of the solenoid. Modify Spreadsheet 30.1 to calculate and plot $x^3 B(x)$ as a function of x. Verify that $x^3 B(x)$ approaches a constant for $x \gg l$.

S3. A circular loop of wire of radius R carries a current I. Using the Biot-Savart law, the magnetic field in the plane of the loop at a distance r from its center for $r < R$ is found to be

$$B = \frac{\mu_0 I}{4\pi R} F(r/R)$$

where

$$F(y) = \int_0^{2\pi} \frac{(1 - y\sin\theta)\,d\theta}{(1 + y^2 - 2y\sin\theta)^{3/2}}$$

Numerically integrate this expression to find F as a function of $y = r/R$. Use a trapezoidal or Simpson's method integration scheme to carry out the numerical integration. Choose any values for I and R; plot B as a function of r/R to show how the field varies inside the loop. What happens as r approaches R?

S4. Consider a multi-layered solenoid of length l centered at the origin whose axis is along the x axis. Construct a computer spreadsheet or write your own computer program to calculate the magnetic field **B** along the x axis. **B** is given by

$$B(x) = \frac{\mu_0 n I N}{2(R_0 - R_i)}\left[(x + a) \ln \frac{R_0 + \sqrt{(x + a)^2 + R_0^2}}{R_i + \sqrt{(x + a)^2 + R_i^2}} \right.$$
$$\left. - (x - a) \ln \frac{R_0 + \sqrt{(x - a)^2 + R_0^2}}{R_i + \sqrt{(x - a)^2 + R_i^2}} \right]$$

where $a = l/2$, N is the total number of layers, n is the number of turns per unit length in each layer, R_1 is the inside radius, and R_0 is the outside radius of the solenoid.[4] Use any reasonable values for the parameters. Plot your results.

[4] For a derivation of this equation, see L. Golden, J. Klein, and L. Tongson, *American Journal of Physics* **56**:846–848, 1988.

Faraday's Law

Induced emf. When a strong magnet is moved toward or away from the coil attached to a galvanometer, an electric current is induced, indicated by the momentary deflection of the galvanometer during the movement of the magnet.   *(Richard Megna / Fundamental Photographs)*

Our studies so far have been concerned with electric fields due to stationary charges and magnetic fields produced by moving charges. This chapter deals with electric fields that originate from changing magnetic fields.

Experiments conducted by Michael Faraday in England in 1831 and independently by Joseph Henry in the United States that same year showed that an electric current could be induced in a circuit by a changing magnetic field. The results of these experiments led to a very basic and important law of electromagnetism known as Faraday's law of induction. This law says that the magnitude of the emf induced in a circuit equals the time rate of change of the magnetic flux through the circuit.

As we shall see, an induced emf can be produced in many ways. For instance, an induced emf and an induced current can be produced in a closed loop of wire when the wire moves into a magnetic field. We shall describe such experiments along with a number of important applications that make use of the phenomenon of electromagnetic induction.

With the treatment of Faraday's law, we complete our introduction to the fundamental laws of electromagnetism. These laws can be summarized in a set of four equations called Maxwell's equations. Together with the Lorentz force law, which we shall discuss briefly, they represent a complete theory for describing the interaction of charged objects. Maxwell's equations relate electric and magnetic fields to each other and to their ultimate source, namely, electric charges.

31.1   FARADAY'S LAW OF INDUCTION

We begin by describing two simple experiments that demonstrate that a current can be produced by a changing magnetic field. First, consider a loop of wire connected to a galvanometer as in Figure 31.1. If a magnet is moved toward the loop, the galvanometer needle will deflect in one direction, as in Figure 31.1a. If the magnet is moved away from the loop, the galvanometer needle will deflect in the opposite direction, as in Figure 31.1b. If the magnet is held stationary relative to the loop, no deflection is observed. Finally, if the magnet is held stationary and the coil is moved either toward or away from the magnet, the needle will also deflect. From these observations, it can be concluded that *a current is set up in the circuit as long as there is relative motion between the magnet and the coil.*[1]

These results are quite remarkable in view of the fact that *a current is set up in the circuit even though there are no batteries in the circuit!* We call such a current an induced current, which is produced by an induced emf.

Now let us describe an experiment, first conducted by Faraday, that is illustrated in Figure 31.2. Part of the apparatus consists of a coil connected to a switch

---

[1] The exact magnitude of the current depends on the particular resistance of the circuit, but the existence of the current (or the algebraic sign) does not.

Joseph Henry, an American physicist who carried out early experiments in electrical induction, was born in Albany, New York, in 1797. The son of a laborer, Henry had little schooling and was forced to go to work at a very young age. After working his way through Albany Academy to study medicine, then engineering, Henry became professor of mathematics and physics in 1826. He later became professor of natural philosophy at New Jersey College (now Princeton University).

In 1848, Henry became the first director of the Smithsonian Institute, where he introduced a weather-forecasting system based on meteorological information received by the electric telegraph. He was also the first president of the Academy of Natural

Joseph Henry

| 1 7 9 7 – 1 8 7 8 |

Science, a position he held until his death in 1878.

Many of Henry's early experiments were with electromagnetism. He improved the electromagnet of William Sturgeon and made one of the first electromagnetic motors. By 1830, Henry had made powerful electromagnets by using many turns of fine insulated wire wound around iron cores. He discovered the phenomenon of self-induction but failed to publish his findings; as a result, credit was given to Michael Faraday.

Henry's contribution to science was ultimately recognized: In 1893 the unit of inductance was named the henry.

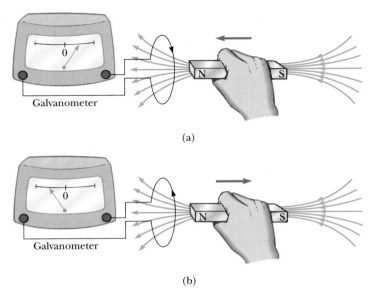

(a)

(b)

FIGURE 31.1   (a) When a magnet is moved toward a loop of wire connected to a galvanometer, the galvanometer deflects as shown. This shows that a current is induced in the loop. (b) When the magnet is moved away from the loop, the galvanometer deflects in the opposite direction, indicating that the induced current is opposite that shown in part (a).

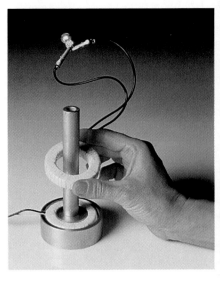

A demonstration of electromagnetic induction. An ac voltage is applied to the lower coil. A voltage is induced in the upper coil as indicated by the illuminated lamp connected to the upper coil. What do you think happens to the lamp's intensity as the upper coil is moved over the vertical tube? *(Courtesy of Central Scientific Co.)*

and a battery. We shall refer to this coil as the primary coil and to the corresponding circuit as the primary circuit. The coil is wrapped around an iron ring to intensify the magnetic field produced by the current through the coil. A second coil, at the right, is also wrapped around the iron ring and is connected to a galvanometer. We shall refer to this as the secondary coil and to the corresponding circuit as the secondary circuit. There is no battery in the secondary circuit and the secondary coil is not connected to the primary coil. The only purpose of this circuit is to show that a current is produced by a change in the magnetic field.

At first sight, you might guess that no current would ever be detected in the secondary circuit. However, something quite amazing happens when the switch in the primary circuit is suddenly closed or opened. At the instant the switch in the primary circuit is closed, the galvanometer in the secondary circuit deflects in one direction and then returns to zero. When the switch is opened, the galvanometer

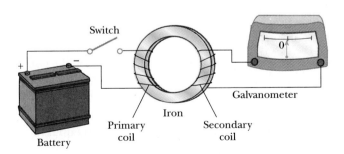

FIGURE 31.2   Faraday's experiment. When the switch in the primary circuit at the left is closed, the galvanometer in the secondary circuit at the right deflects momentarily. The emf induced in the secondary circuit is caused by the changing magnetic field through the coil in this circuit.

deflects in the opposite direction and again returns to zero. Finally, the galvanometer reads zero when there is a steady current in the primary circuit.

As a result of these observations, Faraday concluded that *an electric current can be produced by a changing magnetic field.* A current cannot be produced by a steady magnetic field. The current that is produced in the secondary circuit occurs for only an instant while the magnetic field through the secondary coil is changing. In effect, the secondary circuit behaves as though there were a source of emf connected to it for a short instant. It is customary to say that

> an induced emf is produced in the secondary circuit by the changing magnetic field.

These two experiments have one thing in common. In both cases, an emf is induced in a circuit when the magnetic flux through the circuit changes with time. In fact, a general statement that summarizes such experiments involving induced currents and emfs is as follows:

> The emf induced in a circuit is directly proportional to the time rate of change of magnetic flux through the circuit.

This statement, known as **Faraday's law of induction,** can be written

Faraday's law

$$\varepsilon = -\frac{d\Phi_B}{dt} \tag{31.1}$$

where Φ_B is the magnetic flux threading the circuit (Section 30.6), which can be expressed as

$$\Phi_B = \int \mathbf{B} \cdot d\mathbf{A} \tag{31.2}$$

The integral given by Equation 31.2 is taken over the area bounded by the circuit. The meaning of the negative sign in Equation 31.1 is a consequence of Lenz's law and will be discussed in Section 31.3. If the circuit is a coil consisting of *N* loops all of the same area and if the flux threads all loops, the induced emf is

$$\varepsilon = -N\frac{d\Phi_B}{dt} \tag{31.3}$$

Suppose the magnetic field is uniform over a loop of area *A* lying in a plane as in Figure 31.3. In this case, the flux through the loop is equal to $BA\cos\theta$; hence, the induced emf can be expressed as

$$\varepsilon = -\frac{d}{dt}(BA\cos\theta) \tag{31.4}$$

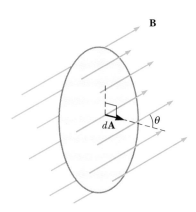

FIGURE 31.3 A conducting loop of area *A* in the presence of a uniform magnetic field **B**, which is at an angle θ with the normal to the loop.

From this expression, we see that an emf can be induced in the circuit in several ways:

- The magnitude of **B** can vary with time.
- The area of the circuit can change with time.
- The angle θ between **B** and the normal to the plane can change with time.
- Any combination of the above can occur.

Some Applications of Faraday's Law

The ground fault interrupter (GFI) is an interesting safety device that protects users of electrical power against electric shock when they touch appliances. Its operation makes use of Faraday's law. Figure 31.4 shows its essential parts. Wire 1 leads from the wall outlet to the appliance to be protected, and wire 2 leads from the appliance back to the wall outlet. An iron ring surrounds the two wires so as to confine the magnetic field set up by each wire. A sensing coil, which can activate a circuit breaker when changes in magnetic flux occur, is wrapped around part of the iron ring. Because the currents in the wires are in opposite directions, the net magnetic field through the sensing coil due to the currents is zero. However, if an insulation fault occurs that connects either the hot or neutral wire to the case, and thus to the safety ground or to the user holding the case, the net magnetic flux through the sensing coil is no longer zero. Because the current is alternating, the magnetic flux through the sensing coil changes with time, producing an induced voltage in the coil. This induced voltage is used to trigger a circuit breaker, stopping the current before it might be harmful to the person using the appliance.

Another interesting application of Faraday's law is the production of sound in an electric guitar. A vibrating string induces an emf in a coil (Fig. 31.5). The pickup coil is placed near the vibrating guitar string, which is made of a metal that can be magnetized. The permanent magnet inside the coil magnetizes the portion of the string nearest the coil. When the string vibrates at some frequency, its magnetized segment produces a changing magnetic flux through the pickup coil. The changing flux induces a voltage in the coil, and the voltage is fed to an

This modern electric range cooks food using the principle of induction. An oscillating current is passed through a coil placed below the cooking surface made of a special glass. The current produces an oscillating magnetic field, which induces a current in the cooking utensil. Since the cooking utensil has some electrical resistance, the electrical energy associated with the induced current transforms into thermal energy, causing the utensil and its contents to heat up. *(Corning Inc.)*

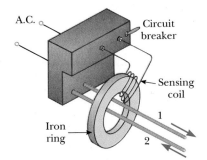

FIGURE 31.4 Essential components of a ground fault interrupter.

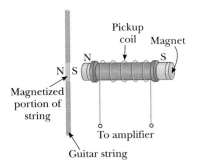

FIGURE 31.5 In an electric guitar, a vibrating string induces a voltage in a pickup coil.

amplifier. The output of the amplifier is sent to the loudspeakers, producing the sound waves that we hear.

EXAMPLE 31.1   One Way to Induce an Emf in a Coil

A coil is wrapped with 200 turns of wire on the perimeter of a square frame of sides 18 cm. Each turn has the same area, equal to that of the frame, and the total resistance of the coil is 2.0 Ω. A uniform magnetic field is turned on perpendicular to the plane of the coil. If the field changes linearly from 0 to 0.50 Wb/m² in a time of 0.80 s, find the magnitude of the induced emf in the coil while the field is changing.

Solution   The area of the loop is $(0.18 \text{ m})^2 = 0.0324 \text{ m}^2$. The magnetic flux through the loop at $t = 0$ is zero since $B = 0$. At $t = 0.80$ s, the magnetic flux through the loop is

$\Phi_B = BA = (0.50 \text{ Wb/m}^2)(0.0324 \text{ m}^2) = 0.0162 \text{ Wb}$. Therefore, the magnitude of the induced emf is

$$|\varepsilon| = \frac{N \Delta \Phi_B}{\Delta t} = \frac{200(0.0162 \text{ Wb} - 0 \text{ Wb})}{0.80 \text{ s}} = 4.1 \text{ V}$$

(Note that 1 Wb = 1 V·s.)

Exercise   What is the magnitude of the induced current in the coil while the field is changing?

Answer   2.0 A.

Michael Faraday

| 1 7 9 1 – 1 8 6 7 |

Michael Faraday was a British physicist and chemist who is often regarded as the greatest experimental scientist of the 1800s. His many contributions to the study of electricity include the invention of the electric motor, electric generator, and transformer, as well as the discovery of electromagnetic induction, the laws of electrolysis, the discovery of benzene, and the theory that the plane of polarization of light is rotated in an electric field.

Faraday was born in 1791 in rural England, but his family moved to London shortly thereafter. One of ten children and the son of a blacksmith, Faraday received a minimal education and became apprenticed to a bookbinder at age 14. He was fascinated by articles on electricity and chemistry and was fortunate to have an employer who allowed him to read books and attend scientific lectures. He received some education in science from the City Philosophical Society.

When Faraday finished his apprenticeship in 1812, he expected to devote himself to bookbinding rather than to science. That same year, Fara-

day attended a lecture by Humphry Davy, who made many contributions in the field of heat and thermodynamics. Faraday sent 386 pages of notes, bound in leather, to Davy; Davy was impressed and appointed Faraday his permanent assistant at the Royal Institution. Faraday toured France and

Italy from 1813 to 1815 with Davy, visiting leading scientists of the time such as Volta and Vauquelin.

Despite his limited mathematical ability, Faraday succeeded in making the basic discoveries on which virtually all our uses of electricity depend. He conceived the fundamental nature of magnetism and, to a degree, that of electricity and light.

A modest man who was content to serve science as best he could, Faraday declined a knighthood and an offer to become president of the Royal Society. He was also a moral man; he refused to take part in the preparation of poison gas for use in the Crimean War.

Faraday died in 1867. His many achievements are recognized by the use of his name. The Faraday constant is the quantity of electricity required to deliver a standard amount of substance in electrolysis, and the SI unit of capacitance is the farad.

(By kind permission of the President and Council of the Royal Society)

EXAMPLE 31.2   An Exponentially Decaying B Field

A plane loop of wire of area A is placed in a region where the magnetic field is perpendicular to the plane. The magnitude of **B** varies in time according to the expression $B = B_0 e^{-at}$. That is, at $t = 0$ the field is B_0, and for $t > 0$, the field decreases exponentially in time (Fig. 31.6). Find the induced emf in the loop as a function of time.

Solution   Since **B** is perpendicular to the plane of the loop, the magnetic flux through the loop at time $t > 0$ is

$$\Phi_B = BA = AB_0 e^{-at}$$

Also, since the coefficient AB_0 and the parameter a are constants, the induced emf can be calculated from Equation 31.1:

$$\mathcal{E} = -\frac{d\Phi_B}{dt} = -AB_0 \frac{d}{dt} e^{-at} = \boxed{aAB_0 e^{-at}}$$

That is, the induced emf decays exponentially in time. Note that the maximum emf occurs at $t = 0$, where $\mathcal{E}_{max} = aAB_0$. Why is this true? The plot of $\mathcal{E}$ versus t is similar to the B versus t curve shown in Figure 31.4.

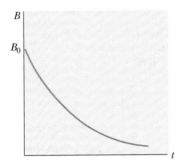

FIGURE 31.6   (Example 31.2) Exponential decrease of the magnetic field with time. The induced emf and induced current have similar time variations.

31.2   MOTIONAL EMF

In Examples 31.1 and 31.2, we considered cases in which an emf is produced in a circuit when the magnetic field changes with time. In this section we describe the so-called **motional emf**, which is the emf induced in a conductor moving through a magnetic field.

First, consider a straight conductor of length ℓ moving with constant velocity through a uniform magnetic field directed into the paper as in Figure 31.7. For simplicity, we shall assume that the conductor is moving perpendicularly to the field. The electrons in the conductor will experience a force along the conductor given by $\mathbf{F} = q\mathbf{v} \times \mathbf{B}$. Under the influence of this force, the electrons will move to the lower end and accumulate there, leaving a net positive charge at the upper end. An electric field is therefore produced within the conductor as a result of this charge separation. The charge at the ends builds up until the magnetic force qvB is balanced by the electric force qE. At this point, charge stops flowing and the condition for equilibrium requires that

$$qE = qvB \quad \text{or} \quad E = vB$$

Since the electric field is constant, the electric field produced in the conductor is related to the potential difference across the ends according to the relationship $V = E\ell$. Thus,

$$V = E\ell = B\ell v$$

where the upper end is at a higher potential than the lower end. Thus, *a potential difference is maintained between the ends of the conductor as long as there is motion through the field. If the motion is reversed, the polarity of V is also reversed.*

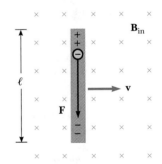

FIGURE 31.7   A straight conducting bar of length ℓ moving with a velocity **v** through a uniform magnetic field **B** directed perpendicular to **v**. An emf equal to $B\ell v$ is induced between the ends of the bar.

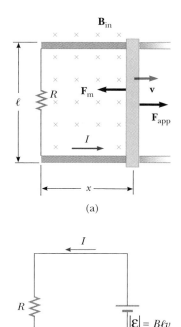

FIGURE 31.8 (a) A conducting bar sliding with a velocity **v** along two conducting rails under the action of an applied force **F**$_{app}$. The magnetic force **F**$_m$ opposes the motion, and a counterclockwise current is induced in the loop. (b) The equivalent circuit of (a).

A more interesting situation occurs if the moving conductor is part of a closed conducting path. This situation is particularly useful for illustrating how a changing magnetic flux can cause an induced current in a closed circuit. Consider a circuit consisting of a conducting bar of length ℓ sliding along two fixed parallel conducting rails as in Figure 31.8a. For simplicity, we assume that the moving bar has zero resistance and that the stationary part of the circuit has a resistance R. A uniform and constant magnetic field **B** is applied perpendicularly to the plane of the circuit. As the bar is pulled to the right with a velocity **v**, under the influence of an applied force **F**$_{app}$, free charges in the bar experience a magnetic force along the length of the bar. This force, in turn, sets up an induced current since the charges are free to move in a closed conducting path. In this case, the rate of change of magnetic flux through the loop and the corresponding induced emf across the moving bar are proportional to the change in area of the loop as the bar moves through the magnetic field. As we shall see, if the bar is pulled to the right with a constant velocity, the work done by the applied force is dissipated in the form of joule heating in the circuit's resistive element.

Since the area of the circuit at any instant is ℓx, the external magnetic flux through the circuit is

$$\Phi_B = B\ell x$$

where x is the width of the circuit, which changes with time. Using Faraday's law, we find that the induced emf is

$$\mathcal{E} = -\frac{d\Phi_B}{dt} = -\frac{d}{dt}(B\ell x) = -B\ell\frac{dx}{dt}$$

$$\mathcal{E} = -B\ell v \tag{31.5}$$

If the resistance of the circuit is R, the magnitude of the induced current is

$$I = \frac{|\mathcal{E}|}{R} = \frac{B\ell v}{R} \tag{31.6}$$

The equivalent circuit diagram for this example is shown in Figure 31.8b.

Let us examine the system using energy considerations. Since there is no battery in the circuit, one might wonder about the origin of the induced current and the electrical energy in the system. We can understand this by noting that the external force does work on the conductor, thereby moving charges through a magnetic field. This causes the charges to move along the conductor with some average drift velocity, and hence a current is established. From the viewpoint of energy conservation, the total work done by the applied force during some time interval should equal the electrical energy that the induced emf supplied in that same period. Furthermore, if the bar moves with constant speed, the work done must equal the energy dissipated as heat in the resistor in this time interval.

As the conductor of length ℓ moves through the uniform magnetic field **B**, it experiences a magnetic force **F**$_m$ of magnitude $I\ell B$ (Section 29.2). The direction of this force is opposite the motion of the bar, or to the left in Figure 31.8a.

If the bar is to move with a constant velocity, the applied force must be equal to and opposite the magnetic force, or to the right in Figure 31.8a. If the magnetic force acted in the direction of motion, it would cause the bar to accelerate once it was in motion, thereby increasing its velocity. This state of affairs would represent a violation of the principle of energy conservation. Using Equation 31.6 and the fact that $F_{app} = I\ell B$, we find that the power delivered by the applied force is

$$P = F_{app}v = (I\ell B)v = \frac{B^2\ell^2v^2}{R} = \frac{V^2}{R} \qquad (31.7)$$

This power is equal to the rate at which energy is dissipated in the resistor, I^2R, as we would expect. It is also equal to the power $I\mathcal{E}$ supplied by the induced emf. This example is a clear demonstration of the conversion of mechanical energy into electrical energy and finally into thermal energy (joule heating).

CONCEPTUAL EXAMPLE 31.3

A circular loop of wire is located in a uniform and constant magnetic field. Describe how an emf can be induced in the loop.

Reasoning According to Faraday's law, an emf is induced in a wire loop if the magnetic flux through the loop changes with time. In this situation, an emf can be induced by either rotating the loop around an arbitrary axis or by changing the shape of the loop.

CONCEPTUAL EXAMPLE 31.4

A spacecraft orbiting the Earth has a coil of wire in it. An astronaut measures a small current in the coil although there is no battery connected to it and there are no magnets on the spacecraft. What is causing the current?

Reasoning As the spacecraft moves through space, it is apparently moving from a region of one magnetic field strength to a region of a different magnetic field strength. The changing magnetic field through the coil induces an emf and a corresponding induced current in the coil.

EXAMPLE 31.5   Emf Induced in a Rotating Bar

A conducting bar of length ℓ rotates with a constant angular speed ω about a pivot at one end. A uniform magnetic field **B** is directed perpendicularly to the plane of rotation, as in Figure 31.9. Find the emf induced between the ends of the bar.

Solution Consider a segment of the bar of length dr, whose velocity is v. According to Equation 31.5, the emf induced in a conductor of this length moving perpendicularly to a field **B** is

$$(1) \qquad d\mathcal{E} = Bv\,dr$$

Each segment of the bar is moving perpendicularly to **B**, so there is an emf generated across each segment; the value of this emf is given by (1). Summing up the emfs induced across

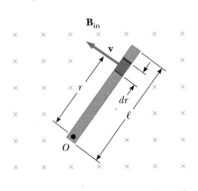

FIGURE 31.9 (Example 31.5) A conducting bar rotating around a pivot at one end in a uniform magnetic field that is perpendicular to the plane of rotation. An emf is induced across the ends of the bar.

all elements, which are in series, gives the total emf between the ends of the bar. That is,

$$\mathcal{E} = \int Bv \, dr$$

In order to integrate this expression, note that the linear speed of an element is related to the angular speed ω through the relationship $v = r\omega$. Therefore, since B and ω are constants, we find that

$$\mathcal{E} = B \int v \, dr = B\omega \int_0^\ell r \, dr = \tfrac{1}{2} B\omega\ell^2$$

EXAMPLE 31.6   Magnetic Force on a Sliding Bar

A bar of mass m and length ℓ moves on two frictionless parallel rails in the presence of a uniform magnetic field directed into the paper (Fig. 31.10). The bar is given an initial velocity v_0 to the right and is released. Find the velocity of the bar as a function of time.

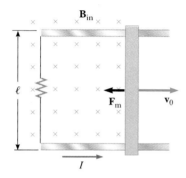

FIGURE 31.10   (Example 31.6) A conducting bar of length ℓ sliding on two fixed conducting rails is given an initial velocity v_0 to the right.

Solution   First note that the induced current is counterclockwise and the magnetic force is $F_m = -I\ell B$, where the negative sign denotes that the force is to the left and retards the motion. This is the only horizontal force acting on the bar, and hence Newton's second law applied to motion in the horizontal direction gives

$$F_x = ma = m\frac{dv}{dt} = -I\ell B$$

Since the induced current is given by Equation 31.6, $I = B\ell v/R$, we can write this expression as

$$m\frac{dv}{dt} = -\frac{B^2 \ell^2}{R} v$$

$$\frac{dv}{v} = -\left(\frac{B^2 \ell^2}{mR}\right) dt$$

Integrating this last equation using the initial condition that $v = v_0$ at $t = 0$, we find that

$$\int_{v_0}^v \frac{dv}{v} = \frac{-B^2 \ell^2}{mR} \int_0^t dt$$

$$\ln\left(\frac{v}{v_0}\right) = -\left(\frac{B^2 \ell^2}{mR}\right) t = -\frac{t}{\tau}$$

where the constant $\tau = mR/B^2 \ell^2$. From this, we see that the velocity can be expressed in the exponential form

$$v = v_0 e^{-t/\tau}$$

Therefore, the velocity of the bar decreases exponentially with time under the action of the magnetic retarding force. Furthermore, if we substitute this result into Equations 31.5 and 31.6, we find that the induced emf and induced current also decrease exponentially with time. That is,

$$I = \frac{B\ell v}{R} = \frac{B\ell v_0}{R} e^{-t/\tau}$$

$$\mathcal{E} = IR = B\ell v_0 e^{-t/\tau}$$

31.3   LENZ'S LAW

The direction of the induced emf and induced current can be found from **Lenz's law,**[2] which can be stated as follows:

A statement of Lenz's law

The polarity of the induced emf is such that it tends to produce a current that will create a magnetic flux to oppose the change in magnetic flux through the loop.

---

[2] Developed by the German physicist Heinrich Lenz (1804–1865).

That is, the induced current tends to keep the original flux through the circuit from changing. The interpretation of this statement depends on the circumstances. As we shall see, this law is a consequence of the law of conservation of energy.

In order to obtain a better understanding of Lenz's law, let us return to the example of a bar moving to the right on two parallel rails in the presence of a uniform magnetic field directed into the paper (Fig. 31.11a). As the bar moves to the right, the magnetic flux through the circuit increases with time since the area of the loop increases. Lenz's law says that the induced current must be in a direction so that the flux it produces opposes the change in the external magnetic flux. Since the flux due to the external field is increasing into the paper, the induced current, if it is to oppose the change, must produce a flux out of the paper. Hence, the induced current must be counterclockwise when the bar moves to the right to give a counteracting flux out of the paper in the region inside the loop. (Use the right-hand rule to verify this direction.) On the other hand, if the bar is moving to the left, as in Figure 31.11b, the magnetic flux through the loop decreases with time. Since the flux is into the paper, the induced current has to be clockwise to produce a flux into the paper inside the loop. In either case, the induced current tends to maintain the original flux through the circuit.

Let us look at this situation from the viewpoint of energy considerations. Suppose that the bar is given a slight push to the right. In the above analysis, we found that this motion leads to a counterclockwise current in the loop. Let us see what happens if we assume that the current is clockwise. For a clockwise current I, the direction of the magnetic force on the sliding bar would be to the right. This force would accelerate the rod and increase its velocity. This, in turn, would cause the area of the loop to increase more rapidly, thus increasing the induced current, which would increase the force, which would increase the current, which would . . . . In effect, the system would acquire energy with no additional input energy. This is clearly inconsistent with all experience and with the law of conservation of energy. Thus, we are forced to conclude that the current must be counterclockwise.

Consider another situation, one in which a bar magnet is moved to the right toward a stationary loop of wire, as in Figure 31.12a. As the magnet moves to the right toward the loop, the magnetic flux through the loop increases with time. To counteract this increase in flux to the right, the induced current produces a flux to the left, as in Figure 31.12b; hence, the induced current is in the direction shown.

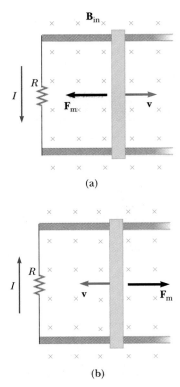

FIGURE 31.11 (a) As the conducting bar slides on the two fixed conducting rails, the magnetic flux through the loop increases in time. By Lenz's law, the induced current must be counterclockwise so as to produce a counteracting flux out of the paper. (b) When the bar moves to the left, the induced current must be clockwise. Why?

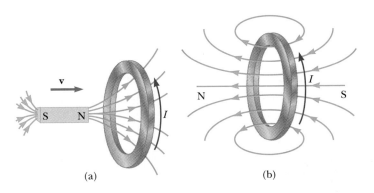

FIGURE 31.12 (a) When the magnet is moved toward the stationary conducting loop, a current is induced in the direction shown. (b) This induced current produces its own flux to the left to counteract the increasing external flux to the right.

Note that the magnetic field lines associated with the induced current oppose the motion of the magnet. Therefore, the left face of the current loop is a north pole and the right face is a south pole.

On the other hand, if the magnet were moving to the left, its flux through the loop, which is toward the right, would decrease in time. Under these circumstances, the induced current in the loop would be in a direction so as to set up a field through the loop directed from left to right in an effort to maintain a constant number of flux lines. Hence, the induced current in the loop would be opposite that shown in Figure 31.12b. In this case, the left face of the loop would be a south pole and the right face would be a north pole.

CONCEPTIONAL EXAMPLE 31.7   Application of Lenz's Law

A coil of wire is placed near an electromagnet as shown in Figure 31.13a. Find the direction of the induced current in the coil (a) at the instant the switch is closed, (b) after the switch has been closed for several seconds, and (c) when the switch is opened.

Reasoning (a) When the switch is closed, the situation changes from a condition in which no lines of flux pass through the coil to one in which lines of flux pass through in the direction shown in Figure 31.13b. To counteract this change in the number of lines, the coil must set up a field from left to right in the figure. This requires a current directed as shown in Figure 31.13b.

(b) After the switch has been closed for several seconds, there is no change in the number of lines through the loop; hence, the induced current is zero.

(c) Opening the switch causes the magnetic field to change from a condition in which flux lines thread through the coil from right to left to a condition of zero flux. The induced current must then be as shown in Figure 31.13c, so as to set up its own field from right to left.

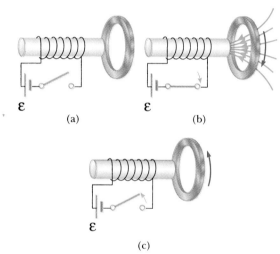

(a)   (b)

(c)

FIGURE 31.13   (Conceptual Example 31.7).

EXAMPLE 31.8   A Loop Moving Through a B Field

A rectangular loop of dimensions ℓ and w and resistance R moves with constant speed v to the right, as in Figure 31.14a. It continues to move with this speed through a region containing a uniform magnetic field **B** directed into the paper and extending a distance $3w$. Plot (a) the flux, (b) the induced emf, and (c) the external force acting on the loop as a function of the position of the loop in the field.

Reasoning and Solution (a) Figure 31.14b shows the flux through the loop as a function of loop position. Before the loop enters the field, the flux is zero. As it enters the field, the flux increases linearly with position. Finally, the flux decreases linearly to zero as the loop leaves the field.

(b) Before the loop enters the field, there is no induced emf since there is no field present (Fig. 31.14c). As the right side of the loop enters the field, the flux inward begins to increase. Hence, according to Lenz's law, the induced current is counterclockwise and the induced emf is given by $-B\ell v$. This motional emf arises from the magnetic force experienced by charges in the right side of the loop. When the loop is entirely in the field, the change in flux is zero, and hence the induced emf vanishes.

From another point of view, the right and left sides of the loop experience magnetic forces that tend to set up currents that cancel one another. As the right side of the loop leaves the field, the flux inward begins to decrease, a clockwise current is induced, and the induced emf is $B\ell v$. As soon as the left side leaves the field, the emf drops to zero.

(c) The external force that must act on the loop to maintain this motion is plotted in Figure 31.14d. When the loop is not in the field, there is no magnetic force on it; hence, the external force on it must be zero if v is constant. When the right side of the loop enters the field, the external force necessary to maintain constant speed must be equal to and opposite the magnetic force on that side, given by $F_m = -I\ell B = -B^2 \ell^2 v/R$. When the loop is entirely in the field, the flux through the loop is not changing with time. Hence, the net emf induced in the loop is zero, and the current is also zero. Therefore, no external force is needed to maintain the motion of the loop. (From another point of view, the

right and left sides of the loop experience equal and opposite forces; hence, the net force is zero.) Finally, as the right side leaves the field, the external force must be equal to and opposite the magnetic force on the left side of the loop. From this analysis, we conclude that power is supplied only when the loop is either entering or leaving the field. Furthermore, this example shows that the induced emf in the loop can be zero even when there is motion through the field! Again, it is emphasized that an emf is induced in the loop only when the magnetic flux through the loop changes in time.

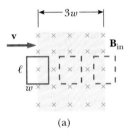

(a)

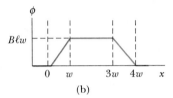

(b)

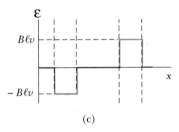

(c)

FIGURE 31.14 (Example 31.8) (a) A conducting rectangular loop of width w and length ℓ moving with a velocity $\mathbf{v}$ through a uniform magnetic field extending a distance $3w$. (b) A plot of the flux as a function of the position of the loop. (c) A plot of the induced emf versus the position of the leading edge. (d) A plot of the force versus position such that the velocity of the loop remains constant.

(d)

31.4 INDUCED EMFS AND ELECTRIC FIELDS

We have seen that a changing magnetic flux induces an emf and a current in a conducting loop. We therefore must conclude that *an electric field is created in the conductor as a result of the changing magnetic flux*. In fact, the law of electromagnetic induction shows that *an electric field is always generated by a changing magnetic flux*, even in free space where no charges are present. However, this induced electric field has properties that are quite different from those of an electrostatic field *produced by stationary charges*.

We can illustrate this point by considering a conducting loop of radius r situated in a uniform magnetic field that is perpendicular to the plane of the loop, as in Figure 31.15. If the magnetic field changes with time, then Faraday's law tells us that an emf given by $\mathcal{E} = -d\Phi_B/dt$ is induced in the loop. The induced current that is produced implies the presence of an induced electric field $\mathbf{E}$, which must be tangent to the loop since all points on the loop are equivalent. The work done in moving a test charge q once around the loop is equal to $q\mathcal{E}$. Since the electric force on the charge is $q\mathbf{E}$, the work done by this force in moving the charge once around

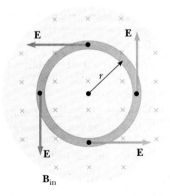

FIGURE 31.15 A loop of radius r in a uniform magnetic field perpendicular to the plane of the loop. If $\mathbf{B}$ changes in time, an electric field is induced in a direction tangent to the loop.

the loop is given by $qE(2\pi r)$, where $2\pi r$ is the circumference of the loop. These two expressions for the work must be equal; therefore, we see that

$$q\mathcal{E} = qE(2\pi r)$$

$$E = \frac{\mathcal{E}}{2\pi r}$$

Using this result, Faraday's law, and the fact that $\Phi_B = BA = \pi r^2 B$ for a circular loop, we find that the induced electric field can be expressed as

$$E = -\frac{1}{2\pi r}\frac{d\Phi_B}{dt} = -\frac{r}{2}\frac{dB}{dt} \qquad (31.8)$$

If the time variation of the magnetic field is specified, the induced electric field can easily be calculated from Equation 31.8. The negative sign indicates that the induced electric field E opposes the change in the magnetic field. It is important to understand that *this result is also valid in the absence of a conductor.* That is, a free charge placed in a changing magnetic field will also experience the same electric field.

The emf for any closed path can be expressed as the line integral of $\mathbf{E} \cdot d\mathbf{s}$ over that path. In more general cases, E may not be constant, and the path may not be a circle. Hence, Faraday's law of induction, $\mathcal{E} = -d\Phi_B/dt$, can be written as

Faraday's law in general form

$$\oint \mathbf{E} \cdot d\mathbf{s} = -\frac{d\Phi_B}{dt} \qquad (31.9)$$

It is important to recognize that *the induced electric field* E *that appears in Equation 31.9 is a nonconservative, time-varying field that is generated by a changing magnetic field.* The field E that satisfies Equation 31.9 could not possibly be an electrostatic field for the following reason. If the field were electrostatic, and hence conservative, the line integral of $\mathbf{E} \cdot d\mathbf{s}$ over a closed loop would be zero, contrary to Equation 31.9.

EXAMPLE 31.9   Electric Field Due to a Solenoid

A long solenoid of radius R has n turns per unit length and carries a time-varying current that varies sinusoidally as $I = I_0 \cos \omega t$, where I_0 is the maximum current and ω is the angular frequency of the current source (Fig. 31.16). (a) Determine the electric field outside the solenoid, a distance r from its axis.

Solution   First, let us consider an external point and take the path for our line integral to be a circle centered on the solenoid, as in Figure 31.16. By symmetry we see that the magnitude of **E** is constant on this path and tangent to it. The magnetic flux through this path is given by $BA = B(\pi R^2)$, and hence Equation 31.9 gives

$$\oint \mathbf{E} \cdot d\mathbf{s} = -\frac{d}{dt}[B(\pi R^2)] = -\pi R^2 \frac{dB}{dt}$$

$$E(2\pi r) = -\pi R^2 \frac{dB}{dt}$$

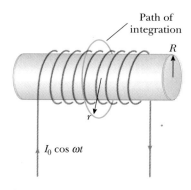

FIGURE 31.16   (Example 31.9) A long solenoid carrying a time-varying current given by $I = I_0 \cos \omega t$. An electric field is induced both inside and outside the solenoid.

Since the magnetic field inside a long solenoid is given by Equation 30.20, $B = \mu_0 nI$, and $I = I_0 \cos \omega t$, we find that

$$E(2\pi r) = -\pi R^2 \mu_0 nI_0 \frac{d}{dt}(\cos \omega t) = \pi R^2 \mu_0 nI_0 \omega \sin \omega t$$

$$E = \frac{\mu_0 nI_0 \omega R^2}{2r} \sin \omega t \qquad \text{(for } r > R)$$

Hence, the electric field varies sinusoidally with time, and its amplitude falls off as $1/r$ outside the solenoid.

(b) What is the electric field inside the solenoid, a distance r from its axis?

Solution For an interior point ($r < R$), the flux threading an integration loop is given by $B(\pi r^2)$. Using the same procedure as in part (a), we find that

$$E(2\pi r) = -\pi r^2 \frac{dB}{dt} = \pi r^2 \mu_0 nI_0 \omega \sin \omega t$$

$$E = \frac{\mu_0 nI_0 \omega}{2} r \sin \omega t \qquad \text{(for } r < R)$$

This shows that the amplitude of the electric field inside the solenoid increases linearly with r and varies sinusoidally with time.

*31.5 GENERATORS AND MOTORS

Generators and motors are important devices that operate on the principle of electromagnetic induction. First, let us consider the **alternating current generator** (or ac generator), a device that converts mechanical energy to electrical energy. In its simplest form, the ac generator consists of a loop of wire rotated by some external means in a magnetic field (Fig. 31.17a). In commercial power plants, the energy required to rotate the loop can be derived from a variety of sources. For example, in a hydroelectric plant, falling water directed against the blades of a turbine produces the rotary motion; in a coal-fired plant, the heat produced by burning coal is used to convert water to steam and this steam is directed against the turbine blades. As the loop rotates, the magnetic flux through it changes with time, inducing an emf and a current in an external circuit. The ends of the loop are connected to slip rings that rotate with the loop. Connections to the external circuit are made by stationary brushes in contact with the slip rings.

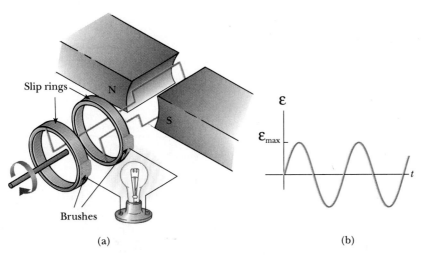

(a)   (b)

FIGURE 31.17 (a) Schematic diagram of an ac generator. An emf is induced in a coil that rotates by some external means in a magnetic field. (b) The alternating emf induced in the loop plotted versus time.

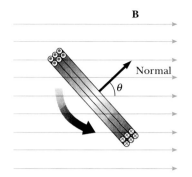

FIGURE 31.18   A loop of area A containing N turns, rotating with constant angular speed ω in the presence of a magnetic field. The emf induced in the loop varies sinusoidally in time.

To put our discussion of the generator on a quantitative basis, suppose that the loop has N turns (a more practical situation), all of the same area A, and suppose that the loop rotates with a constant angular speed ω. If θ is the angle between the magnetic field and the normal to the plane of the loop as in Figure 31.18, then the magnetic flux through the loop at any time t is

$$\Phi_B = BA \cos \theta = BA \cos \omega t$$

where we have used the relationship between angular displacement and angular speed, $\theta = \omega t$. (We have set the clock so that $t = 0$ when $\theta = 0$.) Hence, the induced emf in the coil is

$$\mathcal{E} = -N\frac{d\Phi_B}{dt} = -NAB\frac{d}{dt}(\cos \omega t) = NAB\omega \sin \omega t \qquad (31.10)$$

This result shows that the emf varies sinusoidally with time, as plotted in Figure 31.17b. From Equation 31.10 we see that the maximum emf has the value

$$\mathcal{E}_{\max} = NAB\omega \qquad (31.11)$$

which occurs when $\omega t = 90°$ or $270°$. In other words, $\mathcal{E} = \mathcal{E}_{\max}$ when the magnetic field is in the plane of the coil, and the time rate of change of flux is a maximum. Furthermore, the emf is zero when $\omega t = 0$ or $180°$, that is, when $\mathbf{B}$ is perpendicular to the plane of the coil, and the time rate of change of flux is zero. The frequency for commercial generators in the United States and Canada is 60 Hz, whereas in some European countries, 50 Hz is used. (Recall that $\omega = 2\pi f$, where f is the frequency in hertz.)

EXAMPLE 31.10   Emf Induced in a Generator

An ac generator consists of eight turns of wire each of area $A = 0.0900$ m^2 and total resistance 12.0 Ω. The loop rotates in a magnetic field $B = 0.500$ T at a constant frequency of 60.0 Hz. (a) Find the maximum induced emf.

Solution   First note that

$$\omega = 2\pi f = 2\pi(60.0 \text{ Hz}) = 377 \text{ s}^{-1}.$$

Using Equation 31.11 with the appropriate numerical values gives

$$\mathcal{E}_{\max} = NAB\omega = 8(0.0900 \text{ m}^2)(0.500 \text{ T})(377 \text{ s}^{-1})$$

$$= \boxed{136 \text{ V}}$$

(b) What is the maximum induced current?

Solution   From Ohm's law and the results to part (a), we find that the maximum induced current is

$$I_{\max} = \frac{\mathcal{E}_{\max}}{R} = \frac{136 \text{ V}}{12.0 \text{ }\Omega} = \boxed{11.3 \text{ A}}$$

Exercise   Determine the time variation of the induced emf and induced current when the output terminals are connected by a low-resistance conductor.

Answers

$$\mathcal{E} = \mathcal{E}_{\max} \sin \omega t = (136 \text{ V})\sin 377t$$

$$I = I_{\max} \sin \omega t = (11.3 \text{ A})\sin 377t$$

The **direct current** (dc) **generator** is illustrated in Figure 31.19a. Such generators are used, for instance, to charge storage batteries in older style cars. The components are essentially the same as those of the ac generator, except that the contacts to the rotating loop are made using a split ring, or commutator.

In this configuration, the output voltage always has the same polarity and the current is a pulsating direct current as in Figure 31.19b. The reason for this can be

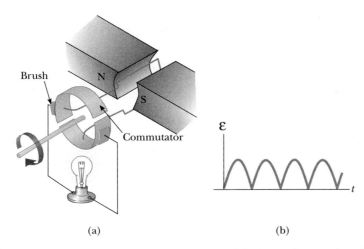

FIGURE 31.19 (a) Schematic diagram of a dc generator. (b) The emf versus time fluctuates in magnitude but always has the same polarity.

understood by noting that the contacts to the split ring reverse their roles every half cycle. At the same time, the polarity of the induced emf reverses; hence, the polarity of the split ring (which is the same as the polarity of the output voltage) remains the same.

A pulsating dc current is not suitable for most applications. To obtain a more steady dc current, commercial dc generators use many armature coils and commutators distributed so that the sinusoidal pulses from the various coils are out of phase. When these pulses are superimposed, the dc output is almost free of fluctuations.

Motors are devices that convert electrical energy into mechanical energy. Essentially, *a motor is a generator operating in reverse.* Instead of generating a current by rotating a loop, a current is supplied to the loop by a battery and the torque acting on the current-carrying loop causes it to rotate.

Useful mechanical work can be done by attaching the rotating armature to some external device. However, as the loop rotates, the changing magnetic flux induces an emf in the loop; this induced emf always acts to reduce the current in the loop. If this were not the case, Lenz's law would be violated. The back emf increases in magnitude as the rotational speed of the armature increases. (The phrase *back emf* is used to indicate an emf that tends to reduce the supplied current.) Since the voltage available to supply current equals the difference between the supply voltage and the back emf, the current through the armature coil is limited by the back emf.

When a motor is first turned on, there is initially no back emf and the current is very large because it is limited only by the resistance of the coil. As the coils begin to rotate, the induced back emf opposes the applied voltage and the current in the coils is reduced. If the mechanical load increases, the motor will slow down, which causes the back emf to decrease. This reduction in the back emf increases the current in the coils and therefore also increases the power needed from the external voltage source. For this reason, the power requirements are greater for starting a motor and for running it under heavy loads. If the motor is allowed to run under no mechanical load, the back emf reduces the current to a value just large enough to overcome energy losses due to heat and friction.

EXAMPLE 31.11   The Induced Current in a Motor

Assume that a motor having coils with a resistance of 10 Ω is supplied by a voltage of 120 V. When the motor is running at its maximum speed, the back emf is 70 V. Find the current in the coils (a) when the motor is first turned on and (b) when the motor has reached maximum speed.

Solution   (a) When the motor is first turned on, the back emf is zero. (The coils are motionless.) Thus the current in the coils is a maximum and equal to

$$I = \frac{\mathcal{E}}{R} = \frac{120 \text{ V}}{10 \text{ } \Omega} = \boxed{12 \text{ A}}$$

(b) At the maximum speed, the back emf has its maximum value. Thus, the effective supply voltage is now that of the external source minus the back emf. Hence, the current is reduced to

$$I = \frac{\mathcal{E} - \mathcal{E}_{\text{back}}}{R} = \frac{120 \text{ V} - 70 \text{ V}}{10 \text{ } \Omega} = \frac{50 \text{ V}}{10 \text{ } \Omega} = \boxed{5.0 \text{ A}}$$

Exercise   If the current in the motor is 8.0 A at some instant, what is the back emf at this time?

Answer   40 V.

*31.6 EDDY CURRENTS

As we have seen, an emf and a current are induced in a circuit by a changing magnetic flux. In the same manner, circulating currents called **eddy currents** are set up in bulk pieces of metal moving through a magnetic field. This can easily be demonstrated by allowing a flat metal plate at the end of a rigid bar to swing as a pendulum through a magnetic field (Fig. 31.20). The metal should be a material such as aluminum or copper. As the plate enters the field, the changing flux creates an induced emf in the plate, which in turn causes the free electrons in the metal to move, producing the swirling eddy currents. According to Lenz's law, the direction of the eddy currents must oppose the change that causes them. For this reason, the eddy currents must produce effective magnetic poles on the plate, which are repelled by the poles of the magnet, thus giving rise to a repulsive force that opposes the motion of the pendulum. (If the opposite were true, the pendulum would accelerate and its energy would increase after each swing, in violation of the law of energy conservation.) Alternatively, the retarding force can be "felt" by pulling a metal sheet through the field of a strong magnet.

As indicated in Figure 31.21, with **B** into the paper, the eddy current is counterclockwise as the swinging plate enters the field in position 1. This is because the external flux into the paper is increasing, and hence by Lenz's law the induced current must provide a flux out of the paper. The opposite is true as the plate leaves the field in position 2, where the current is clockwise. Since the induced eddy current always produces a retarding force F when the plate enters or leaves the field, the swinging plate eventually comes to rest.

If slots are cut in the metal plate as in Figure 31.22, the eddy currents and the corresponding retarding force are greatly reduced. This can be understood since the cuts in the plate result in open circuits for any large current loops that might otherwise be formed.

The braking systems on many subway and rapid transit cars make use of electromagnetic induction and eddy currents. An electromagnet, which can be energized with a current, is positioned near the steel rails. The braking action occurs when a large current is passed through the electromagnet. The relative motion of the magnet and rails induces eddy currents in the rails, and the direction of these currents produces a drag force on the moving vehicle. The loss in mechanical energy of the vehicle is transformed into joule heat. Since the eddy currents decrease steadily in magnitude as the vehicle slows down, the braking effect is quite

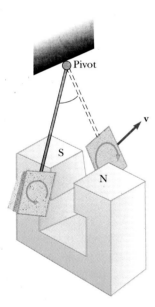

FIGURE 31.20   An apparatus that demonstrates the formation of eddy currents in a conductor moving through a magnetic field. As the plate enters or leaves the field, the changing flux sets up an induced emf, which causes the eddy currents in the plate.

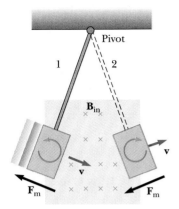

FIGURE 31.21 As the conducting plate enters the field in position 1, the eddy currents are counter-clockwise. However, in position 2, the currents are clockwise. In either case, the plate is repelled by the magnet and eventually comes to rest.

FIGURE 31.22 When slots are cut in the conducting plate, the eddy currents are reduced and the plate swings more freely through the magnetic field.

smooth. Eddy current brakes are also used in some mechanical balances and in various machines.

Eddy currents are often undesirable since they dissipate energy in the form of heat. To reduce this energy loss, the moving conducting parts are often laminated, that is, built up in thin layers separated by a nonconducting material such as lacquer or a metal oxide. This layered structure increases the resistance of the possible paths of the eddy currents and effectively confines the currents to individual layers. Such a laminated structure is used in the cores of transformers and motors to minimize eddy currents and thereby increase the efficiency of these devices.

31.7 MAXWELL'S WONDERFUL EQUATIONS

We conclude this chapter by presenting four equations that can be regarded as the basis of all electrical and magnetic phenomena. These equations, known as Maxwell's equations, after James Clerk Maxwell, are as fundamental to electromagnetic phenomena as Newton's laws are to the study of mechanical phenomena. In fact, the theory developed by Maxwell was more far-reaching than even he imagined at the time, because it turned out to be in agreement with the special theory of relativity, as Einstein showed in 1905. As we shall see, Maxwell's equations represent laws of electricity and magnetism that have already been discussed. However, the equations have additional important consequences. In Chapter 34 we shall show that these equations predict the existence of electromagnetic waves (traveling patterns of electric and magnetic fields), which travel with a speed $c = 1/\sqrt{\mu_0\epsilon_0} \approx 3 \times 10^8$ m/s, the speed of light. Furthermore, the theory shows that such waves are radiated by accelerating charges.

For simplicity, we present **Maxwell's equations** as applied to free space, that is, in the absence of any dielectric or magnetic material. These are the four equations:

$$\oint \mathbf{E} \cdot d\mathbf{A} = \frac{Q}{\epsilon_0} \tag{31.12}$$

$$\oint \mathbf{B} \cdot d\mathbf{A} = 0 \tag{31.13}$$

$$\oint \mathbf{E} \cdot d\mathbf{s} = -\frac{d\Phi_B}{dt} \tag{31.14}$$

$$\oint \mathbf{B} \cdot d\mathbf{s} = \mu_0 I + \epsilon_0 \mu_0 \frac{d\Phi_E}{dt} \tag{31.15}$$

Let us discuss these equations one at a time. Equation 31.12 is Gauss's law, which states that *the total electric flux through any closed surface equals the net charge inside that surface divided by ϵ_0*. This law relates the electric field to the charge distribution, where electric field lines originate on positive charges and terminate on negative charges.

Equation 31.13, which can be considered *Gauss's law in magnetism,* says that *the net magnetic flux through a closed surface is zero.* That is, the number of magnetic field lines that enter a closed volume must equal the number that leave that volume. This implies that magnetic field lines cannot begin or end at any point. If they did, this would mean that isolated magnetic monopoles existed at those points. The fact that isolated magnetic monopoles have not been observed in nature can be taken as a confirmation of Equation 31.13.

Equation 31.14 is *Faraday's law of induction,* which describes the relationship between an electric field and a changing magnetic flux. This law states that *the line integral of the electric field around any closed path (which equals the emf) equals the rate of change of magnetic flux through any surface area bounded by that path.* One consequence of Faraday's law is the current induced in a conducting loop placed in a time-varying magnetic field.

Equation 31.15 is the generalized form of Ampère's law, which describes a relationship between magnetic and electric fields and electric currents. That is, *the line integral of the magnetic field around any closed path is determined by the sum of the net conduction current through that path and the rate of change of electric flux through any surface bounded by that path.*

Once the electric and magnetic fields are known at some point in space, the force on a particle of charge q can be calculated from the expression

$$\mathbf{F} = q\mathbf{E} + q\mathbf{v} \times \mathbf{B} \tag{31.16}$$

This is called the **Lorentz force.** Maxwell's equations, together with this force law, give a complete description of all classical electromagnetic interactions.

It is interesting to note the symmetry of Maxwell's equations. Equations 31.12 and 31.13 are symmetric, apart from the absence of a magnetic monopole term in Equation 31.13. Furthermore, Equations 31.14 and 31.15 are symmetric in that the line integrals of **E** and **B** around a closed path are related to the rate of change of magnetic flux and electric flux, respectively. "Maxwell's wonderful equations," as they were called by John R. Pierce,[3] are of fundamental importance not only to electronics but to all of science. Heinrich Hertz once wrote, "One cannot escape the feeling that these mathematical formulas have an independent existence and

[3] John R. Pierce, *Electrons and Waves,* New York, Doubleday Science Study Series, 1964. Chapter 6 of this interesting book is recommended as supplemental reading.

an intelligence of their own, that they are wiser than we are, wiser even than their discoverers, that we get more out of them than we put into them.''

SUMMARY

Faraday's law of induction states that the emf induced in a circuit is directly proportional to the time rate of change of magnetic flux through the circuit. That is,

$$\mathcal{E} = -\frac{d\Phi_B}{dt} \tag{31.1}$$

where Φ_B is the magnetic flux:

$$\Phi_B = \int \mathbf{B} \cdot d\mathbf{A} \tag{31.2}$$

When a conducting bar of length ℓ moves through a magnetic field $\mathbf{B}$ with a speed v such that $\mathbf{B}$ is perpendicular to the bar, the emf induced in the bar (the so-called **motional emf**) is

$$\mathcal{E} = -B\ell v \tag{31.5}$$

Lenz's law states that the induced current and induced emf in a conductor are in such a direction as to oppose the change that produced them.

A general form of **Faraday's law of induction** is

$$\mathcal{E} = \oint \mathbf{E} \cdot d\mathbf{s} = -\frac{d\Phi_B}{dt} \tag{31.9}$$

where $\mathbf{E}$ is a nonconservative, time-varying electric field that is produced by the changing magnetic flux.

When used with the Lorentz force law, $\mathbf{F} = q\mathbf{E} + q\mathbf{v} \times \mathbf{B}$, **Maxwell's equations**, given below in integral form, describe all electromagnetic phenomena:

$$\oint \mathbf{E} \cdot d\mathbf{A} = \frac{Q}{\epsilon_0} \tag{31.12}$$

$$\oint \mathbf{B} \cdot d\mathbf{A} = 0 \tag{31.13}$$

$$\oint \mathbf{E} \cdot d\mathbf{s} = -\frac{d\Phi_B}{dt} \tag{31.14}$$

$$\oint \mathbf{B} \cdot d\mathbf{s} = \mu_0 I + \epsilon_0 \mu_0 \frac{d\Phi_E}{dt} \tag{31.15}$$

The last two equations are of particular importance for the material discussed in this chapter. Faraday's law describes how an electric field can be induced by a changing magnetic flux. Similarly, the Ampère-Maxwell law describes how a magnetic field can be produced by both a conduction current and a changing electric flux.

QUESTIONS

1. What is the difference between magnetic flux and magnetic field?
2. A loop of wire is placed in a uniform magnetic field. For what orientation of the loop is the magnetic flux a maximum? For what orientation is the flux zero?
3. As the conducting bar in Figure 31.23 moves to the right, an electric field is set up directed downward. If the bar were moving to the left, explain why the electric field would be upward.

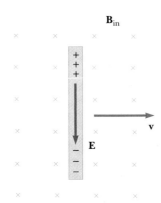

FIGURE 31.23   (Questions 3 and 4).

4. As the bar in Figure 31.23 moves perpendicular to the field, is an external force required to keep it moving with constant speed?
5. The bar in Figure 31.24 moves on rails to the right with a velocity **v**, and the uniform, constant magnetic field is directed out of the page. Why is the induced current clockwise? If the bar were moving to the left, what would be the direction of the induced current?

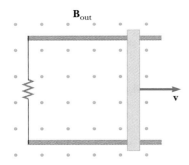

FIGURE 31.24   (Questions 5 and 6).

6. Explain why an external force is necessary to keep the bar in Figure 31.24 moving with a constant speed.
7. A large circular loop of wire lies in the horizontal plane. A bar magnet is dropped through the loop. If the axis of the magnet remains horizontal as it falls, describe the emf induced in the loop. How is the situation altered if the axis of the magnet remains vertical as it falls?
8. When a small magnet is moved toward a solenoid, an emf is induced in the coil. However, if the magnet is moved around inside a toroid, there is no induced emf. Explain.
9. Will dropping a magnet down a long copper tube produce a current in the tube? Explain.
10. How is electrical energy produced in dams (that is, how is the energy of motion of the water converted to ac electricity)?
11. In a beam-balance scale, an aluminum plate is sometimes used to slow the oscillations of the beam near equilibrium. The plate is mounted at the end of the beam and moves between the poles of a small horseshoe magnet attached to the frame. Why are the oscillations of the beam strongly damped near equilibrium?
12. What happens when the speed at which the coil of a generator is rotated is increased?
13. Could a current be induced in a coil by rotating a magnet inside the coil? If so, how?
14. When the switch in Figure 31.25a is closed, a current is set up in the coil and the metal ring springs upward (Fig. 31.25b). Explain this behavior.

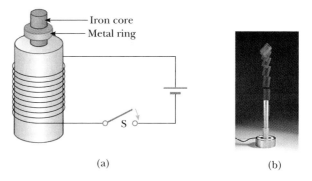

(a)   (b)

FIGURE 31.25   (Questions 14 and 15).   *(Photo courtesy of Central Scientific Co.)*

15. Assume that the battery in Figure 31.25a is replaced by an ac source and the switch is held closed. If held down, the metal ring on top of the solenoid becomes hot. Why?
16. Do Maxwell's equations allow for the existence of magnetic monopoles?

PROBLEMS

Section 31.1 Faraday's Law of Induction

1. A 50-turn rectangular coil of dimensions 5.0 cm × 10.0 cm is dropped from a position where $B = 0$ to a new position where $B = 0.50$ T and is directed perpendicularly to the plane of the coil. Calculate the resulting average emf induced in the coil if the displacement occurs in 0.25 s.

2. A flat loop of wire consisting of a single turn of cross-sectional area 8.0 cm² is perpendicular to a magnetic field that increases uniformly in magnitude from 0.50 T to 2.50 T in 1.0 s. What is the resulting induced current if the loop has a resistance of 2.0 Ω?

3. A powerful electromagnet has a field of 1.6 T and a cross-sectional area of 0.20 m². If we place a coil having 200 turns and a total resistance of 20 Ω around the electromagnet and then turn off the power to the electromagnet in 20 ms, what is the current induced in the coil?

4. In Figure P31.4 find the current through section PQ, which has a length $a = 65.0$ cm. The circuit is located in a magnetic field whose magnitude varies with time according to the expression $B = (1.00 \times 10^{-3} \text{ T/s})\,t$. Assume the resistance per unit length of the wire is $0.100 \; \Omega/\text{m}$.

4A. In Figure P31.4 find the current through section PQ, which has resistance R and length a. The circuit is located in a magnetic field whose magnitude varies with time according to the expression $B = At$, where A is a constant having units of teslas/second.

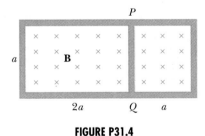

FIGURE P31.4

5. The 10.0-Ω square loop in Figure P31.5, is placed in a uniform 0.10-T magnetic field directed perpendicular to the plane of the loop. The loop, which is hinged at each vertex, is pulled as shown until the separation between points A and B is 3.0 m. If the process takes 0.10 s, what is the average current generated in the loop?

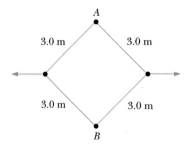

FIGURE P31.5

6. A tightly wound circular coil has 50 turns, each of radius 0.10 m. A uniform magnetic field is turned on along a direction perpendicular to the plane of the coil. If the field increases linearly from 0 to 0.60 T in 0.20 s, what emf is induced in the coil?

7. A 30-turn circular coil of radius 4 cm and resistance 1 Ω is placed in a magnetic field directed perpendicularly to the plane of the coil. The magnitude of the magnetic field varies in time according to the expression $B = 0.010t + 0.040t^2$, where t is in seconds and B is in tesla. Calculate the induced emf in the coil at $t = 5.0$ s.

8. A circular wire loop of radius 0.50 m lies in a plane perpendicular to a uniform magnetic field of magnitude 0.40 T. If in 0.10 s the wire is reshaped into a square but remains in the same plane, what is the magnitude of the average induced emf in the wire during this time?

9. A flat loop of wire of area 14 cm² and two turns is perpendicular to a magnetic field whose magnitude decays in time according to $B = (0.50 \text{ T})e^{-t/7}$. What is the induced emf as a function of time?

10. A rectangular loop of area A is placed in a region where the magnetic field is perpendicular to the plane of the loop. The magnitude of the field is allowed to vary in time according to $B = B_0 e^{-t/\tau}$, where B_0 and τ are constants. The field has a value of B_0 at $t \leq 0$. (a) Use Faraday's law to show that the emf induced in the loop is

$$\mathcal{E} = \frac{AB_0}{\tau} e^{-t/\tau}$$

(b) Obtain a numerical value for $\mathcal{E}$ at $t = 4.0$ s when $A = 0.16$ m², $B_0 = 0.35$ T, and $\tau = 2.0$ s. (c) For the values of A, B_0, and τ given in part (b), what is the maximum value of $\mathcal{E}$?

□ indicates problems that have full solutions available in the Student Solutions Manual and Study Guide.

11. A long solenoid has 400 turns per meter and carries a current $I = (30 \text{ A})(1 - e^{-1.6t})$. Inside the solenoid and coaxial with it is a loop that has a radius of 6.0 cm and consists of a total of 250 turns of fine wire. What emf is induced in the loop by the changing current? (See Fig. P31.11.)

11A. A long solenoid has n turns per meter and carries a current $I = I_0(1 - e^{-\alpha t})$. Inside the solenoid and coaxial with it is a loop that has a radius R and consists of a total of N turns of fine wire. What emf is induced in the loop by the changing current? (See Fig. P31.11.)

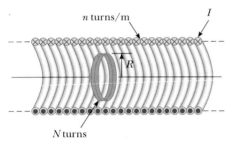

FIGURE P31.11

12. A magnetic field of 0.20 T exists in the region enclosed by a solenoid that has 500 turns and a diameter of 10 cm. Within what period of time must the field be reduced to zero if the average magnitude of the induced emf within the coil during this time interval is to be 10 kV?

13. A coil formed by wrapping 50 turns of wire in the shape of a square is positioned in a magnetic field so that the normal to the plane of the coil makes an angle of 30° with the direction of the field. When the magnitude of the magnetic field is increased uniformly from 200 μT to 600 μT in 0.40 s, an emf of 80 mV is induced in the coil. What is the total length of the wire?

14. A long, straight wire carries a current $I = I_0 \sin(\omega t + \phi)$ and lies in the plane of a rectangular loop of N turns of wire, as shown in Figure P31.14. The quantities I_0, ω, and ϕ are all constants. Determine the emf induced in the loop by the magnetic field created by the current in the straight wire. Assume $I_0 = 50$ A, $\omega = 200\pi$ s^{-1}, $N = 100$, $a = b = 5.0$ cm, and $\ell = 20$ cm.

15. A two-turn circular wire loop of radius 0.500 m lies in a plane perpendicular to a uniform magnetic field of magnitude 0.40 T. If the wire is reshaped from a two-turn circle to a one-turn circle in 0.10 s (while remaining in the same plane), what is the magnitude of the average induced emf in the wire during this time?

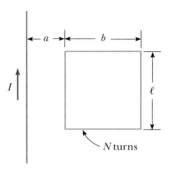

FIGURE P31.14

15A. A two-turn circular wire loop of radius R lies in a plane perpendicular to a uniform magnetic field of magnitude B. If the wire is reshaped from a two-turn circle to a one-turn circle in a time t (while remaining in the same plane), what is the magnitude of the average induced emf in the wire during this time?

16. A toroid having a rectangular cross-section ($a = 2.0$ cm by $b = 3.0$ cm) and inner radius $R = 4.0$ cm consists of 500 turns of wire that carries a current $I = I_0 \sin \omega t$, with $I_0 = 50$ A and a frequency $f = \omega/2\pi = 60$ Hz. A loop that consists of 20 turns of wire links the toroid, as in Figure P31.16. Determine the emf induced in the loop by the changing current I.

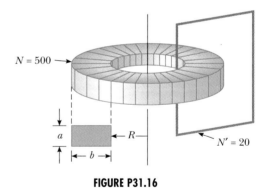

FIGURE P31.16

Section 31.2   Motional Emf
Section 31.3   Lenz's Law

17. A Boeing-747 jet with a wing span of 60.0 m is flying horizontally at a speed of 300 m/s over Phoenix, where the direction of the Earth's magnetic field is 58° below the horizontal. If the magnitude of the magnetic field is 50.0 μT, what is the voltage generated between the wing tips?

18. Consider the arrangement shown in Figure P31.18. Assume that $R = 6.0$ Ω, $\ell = 1.2$ m, and a uniform 2.5-T magnetic field is directed into the page. At what speed should the bar be moved to produce a current of 0.50 A in the resistor?

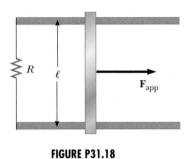

FIGURE P31.18

19. In the arrangement shown in Figure P31.18, the resistor is 6.0 Ω and a 2.5-T magnetic field is directed into the paper. Let $\ell = 1.2$ m and neglect the mass of the bar. (a) Calculate the applied force required to move the bar to the right at a constant speed of 2.0 m/s. (b) At what rate is energy dissipated in the resistor?

20. In Figure P31.20, the bar magnet is moved toward the loop. Is $V_a - V_b$ positive, negative, or zero? Explain.

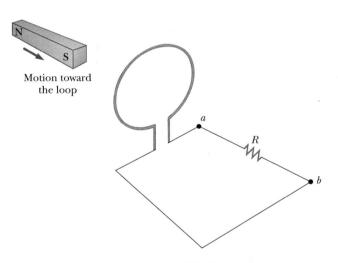

FIGURE P31.20

21. Over a region where the vertical component of the Earth's magnetic field is 40.0 μT directed downward, a 5.00-m length of wire is held along an east-west direction and moved horizontally to the north at 10.0 m/s. Calculate the potential difference between the ends of the wire and determine which end is positive.

22. A metal rod is sliding on a metal ring of radius R, shown in Figure P31.22. There is a uniform magnetic field inside the ring, and the rod moves at constant speed v. (a) Find the induced emf in the rod when it

is at a distance d from the center of the ring. (b) Plot the emf as a function of d.

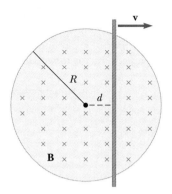

FIGURE P31.22

23. A helicopter has blades of length 3.0 m, rotating at 2.0 rev/s around a central hub. If the vertical component of the Earth's magnetic field is 0.50×10^{-4} T, what is the emf induced between the blade tip and the center hub?

24. A metal bar spins at a constant rate in the magnetic field of the Earth as in Figure 31.9. The rotation occurs in a region where the component of the Earth's magnetic field perpendicular to the plane of rotation is 3.3×10^{-5} T. If the bar is 1.0 m in length and its angular speed is 5π rad/s, what potential difference is developed between its ends?

25. Two parallel rails having negligible resistance are 10.0 cm apart and are connected by a 5.00-Ω resistor. The circuit also contains 10.0-Ω and 15.0-Ω metal rods sliding along the rails and moving away from the resistor at the velocities shown in Figure P31.25. A uniform 0.01-T magnetic field is applied perpendicular to the plane of the rails. Determine the current in the 5.00-Ω resistor.

25A. Two parallel rails having negligible resistance are a distance d apart and are connected by resistor R_1. The circuit also contains two metal rods having resistances R_2 and R_3 sliding along the rails (Fig. P31.25). The rods move away from the resistor at constant speeds v_2 and v_3, respectively. A uniform magnetic field of magnitude B is applied perpendic-

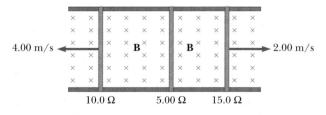

FIGURE P31.25

ularly to the plane of the rails. Determine the current in the resistor R_1.

26. Find the power dissipated in the 12.0-Ω resistor in Figure P31.26. The 0.675-T uniform magnetic field is directed into the plane of the circuit and the 50.0-cm-long conductor moves at a speed $v = 4.20$ m/s.

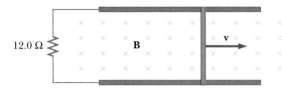

FIGURE P31.26

27. Use Lenz's law to answer the following questions concerning the direction of induced currents. (a) What is the direction of the induced current in resistor R in Figure P31.27a when the bar magnet is moved to the left? (b) What is the direction of the current induced in the resistor R right after the switch S in Figure P31.27b is closed? (c) What is the direction of the induced current in R when the current I in Figure P31.27c decreases rapidly to zero? (d) A copper bar is moved to the right while its axis is maintained perpendicularly to a magnetic field, as in Figure P31.27d. If the top of the bar becomes positive relative to the bottom, what is the direction of the magnetic field?

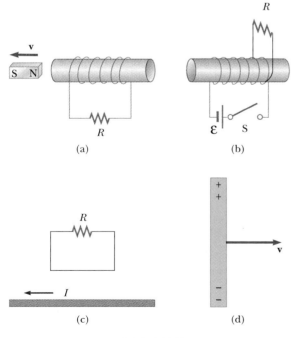

(a)   (b)

(c)   (d)

FIGURE P31.27

28. A conducting rectangular loop of mass M, resistance R, and dimensions w by ℓ falls from rest into a magnetic field **B** as in Figure P31.28. The loop accelerates until it reaches a terminal speed v_t. (a) Show that

$$v_t = \frac{MgR}{B^2 w^2}$$

(b) Why is v_t proportional to R? (c) Why is it inversely proportional to B^2?

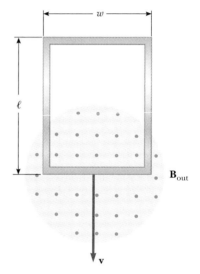

FIGURE P31.28

29. A 0.15-kg wire in the shape of a closed rectangle 1.0 m wide and 1.5 m long has a total resistance of 0.75 Ω. The rectangle is allowed to fall through a magnetic field directed perpendicularly to the direction of motion of the rectangle (Fig. P31.28). The rectangle accelerates downward until it acquires a constant speed of 2.0 m/s with its top not yet in that region of the field. Calculate the magnitude of **B**.

Section 31.4   Induced Emfs and Electric Fields

30. The current in a solenoid is increasing at a rate of 10 A/s. The cross-sectional area of the solenoid is π cm^2, and there are 300 turns on its 15-cm length. What is the induced emf opposing the increasing current?

31. A single-turn, circular loop of radius R is coaxial with a long solenoid of radius 0.030 m and length 0.75 m and having 1500 turns (Fig. P31.31). The variable resistor is changed so that the solenoid current decreases linearly from 7.2 A to 2.4 A in 0.30 s. Calculate the induced emf in the loop.

31A. A single-turn, circular loop of radius R is coaxial with a long solenoid of radius r and length ℓ and having N

turns (Fig. P31.31). The variable resistor is changed so that the solenoid current decreases linearly from I_1 to I_2 in an interval Δt. Find the induced emf in the loop.

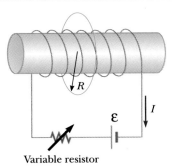

FIGURE P31.31

32. A coil of 15 turns and radius 10 cm surrounds a long solenoid of radius 2.0 cm and 1.0×10^3 turns/meter (Fig. P31.32). If the current in the solenoid changes as $I = (5.0 \text{ A}) \sin(120t)$, what is the induced emf in the 15-turn coil?

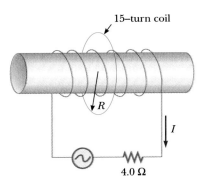

FIGURE P31.32

33. A magnetic field directed into the page changes with time according to $B = (0.030t^2 + 1.4)$ T, where t is in seconds. The field has a circular cross-section of radius $R = 2.5$ cm (Fig. P31.33). What are the magnitude and direction of the electric field at point P_1 when $t = 3.0$ s and $r_1 = 0.020$ m?

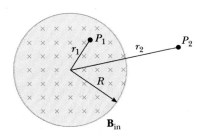

FIGURE P31.33

34. For the situation described in Figure P31.33, the magnetic field changes with time according to $B = (2.0t^3 - 4.0t^2 + 0.80)$ T, and $r_2 = 2R = 5.0$ cm. (a) Calculate the magnitude and direction of the force exerted on an electron located at point P_2 when $t = 2.0$ s. (b) At what time is this force equal to zero?

35. A long solenoid with 1000 turns/meter and radius 2.0 cm carries an oscillating current $I = (5.0 \text{ A}) \sin(100\pi t)$. What is the electric field induced at a radius $r = 1.0$ cm from the axis of the solenoid? What is the direction of this electric field when the current is increasing counterclockwise in the coil?

36. In 1832 Faraday proposed that the apparatus shown in Figure P31.36 could be used to generate electric current from the flowing water in the Thames River. Two conducting planes of lengths a and widths b are placed facing one another on opposite sides of the river, a distance w apart. The flow velocity of the river is v and the vertical component of the Earth's magnetic field is B. (a) Show that the current in the load resistor R is

$$I = \frac{abvB}{\rho + abR/w}$$

where ρ is the electrical resistivity of the water. (b) Calculate the short-circuit current ($R = 0$) if $a = 100$ m, $b = 5.00$ m, $v = 3.00$ m/s, $B = 0.500$ μT, and $\rho = 100$ $\Omega \cdot$m.

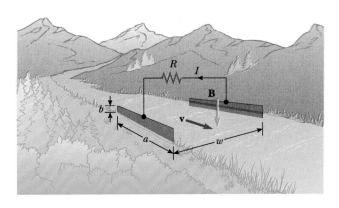

FIGURE P31.36

37. An aluminum ring of radius 5.0 cm and resistance 3.0×10^{-4} Ω is placed on top of a long air-core solenoid with 1000 turns per meter and radius 3.0 cm as in Figure P31.37. At the location of the ring, the magnetic field due to the current in the solenoid is one-half that at the center of the solenoid. If the current in the solenoid is increasing at a rate of 270 A/s, (a) what is the induced current in the ring? (b) At the center of the ring, what is the magnetic field produced by the induced current in the ring? (c) What is the direction of this field?

37A. An aluminum ring of radius r_1 and resistance R is placed on top of a long air-core solenoid with n turns per meter and radius r_2 as in Figure P31.37. At the location of the ring, the magnetic field due to the current in the solenoid is one-half that at the center of the solenoid. If the current in the solenoid is increasing at a rate $\Delta I / \Delta t$, (a) what is the induced current in the ring? (b) At the center of the ring, what is the magnetic field produced by the induced current in the ring? (c) What is the direction of this field?

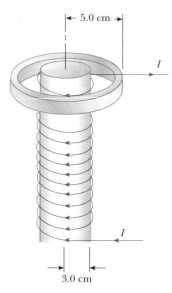

FIGURE P31.37

38. A circular coil enclosing an area of 100 cm² is made of 200 turns of copper wire as shown in Figure P31.38. Initially, a 1.10-T uniform magnetic field points perpendicularly upward through the plane of the coil. The direction of the field then reverses. During the time the field is changing its direction, how much charge flows through the coil if $R = 5.0 \ \Omega$?

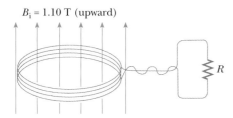

$B_i = 1.10$ T (upward)

R

FIGURE P31.38

*Section 31.5 Generators and Motors

39. A square coil (20 cm × 20 cm) that consists of 100 turns of wire rotates about a vertical axis at 1500 rev/min, as indicated in Figure P31.39. The horizontal component of the Earth's magnetic field at the location of the coil is 2.0×10^{-5} T. Calculate the maximum emf induced in the coil by this field.

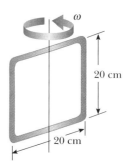

ω

20 cm

20 cm

FIGURE P31.39

40. A 25-turn circular loop of wire has a diameter of 1.0 m. In 0.20 s it is flipped 180° at a location where the magnitude of the Earth's magnetic field is 50 μT. What is the emf generated in the loop?

41. A loop of area 0.10 m² is rotating at 60 rev/s with the axis of rotation perpendicular to a 0.20-T magnetic field. (a) If there are 1000 turns on the loop, what is the maximum voltage induced in it? (b) When the maximum induced voltage occurs, what is the orientation of the loop with respect to the magnetic field?

42. In a 250-turn automotive alternator, the magnetic flux in each turn is $\Phi = (2.5 \times 10^{-4} \text{ Wb}) \cos(\omega t)$, where ω is the angular frequency of the alternator. The alternator rotates three times for each engine rotation. When the engine is running at 1000 rpm, determine (a) the induced emf in the alternator as a function of time and (b) the maximum emf in the alternator.

43. A long solenoid, the axis of which coincides with the x axis, consists of 200 turns/m of wire that carries a steady current of 15 A. A coil is formed by wrapping 30 turns of thin wire around a frame that has a radius of 8.0 cm. The coil is placed inside the solenoid and mounted on an axis that is a diameter of the coil and coincides with the y axis. The coil is then rotated with an angular speed of 4π rad/s. (The plane of the coil is in the yz plane at $t = 0$.) Determine the emf developed in the coil.

44. The rotating loop in an ac generator is a square 10 cm on a side. It is rotated at 60 Hz in a uniform field of 0.80 T. Calculate (a) the flux through the loop as a function of time, (b) the emf induced in the loop, (c) the current induced in the loop for a loop resistance of 1.0 Ω, (d) the power dissipated in the

loop, and (e) the torque that must be exerted to rotate the loop.

45. (a) What is the maximum torque delivered by an electric motor if it has 80 turns of wire wrapped on a rectangular coil, of dimensions 2.5 cm by 4.0 cm? Assume that the motor uses 10 A of current and that a uniform 0.80-T magnetic field exists within the motor. (b) If the motor rotates at 3600 rev/min, what is the peak power produced by the motor?

46. A semicircular conductor of radius $R = 0.25$ m is rotated about the axis AC at a constant rate of 120 rev/min (Fig. P31.46). A uniform magnetic field in all of the lower half of the figure is directed out of the plane of rotation and has a magnitude of 1.3 T. (a) Calculate the maximum value of the emf induced in the conductor. (b) What is the value of the average induced emf for each complete rotation? (c) How would the answers to (a) and (b) change if **B** were allowed to extend a distance R above the axis of rotation? Sketch the emf versus time (d) when the field is as drawn in Figure P31.46 and (e) when the field is extended as described in (c).

46A. A semicircular conductor of radius R rotates about the axis AC at a constant angular speed ω (Fig. P31.46). A uniform magnetic field in all of the lower half of the figure is directed out of the plane of rotation and has a magnitude B. (a) Find the maximum emf induced in the conductor. (b) What is the value of the average induced emf for each complete rotation?

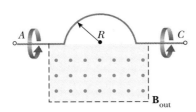

FIGURE P31.46

47. A small rectangular coil composed of 50 turns of wire has an area of 30 cm² and carries a current of 1.5 A. When the plane of the coil makes an angle of 30° with a uniform magnetic field, the torque on the coil is 0.10 N·m. What is the magnitude of the magnetic field?

48. A bar magnet is spun at constant angular speed ω around an axis as shown in Figure P31.48. A flat rectangular conducting loop surrounds the magnet, and at $t = 0$ the magnet is oriented as shown. Sketch the induced current in the loop as a function of time, plotting counterclockwise currents as positive and clockwise currents as negative.

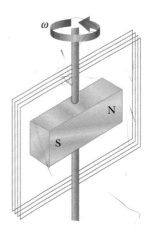

FIGURE P31.48

*Section 31.6   Eddy Currents

49. A rectangular loop with resistance R has N turns, each of length ℓ and width w as shown in Figure P31.49. The loop moves into a uniform magnetic field **B** with velocity **v**. What are the magnitude and direction of the resultant force on the loop (a) as it enters the magnetic field, (b) as it moves within the field, (c) as it leaves the field?

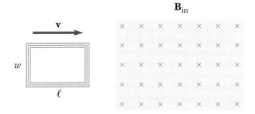

FIGURE P31.49

50. A dime is suspended from a thread and hung between the poles of a strong horseshoe magnet as shown in Figure P31.50. The dime rotates at constant angular speed ω about a vertical axis. Letting θ be the angle between the direction of **B** and the normal to the face of the dime, sketch a graph of the torque due to induced currents as a function of θ for $0 \leqslant \theta \leqslant 2\pi$.

Section 31.7   Maxwell's Wonderful Equations

51. A proton moves through a uniform electric field $E = 50j$ V/m and a uniform magnetic field $B = (0.20i + 0.30j + 0.40k)$ T. Determine the acceleration of the proton when it has a velocity $v = 200i$ m/s.

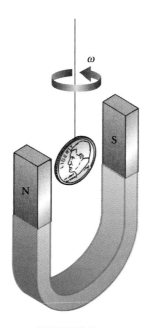

FIGURE P31.50

52. An electron moves through a uniform electric field $\mathbf{E} = (2.5\mathbf{i} + 5.0\mathbf{j})$ V/m and a uniform magnetic field $\mathbf{B} = 0.40\mathbf{k}$ T. Determine the acceleration of the electron when it has a velocity $\mathbf{v} = 10\mathbf{i}$ m/s.

ADDITIONAL PROBLEMS

53. A conducting rod moves with a constant velocity $\mathbf{v}$ perpendicular to a long, straight wire carrying a current I as in Figure P31.53. Show that the emf generated between the ends of the rod is

$$|\mathcal{E}| = \frac{\mu_0 vI}{2\pi r}\ell$$

In this case, note that the emf decreases with increasing r, as you might expect.

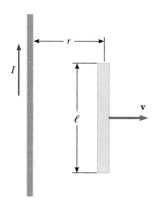

FIGURE P31.53

54. A circular loop of wire 5.0 cm in radius is in a uniform magnetic field, with the plane of the loop perpendicular to the direction of the field (Fig. P31.54). The magnetic field varies with time according to $B(t) = a + bt$, where $a = 0.20$ T and $b = 0.32$ T/s. (a) Calculate the magnetic flux through the loop at $t = 0$. (b) Calculate the emf induced in the loop. (c) If the resistance of the loop is 1.2 Ω, what is the induced current? (d) At what rate is electric energy being dissipated in the loop?

54A. A circular loop of wire of radius r is in a uniform magnetic field, with the plane of the loop perpendicular to the direction of the field (Fig. P31.54). The magnetic field varies with time according to $B(t) = a + bt$, where a and b are constants. (a) Calculate the magnetic flux through the loop at $t = 0$. (b) Calculate the emf induced in the loop. (c) If the resistance of the loop is R, what is the induced current? (d) At what rate is electric energy being dissipated in the loop?

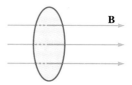

FIGURE P31.54

55. Consider a long solenoid of length ℓ containing a core of permeability μ. The core material is magnetized by increasing the current in the coil, so as to produce a changing field dB/dt. (a) Show that the rate at which work is done against the induced emf in the coil is

$$\frac{dW}{dt} = I\mathcal{E} = HA\ell\,\frac{dB}{dt}$$

where A is the cross-sectional area of the solenoid. (*Hint:* Use Faraday's law to find $\mathcal{E}$ and use Equation 30.34.) (b) Use the result of part (a) to show that the total work done in a complete hysteresis cycle equals the area enclosed by the B versus H curve (Fig. 30.31).

56. In Figure P31.56, a uniform magnetic field decreases at a constant rate $dB/dt = -K$, where K is a positive constant. A circular loop of wire of radius a containing a resistance R and a capacitance C is placed with its plane normal to the field. (a) Find the charge Q on the capacitor when it is fully charged. (b) Which plate is at the higher potential? (c) Discuss the force that causes the separation of charges.

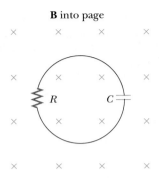

B into page

FIGURE P31.56

57. A rectangular coil of 60 turns, dimensions 0.10 m by 0.20 m, and total resistance 10 Ω rotates with angular speed 30 rad/s about the y axis in a region where a 1.0-T magnetic field is directed along the x axis. The rotation is initiated so that the plane of the coil is perpendicular to the direction of **B** at $t = 0$. Calculate (a) the maximum induced emf in the coil, (b) the maximum rate of change of magnetic flux through the coil, (c) the induced emf at $t = 0.050$ s, and (d) the torque exerted on the loop by the magnetic field at the instant when the emf is a maximum.

58. A bar of mass m, length d, and resistance R slides without friction on parallel rails as shown in Figure P31.58. A battery that maintains a constant emf $\mathcal{E}$ is connected between the rails, and a constant magnetic field **B** is directed perpendicularly to the plane of the page. If the bar starts from rest, show that at time t it moves with a speed

$$v = \frac{\mathcal{E}}{Bd}(1 - e^{-B^2 d^2 t / mR})$$

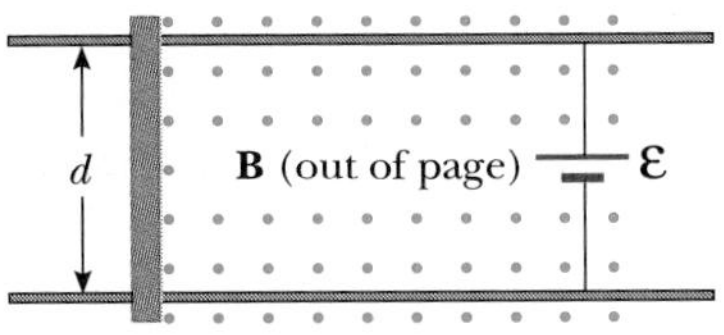

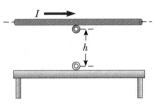

FIGURE P31.58

59. A small circular copper washer of radius 0.500 cm is held directly below a long, straight wire carrying a current of 10.0 A and 0.500 m above the top of the table in Figure P31.59. (a) If the washer is dropped from rest, what is the magnitude of the average emf induced in it from the time it is released to the moment it hits the tabletop? Assume that the magnetic field through the washer is the same as the magnetic field at its center. (b) What is the direction of the induced current in the washer?

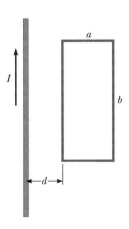

FIGURE P31.59

60. To monitor the breathing of a hospital patient, a thin belt is girded around the patient's chest. The belt is a 200-turn coil. When the patient inhales, the area encircled by the coil increases by 39 cm². The magnitude of the Earth's magnetic field is 50 μT and makes an angle of 28° with the plane of the coil. If a patient takes 1.8 s to inhale, find the average induced emf in the coil during this time.

61. An automobile has a vertical radio antenna 1.2 m long. The automobile travels at 65 km/h on a horizontal road where the Earth's magnetic field is 50 μT directed downward (toward the north) at an angle of 65° below the horizontal. (a) Specify the direction that the automobile should move in order to generate the maximum motional emf in the antenna, with the top of the antenna positive relative to the bottom. (b) Calculate the magnitude of this induced emf.

62. A long, straight wire is parallel to one edge and in the plane of a single-turn rectangular loop as in Figure P31.62. (a) If the current in the long wire varies in time as $I = I_0 e^{-t/\tau}$, show that the induced emf in the loop is

$$\mathcal{E} = \frac{\mu_0 bI}{2\pi\tau} \ln\left(1 + \frac{a}{d}\right)$$

(b) Calculate the induced emf at $t = 5.0$ s taking $I_0 = 10$ A, $d = 3.0$ cm, $a = 6.0$ cm, $b = 15$ cm, and $\tau = 5.0$ s.

FIGURE P31.62

63. A conducting rod of length ℓ moves with velocity $\mathbf{v}$ parallel to a long wire carrying a steady current I. The axis of the rod is maintained perpendicular to the wire with the near end a distance r away, as shown in Figure P31.63. Show that the emf induced in the rod is

$$|\mathcal{E}| = \frac{\mu_0 I}{2\pi}\, v \ln\left(1 + \frac{\ell}{r}\right)$$

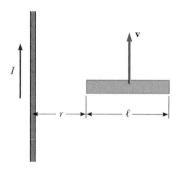

FIGURE P31.63

64. A rectangular loop of dimensions ℓ and w moves with a constant velocity $\mathbf{v}$ away from a long wire that carries a current I in the plane of the loop (Fig. P31.64). The total resistance of the loop is R. Derive an expression that gives the current in the loop at the instant the near side is a distance r from the wire.

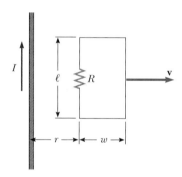

FIGURE P31.64

65. A plane of a square loop of wire with edge length $a = 0.20$ m is perpendicular to the Earth's magnetic field at a point where $B = 15$ μT, as in Figure P31.65. The total resistance of the loop and the wires connecting it to the galvanometer is 0.50 Ω. If the loop is suddenly collapsed by horizontal forces as shown, what total charge passes through the galvanometer?

65A. A plane of a square loop of wire with edge length a is perpendicular to the Earth's magnetic field at a point where the magnitude of the magnetic field is B,

as in Figure P31.65. The total resistance of the loop and the wires connecting it to the galvanometer is R. If the loop is suddenly collapsed by horizontal forces as shown, what total charge passes through the galvanometer?

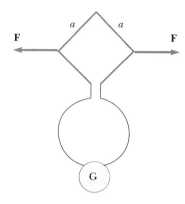

FIGURE P31.65

66. A horizontal wire is free to slide on the vertical rails of a conducting frame, as in Figure P31.66. The wire has mass m and length ℓ, and the resistance of the circuit is R. If a uniform magnetic field is directed perpendicularly to the frame, what is the terminal speed of the wire as it falls under the influence of gravity?

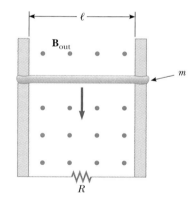

FIGURE P31.66

67. The magnetic flux threading a metal ring varies with time t according to $\Phi_B = 3(at^3 - bt^2)$ T·m², with $a = 2.0$ s^{-3} and $b = 6.0$ s^{-2}. The resistance of the ring is 3.0 Ω. Determine the maximum current induced in the ring during the interval from $t = 0$ to $t = 2.0$ s.

67A. The magnetic flux threading a metal ring varies with time t according to $\Phi_B = 3(at^3 - bt^2)$ T·m², where a and b are constants. The resistance of the ring is R.

Determine the maximum current induced in the ring during the interval from $t = 0$ to some later time t.

68. The bar of mass m in Figure P31.68 is pulled horizontally across parallel rails by a massless string that passes over an ideal pulley and is attached to a suspended mass M. The uniform magnetic field has a magnitude B, and the distance between the rails is ℓ. The rails are connected at one end by a load resistor R. Derive an expression that gives the horizontal speed of the bar as a function of time, assuming that the suspended mass is released with the bar at rest at $t = 0$. Assume no friction between rails and bar.

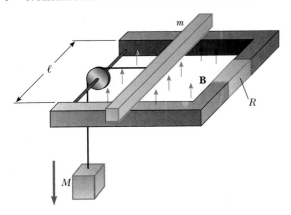

FIGURE P31.68

69. In Figure P31.69, the rolling axle, 1.5 m long, is pushed along horizontal rails at a constant speed $v = 3.0$ m/s. A resistor $R = 0.40\ \Omega$ is connected to the rails at points a and b, directly opposite each other. (The wheels make good electrical contact with the rails, and so the axle, rails, and R form a closed-loop circuit. The only significant resistance in the circuit is R.) There is a uniform magnetic field $B = 0.08$ T vertically downward. (a) Find the induced current I in the resistor. (b) What horizontal force F is required to keep the axle rolling at constant speed? (c) Which end of the resistor, a or b, is at the higher electric potential? (d) After the axle rolls past the resistor, does the current in R reverse direction?

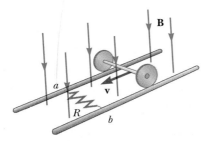

FIGURE P31.69

70. Two infinitely long solenoids (seen in cross-section) thread a circuit as in Figure P31.70. The magnitude of **B** inside each is the same and is increasing at the rate of 100 T/s. What is the current in each resistor?

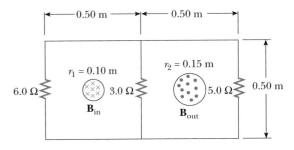

FIGURE P31.70

71. Figure P31.71 shows a circular loop of radius r that has a resistance R spread uniformly throughout its length. The loop's plane is normal to the magnetic field **B** that decreases at a constant rate $dB/dt = -K$, where K is a positive constant. What are (a) the direction and (b) the value of the induced current? (c) Which point, a or b, is at the higher potential? Explain. (d) Discuss what force causes the current in the loop.

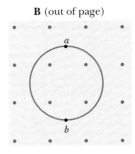

B (out of page)

FIGURE P31.71

72. A wire 30.0 cm long is held parallel to and 80.0 cm above a long wire carrying 200 A and resting on the floor (Fig. P31.72). The 30.0-cm wire is released and falls, remaining parallel with the current-carrying wire as it falls. Assume that the falling wire accelerates at 9.80 m/s² and derive an equation for the emf induced in it. Express your result as a function of the time t after the wire is dropped. What is the induced emf 0.30 s after the wire is released?

72A. A wire of length L is held parallel to and a distance h above a long wire carrying a current I and resting on the floor (Fig. P31.72). The wire of length L is released and falls, remaining parallel with the current-carrying wire as it falls. Assuming that the falling wire is in free fall with an acceleration g, derive an equation for the emf induced in it. Express your result as a function of the time t after the wire is dropped.

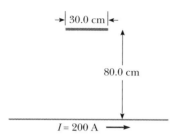

FIGURE P31.72

73. (a) A loop of wire in the shape of a rectangle of width w and length L and a long, straight wire carrying a current I lie on a tabletop as shown in Figure P31.73. (a) Determine the magnetic flux through the loop. (b) Suppose the current is changing with time according to $I = a + bt$, where a and b are constant. Determine the induced emf in the loop if $b = 10.0$ A/s, $h = 1.00$ cm, $w = 10.0$ cm, and $L = 100$ cm.

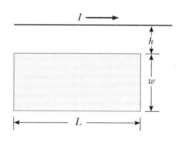

FIGURE P31.73

74. The wire shown in Figure P31.74 is bent in the shape of a tent, with $\theta = 60°$ and $L = 1.5$ m, and is placed in a 0.30-T magnetic field directed perpendicular to the tabletop. The wire is hinged at points a and b. If

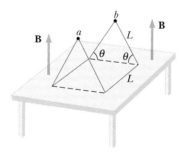

FIGURE P31.74

the tent is flattened out on the table in 0.10 s, what is the average emf induced in the wire during this time?

SPREADSHEET PROBLEMS

S1. The size and orientation of a flat surface of area A can be described by a vector $\mathbf{A} = A\hat{n}$, where $\hat{n}$ is a unit vector perpendicular to the surface. Suppose that a magnetic field $\mathbf{B}$ exists in the region of this surface. If the field is constant over the area A, then the magnetic flux, ϕ, through the surface is $\phi = \mathbf{B} \cdot \mathbf{A} = BA \cos\theta = B_x A_x + B_y A_y + B_z A_z$, where $\mathbf{A} = A_x\mathbf{i} + A_y\mathbf{j} + A_z\mathbf{k}$ and $\mathbf{B} = B_x\mathbf{i} + B_y\mathbf{j} + B_z\mathbf{k}$. (Fig. PS31.1). Spreadsheet 31.1 will calculate the flux as a function of time. It will also numerically differentiate the flux to find the induced emf, $\mathcal{E} = -\Delta\phi/\Delta t$. (a) Set $A_x = 0$, $A_y = 0$, $A_z = 0.2$ m², $B_x = 0$, $B_y = 0.5$ T, and $B_z = 0.6$ T at $t = 0$. Copy these values down through $t = 4.5$ s. What is the induced emf? (b) Modify the spreadsheet so that B_z increases with time, $B_z = 0.2t$, where t is in seconds and B_z is in teslas. What is the induced emf?

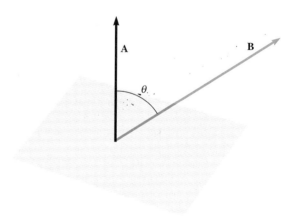

FIGURE PS31.1   Faraday's Law—Induced emf.

S2. Modify Spreadsheet 31.1 so that $\mathbf{A} = 0.02 \sin(\omega t)\mathbf{i} + 0.02 \cos(\omega t) \mathbf{k}$, where A is in square meters. Set $\mathbf{B} = 0.5$ T $\mathbf{k}$. (a) What physical situation does this variation in $\mathbf{A}$ correspond to? (b) Let $\omega = 1$ rad/s. View the included graph, and describe the induced emf. (c) Increase ω to 2 rad/s. How does the induced emf change from part (b)?

S3. (a) With $\mathbf{A}$ as given in Problem S2, modify Spreadsheet 31.1 so that $B_z = 0.2t$, where t is in seconds and B_z is in teslas. View the included graph, and explain your numerical results. (b) Choose any other time dependence for $\mathbf{B}$. Explore the consequences of your choice.

CHAPTER 32

Inductance

This photograph of water-driven generators was taken at the Bonneville Dam in Oregon. Hydroelectric power is generated when water from a dam passes through the generators under the influence of gravity, which causes turbines in the generator to rotate. The mechanical energy of the rotating turbines is transformed into electrical energy using the principle of electromagnetic induction, which you will study in this chapter. *(David Weintraub/Photo Researchers)*

I n the previous chapter, we saw that currents and emfs are induced in a circuit when the magnetic flux through the circuit changes with time. This electromagnetic induction has some practical consequences, which we describe in this chapter. First, we describe an effect known as *self-induction,* in which a time-varying current in a conductor induces in the conductor an emf that opposes the external emf that set up the current. Self-induction is the basis of the *inductor,* an electrical element that plays an important role in circuits that use time-varying currents. We discuss the energy stored in the magnetic field of an inductor and the energy density associated with a magnetic field.

Next, we study how an emf is induced in a circuit as a result of a changing magnetic flux produced by an external circuit, which is the basic principle of *mutual induction.* Finally, we examine the characteristics of circuits containing inductors, resistors, and capacitors in various combinations.

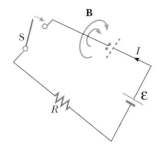

FIGURE 32.1 After the switch is closed, the current produces a magnetic flux through the loop. As the current increases toward its equilibrium value, the flux changes in time and induces an emf in the loop. The battery drawn with dashed lines is a symbol for the self-induced emf.

32.1   SELF-INDUCTANCE

Consider a circuit consisting of a switch, resistor, and source of emf, as in Figure 32.1. At the moment the switch is thrown to its closed position, the current doesn't immediately jump from zero to its maximum value, $\mathcal{E}/R$. The law of electromagnetic induction (Faraday's law) prevents this from occurring. What happens is the following: As the current increases with time, the magnetic flux through the loop due to this current also increases with time. This increasing flux induces in the circuit an emf that opposes the change in the net magnetic flux through the loop. By Lenz's law, the direction of the electric field induced in the wires must be opposite the direction of the current, and this opposing emf results in a gradual increase in the current. This effect is called *self-induction* because the changing flux through the circuit arises from the circuit itself. The emf $\mathcal{E}_L$ setup in this case is called a **self-induced emf.**

To obtain a quantitative description of self-induction, we recall from Faraday's law that the induced emf is equal to the negative time rate of change of the magnetic flux. The magnetic flux is proportional to the magnetic field, which in turn is proportional to the current in the circuit. Therefore, *the self-induced emf is always proportional to the time rate of change of the current.* For a closely spaced coil of N turns (a toroid or an ideal solenoid), we find that

Self-induced emf

$$\mathcal{E}_L = -N\frac{d\Phi_B}{dt} = -L\frac{dI}{dt} \tag{32.1}$$

where L is a proportionality constant, called the **inductance** of the coil, that depends on the geometry of the circuit and other physical characteristics. From this expression, we see that the inductance of a coil containing N turns is

Inductance of an *N*-turn coil

$$L = \frac{N\Phi_B}{I} \tag{32.2}$$

where it is assumed that the same flux passes through each turn. Later we shall use this equation to calculate the inductance of some special current geometries.

From Equation 32.1, we can also write the inductance as the ratio

Inductance

$$L = -\frac{\mathcal{E}_L}{dI/dt} \tag{32.3}$$

This is usually taken to be the defining equation for the inductance of any coil, regardless of its shape, size, or material characteristics. Just as resistance is a measure of the opposition to current, inductance is a measure of the opposition to any change in current.

The SI unit of inductance is the **henry** (H), which, from Equation 32.3, is seen to be equal to 1 volt-second per ampere:

$$1\ \text{H} = 1\ \frac{\text{V}\cdot\text{s}}{\text{A}}$$

As we shall see, *the inductance of a device depends on its geometry.* Induction calculations can be quite difficult for complicated geometries, but the following examples involve simple situations for which inductances are easily evaluated.

EXAMPLE 32.1   Inductance of a Solenoid

Find the inductance of a uniformly wound solenoid having N turns and length ℓ. Assume that ℓ is long compared with the radius and that the core of the solenoid is air.

Solution   In this case, we can take the interior magnetic field to be uniform and given by Equation 30.20:

$$B = \mu_0 nI = \mu_0 \frac{N}{\ell} I$$

where n is the number of turns per unit length, N/ℓ. The magnetic flux through each turn is

$$\Phi_B = BA = \mu_0 \frac{NA}{\ell} I$$

where A is the cross-sectional area of the solenoid. Using this expression and Equation 32.2, we find that

$$L = \frac{N\Phi_B}{I} = \frac{\mu_0 N^2 A}{\ell} \tag{32.4}$$

This shows that L depends on geometry and is proportional to the square of the number of turns. Because $N = n\ell$, we can also express the result in the form

$$L = \mu_0 \frac{(n\ell)^2}{\ell} A = \mu_0 n^2 A\ell = \mu_0 n^2 \text{ (volume)} \tag{32.5}$$

where $A\ell$ is the volume of the solenoid.

EXAMPLE 32.2   Calculating Inductance and Emf

(a) Calculate the inductance of a solenoid containing 300 turns if the length of the solenoid is 25.0 cm and its cross-sectional area is 4.00 cm² = 4.00×10^{-4} m².

Solution   Using Equation 32.4 we get

$$L = \frac{\mu_0 N^2 A}{\ell} = (4\pi \times 10^{-7} \text{ Wb/A} \cdot \text{m}) \frac{(300)^2 (4.00 \times 10^{-4} \text{ m}^2)}{25.0 \times 10^{-2} \text{ m}}$$

$$= 1.81 \times 10^{-4} \text{ Wb/A} = \boxed{0.181 \text{ mH}}$$

(b) Calculate the self-induced emf in the solenoid described in part (a) if the current through it is decreasing at the rate of 50.0 A/s.

Solution   Using Equation 32.1 and given that $dI/dt = 50.0$ A/s, we get

$$\mathcal{E}_L = -L \frac{dI}{dt} = -(1.81 \times 10^{-4} \text{ H})(-50.0 \text{ A/s})$$

$$= \boxed{9.05 \text{ mV}}$$

32.2   *RL* CIRCUITS

Any circuit that contains a coil, such as a solenoid, has a self-inductance that prevents the current from increasing or decreasing instantaneously. A circuit element that has a large inductance is called an **inductor**, symbol ⎯ℓℓℓℓ⎯. We always assume that the self-inductance of the remainder of a circuit is negligible compared with that of the inductor.

Consider the circuit shown in Figure 32.2, where the battery has negligible internal resistance. Suppose the switch S is closed at $t = 0$. The current begins to increase, and because of the increasing current, the inductor produces a back emf that opposes the increasing current. In other words, the inductor acts like a battery whose polarity is opposite that of the real battery in the circuit. The back emf is

$$\mathcal{E}_L = -L \frac{dI}{dt}$$

Since the current is increasing, dI/dt is positive; therefore, $\mathcal{E}_L$ is negative. This negative value corresponds to the fact that there is a potential drop in going from a to b across the inductor. For this reason, point a is at a higher potential than point b, as illustrated in Figure 32.2.

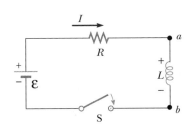

FIGURE 32.2   A series *RL* circuit. As the current increases toward its maximum value, the inductor produces an emf that opposes the increasing current.

With this in mind, we can apply Kirchhoff's loop equation to this circuit:

$$\mathcal{E} - IR - L\frac{dI}{dt} = 0 \tag{32.6}$$

where IR is the voltage drop across the resistor. We must now look for a solution to this differential equation, which is similar to that of the *RC* circuit (Section 28.4).

To obtain a mathematical solution of Equation 32.6, it is convenient to change variables by letting $x = \dfrac{\mathcal{E}}{R} - I$, so that $dx = -dI$. With these substitutions, Equation 32.6 can be written

$$x + \frac{L}{R}\frac{dx}{dt} = 0$$

$$\frac{dx}{x} = -\frac{R}{L}dt$$

Integrating this last expression gives

$$\ln\frac{x}{x_0} = -\frac{R}{L}t$$

where the integrating constant is taken to be $-\ln x_0$. Taking the antilog of this result gives

$$x = x_0 e^{-Rt/L}$$

Since at $t = 0$, $I = 0$, we note that $x_0 = \mathcal{E}/R$. Hence, the last expression is equivalent to

$$\frac{\mathcal{E}}{R} - I = \frac{\mathcal{E}}{R}e^{-Rt/L}$$

$$I = \frac{\mathcal{E}}{R}(1 - e^{-Rt/L})$$

which represents the solution of Equation 32.6.

This mathematical solution of Equation 32.6, which represents the current as a function of time, can also be written:

$$I(t) = \frac{\mathcal{E}}{R}(1 - e^{-t/\tau}) \tag{32.7}$$

where the constant τ is the time constant of the *RL* circuit:

$$\tau = L/R \tag{32.8}$$

Physically, τ is the time it takes the current to reach $(1 - e^{-1}) = 0.632$ of its final value, $\mathcal{E}/R$.

Figure 32.3 graphs the current versus time, where $I = 0$ at $t = 0$. Note that the equilibrium value of the current, which occurs at $t = \infty$, is $\mathcal{E}/R$. This can be seen by setting dI/dt equal to zero in Equation 32.6 (at equilibrium, the change in the

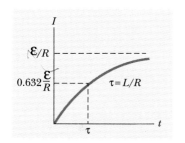

FIGURE 32.3   Plot of the current versus time for the *RL* circuit shown in Figure 32.2. The switch is closed at $t = 0$, and the current increases toward its maximum value, $\mathcal{E}/R$. The time constant τ is the time it takes I to reach 63% of its maximum value.

current is zero) and solving for the current. Thus, we see that the current rises very fast initially and then gradually approaches the equilibrium value $\mathcal{E}/R$ as $t \to \infty$.

We can show that Equation 32.7 is a solution of Equation 32.6 by computing dI/dt and noting that $I = 0$ at $t = 0$. Taking the first time derivative of Equation 32.7, we get

$$\frac{dI}{dt} = \frac{\mathcal{E}}{L} e^{-t/\tau} \qquad (32.9)$$

Substitution of this result for the dI/dt term in Equation 32.6 together with the value of I given by Equation 32.7 will indeed verify that our solution satisfies Equation 32.6. That is,

$$\mathcal{E} - IR - L\frac{dI}{dt} = 0$$

$$\mathcal{E} - \frac{\mathcal{E}}{R}(1 - e^{-t/\tau})R - L\left(\frac{\mathcal{E}}{L}e^{-t/\tau}\right) = 0$$

$$\mathcal{E} - \mathcal{E} + \mathcal{E}e^{-t/\tau} - \mathcal{E}e^{-t/\tau} = 0$$

From Equation 32.9 we see that the time rate of increase of current is a maximum (equal to $\mathcal{E}/L$) at $t = 0$ and falls off exponentially to zero as $t \to \infty$ (Fig. 32.4).

Now consider the *RL* circuit arranged as shown in Figure 32.5. The circuit contains two switches that operate so that when one is closed, the other is opened. Suppose that S_1 is closed for a long enough time to allow the current to reach its equilibrium value, $\mathcal{E}/R$. If we call $t = 0$ the instant at which S_1 is thrown open and S_2 is simultaneously thrown closed, we have a circuit with no battery ($\mathcal{E} = 0$). If we

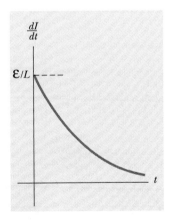

FIGURE 32.4   Plot of dI/dt versus time for the *RL* circuit shown in Figure 32.2. The time rate of change of current is a maximum at $t = 0$ when the switch is closed. The rate decreases exponentially with time as I increases toward its maximum value.

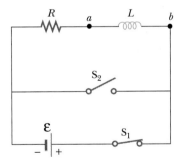

FIGURE 32.5   An *RL* circuit containing two switches. When S_1 is closed and S_2 is open as shown, the battery is in the circuit. At the instant S_2 is closed, S_1 is opened and the battery is removed from the circuit.

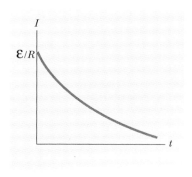

FIGURE 32.6 Current versus time for the circuit shown in Figure 32.5. At $t < 0$, S_1 is closed and S_2 is open. At $t = 0$, S_2 is closed, S_1 is open, and the current has its maximum value $\mathcal{E}/R$.

apply Kirchhoff's circuit law to the upper loop containing the resistor and inductor, we obtain

$$IR + L\frac{dI}{dt} = 0$$

It is left as a problem (Problem 18) to show that the solution of this differential equation is

$$I(t) = \frac{\mathcal{E}}{R}\,e^{-t/\tau} = I_0 e^{-t/\tau} \tag{32.10}$$

where the current at $t = 0$ is $I_0 = \mathcal{E}/R$ and $\tau = L/R$.

The graph of the current versus time (Fig. 32.6) shows that the current is continuously decreasing with time, as would be expected. Furthermore, note that the slope, dI/dt, is always negative and has its maximum value at $t = 0$. The negative slope signifies that $\mathcal{E}_L = -L(dI/dt)$ is now positive; that is, point a is at a lower potential than point b in Figure 32.5.

EXAMPLE 32.3   Time Constant of an *RL* Circuit

The switch in Figure 32.7a is closed at $t = 0$. (a) Find the time constant of the circuit.

Solution   The time constant is given by Equation 32.8

$$\tau = \frac{L}{R} = \frac{30.0 \times 10^{-3}\ \text{H}}{6.00\ \Omega} = \boxed{5.00\ \text{ms}}$$

(b) Calculate the current in the circuit at $t = 2.00$ ms.

Solution   Using Equation 32.7 for the current as a function of time (with t and τ in milliseconds), we find that

at $t = 2.00$ ms

$$I = \frac{\mathcal{E}}{R}\,(1 - e^{-t/\tau}) = \frac{12.0\ \text{V}}{6.00\ \Omega}\,(1 - e^{-0.400}) = \boxed{0.659\ \text{A}}$$

A plot of Equation 32.7 for this circuit is given in Figure 32.7b.

Exercise   Calculate the current in the circuit and the voltage across the resistor after one time constant has elapsed.

Answer   1.37 A, 7.56 V.

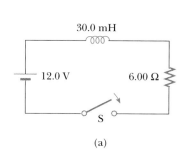

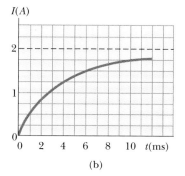

FIGURE 32.7   (Example 32.3) (a) The switch in this *RL* circuit is closed at $t = 0$. (b) A graph of the current versus time for the circuit in part (a).

32.3   ENERGY IN A MAGNETIC FIELD

Because the emf induced by an inductor prevents a battery from establishing an instantaneous current, the battery has to do work against the inductor to create a current. Part of the energy supplied by the battery goes into joule heat dissipated in the resistor, while the remaining energy is stored in the inductor. If we multiply each term in Equation 32.6 by I and rearrange the expression, we get

$$I\mathcal{E} = I^2R + LI\frac{dI}{dt} \tag{32.11}$$

This expression tells us that the rate at which energy is supplied by the battery, $I\mathcal{E}$, equals the sum of the rate at which joule heat is dissipated in the resistor, I^2R, and the rate at which energy is stored in the inductor, $LI(dI/dt)$. Thus, Equation 32.11 is simply an expression of energy conservation. If we let U_B denote the energy stored in the inductor at any time (where the subscript B denotes energy stored in the magnetic field of the inductor), then the rate dU_B/dt at which energy is stored can be written

$$\frac{dU_B}{dt} = LI\frac{dI}{dt}$$

To find the total energy stored in the inductor, we can rewrite this expression as $dU_B = LI\, dI$ and integrate:

$$U_B = \int_0^{U_B} dU_B = \int_0^I LI\, dI$$

$$U_B = \tfrac{1}{2}LI^2 \tag{32.12}$$

Energy stored in an inductor

where L is constant and can be removed from the integral. Equation 32.12 represents the energy stored in the magnetic field of the inductor when the current is I. Note that this equation is similar in form to the equation for the energy stored in the electric field of a capacitor, $Q^2/2C$ (Eq. 26.10). In either case, we see that it takes work to establish a field.

We can also determine the energy per unit volume, or energy density, stored in a magnetic field. For simplicity, consider a solenoid whose inductance is given by Equation 32.5:

$$L = \mu_0 n^2 A\ell$$

The magnetic field of a solenoid is given by Equation 30.20:

$$B = \mu_0 nI$$

Substituting the expression for L and $I = B/\mu_0 n$ into Equation 32.12 gives

$$U_B = \tfrac{1}{2}LI^2 = \tfrac{1}{2}\mu_0 n^2 A\ell\left(\frac{B}{\mu_0 n}\right)^2 = \frac{B^2}{2\mu_0}(A\ell) \tag{32.13}$$

Because $A\ell$ is the volume of the solenoid, the energy stored per unit volume in a magnetic field is

$$u_B = \frac{U_B}{A\ell} = \frac{B^2}{2\mu_0} \tag{32.14}$$

Magnetic energy density

Although Equation 32.14 was derived for the special case of a solenoid, it is valid for any region of space in which a magnetic field exists. Note that Equation 32.14 is similar in form to the equation for the energy per unit volume stored in an electric field, given by $\tfrac{1}{2}\epsilon_0 E^2$ (Eq. 26.12). In both cases, the energy density is proportional to the square of the field strength.

EXAMPLE 32.4   What Happens to the Energy in the Inductor?

Consider once again the *RL* circuit shown in Figure 32.5, in which switch S_2 is closed at the instant S_1 is opened (at $t = 0$). Recall that the current in the upper loop decays exponentially with time according to the expression $I = I_0 e^{-t/\tau}$, where $I_0 = \mathcal{E}/R$ is the initial current in the circuit and $\tau = L/R$ is the time constant. Let us show explicitly that all the energy stored in the magnetic field of the inductor gets dissipated as heat in the resistor.

Solution   That rate at which energy is dissipated in the resistor, dU/dt, (or the power) is equal to I^2R, where I is the instantaneous current:

$$\frac{dU}{dt} = I^2R = (I_0 e^{-Rt/L})^2R = I_0{}^2Re^{-2Rt/L}$$

To find the total energy dissipated in the resistor, we integrate this expression over the limits $t = 0$ to $t = \infty$ (∞ because it takes an infinite time for the current to reach zero):

$$U = \int_0^\infty I_0{}^2Re^{-2Rt/L}\,dt = I_0{}^2R\int_0^\infty e^{-2Rt/L}\,dt \qquad (1)$$

The value of the definite integral is $L/2R$, and so U becomes

$$U = I_0{}^2R\left(\frac{L}{2R}\right) = \frac{1}{2}LI_0{}^2$$

Note that this is equal to the initial energy stored in the magnetic field of the inductor, given by Equation 32.13, as we set out to prove.

Exercise   Show that the integral on the right-hand side of Equation (1) has the value $L/2R$.

EXAMPLE 32.5   The Coaxial Cable

A long coaxial cable consists of two concentric cylindrical conductors of radii a and b and length ℓ, as in Figure 32.8. The inner conductor is assumed to be a thin cylindrical shell. Each conductor carries a current I (the outer one being a return path). (a) Calculate the self-inductance L of this cable.

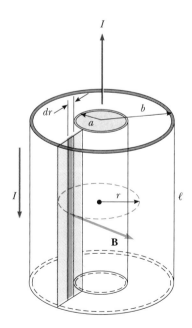

FIGURE 32.8   (Example 32.5) Section of a long coaxial cable. The inner and outer conductors carry equal and opposite currents.

Solution   To obtain L, we must know the magnetic flux through any cross-section between the two conductors. From Ampère's law (Section 30.3), it is easy to see that the magnetic field between the conductors is $B = \mu_0 I/2\pi r$. The field is zero outside the conductors $(r > b)$ because the net current through a circular path surrounding both wires is zero, and hence from Ampère's law, $\oint \mathbf{B} \cdot d\mathbf{s} = 0$. The field is zero inside the inner conductor because it is hollow and there is no current within a radius $r < a$.

The magnetic field is perpendicular to the shaded rectangular strip of length ℓ and width $(b - a)$, the cross-section of interest. Dividing this rectangle into strips of width dr, we see that the area of each strip is $\ell\,dr$ and the flux through each strip is $B\,dA = B\ell\,dr$. Hence, the total flux through any cross-section is

$$\Phi_B = \int B\,dA = \int_a^b \frac{\mu_0 I}{2\pi r}\ell\,dr = \frac{\mu_0 I\ell}{2\pi}\int_a^b \frac{dr}{r} = \frac{\mu_0 I\ell}{2\pi}\ln\left(\frac{b}{a}\right)$$

Using this result, we find that the self-inductance of the cable is

$$L = \frac{\Phi_B}{I} = \boxed{\frac{\mu_0 \ell}{2\pi}\ln\left(\frac{b}{a}\right)}$$

(b) Calculate the total energy stored in the magnetic field of the cable.

Solution   Using Equation 32.13 and the results to part (a) gives

$$U_B = \tfrac{1}{2}LI^2 = \boxed{\frac{\mu_0 \ell I^2}{4\pi}\ln\left(\frac{b}{a}\right)}$$

*32.4 MUTUAL INDUCTANCE

Very often the magnetic flux through a circuit varies with time because of varying currents in nearby circuits. This condition induces an emf through a process known as mutual induction, so-called because it depends on the interaction of two circuits.

Consider two closely wound coils as shown in the cross-sectional view of Figure 32.9. The current I_1 in coil 1, which has N_1 turns, creates magnetic field lines, some of which pass through coil 2, which has N_2 turns. The corresponding flux through coil 2 produced by coil 1 is represented by Φ_{21}. We define the **mutual inductance** M_{21} of coil 2 with respect to coil 1 as the ratio of $N_2\Phi_{21}$ and the current I_1:

$$M_{21} \equiv \frac{N_2\Phi_{21}}{I_1} \tag{32.15}$$

$$\Phi_{21} = \frac{M_{21}}{N_2} I_1$$

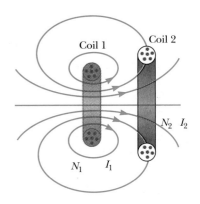

FIGURE 32.9   A cross-sectional view of two adjacent coils. A current in coil 1 sets up a magnetic flux, part of which passes through coil 2.

The mutual inductance depends on the geometry of both circuits and on their orientation with respect to one another. Clearly, as the circuit separation increases, the mutual inductance decreases because the flux linking the circuits decreases.

If the current I_1 varies with time, we see from Faraday's law and Equation 32.15 that the emf induced in coil 2 by coil 1 is

$$\mathcal{E}_2 = -N_2\frac{d\Phi_{21}}{dt} = -M_{21}\frac{dI_1}{dt} \tag{32.16}$$

Similarly, if the current I_2 varies with time, the emf induced in coil 1 by coil 2 is

$$\mathcal{E}_1 = -M_{12}\frac{dI_2}{dt} \tag{32.17}$$

These results are similar in form to Equation 32.1 for the self-induced emf $\mathcal{E} = -L(dI/dt)$. *The emf induced by mutual induction in one coil is always proportional to the rate of current change in the other coil.* If the rates at which the currents change with time are equal (that is, if $dI_1/dt = dI_2/dt$), then $\mathcal{E}_1 = \mathcal{E}_2$. Although the proportionality constants M_{12} and M_{21} appear to be different, it can be shown that they are equal. Thus, taking $M_{12} = M_{21} = M$, Equations 32.16 and 32.17 become

$$\mathcal{E}_2 = -M\frac{dI_1}{dt} \quad \text{and} \quad \mathcal{E}_1 = -M\frac{dI_2}{dt}$$

The unit of mutual inductance is also the henry.

EXAMPLE 32.6   *Mutual Inductance of Two Solenoids*

A long solenoid of length ℓ has N_1 turns, carries a current I, and has a cross-sectional area A. A second coil containing N_2 turns is wound around the center of the first coil, as in Figure 32.10. Find the mutual inductance of the system.

Solution   If the solenoid carries a current I_1, the magnetic field at its center is

$$B = \frac{\mu_0 N_1 I_1}{\ell}$$

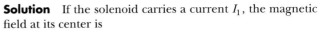

Since the flux Φ_{21} through coil 2 due to coil 1 is BA, the mutual inductance is

$$M = \frac{N_2 \Phi_{21}}{I_1} = \frac{N_2 BA}{I_1} = \mu_0 \frac{N_1 N_2 A}{\ell}$$

Exercise   Calculate the mutual inductance of two solenoids for which $N_1 = 500$ turns, $A = 3 \times 10^{-3}$ m^2, $\ell = 0.5$ m, and $N_2 = 8$ turns.

Answer   30.2 μH.

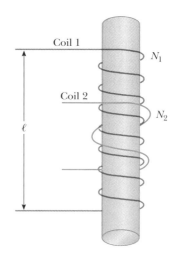

FIGURE 32.10   (Example 32.6) A small coil of N_2 turns wrapped around the center of a long solenoid of N_1 turns.

32.5   OSCILLATIONS IN AN *LC* CIRCUIT

When a charged capacitor is connected to an inductor as in Figure 32.11 and the switch is then closed, both the current and the charge on the capacitor oscillate. If the resistance of the circuit is zero, no energy is dissipated as joule heat and the oscillations persist. In this section we neglect the resistance in the circuit.

In the following analysis, let us assume that the capacitor has an initial charge Q_{max} (the maximum charge) and that the switch is thrown closed at $t = 0$. It is convenient to describe what happens from an energy viewpoint.

When the capacitor is fully charged, the total energy U in the circuit is stored in the electric field of the capacitor and is equal to $Q_{max}^2/2C$ (Eq. 26.10). At this time, the current is zero and so there is no energy stored in the inductor. As the capacitor begins to discharge, the energy stored in its electric field decreases. At the same time, the current increases and some energy is now stored in the magnetic field of the inductor. Thus, we see that energy is transferred from the electric field of the capacitor to the magnetic field of the inductor. When the capacitor is fully discharged, it stores no energy. At this time, the current reaches its maximum value and all of the energy is stored in the inductor. The process then repeats in the reverse direction. The energy continues to oscillate between the inductor and capacitor indefinitely.

A graphical description of this energy transfer is shown in Figure 32.12. The circuit behavior is analogous to the oscillating mass-spring system studied in Chapter 13. The potential energy stored in a stretched spring, $\frac{1}{2}kx^2$, is analogous to the potential energy stored in the capacitor, $Q_{max}^2/2C$. The kinetic energy of the moving mass, $\frac{1}{2}mv^2$, is analogous to the energy stored in the inductor, $\frac{1}{2}LI^2$, which requires the presence of moving charges. In Figure 32.12a, all of the energy is stored as potential energy in the capacitor at $t = 0$ (since $I = 0$). In Figure 32.12b, all of the energy is stored as "kinetic" energy in the inductor, $\frac{1}{2}LI_{max}^2$, where I_{max} is the maximum current. At intermediate points, part of the energy is potential energy and part is kinetic energy.

Consider some arbitrary time t after the switch is closed, so that the capacitor has a charge Q and the current is I. At this time, both elements store energy, but the sum of the two energies must equal the total initial energy U stored in the fully charged capacitor at $t = 0$:

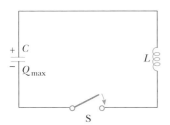

FIGURE 32.11   A simple *LC* circuit. The capacitor has an initial charge Q_{max}, and the switch is thrown closed at $t = 0$.

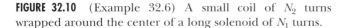

Total energy stored in the *LC* circuit

$$U = U_C + U_L = \frac{Q^2}{2C} + \frac{1}{2}LI^2 \qquad (32.18)$$

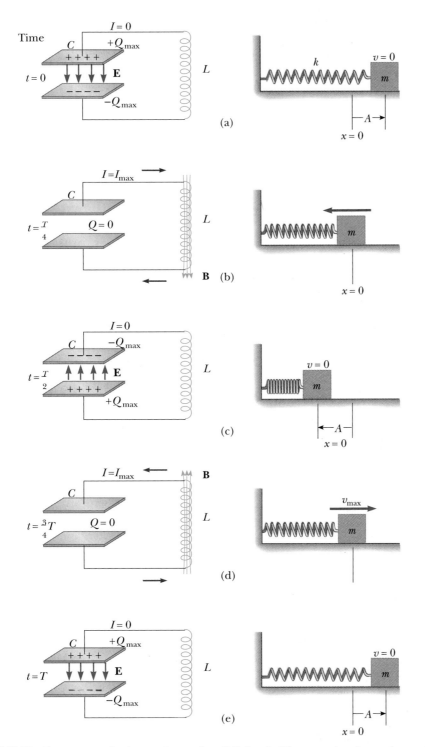

FIGURE 32.12   Energy transfer in a resistanceless *LC* circuit. The capacitor has a charge Q_{max} at $t = 0$, the instant at which the switch is thrown closed. The mechanical analog of this circuit is a mass-spring system.

Since we have assumed the circuit resistance to be zero, no energy is dissipated as joule heat and hence *the total energy must remain constant in time*. This means that $dU/dt = 0$. Therefore, by differentiating Equation 32.18 with respect to time while noting that Q and I vary with time, we get

$$\frac{dU}{dt} = \frac{d}{dt}\left(\frac{Q^2}{2C} + \tfrac{1}{2}LI^2\right) = \frac{Q}{C}\frac{dQ}{dt} + LI\frac{dI}{dt} = 0 \qquad (32.19)$$

We can reduce this to a differential equation in one variable by using the relationship $I = dQ/dt$. From this, it follows that $dI/dt = d^2Q/dt^2$. Substitution of these relationships into Equation 32.19 gives

$$L\frac{d^2Q}{dt^2} + \frac{Q}{C} = 0$$

$$\frac{d^2Q}{dt^2} = -\frac{1}{LC}Q \qquad (32.20)$$

We can solve for Q by noting that Equation 32.20 is of the same form as the analogous Equation 13.14 for a mass-spring system:

$$\frac{d^2x}{dt^2} = -\frac{k}{m}x = -\omega^2 x$$

where k is the spring constant, m is the mass, and $\omega = \sqrt{k/m}$. The solution of this equation has the general form

$$x = A\cos(\omega t + \phi)$$

where ω is the angular frequency of the simple harmonic motion, A is the amplitude of motion (the maximum value of x), and ϕ is the phase constant; the values of A and ϕ depend on the initial conditions. Since it is of the same form as the differential equation of the simple harmonic oscillator, Equation 32.20 has the solution

$$Q = Q_{max}\cos(\omega t + \phi) \qquad (32.21)$$

where Q_{max} is the maximum charge of the capacitor and the angular frequency ω is

$$\omega = \frac{1}{\sqrt{LC}} \qquad (32.22)$$

Note that *the angular frequency of the oscillations depends solely on the inductance and capacitance of the circuit.*

Because Q varies harmonically, the current also varies harmonically. This is easily shown by differenting Equation 32.21 with respect to time:

$$I = \frac{dQ}{dt} = -\omega Q_{max}\sin(\omega t + \phi) \qquad (32.23)$$

To determine the value of the phase angle ϕ, we examine the initial conditions, which in our situation require that at $t = 0$, $I = 0$, and $Q = Q_{max}$. Setting $I = 0$ at $t = 0$ in Equation 32.23 gives

$$0 = -\omega Q_{max} \sin \phi$$

which shows that $\phi = 0$. This value for ϕ is also consistent with Equation 32.21 and with the condition that $Q = Q_{max}$ at $t = 0$. Therefore, in our case, the time variation of Q and that of I are

$$Q = Q_{max} \cos \omega t \qquad (32.24)$$

$$I = -\omega Q_{max} \sin \omega t = -I_{max} \sin \omega t \qquad (32.25)$$

where $I_{max} = \omega Q_{max}$ is the maximum current in the circuit.

Graphs of Q versus t and I versus t are shown in Figure 32.13. Note that the charge on the capacitor oscillates between the extreme values Q_{max} and $-Q_{max}$, and the current oscillates between I_{max} and $-I_{max}$. Furthermore, the current is 90° out of phase with the charge. That is, when the charge reaches an extreme value, the current is zero, and when the charge is zero, the current has an extreme value.

Let us return to the energy of the LC circuit. Substituting Equations 32.24 and 32.25 in Equation 32.18, we find that the total energy is

$$U = U_C + U_L = \frac{Q_{max}^2}{2C} \cos^2 \omega t + \frac{LI_{max}^2}{2} \sin^2 \omega t \qquad (32.26)$$

This expression contains all of the features described qualitatively at the beginning of this section. It shows that the energy of the system continuously oscillates between energy stored in the electric field of the capacitor and energy stored in the magnetic field of the inductor. When the energy stored in the capacitor has its maximum value, $Q_{max}^2/2C$, the energy stored in the inductor is zero. When the energy stored in the inductor has its maximum value, $\frac{1}{2}LI_{max}^2$, the energy stored in the capacitor is zero.

Plots of the time variations of U_C and U_L are shown in Figure 32.14. Note that the sum $U_C + U_L$ is a constant and equal to the total energy, $Q_{max}^2/2C$. An analytical proof of this is straightforward. The maximum energy stored in the capacitor (when $I = 0$) must equal the maximum energy stored in the inductor (when $Q = 0$), so

$$\frac{Q_{max}^2}{2C} = \frac{1}{2}LI_{max}^2$$

Using this expression in Equation 32.26 for the total energy gives

$$U = \frac{Q_{max}^2}{2C} (\cos^2 \omega t + \sin^2 \omega t) = \frac{Q_{max}^2}{2C} \qquad (32.27)$$

because $\cos^2 \omega t + \sin^2 \omega t = 1$.

In our idealized situation, the oscillations in the circuit persist indefinitely, but you should note that the total energy U remains constant only if energy losses are neglected. In actual circuits, there is always some resistance and so energy will be lost in the form of heat. (In fact, even when the energy losses due to wire resistance are neglected, energy is also lost in the form of electromagnetic waves radiated by the circuit.)

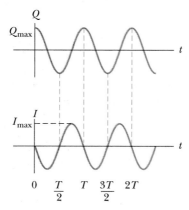

FIGURE 32.13   Graphs of charge versus time and current versus time for a resistanceless LC circuit. Note that Q and I are 90° out of phase with each other.

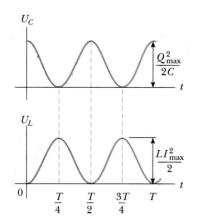

FIGURE 32.14   Plots of U_C versus t and U_L versus t for a resistanceless LC circuit. The sum of the two curves is a constant and equal to the total energy stored in the circuit.

EXAMPLE 32.7   An Oscillatory *LC* Circuit

In Figure 32.15, the capacitor is initially charged when S_1 is open and S_2 is closed. Then S_1 is thrown closed at the same instant that S_2 is opened so that the capacitor is shorted across the inductor. (a) Find the frequency of oscillation.

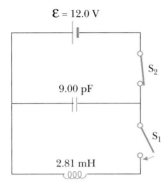

FIGURE 32.15   (Example 32.7) First the capacitor is fully charged with the switch S_1 open and S_2 closed. Then, S_1 is thrown closed at the same time that S_2 is thrown open.

Solution   Using Equation 32.22 gives for the frequency

$$f = \frac{\omega}{2\pi} = \frac{1}{2\pi\sqrt{LC}}$$

$$= \frac{1}{2\pi[(2.81 \times 10^{-3}\,\text{H})(9.00 \times 10^{-12}\,\text{F})]^{1/2}}$$

$$= \boxed{1.00 \times 10^6\,\text{Hz}}$$

(b) What are the maximum values of charge on the capacitor and current in the circuit?

Solution   The initial charge on the capacitor equals the maximum charge, and since $C = Q/V$, we get

$$Q_{\text{max}} = CV = (9.00 \times 10^{-12}\,\text{F})(12.0\,\text{V}) = \boxed{1.08 \times 10^{-10}\,\text{C}}$$

From Equation 32.25, we see that the maximum current is related to the maximum charge:

$$I_{\text{max}} = \omega Q_{\text{max}} = 2\pi f Q_{\text{max}}$$
$$= (2\pi \times 10^6\,\text{s}^{-1})(1.08 \times 10^{-10}\,\text{C})$$

$$= \boxed{6.79 \times 10^{-4}\,\text{A}}$$

(c) Determine the charge and current as functions of time.

Solution   Equations 32.24 and 32.25 give the following expressions for the time variation of Q and I:

$$Q = Q_{\text{max}}\cos\omega t = \boxed{(1.08 \times 10^{-10}\,\text{C})\cos\omega t}$$

$$I = -I_{\text{max}}\sin\omega t = \boxed{(-6.79 \times 10^{-4}\,\text{A})\sin\omega t}$$

where

$$\omega = 2\pi f = 2\pi \times 10^6\,\text{rad/s}$$

Exercise   What is the total energy stored in the circuit?

Answer $6.48 \times 10^{-10}\,\text{J}$.

*32.6   THE *RLC* CIRCUIT

We now turn our attention to a more realistic circuit consisting of an inductor, a capacitor, and a resistor connected in series, as in Figure 32.16. We assume that the capacitor has an initial charge Q_{max} before the switch is closed. Once the switch is thrown closed and a current is established, the total energy stored in the circuit at any time is given, as before, by Equation 32.18. That is, the energy stored in the capacitor is $Q^2/2C$, and the energy stored in the inductor is $\frac{1}{2}LI^2$. However, the total energy is no longer constant, as it was in the *LC* circuit, because of the presence of a resistor, which dissipates energy as heat. Since the rate of energy dissipation through a resistor is I^2R, we have

$$\frac{dU}{dt} = -I^2R$$

where the negative sign signifies that U is decreasing in time. Substituting this result into Equation 32.19 gives

$$LI\frac{dI}{dt} + \frac{Q}{C}\frac{dQ}{dt} = -I^2R \qquad (32.28)$$

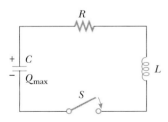

FIGURE 32.16   A series *RLC* circuit. The capacitor has a charge Q_{max} at $t = 0$ the instant at which the switch is thrown closed.

Using the fact that $I = dQ/dt$ and $dI/dt = d^2Q/dt^2$, and dividing Equation 32.28 by I, we get

$$L\frac{d^2Q}{dt^2} + R\frac{dQ}{dt} + \frac{Q}{C} = 0 \qquad (32.29)$$

Note that the *RLC* circuit is analogous to the damped harmonic oscillator discussed in Section 13.6 and illustrated in Figure 32.17. The equation of motion for this mechanical system is

$$m\frac{d^2x}{dt^2} + b\frac{dx}{dt} + kx = 0 \qquad (32.30)$$

Comparing Equations 32.29 and 32.30, we see that Q corresponds to x, L to m, R to the damping constant b, and C to $1/k$, where k is the force constant of the spring.

Because the analytical solution of Equation 32.29 is cumbersome, we give only a qualitative description of the circuit behavior.

In the simplest case, when $R = 0$, Equation 32.29 reduces to that of a simple *LC* circuit, as expected, and the charge and the current oscillate sinusoidally in time.

Next consider the situation where R is reasonably small. In this case, the solution of Equation 32.29 is

$$Q = Q_{max}e^{-Rt/2L}\cos\omega_d t \qquad (32.31)$$

where

$$\omega_d = \left[\frac{1}{LC} - \left(\frac{R}{2L}\right)^2\right]^{1/2} \qquad (32.32)$$

That is, the charge oscillates with damped harmonic motion in analogy with a mass-spring system moving in a viscous medium. From Equation 32.32, we see that, when $R \ll \sqrt{4L/C}$, the frequency ω_d of the damped oscillator is close to that of the undamped oscillator, $1/\sqrt{LC}$. Because $I = dQ/dt$, it follows that the current also undergoes damped harmonic motion. A plot of the charge versus time for the damped oscillator is shown in Figure 32.18. Note that the maximum value of Q decreases after each oscillation, just as the amplitude of a damped harmonic oscillator decreases in time.

When we consider larger values of R, we find that the oscillations damp out more rapidly; in fact, there exists a critical resistance value R_c above which no oscillations occur. The critical value is given by $R_c = \sqrt{4L/C}$. A system with $R = R_c$ is said to be critically damped. When R exceeds R_c, the system is said to be over-damped (Fig. 32.19).

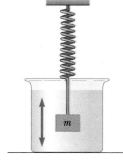

FIGURE 32.17 A mass-spring system moving in a viscous medium with damped harmonic motion is analogous to an *RLC* circuit.

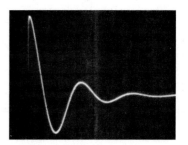

Oscilloscope pattern showing the decay in the oscillations of an *RLC* circuit. The parameters used were $R = 75\ \Omega$, $L = 10$ mH, $C = 0.19\ \mu$F, and $f = 300$ Hz. *(Courtesy of J. Rudmin)*

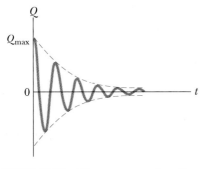

FIGURE 32.18 Charge versus time for a damped *RLC* circuit. This occurs for $R \ll \sqrt{4L/C}$. The Q versus t curve represents a plot of Equation 32.31.

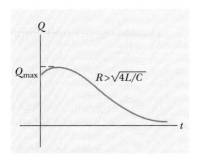

FIGURE 32.19 Plot of Q versus t for an overdamped *RLC* circuit, which occurs for values of $R > \sqrt{4L/C}$.

SUMMARY

When the current in a coil changes with time, an emf is induced in the coil according to Faraday's law. The **self-induced emf** is

$$\mathcal{E}_L = -L\frac{dI}{dt} \tag{32.1}$$

where L is the **inductance** of the coil. Inductance is a measure of the opposition of a device to a change in current. Inductance has the SI unit of **henry** (H), where $1\ \text{H} = 1\ \text{V·s/A}$.

The inductance of any coil is

$$L = \frac{N\Phi_B}{I} \tag{32.2}$$

where Φ_B is the magnetic flux through the coil and N is the total number of turns. The inductance of a device depends on its geometry. For example, the inductance of an air-core solenoid is

$$L = \frac{\mu_0 N^2 A}{\ell} \tag{32.4}$$

where A is the cross-sectional area and ℓ is the length of the solenoid.

If a resistor and inductor are connected in series to a battery of emf $\mathcal{E}$, and a switch in the circuit is thrown closed at $t = 0$, the current in the circuit varies in time according to the expression

$$I(t) = \frac{\mathcal{E}}{R}(1 - e^{-t/\tau}) \tag{32.7}$$

where $\tau = L/R$ is the time constant of the RL circuit. That is, the current rises to an equilibrium value of $\mathcal{E}/R$ after a time that is long compared to τ. If the battery is removed from the circuit, the current decays exponentially with time according to the expression

$$I(t) = \frac{\mathcal{E}}{R}e^{-t/\tau} \tag{32.10}$$

where $\mathcal{E}/R$ is the initial current in the circuit.

The energy stored in the magnetic field of an inductor carrying a current I is

$$U_B = \tfrac{1}{2}LI^2 \tag{32.12}$$

The energy per unit volume at a point where the magnetic field is B is

$$u_B = \frac{B^2}{2\mu_0} \tag{32.14}$$

In an LC circuit with zero resistance, the charge on the capacitor and the current in the circuit vary in time according to the expressions

$$Q = Q_{max}\cos(\omega t + \phi) \tag{32.21}$$

$$I = \frac{dQ}{dt} = -\omega Q_{max}\sin(\omega t + \phi) \tag{32.23}$$

where Q_{max} is the maximum charge on the capacitor, ϕ is a phase constant, and ω is the angular frequency of oscillation:

$$\omega = \frac{1}{\sqrt{LC}} \qquad (32.22)$$

The energy in an *LC* circuit continuously transfers between energy stored in the capacitor and energy stored in the inductor. The total energy of the *LC* circuit at any time *t* is

$$U = U_C + U_L = \frac{Q^2_{max}}{2C} \cos^2 \omega t + \frac{LI^2_{max}}{2} \sin^2 \omega t \qquad (32.26)$$

At $t = 0$, all of the energy is stored in the electric field of the capacitor ($U = Q^2_{max}/2C$). Eventually, all of this energy is transferred to the inductor ($U = LI^2_{max}/2$). However, the total energy remains constant because the energy losses are neglected in the ideal *LC* circuit.

The charge and current in an *RLC* circuit exhibit a damped harmonic behavior for small values of *R*. This is analogous to the damped harmonic motion of a mass-spring system in which friction is present.

QUESTIONS

1. Why is the induced emf that appears in an inductor called a "counter" or "back" emf?
2. The current in a circuit containing a coil, resistor, and battery has reached a constant value. Does the coil have an inductance? Does the coil affect the value of the current?
3. Does the inductance of a coil depend on the current in the coil? What other parameters affect the inductance of a coil?
4. How can a long piece of wire be wound on a spool so that the wire has a negligible self-inductance?
5. A long, fine wire is wound as a solenoid with a self-inductance *L*. If it is connected across the terminals of a battery, how does the maximum current depend on *L*?
6. For the series *RL* circuit shown in Figure 32.20, can the back emf ever be greater than the battery emf? Explain.

7. Suppose the switch in Figure 32.20 has been closed for a long time and is suddenly opened. Does the current instantaneously drop to zero? Why does a spark appear at the switch contacts at the instant the switch is thrown open?
8. If the current in an inductor is doubled, by what factor does the stored energy change?
9. Discuss the similarities between the energy stored in the electric field of a charged capacitor and the energy stored in the magnetic field of a current-carrying coil.
10. What is the inductance of two inductors connected in series?
11. Discuss how mutual inductance arises between the primary and secondary coils in a transformer.
12. The centers of two circular loops are separated by a fixed distance. For what relative orientation of the loops is their mutual inductance a maximum? a minimum?
13. Two solenoids are connected in series so that each carries the same current at any instant. Is mutual induction present? Explain.
14. In the *LC* circuit shown in Figure 32.12, the charge on the capacitor is sometimes zero, even though there is current in the circuit. How is this possible?
15. If the resistance of the wires in an *LC* circuit were not zero, would the oscillations persist? Explain.
16. How can you tell whether an *RLC* circuit is overdamped or underdamped?
17. What is the significance of critical damping in an *RLC* circuit?

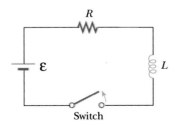

FIGURE 32.20 (Questions 6 and 7).

PROBLEMS

Section 32.1   Self-Inductance

1. A 2.00-H inductor carries a steady current of 0.500 A. When the switch in the circuit is thrown open, the current disappears in 10.0 ms. What is the average induced emf in the inductor during this time?

2. A spring has a radius of 4.00 cm and an inductance of 125 μH when extended to a length of 2.00 m. Find an approximate value for the total number of turns in the spring?

3. A coiled telephone cord has 70 turns, a cross-sectional diameter of 1.3 cm, and an unstretched length of 60 cm. Determine an approximate value for the self-inductance of the unstretched cord.

4. A small air-core solenoid has a length of 4.0 cm and a radius of 0.25 cm. If the inductance is to be 0.060 mH, how many turns per centimeter are required?

5. An emf induced in a solenoid of inductance L changes in time as $\mathcal{E} = \mathcal{E}_0 e^{-kt}$. Find the total charge that passes through the solenoid.

6. Calculate the magnetic flux through a 300-turn, 7.20-mH coil when the current in the coil is 10.0 mA.

6A. Calculate the magnetic flux through an N-turn coil having inductance L when the coil carries a current I.

7. A 40.0-mA current is carried by a uniformly wound air-core solenoid with 450 turns, a 15.0-mm diameter, and 12.0-cm length. Compute (a) the magnetic field inside the solenoid, (b) the magnetic flux through each turn, and (c) the inductance of the solenoid. (d) Which of these quantities depends on the current?

8. A 0.388-mH inductor has a length that is four times its diameter. If it is wound with 22 turns per centimeter, what is its length?

9. An emf of 36 mV is induced in a 400-turn coil at an instant when the current has a value of 2.8 A and is changing at a rate of 12 A/s. What is the total magnetic flux through the coil?

10. The current in a 90-mH inductor changes with time as $I = t^2 - 6t$ (in SI units). Find the magnitude of the induced emf at (a) $t = 1.0$ s and (b) $t = 4.0$ s. (c) At what time is the emf zero?

11. A 10.0-mH inductor carries a current $I = I_{max} \sin \omega t$, with $I_{max} = 5.00$ A and $\omega/2\pi = 60.0$ Hz. What is the back emf as a function of time?

12. A solenoid inductor is 20.0 cm long and has a cross-sectional area of 5.00 cm^2. When the current through the solenoid decreases at a rate of 0.625 A/s, the induced emf is 200 μV. Find the number of turns/unit length of the solenoid.

13. Two coils, A and B, are wound using equal lengths of wire. Each coil has the same number of turns per unit length, but coil A has twice as many turns as coil B. What is the ratio of the self-inductance of A to the self-inductance of B? (*Note:* The radii of the two coils are not equal.)

14. A toroid has a major radius R and a minor radius r, and is tightly wound with N turns of wire, as shown in Figure P32.14. If $R \gg r$, the magnetic field within the region of the toroid of cross-sectional area $A = \pi r^2$ is essentially that of a long solenoid that has been bent into a large circle of radius R. Using the uniform field of a long solenoid, show that the self-inductance of such a toroid is approximately

$$L \cong \frac{\mu_0 N^2 A}{2\pi R}$$

(An exact expression for the inductance of a toroid with a rectangular cross-section is derived in Problem 78.)

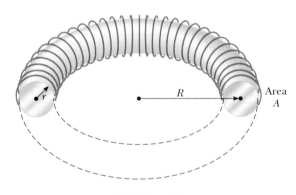

FIGURE P32.14

15. A solenoid has 120 turns uniformly wrapped around a wooden core, which has a diameter of 10.0 mm and a length of 9.00 cm. (a) Calculate the inductance of the solenoid. (b) The wooden core is replaced with a soft iron rod that has the same dimensions, but a magnetic permeability $\kappa_m = 800\mu_0$. What is the new inductance?

16. An inductor in the form of a solenoid contains 420 turns, is 16.0 cm in length, and has a cross-sectional area of 3.00 cm^2. What uniform rate of decrease of current through the inductor induces an emf of 175 μV?

□ indicates problems that have full solutions available in the Student Solutions Manual and Study Guide.

16A. An inductor in the form of a solenoid contains N turns, has a length ℓ, and has cross-sectional area A. What uniform rate of decrease of current through the inductor induces an emf $\mathcal{E}$?

Section 32.2   RL Circuits

17. The switch in Figure P32.17 is closed at time $t = 0$. Find the current in the inductor and the current through the switch as functions of time.

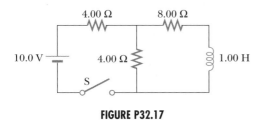

FIGURE P32.17

18. Show that $I = I_0 e^{-t/\tau}$ is a solution of the differential equation

$$IR + L\frac{dI}{dt} = 0$$

where $\tau = L/R$ and $I_0 = \mathcal{E}/R$ is the current at $t = 0$.

19. Calculate the resistance in an RL circuit in which $L = 2.5$ H and the current increases to 90% of its final value in 3.0 s.

20. In an RL series circuit (Fig. 32.2), the maximum current is 0.500 A. After the switch is thrown, a current of 0.250 A is reached in 0.150 s, and then the voltage across the resistor is 20.0 V. Calculate the values of R, L, and $\mathcal{E}$ for this circuit.

21. A series RL circuit with $L = 3.00$ H and a series RC circuit with $C = 3.00$ μF have the same time constant. If the two circuits have the same resistance R, (a) what is the value of R and (b) what is the time constant?

21A. A series RL circuit and a series RC circuit have the same time constant. If the two circuits have the same resistance R, (a) what is the value of R in terms of L and C, and (b) what is the time constant in terms of L and C?

22. An inductor that has an inductance of 15.0 H and a resistance of 30.0 Ω is connected across a 100-V battery. What is the rate of increase of the current (a) at $t = 0$ and (b) at $t = 1.50$ s?

23. A 12-V battery is about to be connected to a series circuit containing a 10-Ω resistor and a 2.0-H inductor. How long will it take the current to reach (a) 50% and (b) 90% of its final value?

24. A current pulse is fed to the partial circuit shown in Figure P32.24. The current begins at zero, then becomes 10.0 A for 200 μs, and then is zero once again.

Determine the voltage across the inductor as a function of time.

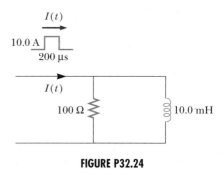

FIGURE P32.24

25. A 140-mH inductor and a 4.9-Ω resistor are connected with a switch to a 6.0-V battery as shown in Figure P32.25. (a) If the switch is thrown to the left (connecting the battery), how much time elapses before the current reaches 220 mA? (b) What is the current in the inductor 10.0 s after the switch is closed? (c) Now the switch is quickly thrown from A to B. How much time elapses before the current falls to 160 mA?

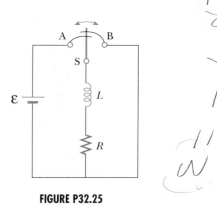

FIGURE P32.25

26. When the switch in Figure P32.26 is thrown closed, the current takes 3.00 ms to reach 98% of its final value. If $R = 10.0$ Ω, what is the inductance?

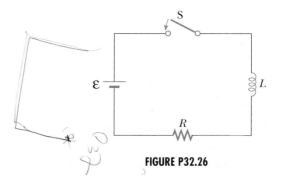

FIGURE P32.26

27. For $\mathcal{E} = 6.00$ V, $L = 24.0$ mH, and $R = 10.0$ Ω in Figure P32.26, find (a) the current 0.500 ms after S is thrown closed and (b) the maximum current.

28. Consider two ideal inductors, L_1 and L_2, that have *zero* internal resistance and are far apart so that their mutual inductance is zero. (a) If these inductors are connected in series, show that they are equivalent to a single ideal inductor having $L_{eq} = L_1 + L_2$. (b) If these same inductors are connected in parallel, show that they are equivalent to a single ideal inductor having $1/L_{eq} = 1/L_1 + 1/L_2$. (c) Now consider two inductors, L_1 and L_2, that have *nonzero* internal resistance R_1 and R_2, respectively, but are still far apart so that their mutual inductance is zero. If these inductors are connected in series show that they are equivalent to a single inductor having $L_{eq} = L_1 + L_2$ and $R_{eq} = R_1 + R_2$. (d) If these same inductors are now connected in parallel, is it necessarily true that they are equivalent to a single ideal inductor having $1/L_{eq} = 1/L_1 + 1/L_2$ and $1/R_{eq} = 1/R_1 + 1/R_2$? Explain.

29. Let $L = 3.00$ H, $R = 8.00$ Ω, and $\mathcal{E} = 36.0$ V in Figure P32.26. (a) Calculate the ratio of the potential difference across the resistor to that across the inductor when $I = 2.00$ A. (b) Calculate the voltage across the inductor when $I = 4.50$ A.

30. In the circuit shown in Figure P32.30, switch S_1 is closed first, and after a certain period of time the current through L_1 is 0.60 A. Then switch S_2 is closed. Find the currents through the coils the moment switch S_2 is closed. Assume that the resistances of the coils are negligible, and take $\mathcal{E} = 12.0$ V, $r = 10.0$ Ω, $L_1 = 2.00$ H, and $L_2 = 6.00$ H.

30A. In the circuit shown in Figure P32.30, switch S_1 is closed first, and after a certain period of time the current through L_1 is I_1. Then switch S_2 is closed. Find the currents through the coils the moment switch S_2 is closed. Assume that the resistances of the coils are negligible.

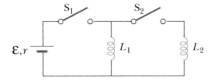

FIGURE P32.30

31. One application of an *RL* circuit is the generation of time-varying high-voltage from a low-voltage source, as shown in Figure P32.31. (a) What is the current in the circuit a long time after the switch has been in position A? (b) Now the switch is thrown quickly from A to B. Compute the initial voltage across each resistor and the inductor. (c) How much time elapses before the voltage across the inductor drops to 12 V?

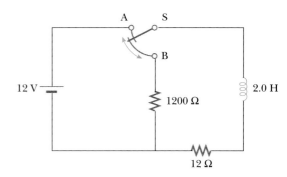

FIGURE P32.31

Section 32.3 Energy in a Magnetic Field

32. Calculate the energy associated with the magnetic field of a 200-turn solenoid in which a current of 1.75 A produces a flux of 3.70×10^{-4} Wb in each turn.

33. An air-core solenoid with 68 turns is 8.0 cm long and has a diameter of 1.2 cm. How much energy is stored in its magnetic field when it carries a current of 0.77 A?

34. Consider the circuit shown in Figure P32.34. What energy is stored in the inductor when the current reaches its final equilibrium value after the switch is closed?

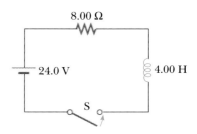

FIGURE P32.34

35. A 10.0-V battery, a 5.00-Ω resistor, and a 10.0-H inductor are connected in series. After the current in the circuit has reached its maximum value, calculate (a) the power supplied by the battery, (b) the power dissipated in the resistor, (c) the power dissipated in the inductor, and (d) the energy stored in the magnetic field of the inductor.

36. At $t = 0$, an emf of 500 V is applied to a coil that has an inductance of 0.80 H and a resistance of 30 Ω. (a) Find the energy stored in the magnetic field when the current reaches half its maximum value. (b) After the emf is connected, how long does it take the current to reach this value?

37. The magnetic field inside a superconducting solenoid is 4.5 T. The solenoid has an inner diameter of 6.2 cm and a length of 26 cm. Determine (a) the

magnetic energy density in the field and (b) the energy stored in the magnetic field within the solenoid.

38. A uniform electric field of magnitude 6.80×10^5 V/m throughout a cylindrical volume results in a total energy of $3.40 \ \mu J$. What magnetic field over this same region stores the same total energy?

39. On a clear day, there is a 100-V/m vertical electric field near the Earth's surface. At the same time, the Earth's magnetic field has a magnitude of 0.500×10^{-4} T. Compute the energy density of the two fields.

40. A 15.0-V battery is connected to an RL circuit for which $L = 0.600$ H and $R = 7.00 \ \Omega$. When the current has reached one half of its final value, what is the total magnetic energy stored in the inductor?

41. Two inductors, $L_1 = 85 \ \mu H$ and $L_2 = 200 \ \mu H$, are connected in series with an 850-mA dc power supply. Calculate the energy stored in each inductor.

42. In the circuit of Figure P32.42, $\mathcal{E} = 50.0$ V, $R = 250 \ \Omega$, and $C = 0.50 \ \mu F$. The switch S is closed for a long time and no voltage is measured across the capacitor. After the switch is opened, the voltage across the capacitor reaches a maximum value of 150 V. What is the inductance, L?

42A. In the circuit of Figure P32.42, the switch S is closed for a long time, and no voltage is measured across the capacitor. After the switch is opened, the voltage across the capacitor reaches a maximum value of V. Find an expression for the inductance, L.

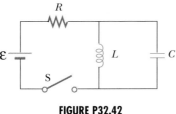

FIGURE P32.42

43. An inductor has a self-inductance of 20.0 H and a resistance of $10.0 \ \Omega$. At $t = 0.10$ s after this inductor is connected to a 12.0-V battery, calculate (a) the stored magnetic power, (b) the power dissipated in the resistor, and (c) the power delivered by the battery.

44. The magnitude of the magnetic field outside a sphere of radius R is $B = B_0 (R/r)^2$, where B_0 is a constant. Determine the total energy stored in the magnetic field outside the sphere and evaluate your result for $B_0 = 5.0 \times 10^{-5}$ T and $R = 6.0 \times 10^6$ m, values appropriate for the Earth's magnetic field.

*Section 32.4 Mutual Inductance

45. Two coils are close to each other. The first coil carries a time-varying current given by $I(t) = (5.0 \ A)e^{-0.025t}$

$\sin(377t)$. At $t = 0.80$ s, the voltage measured across the second coil is -3.2 V. What is the mutual inductance of the coils?

46. Two coils, held in fixed positions, have a mutual inductance of $100 \ \mu H$. What is the maximum voltage in one when the second coil carries a sinusoidal current given by $I(t) = (10.0 \ A) \sin(1000t)$?

47. An emf of 96.0 mV is induced in the windings of a coil when the current in a nearby coil is increasing at the rate of 1.20 A/s. What is the mutual inductance of the two coils?

48. Two inductors having self-inductances $L_1 = 10.0$ H and $L_2 = 5.00$ H are connected in parallel as in Figure P32.48a. The mutual inductance between the two inductors is $M = 6.50$ H. Determine the equivalent self-inductance, L_{eq}, for the system (Fig. P32.48b).

48A. Two inductors having self-inductances L_1 and L_2 are connected in parallel as in Figure P32.48a. The mutual inductance between the two inductors is M. Determine the equivalent self-inductance, L_{eq}, for the system (Fig. P32.48b).

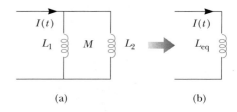

(a)   (b)

FIGURE P32.48

49. A coil of 50 turns is wound on a long solenoid as shown in Figure 32.10. The solenoid has a cross-sectional area of 8.8×10^{-3} m^2 and is wrapped uniformly with 1000 turns per meter of length. Calculate the mutual inductance of the two windings.

50. A 70-turn solenoid is 5.0 cm long and 1.0 cm in diameter and carries a 2.0-A current. A single loop of wire, 3.0 cm in diameter, is held so that the plane of the loop is perpendicular to the long axis of the solenoid. What is the mutual inductance of the two if the plane of the loop passes through the solenoid 2.5 cm from one end?

51. Two solenoids A and B spaced closely to each other and sharing the same cylindrical axis have 400 and 700 turns, respectively. A current of 3.5 A in coil A produces a flux of 300 μWb at the center of A and a flux of 90 μWb at the center of B. (a) Calculate the mutual inductance of the two solenoids. (b) What is the self-inductance of A? (c) What emf is induced in B when the current in A increases at the rate of 0.50 A/s?

52. Two single-turn circular loops of wire have radii R

and r, with $R \gg r$. The loops lie in the same plane and are concentric. (a) Show that the mutual inductance of the pair is $M = \mu_0 \pi r^2/2R$. (*Hint:* Assume that the larger loop carries a current I and compute the resulting flux through the smaller loop.) (b) Evaluate M for $r = 2.00$ cm and $R = 20.0$ cm.

Section 32.5 Oscillations in an *LC* Circuit

53. A 1.00-μF capacitor is charged by a 40.0-V power supply. The fully charged capacitor is then discharged through a 10.0-mH inductor. Find the maximum current in the resulting oscillations.

54. An *LC* circuit consists of a 20-mH inductor and a 0.50-μF capacitor. If the maximum instantaneous current is 0.10 A, what is the greatest potential difference across the capacitor?

55. A 1.00-mH inductor and a 1.00-μF capacitor are connected in series. The current in the circuit is described by $I = 20.0t$, where t is in seconds and I is in amperes. The capacitor initially has no charge. Determine (a) the voltage across the inductor as a function of time, (b) the voltage across the capacitor as a function of time, (c) the time when the energy stored in the capacitor first exceeds that in the inductor.

55A. An inductor having inductance L and a capacitor having capacitance C are connected in series. The current in the circuit is described by $I = Kt$, where t is in seconds and I is in amperes. The capacitor initially has no charge. Determine (a) the voltage across the inductor as a function of time, (b) the voltage across the capacitor as a function of time, and (c) the time when the energy stored in the capacitor first exceeds that in the inductor.

56. Calculate the inductance of an *LC* circuit that oscillates at 120 Hz when the capacitance is 8.00 μF.

57. A fixed inductance $L = 1.05$ μH is used in series with a variable capacitor in the tuning section of a radio. What capacitance tunes the circuit into the signal from a station broadcasting at 6.30 MHz?

58. An *LC* circuit like the one in Figure 32.11 contains an 82-mH inductor and a 17-μF capacitor that initially carries a 180-μC charge. The switch is thrown closed at $t = 0$. (a) Find the frequency (in hertz) of the resulting oscillations. At $t = 1.0$ ms, find (b) the charge on the capacitor and (c) the current in the circuit.

59. (a) What capacitance must be combined with a 45.0-mH inductor in order to achieve a resonant frequency of 125 Hz? (b) What time interval elapses between accumulations of maximum charge of the same sign on a given plate of the capacitor?

60. The switch in Figure P32.60 is connected to point a for a long time. After the switch is thrown to point b, find (a) the frequency of oscillation in the *LC* circuit, (b) the maximum charge that builds up on the capacitor, (c) the maximum current in the inductor, and (d) the total energy stored in the circuit at $t = 3.0$ s.

60A. The switch in Figure P32.60 is connected to point a for a long time. After the switch is thrown to point b, find (in terms of $\mathcal{E}$, R, L, and C) (a) the frequency of oscillation in the *LC* circuit, (b) the maximum charge on the capacitor, (c) the maximum current in the inductor, and (d) the total energy stored in the circuit at time t.

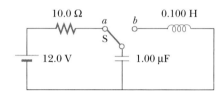

FIGURE P32.60

61. An *LC* circuit like that in Figure 32.11 consists of a 3.30-H inductor and an 840-pF capacitor, initially carrying a 105-μC charge. At $t = 0$ the switch is thrown closed. Compute the following quantities at $t = 2.00$ ms: (a) the energy stored in the capacitor, (b) the energy stored in the inductor, and (c) the total energy in the circuit.

62. A 6.0-V battery is used to charge a 50-μF capacitor. The capacitor is then discharged through a 0.34-mH inductor. Find (a) the maximum charge on the capacitor, (b) the maximum current in the circuit, and (c) the maximum energy stored in each component.

*Section 32.6 The *RLC* Circuit

63. In Figure 32.16, let $R = 7.60$ Ω, $L = 2.20$ mH, and $C = 1.80$ μF. (a) Calculate the frequency of the damped oscillation of the circuit. (b) What is the critical resistance?

64. Consider a series *LC* circuit in which $L = 2.18$ H and $C = 6.00$ nF. What is the maximum value of a resistor that, inserted in series with L and C, allows the circuit to continue to oscillate?

65. Consider an *LC* circuit in which $L = 500$ mH and $C = 0.100$ μF. (a) What is the resonant frequency (ω_0)? (b) If a resistance of 1.00 kΩ is introduced into this circuit, what is the frequency of the (damped) oscillations? (c) What is the percent difference between the two frequencies?

66. Electrical oscillations are initiated in a series circuit containing a capacitance C, inductance L, and resistance R. (a) If $R \ll \sqrt{4L/C}$ (weak damping), how much time elapses before the current falls off to 50% of its initial value? (b) How long does it take the energy to decrease to 50% of its initial value?

67. Show that Equation 32.29 in the text is consistent with Kirchhoff's loop law as applied to Figure 32.16.

68. Consider an *RLC* series circuit consisting of a charged 500-μF capacitor connected to a 32-mH inductor and a resistor *R*. Calculate the frequency of the oscillations (in Hertz) for (a) $R = 0$ (no damping); (b) $R = 16\ \Omega$ (critical damping: $R = \sqrt{4L/C}$); (c) $R = 4.0\ \Omega$ (underdamped: $R < \sqrt{4L/C}$); and (d) $R = 64\ \Omega$ (overdamped: $R > \sqrt{4L/C}$).

ADDITIONAL PROBLEMS

69. An inductor that has a resistance of $0.50\ \Omega$ is connected to a 5.0-V battery. One second after the switch is closed, the current in the circuit is 4.0 A. Calculate the inductance.

70. A soft iron rod ($\mu = 800\mu_0$) is used as the core of a solenoid. The rod has a diameter of 24 mm and is 10 cm long. A 10-m piece of 22-gauge copper wire (diameter = 0.644 mm) is wrapped around the rod in a single uniform layer, except for a 10-cm length at each end to be used for connections. (a) How many turns of this wire can be wrapped around the rod? (*Hint:* The radius of the wire adds to the diameter of the rod in determining the circumference of each turn. Also, the wire spirals diagonally along the surface of the rod.) (b) What is the resistance of this inductor? (c) What is its inductance?

71. An 820-turn wire coil of resistance $24.0\ \Omega$ is placed on top of a 12 500-turn, 7.00-cm-long solenoid, as in Figure P32.71. Both coil and solenoid have cross-sectional areas of 1.00×10^{-4} m². (a) How long does it take the solenoid current to reach 63.2 percent its maximum value? Determine (b) the average back emf caused by the self-inductance of the solenoid

during this interval, (c) the average rate of change in magnetic flux through the coil during this interval, and (d) the magnitude of the average induced current in the coil.

72. A capacitor in a series *LC* circuit has an initial charge *Q* and is being discharged. Find, in terms of *L* and *C*, the flux through the coil when the charge on the capacitor is $Q/2$.

73. The inductor in Figure P32.73 has negligible resistance. When the switch is thrown open after having been closed for a long time, the current in the inductor drops to 0.25 A in 0.15 s. What is the inductance of the inductor?

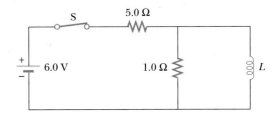

FIGURE P32.73

74. A platinum wire 2.5 mm in diameter is connected in series to a 100-μF capacitor and a 1.2×10^{-3} μH inductor to form an *RLC* circuit. The resistivity of platinum is 11×10^{-8} $\Omega \cdot$m. Calculate the maximum length of wire for which the current oscillates.

75. Assume that the switch in Figure P32.75 is initially in position 1. Show that if the switch is thrown from position 1 to position 2, all the energy stored in the magnetic field of the inductor is dissipated as thermal energy in the resistor.

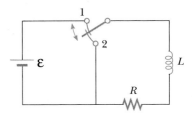

FIGURE P32.75

76. The lead-in wires from a TV antenna are often constructed in the form of two parallel wires (Fig. P32.76). (a) Why does this configuration of conductors have an inductance? (b) What constitutes the flux loop for this configuration? (c) Neglecting any magnetic flux inside the wires, show that the inductance of a length *x* of this type of lead-in is

$$L = \frac{\mu_0 x}{\pi} \ln\left(\frac{w - a}{a}\right)$$

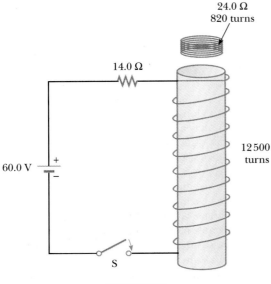

FIGURE P32.71

where a is the radius of the wires and w is their center-to-center separation.

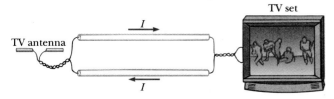

FIGURE P32.76

77. At $t = 0$, the switch in Figure P32.77 is thrown closed. By using Kirchhoff's laws for the instantaneous currents and voltages in this two-loop circuit, show that the current in the inductor is

$$I(t) = \frac{\mathcal{E}}{R_1}[1 - e^{-(R'/L)t}]$$

where $R' = R_1 R_2 / (R_1 + R_2)$.

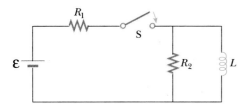

FIGURE P32.77

78. The toroid in Figure P32.78 consists of N turns and has a rectangular cross-section. Its inner and outer radii are a and b, respectively. (a) Show that

$$L = \frac{\mu_0 N^2 h}{2\pi} \ln\left(\frac{b}{a}\right)$$

(b) Using this result, compute the self-inductance of a 500-turn toroid for which $a = 10.0$ cm, $b = 12.0$ cm, and $h = 1.00$ cm. (c) In Problem 14, an approximate formula for the inductance of a toroid with $R \gg r$ was derived. To get a feel for the accuracy of this result, use the expression in Problem 14 to compute the (approximate) inductance of the toroid described in part (b).

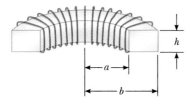

FIGURE P32.78

79. In Figure P32.79, the switch is closed at $t < 0$, and steady-state conditions are established. The switch is now thrown open at $t = 0$. (a) Find the initial voltage $\mathcal{E}_0$ across L just after $t = 0$. Which end of the coil is at the higher potential: a or b? (b) Make freehand graphs of the currents in R_1 and in R_2 as a function of time, treating the steady-state directions as positive. Show values before and after $t = 0$. (c) How long after $t = 0$ is the current in R_2 2.0 mA?

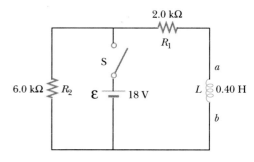

FIGURE P32.79

80. The switch in Figure P32.80 is thrown closed at $t = 0$. Before the switch is closed, the capacitor is uncharged and all currents are zero. Determine the currents in L, C, and R and the potential differences across L, C, and R (a) the instant after the switch is closed and (b) long after it is closed.

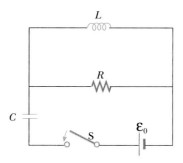

FIGURE P32.80

81. Two long parallel wires, each of radius a, have their centers a distance d apart and carry equal currents in opposite directions. Neglecting the flux within the wires, calculate the inductance per unit length.

82. An air-core solenoid 0.50 m in length contains 1000 turns and has a cross-sectional area of 1.0 cm². (a) Neglecting end effects, what is the self-inductance? (b) A secondary winding wrapped around the center of the solenoid has 100 turns. What is the mutual inductance? (c) The secondary winding carries a constant current of 1.0 A, and the solenoid is connected to a load of 1.0 kΩ. The constant current is suddenly stopped. How much charge flows through the load resistor?

83. To prevent damage from arcing in an electric motor, a discharge resistor is sometimes placed in parallel with the armature. If the motor is suddenly unplugged while running, this resistor limits the voltage that appears across the armature coils. Consider a 12-V dc motor that has an armature that has a resistance of 7.5 Ω and an inductance of 450 mH. Assume the back emf in the armature coils is 10 V when the motor is running at normal speed. (The equivalent circuit for the armature is shown in Fig. P32.83.) Calculate the maximum resistance R that limits the voltage across the armature to 80 V when the motor is unplugged.

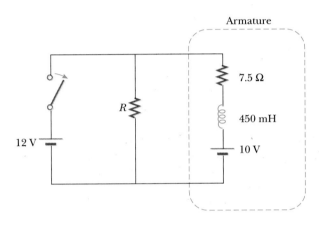

FIGURE P32.83

84. A battery is in series with a switch and a 2.0-H inductor whose windings have a resistance R. After the switch is thrown closed, the current rises to 80% of its final value in 0.40 s. Find R.

85. Initially, the capacitor in a series LC circuit is charged. A switch is closed, allowing the capacitor to discharge, and 0.50 μs later the energy stored in the capacitor is one-fourth its initial value. Determine L if $C = 5.0$ pF.

85A. Initially, the capacitor in a series LC circuit is charged. A switch is closed, allowing the capacitor to discharge, and t seconds later the energy stored in the capacitor is one-fourth its initial value. Determine L if C is known.

86. A toroid has two sets of windings, each spread uniformly around the toroid, with total turns N_1 and N_2, respectively. The toroid has a circumferential length ℓ and a cross-sectional area A. (a) Write expressions for the self-inductances L_1 and L_2 when each coil is used alone. (b) Derive an expression for the mutual inductance M of the two coils. (c) Show that $M^2 = L_1 L_2$. (This expression is true only when all the flux through one coil also passes through the other coil.)

SPREADSHEET PROBLEMS

S1. Spreadsheet 32.1 calculates the current and the energy stored in the magnetic field of an RL circuit when the circuit is charging and when it is discharging. Use $R = 1000\ \Omega$, $L = 0.35$ H, and $\mathcal{E} = 10$ V. (a) What is the time constant of the circuit? From the graph of the current versus time when the circuit is charging, how much time has elapsed when the current is 50% of its maximum value? 90%? 99%? Give your answers both in seconds and in multiples of the time constant. (b) Repeat for the case when the circuit is discharging. (c) How much time has elapsed when the energy is 50% of its maximum value for the two cases? 90%? 99%?

S2. A coil of self-inductance L carries a current given by $I = I_{\max} \sin 2\pi ft$. The self-induced emf in the coil is $\mathcal{E}_L = -L\ dI/dt$. Develop a spreadsheet to calculate I as a function of time. Numerically differentiate the current and calculate $\mathcal{E}$. Choose $I_{\max} = 2.00$ A, $f = 60.0$ Hz, and $L = 10.0$ mH. Plot $\mathcal{E}$ versus t.

CHAPTER 33

Alternating Current Circuits

Line repair crews working on transmission lines. *(Tom Pantages)*

I n this chapter, we describe alternating current (ac) circuits. We investigate the characteristics of circuits containing familiar elements and driven by a sinusoidal voltage. Our discussion is limited to simple series circuits containing resistors, inductors, and capacitors, and we find that the ac current in each element is proportional to the instantaneous ac voltage across the element. We also find that when the applied voltage is sinusoidal, the current in each element is also sinusoidal but not necessarily in phase with the applied voltage. We conclude the chapter with two sections concerning the characteristics of *RC* filters, transformers, and power transmission.

33.1   AC SOURCES AND PHASORS

An ac circuit consists of circuit elements and a generator that provides the alternating current. The basic principle of the ac generator is a direct consequence of Faraday's law of induction. When a coil is rotated in a magnetic field at constant angular frequency ω, a sinusoidal voltage (emf) is induced in the coil. This instantaneous voltage v is

$$v = V_{max} \sin \omega t$$

where V_{max} is the maximum output voltage of the ac generator, or the **voltage amplitude**. The angular frequency is given by

$$\omega = 2\pi f = \frac{2\pi}{T}$$

where f is the frequency of the source and T is the period. Commercial electric-power plants in the United States use a frequency of 60 Hz, which corresponds to an angular frequency of 377 rad/s.

The primary aim of this chapter can be summarized as follows: Consider an ac generator connected to a series circuit containing R, L, and C elements. If the voltage amplitude and frequency of the generator are given, together with the values of R, L, and C, find the amplitude and phase constant of the current. In order to simplify our analysis of circuits containing two or more elements, we use graphical constructions called *phasor diagrams*. In these constructions, alternating quantities, such as current and voltage, are represented by rotating vectors called **phasors**. The length of the phasor represents the amplitude (maximum value) of the quantity, while the projection of the phasor onto the vertical axis represents the instantaneous value of that quantity. As we shall see, the method of combining several sinusoidally varying currents or voltages with different phases is greatly simplified using this procedure.

33.2   RESISTORS IN AN AC CIRCUIT

Consider a simple ac circuit consisting of a resistor and an ac generator (—⊙—), as in Figure 33.1. At any instant, the algebraic sum of the potential increases and decreases around a closed loop in a circuit must be zero (Kirchhoff's loop equation). Therefore, $v - v_R = 0$, or

$$v = v_R = V_{max} \sin \omega t \qquad (33.1)$$

where v_R is the *instantaneous voltage drop across the resistor*. Therefore, the instantaneous current in the resistor is

$$i_R = \frac{v}{R} = \frac{V_{max}}{R} \sin \omega t = I_{max} \sin \omega t \qquad (33.2)$$

where I_{max} is the maximum current:

$$I_{max} = \frac{V_{max}}{R}$$

From Equations 33.1 and 33.2, we see that the instantaneous voltage drop across the resistor is

$$v_R = I_{max} R \sin \omega t \qquad (33.3)$$

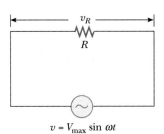

FIGURE 33.1   A circuit consisting of a resistor R connected to an ac generator, designated by the symbol —⊙—.

Maximum current in a resistor

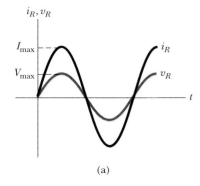

(a)

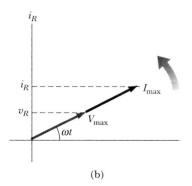

(b)

FIGURE 33.2   (a) Plots of the current and voltage across a resistor as functions of time. The current is in phase with the voltage, which means that the voltage is zero when the current is zero, maximum when the current is maximum, and minimum when the current is minimum. (b) A phasor diagram for the resistive circuit, showing that the current is in phase with the voltage.

Because i_R and v_R both vary as $\sin \omega t$ and reach their maximum values at the same time as in Figure 33.2, they are said to be in phase. A phasor diagram is used to represent phase relationships. The lengths of the arrows correspond to V_{max} and I_{max}. The projections of the arrows onto the vertical axis give v_R and i_R. In the case of the single-loop resistive circuit, the current and voltage phasors lie along the same line, as in Figure 33.2b, because i_R and v_R are in phase.

Note that *the average value of the current over one cycle is zero.* That is, the current is maintained in the positive direction for the same amount of time and at the same magnitude as it is maintained in the negative direction. However, the direction of the current has no effect on the behavior of the resistor. This can be understood by realizing that collisions between electrons and the fixed atoms of the resistor result in an increase in the temperature of the resistor. Although this temperature increase depends on the magnitude of the current, it is independent of the direction of the current.

This discussion can be made quantitative by recalling that the rate at which electrical energy is converted to heat in a resistor is the power $P = i^2 R$, where i is the instantaneous current in the resistor. Since the heating effect of a current is proportional to the square of the current, it makes no difference whether the current is direct or alternating, that is, whether the sign associated with the current is positive or negative. However, the heating effect produced by an alternating current having a maximum value I_{max} is not the same as that produced by a direct current of the same value. This is because the alternating current is at this maximum value for only a very brief instant of time during each cycle. What is of importance in an ac circuit is an average value of current referred to as the rms current. The notation **rms** refers to root mean square, which means the square root of the average value of the square of the current. Because I^2 varies as $\sin^2 \omega t$, and because the average value of i^2 is $\frac{1}{2}I_{max}^2$ (Fig. 33.3), the rms current is[1]

$$I_{rms} = \frac{I_{max}}{\sqrt{2}} = 0.707 I_{max} \tag{33.4}$$

This equation says that an alternating current whose maximum value is 2.00 A produces in a resistor the same heating effect as a direct current of $(0.707)(2.00) = 1.41$ A. Thus, we can say that the average power dissipated in a resistor that carries an alternating current is $P_{av} = I_{rms}^2 R$.

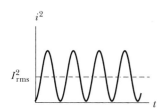

FIGURE 33.3   Plot of the square of the current in a resistor versus time. The rms current is the square root of the average of the square of the current.

[1] The fact that the square root of the average value of the square of the current is equal to $I_{max}/\sqrt{2}$ can be shown as follows. The current in the circuit varies with time according to the expression $i = I_{max} \sin \omega t$, so that $i^2 = I_{max}^2 \sin^2 \omega t$. Therefore we can find the average value of i^2 by calculating the average value of $\sin^2 \omega t$. Note that a graph of $\cos^2 \omega t$ versus time is identical to a graph of $\sin^2 \omega t$ versus time, except that the points are shifted on the time axis. Thus, the time average of $\sin^2 \omega t$ is equal to the time average of $\cos^2 \omega t$ when taken over one or more complete cycles. That is,

$$(\sin^2 \omega t)_{av} = (\cos^2 \omega t)_{av}$$

With this fact and the trigonometric identity $\sin^2 \theta + \cos^2 \theta = 1$, we get

$$(\sin^2 \omega t)_{av} + (\cos^2 \omega t)_{av} = 2(\sin^2 \omega t)_{av} = 1$$

$$(\sin^2 \omega t)_{av} = \tfrac{1}{2}$$

When this result is substituted in the expression $i^2 = I_{max}^2 \sin^2 \omega t$, we get $(i^2)_{av} = I_{rms}^2 = I_{max}^2/2$, or $I_{rms} = I_{max}/\sqrt{2}$, where I_{rms} is the rms current. The factor of $1/\sqrt{2}$ is only valid for sinusoidally varying currents. Other waveforms such as sawtooth variations have different factors.

TABLE 33.1   Notation Used in This Chapter

	Voltage	Current
Instantaneous value	v	i
Maximum value	V_{max}	I_{max}
rms value	V_{rms}	I_{rms}

Alternating voltages are also best discussed in terms of rms voltages, and the relationship here is identical to the above; that is, the rms voltage is

$$V_{\text{rms}} = \frac{V_{\text{max}}}{\sqrt{2}} = 0.707 \, V_{\text{max}} \qquad (33.5) \qquad \text{rms voltage}$$

When speaking of measuring a 120-V ac voltage from an electric outlet, we are really referring to an rms voltage of 120 V. A quick calculation using Equation 33.5 shows that such an ac voltage actually has a maximum value of about 170 V. In this chapter we use rms values when discussing alternating currents and voltages. One reason for this is that ac ammeters and voltmeters are designed to read rms values. Furthermore, with rms values, many of the equations we use have the same form as their direct-current counterparts. Table 33.1 summarizes the notation used in this chapter.

EXAMPLE 33.1   What Is the rms Current?

The output of a generator is given by $v = 200 \sin \omega t$. Find the rms current in the circuit when this generator is connected to a 100-Ω resistor.

Solution Comparing this expression for the voltage output with the general form, $v = V_{\text{max}} \sin \omega t$, we see that $V_{\text{max}} = 200$ V. Thus, the rms voltage is

$$V_{\text{rms}} = \frac{V_{\text{max}}}{\sqrt{2}} = \frac{200 \text{ V}}{\sqrt{2}} = 141 \text{ V}$$

The calculated rms voltage can be used with Ohm's law to find the rms current in the circuit:

$$I_{\text{rms}} = \frac{V_{\text{rms}}}{R} = \frac{141 \text{ V}}{100 \text{ }\Omega} = \boxed{1.41 \text{ A}}$$

Exercise Find the maximum current in the circuit.

Answer 2.00 A.

33.3   INDUCTORS IN AN AC CIRCUIT

Now consider an ac circuit consisting only of an inductor connected to the terminals of an ac generator, as in Figure 33.4. Because the induced emf in the inductor is $L\,dI/dt$, Kirchhoff's loop rule applied to the circuit gives

$$v - L\frac{di}{dt} = 0$$

When we rearrange this equation and substitute $V_{\text{max}} \sin \omega t$ for v, we get

$$L\frac{di}{dt} = V_{\text{max}} \sin \omega t \qquad (33.6)$$

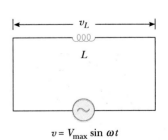

FIGURE 33.4 A circuit consisting of an inductor L connected to an ac generator.

Integrating this expression[2] gives the current as a function of time:

$$i_L = \frac{V_{max}}{L} \int \sin \omega t \, dt = -\frac{V_{max}}{\omega L} \cos \omega t \tag{33.7}$$

When we use the trigonometric identity $\cos \omega t = -\sin(\omega t - \pi/2)$, we can express Equation 33.7 as

$$i_L = \frac{V_{max}}{\omega L} \sin\left(\omega t - \frac{\pi}{2}\right) \tag{33.8}$$

Comparing this result with Equation 33.6 clearly shows that the current and voltage are out of phase with each other by $\pi/2$ rad, or 90°. A plot of voltage and current versus time is given in Figure 33.5a. The voltage reaches its maximum value one quarter of an oscillation period before the current reaches its maximum value. The corresponding phasor diagram for this circuit is shown in Figure 33.5b. Thus, we see that

The current in an inductor lags the voltage by 90°

for a sinusoidal applied voltage, the current in an inductor always lags behind the voltage across the inductor by 90°.

This lag can be understood by noting that because the voltage across the inductor is proportional to di/dt, the value of v_L is largest when the current is changing most rapidly. Since i versus t is a sinusoidal curve, di/dt (the slope) is maximum when the curve goes through zero. This shows that v_L reaches its maximum value when the current is zero.

From Equation 33.7 we see that the current reaches its maximum values when $\cos \omega t = 1$:

Maximum current in an inductor

$$I_{max} = \frac{V_{max}}{\omega L} = \frac{V_{max}}{X_L} \tag{33.9}$$

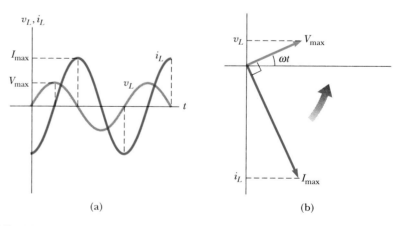

(a)   (b)

FIGURE 33.5   (a) Plots of the current and voltage across an inductor as functions of time. The current lags the voltage by 90°. (b) The phasor diagram for the inductive circuit. The angle between the current phasor and voltage phasor is 90°.

---

[2] The constant of integration is neglected here since it depends on the initial conditions, which are not important for this situation.

where the quantity X_L, called the **inductive reactance**, is

$$X_L = \omega L \tag{33.10}$$

The expression for the rms current is similar to Equation 33.9, with V_{max} replaced by V_{rms}.

Inductive reactance, like resistance, has units of ohms. The maximum current decreases as the inductive reactance increases for a given applied voltage. However, unlike resistance, reactance depends on frequency as well as the characteristics of the inductor. Note that the reactance of an inductor increases as the frequency of the current increases. This is because at higher frequencies, the instantaneous current must change more rapidly than it does at the lower frequencies, which in turn causes an increase in the induced emf associated with a given peak current.

Using Equations 33.6 and 33.9, we find that the instantaneous voltage drop across the inductor is

$$v_L = L\frac{di}{dt} = V_{max} \sin \omega t = I_{max} X_L \sin \omega t \tag{33.11}$$

We can think of Equation 33.11 as Ohm's law for an inductive circuit. As an exercise, you should show that X_L has the SI unit of ohm.

EXAMPLE 33.2   A Purely Inductive ac Circuit

In a purely inductive ac circuit (Fig. 33.4), $L = 25.0$ mH and the rms voltage is 150 V. Find the inductive reactance and rms current in the circuit if the frequency is 60.0 Hz.

Solution   First, recall from Equation 13.4 that $\omega = 2\pi f = 2\pi(60.0) = 377$ s^{-1}. Equation 33.10 then gives

$$X_L = \omega L = (377 \text{ s}^{-1})(25.0 \times 10^{-3} \text{ H}) = \boxed{9.43\ \Omega}$$

The rms current is

$$I_{rms} = \frac{V_L}{X_L} = \frac{150 \text{ V}}{9.43\ \Omega} = \boxed{15.9 \text{ A}}$$

Exercise   Calculate the inductive reactance and rms current in the circuit if the frequency is 6.00 kHz.

Answers   943 Ω, 0.159 A.

33.4   CAPACITORS IN AN AC CIRCUIT

Figure 33.6 shows an ac circuit consisting of a capacitor connected across the terminals of an ac generator. Kirchhoff's loop rule applied to this circuit gives $v - v_C = 0$, or

$$v = v_C = V_{max} \sin \omega t \tag{33.12}$$

where v_C is the *instantaneous voltage drop across the capacitor*. From the definition of capacitance, $v_C = Q/C$, and this value for v_C substituted into Equation 33.12 gives

$$Q = CV_{max} \sin \omega t \tag{33.13}$$

Since $i = dQ/dt$, differentiating Equation 33.13 gives the instantaneous current in the circuit:

$$i_C = \frac{dQ}{dt} = \omega CV_{max} \cos \omega t \tag{33.14}$$

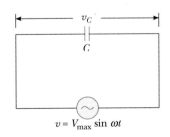

FIGURE 33.6   A circuit consisting of a capacitor C connected to an ac generator.

Here again we see that the current is not in phase with the voltage drop across the capacitor, given by Equation 33.12. Using the trigonometric identity $\cos \omega t = \sin(\omega t + \frac{\pi}{2})$, we can express Equation 33.14 in the alternative form

$$i_C = \omega C V_{max} \sin\left(\omega t + \frac{\pi}{2}\right) \qquad (33.15)$$

Comparing this expression with Equation 33.12, we see that the current is $\pi/2$ rad = 90° out of phase with the voltage across the capacitor. A plot of current and voltage versus time (Fig. 33.7a) shows that the current reaches its maximum value one quarter of a cycle sooner than the voltage reaches its maximum value. The corresponding phasor diagram in Figure 33.7b also shows that

---
The current leads the voltage across a capacitor by 90°

for a sinusoidally applied emf, the current always leads the voltage across a capacitor by 90°.

From Equation 33.14, we see that the current in the circuit reaches its maximum value when $\cos \omega t = 1$:

$$I_{max} = \omega C V_{max} = \frac{V_{max}}{X_C} \qquad (33.16)$$

where X_C is called the **capacitive reactance**:

Capacitive reactance

$$X_C = \frac{1}{\omega C} \qquad (33.17)$$

The SI unit of X_C is also the ohm. The rms current is given by an expression similar to Equation 33.16, with V_{max} replaced by V_{rms}.

Combining Equations 33.12 and 33.16, we can express the instantaneous voltage drop across the capacitor as

$$v_C = V_{max} \sin \omega t = I_{max} X_C \sin \omega t \qquad (33.18)$$

As the frequency of the circuit increases, the maximum current increases but the

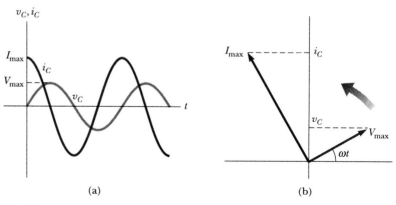

(a)   (b)

FIGURE 33.7   (a) Plots of the current and voltage across the capacitor as functions of time. The voltage lags behind the current by 90°. (b) Phasor diagram for the purely capacitive circuit. Projections of the phasors onto the vertical axis gives the instantaneous values v_C and i_C.

reactance decreases. For a given maximum applied voltage V_{max}, the current increases as the frequency increases. As the frequency approaches zero, the capacitive reactance approaches infinity and so the current approaches zero. This makes sense because the circuit approaches dc conditions as $\omega \rightarrow 0$. Of course, no current passes through a capacitor under steady-state dc conditions.

CONCEPTUAL EXAMPLE 33.3

Explain why the reactance of a capacitor decreases with increasing frequency, while the reactance of an inductor increases with increasing frequency.

Reasoning As the frequency of a capacitive circuit increases, the polarities of the charged plates must change more rapidly with time, corresponding to a larger current. The capacitive reactance varies as the inverse of the frequency, and hence approaches zero as f approaches infinity.

The current is zero in a dc capacitive circuit, which corresponds to zero frequency and infinite reactance. The inductive reactance is proportional to the frequency and, therefore, increases with increasing frequency. At the higher frequencies, the current changes more rapidly, which according to Faraday's law results in an increase in the back emf associated with an inductor and a corresponding decrease in current.

EXAMPLE 33.4   A Purely Capacitive ac Circuit

An 8.00-μF capacitor is connected to the terminals of a 60.0-Hz ac generator whose rms voltage is 150 V. Find the capacitive reactance and the rms current in the circuit.

Solution Using the Equation 33.17 and the fact that $\omega = 2\pi f = 377$ s^{-1} (Eq. 13.4) gives

$$X_C = \frac{1}{\omega C} = \frac{1}{(377 \text{ s}^{-1})(8.00 \times 10^{-6} \text{ F})} = \boxed{332 \ \Omega}$$

Hence, the rms current is

$$I_{rms} = \frac{V_{rms}}{X_C} = \frac{150 \text{ V}}{332 \ \Omega} = \boxed{0.452 \text{ A}}$$

Exercise If the frequency is doubled, what happens to the capacitive reactance and the current?

Answer X_C halved, I_{max} doubled.

33.5   THE *RLC* SERIES CIRCUIT

Figure 33.8a shows a circuit containing a resistor, an inductor, and a capacitor connected in series across an ac-voltage source. As before, we assume that the applied voltage varies sinusoidally with time. It is convenient to assume that the applied voltage is given by

$$v = V_{max} \sin \omega t$$

while the current varies as

$$i = I_{max} \sin(\omega t - \phi)$$

where ϕ is the **phase angle** between the current and the applied voltage. Our aim is to determine ϕ and I_{max}. Figure 33.8b shows the voltage versus time across each element in the circuit and their phase relationships.

In order to solve this problem, we must analyze the phasor diagram for this circuit. First, note that because the elements are in series, the current everywhere in the circuit must be the same at any instant. That is, *the current at all points in a series ac circuit has the same amplitude and phase.* Therefore, as we found in the previous sections, the voltage across each element has different amplitudes and

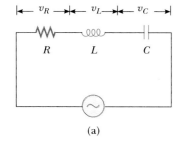

(a)

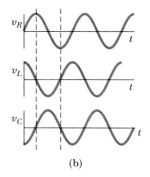

(b)

FIGURE 33.8   (a) A series circuit consisting of a resistor, an inductor, and a capacitor connected to an ac generator. (b) Phase relationships in the series *RLC* circuit.

phases, as summarized in Figure 33.9. In particular, the voltage across the resistor is in phase with the current, the voltage across the inductor leads the current by 90°, and the voltage across the capacitor lags behind the current by 90°. Using these phase relationships, we can express the instantaneous voltage drops across the three elements as

$$v_R = I_{max} R \sin \omega t = V_R \sin \omega t \qquad (33.19)$$

$$v_L = I_{max} X_L \sin\left(\omega t + \frac{\pi}{2}\right) = V_L \cos \omega t \qquad (33.20)$$

$$v_C = I_{max} X_C \sin\left(\omega t - \frac{\pi}{2}\right) = -V_C \cos \omega t \qquad (33.21)$$

where V_R, V_L, and V_C are the voltage amplitudes across each element:

$$V_R = I_{max} R \qquad V_L = I_{max} X_L \qquad V_C = I_{max} X_C$$

At this point, we could proceed by noting that the instantaneous voltage v across the three elements equals the sum

$$v = v_R + v_L + v_C$$

Although this analytical approach is correct, it is simpler to obtain the sum by examining the phasor diagram.

Because the current in each element is the same at any instant, we can obtain the resulting phasor diagram by combining the three phasor pairs shown in Figure 33.9 to obtain Figure 33.10a, where a single phasor I_{max} is used to represent the current in each element. To obtain the vector sum of these voltages, it is convenient to redraw the phasor diagram as in Figure 33.10b. From this diagram, we see that the vector sum of the voltage amplitudes V_R, V_L, and V_C equals a phasor whose length is the maximum applied voltage, V_{max}, where the phasor V_{max} makes an angle ϕ with the current phasor, I_{max}. Note that the voltage phasors V_L and V_C are in opposite directions along the same line, and hence we are able to construct the difference phasor $V_L - V_C$, which is perpendicular to the phasor V_R. From the right triangle in Figure 33.10b, we see that

$$V_{max} = \sqrt{V_R{}^2 + (V_L - V_C)^2} = \sqrt{(I_{max} R)^2 + (I_{max} X_L - I_{max} X_C)^2}$$

$$V_{max} = I_{max} \sqrt{R^2 + (X_L - X_C)^2} \qquad (33.22)$$

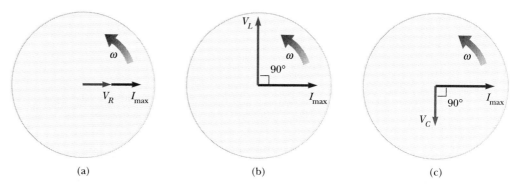

(a)   (b)   (c)

FIGURE 33.9   Phase relationships between the peak voltage and current phasors for (a) a resistor, (b) an inductor, and (c) a capacitor.

Therefore, we can express the maximum current as

$$I_{max} = \frac{V_{max}}{\sqrt{R^2 + (X_L - X_C)^2}}$$

The **impedance** Z of the circuit is defined to be

$$Z \equiv \sqrt{R^2 + (X_L - X_C)^2} \qquad (33.23)$$

where impedance also has the SI unit of ohm. Therefore, we can write Equation 33.22 in the form

$$V_{max} = I_{max} Z \qquad (33.24)$$

We can regard Equation 33.24 as a generalized Ohm's law applied to an ac circuit. Note that the current in the circuit depends upon the resistance, the inductance, the capacitance, and the frequency since the reactances are frequency dependent.

By removing the common factor I_{max} from each phasor in Figure 33.10, we can also construct an impedance triangle, shown in Figure 33.11. From this phasor diagram, we find that the phase angle ϕ between the current and voltage is

$$\tan \phi = \frac{X_L - X_C}{R} \qquad (33.25)$$

For example, when $X_L > X_C$ (which occurs at high frequencies), the phase angle is positive, signifying that the current lags behind the applied voltage, as in Figure 33.10. On the other hand, if $X_L < X_C$, the phase angle is negative, signifying that the current leads the applied voltage. Finally, when $X_L = X_C$, the phase angle is zero. In this case, the ac impedance equals the resistance and the current has its maximum value, given by V_{max}/R. The frequency at which this occurs is called the *resonance frequency*, and is described further in Section 33.7.

Figure 33.12 gives impedance values and phase angles for various series circuits containing different combinations of circuit elements.

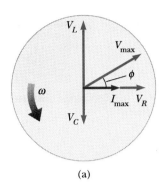

(a)

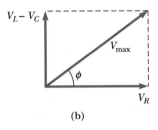

(b)

FIGURE 33.10 (a) The phasor diagram for the series *RLC* circuit shown in Figure 33.8. Note that the phasor V_R is in phase with the current phasor I_{max}, the phasor V_L leads I_{max} by 90°, and the phasor V_C lags I_{max} by 90°. The total voltage V_{max} makes an angle ϕ with I_{max}. (b) Simplified version of the phasor diagram shown in part (a).

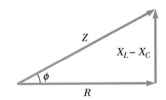

FIGURE 33.11 The impedance triangle for a series *RLC* circuit gives the relationship $Z = \sqrt{R^2 + (X_L - X_C)^2}$.

Circuit Elements	Impedance, Z	Phase angle, ϕ
R ⏤WWW⏤	R	0°
C ⏤┤├⏤	X_C	−90°
L ⏤ೲ⏤	X_L	+90°
R　C ⏤WWW┤├⏤	$\sqrt{R^2 + X_C^2}$	Negative, between −90° and 0°
R　L ⏤WWW─ೲ⏤	$\sqrt{R^2 + X_L^2}$	Positive, between 0° and 90°
R　L　C ⏤WWW─ೲ┤├⏤	$\sqrt{R^2 + (X_L - X_C)^2}$	Negative if $X_C > X_L$ Positive if $X_C < X_L$

FIGURE 33.12 The impedance values and phase angles for various circuit element combinations. In each case, an ac voltage (not shown) is applied across the combination of elements (that is, across the dots).

Oscilloscope Simulator

The oscilloscope is a principal laboratory instrument for measuring and viewing electrical phenomena. It is especially important for electrical engineering students or anyone who intends to work in areas involving electronics. The oscilloscope simulator duplicates the behavior and appearance of an oscilloscope. The simulator offers two modes of operation. In the tutorial mode, you can click on a component to view a message describing how that component operates. In the second mode of operation, the experimental mode, you can select different input signals and observe the signal as it would appear on an oscilloscope screen.

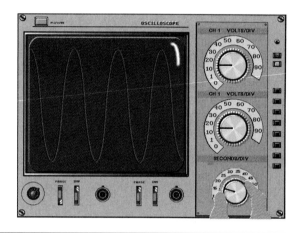
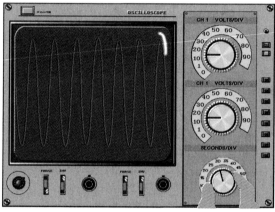

EXAMPLE 33.5   Analyzing a Series *RLC* Circuit

Analyze a series *RLC* ac circuit for which $R = 250\ \Omega$, $L = 0.600$ H, $C = 3.50\ \mu$F, $\omega = 377$ s^{-1}, and $V_{max} = 150$ V.

Solution   The reactances are $X_L = \omega L = 226\ \Omega$ and $X_C = 1/\omega C = 758\ \Omega$. Therefore, the impedance is

$$Z = \sqrt{R^2 + (X_L - X_C)^2}$$
$$= \sqrt{(250\ \Omega)^2 + (226\ \Omega - 758\ \Omega)^2} = 588\ \Omega$$

The maximum current is

$$I_{max} = \frac{V_{max}}{Z} = \frac{150\ \text{V}}{588\ \Omega} = 0.255\ \text{A}$$

The phase angle between the current and voltage is

$$\phi = \tan^{-1}\left(\frac{X_L - X_C}{R}\right) = \tan^{-1}\left(\frac{226 - 758}{250}\right) = -64.8°$$

Since the circuit is more capacitive than inductive, ϕ is negative and the current leads the applied voltage.

The maximum voltages across each element are given by

$$V_R = I_{max}R = (0.255\ \text{A})(250\ \Omega) = 63.8\ \text{V}$$

$$V_L = I_{max}X_L = (0.255\ \text{A})(226\ \Omega) = 57.6\ \text{V}$$

$$V_C = I_{max}X_C = (0.255\ \text{A})(758\ \Omega) = 193\ \text{V}$$

Using Equations 33.19, 33.20, and 33.21, we find that the instantaneous voltages across the three elements can be written

$$v_R = (63.8\ \text{V})\sin 377t$$

$$v_L = (57.6\ \text{V})\cos 377t$$

$$v_C = (-193\ \text{V})\cos 377t$$

and the applied voltage is $v = 150\sin(\omega t - 64.8°)$. The sum of the maximum voltages across each element is $V_R + V_L + V_C = 314$ V, which is much larger than the maximum voltage of the generator, 150 V. The former is a meaningless quantity. This is because when harmonically varying quantities are added, *both their amplitudes and their phases* must be taken into account and we know that the peak voltages across the different circuit elements occur at different times. That is, the voltages must be added in a way that takes account of the different phases. When this is done, Equation 33.22 is satisfied. You should verify this result.

EXAMPLE 33.6   **Finding *L* from a Phasor Diagram**

In a series *RLC* circuit, the applied voltage has a maximum value of 120 V and oscillates at a frequency of 60.0 Hz. The circuit contains an inductor whose inductance can be varied,

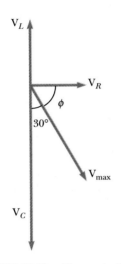

FIGURE 33.13   (Example 33.6).

$R = 800\ \Omega$, and $C = 4.00\ \mu\text{F}$. Determine the value of L such that the voltage across the capacitor is out of phase with the applied voltage by 30.0°, with V_{max} leading V_C.

Solution   The phase relationships for the voltage drops across the elements in the circuit are shown in Figure 33.13. From the figure, we see that the phase angle is 60.0°. This is because the phasors representing I_{max} and V_R are in the same direction (they are in phase). From Equation 33.25, we find that

$$X_L = X_C + R \tan \phi \qquad (1)$$

Substituting Equations 33.10 and 33.17 into (1) gives

$$2\pi f L = \frac{1}{2\pi f C} + R \tan \phi$$

or

$$L = \frac{1}{2\pi f}\left[\frac{1}{2\pi f C} + R \tan \phi\right] \qquad (2)$$

Substituting the given values into (2) gives $L = 5.44$ H.

33.6   POWER IN AN AC CIRCUIT

As we see in this section, *there are no power losses associated with pure capacitors and pure inductors in an ac circuit.* (A pure inductor is defined as one having no resistance or capacitance.) First, let us analyze the power dissipated in an ac circuit containing only a generator and a capacitor.

When the current begins to increase in one direction in an ac circuit, charge begins to accumulate on the capacitor and a voltage drop appears across it. When this voltage drop reaches its peak value, the energy stored in the capacitor is $\frac{1}{2}CV_{\text{max}}^2$. However, this energy storage is only momentary. The capacitor is charged and discharged twice during each cycle. In this process, charge is delivered to the capacitor during two quarters of the cycle and is returned to the voltage source during the remaining two quarters. Therefore, *the average power supplied by the source is zero.* In other words, *a capacitor in an ac circuit does not dissipate energy.*

Similarly, the voltage source must do work against the back emf of the inductor, which carries a current. When the current reaches its peak value, the energy stored in the inductor is a maximum and is given by $\frac{1}{2}LI_{\text{max}}^2$. When the current begins to decrease in the circuit, this stored energy is returned to the source as the inductor attempts to maintain the current in the circuit.

When we studied dc circuits in Chapter 28, we found that the power delivered by a battery to a circuit is equal to the product of the current and the emf of the battery. Likewise, the instantaneous power delivered by an ac generator to any circuit is the product of the generator current and the applied voltage. For the *RLC* circuit shown in Figure 33.8, we can express the instantaneous power P as

$$\begin{aligned}P = iv &= I_{\text{max}} \sin(\omega t - \phi)\, V_{\text{max}} \sin \omega t \\ &= I_{\text{max}} V_{\text{max}} \sin \omega t \sin(\omega t - \phi)\end{aligned} \qquad (33.26)$$

Clearly this result is a complicated function of time and therefore not very useful from a practical viewpoint. What is generally of interest is the average power over one or more cycles. Such an average can be computed by first using the trigonometric identity $\sin(\omega t - \phi) = \sin \omega t \cos \phi - \cos \omega t \sin \phi$. Substituting this into Equation 33.26 gives

$$P = I_{max} V_{max} \sin^2 \omega t \cos \phi - I_{max} V_{max} \sin \omega t \cos \omega t \sin \phi \qquad (33.27)$$

We now take the time average of P over one or more cycles, noting that I_{max}, V_{max}, ϕ, and ω are all constants. The time average of the first term on the right of Equation 33.27 involves the average value of $\sin^2 \omega t$, which is $\frac{1}{2}$, as shown in footnote 1. The time average of the second term on the right is identically zero because $\sin \omega t \cos \omega t = \frac{1}{2} \sin 2\omega t$, and the average value of $\sin 2\omega t$ is zero. Therefore, we can express the **average power** P_{av} as

$$P_{av} = \tfrac{1}{2} I_{max} V_{max} \cos \phi \qquad (33.28)$$

It is convenient to express the average power in terms of the rms current and rms voltage defined by Equations 33.4 and 33.5. Using these defined quantities, the average power becomes

Average power

$$P_{av} = I_{rms} V_{rms} \cos \phi \qquad (33.29)$$

where the quantity $\cos \phi$ is called the **power factor**. By inspecting Figure 33.10, we see that the maximum voltage drop across the resistor is given by $V_R = V_{max} \cos \phi = I_{max} R$. Using Equation 33.3 and the fact that $\cos \phi = I_{max} R / V_{max}$, we find that P_{av} can be expressed as

$$P_{av} = I_{rms} V_{rms} \cos \phi = I_{rms} \left(\frac{V_{max}}{\sqrt{2}} \right) \frac{I_{max} R}{V_{max}} = I_{rms} \frac{I_{max} R}{\sqrt{2}}$$

$$P_{av} = I_{rms}^2 R \qquad (33.30)$$

In other words, the *average power delivered by the generator is dissipated as heat in the resistor,* just as in the case of a dc circuit. *There is no power loss in an ideal inductor or capacitor.* When the load is purely resistive, then $\phi = 0$, $\cos \phi = 1$, and from Equation 33.29 we see that $P_{av} = I_{rms} V_{rms}$.

EXAMPLE 33.7   Average Power in a *RLC* Series Circuit

Calculate the average power delivered to the series *RLC* circuit described in Example 33.5.

Solution   First, let us calculate the rms voltage and rms current:

$$V_{rms} = \frac{V_{max}}{\sqrt{2}} = \frac{150 \text{ V}}{\sqrt{2}} = 106 \text{ V}$$

$$I_{rms} = \frac{I_{max}}{\sqrt{2}} = \frac{V_{max}/Z}{\sqrt{2}} = \frac{0.255 \text{ A}}{\sqrt{2}} = 0.180 \text{ A}$$

Since $\phi = -64.8°$, the power factor, $\cos \phi$, is 0.426, and hence the average power is

$$P_{av} = I_{rms} V_{rms} \cos \phi = (0.180 \text{ A})(106 \text{ V})(0.426)$$

$$= \boxed{8.13 \text{ W}}$$

The same result can be obtained using Equation 33.30.

33.7 RESONANCE IN A SERIES *RLC* CIRCUIT

A series *RLC* circuit is said to be in resonance when the current has its maximum value. In general, the rms current can be written

$$I_{rms} = \frac{V_{rms}}{Z} \tag{33.31}$$

where Z is the impedance. Substituting Equation 33.23 into 33.31 gives

$$I_{rms} = \frac{V_{rms}}{\sqrt{R^2 + (X_L - X_C)^2}} \tag{33.32}$$

Because the impedance depends on the frequency of the source, we see that the current in the *RLC* circuit also depends on the frequency. Note that the current reaches its peak when $X_L = X_C$, corresponding to $Z = R$. The frequency ω_0 at which this occurs is called the **resonance frequency** of the circuit. To find ω_0, we use the condition $X_L = X_C$, from which we get $\omega_0 L = 1/\omega_0 C$, or

$$\omega_0 = \frac{1}{\sqrt{LC}} \tag{33.33}$$

Resonance frequency

Note that this frequency also corresponds to the natural frequency of oscillation of an *LC* circuit (Section 32.5). Therefore, the current in a series *RLC* circuit reaches its maximum value when the frequency of the applied voltage matches the natural oscillator frequency, which depends only on L and C. Furthermore, at this frequency the current is in phase with the applied voltage.

A plot of the rms current versus frequency for a series *RLC* circuit is shown in Figure 33.14a. The data that are plotted assume a constant rms voltage of 5.0 mV,

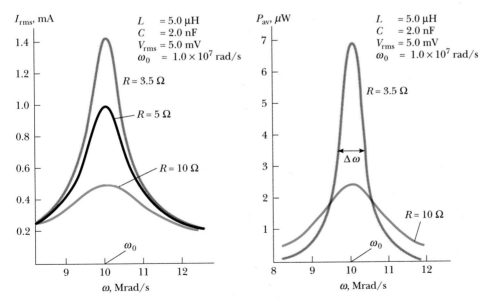

FIGURE 33.14 (a) Plots of the rms current versus frequency for a series *RLC* circuit for three values of *R*. Note that the current reaches its peak value at the resonance frequency ω_0. (b) Plots of the average power versus frequency for the series *RLC* circuit for two values of *R*.

$L = 5.0 \ \mu H$, and $C = 2.0$ nF. The three curves correspond to three values of R. Note that in each case, the current reaches its maximum value at the resonance frequency, ω_0. Furthermore, the curves become narrower and taller as the resistance decreases.

By inspecting Equation 33.32, it must be concluded that, when $R = 0$, the current would become infinite at resonance. Although the equation predicts this, real circuits always have some resistance, which limits the value of the current.

Mechanical systems can also exhibit resonances. For example, when an undamped mass-spring system is driven at its natural frequency of oscillation, its amplitude increases with time, as we discussed in Chapter 13. Large-amplitude mechanical vibrations can be disastrous, as in the case of the Tacoma Narrows Bridge collapse.

It is also interesting to calculate the average power as a function of frequency for a series *RLC* circuit. Using Equations 33.30 and 33.31, we find that

$$P_{av} = I_{rms}^2 R = \frac{V_{rms}^2}{Z^2} R = \frac{V_{rms}^2 R}{R^2 + (X_L - X_C)^2} \tag{33.34}$$

Since $X_L = \omega L$, $X_C = 1/\omega C$, and $\omega_0^2 = 1/LC$, the factor $(X_L - X_C)^2$ can be expressed as

$$(X_L - X_C)^2 = \left(\omega L - \frac{1}{\omega C} \right)^2 = \frac{L^2}{\omega^2}(\omega^2 - \omega_0^2)^2$$

Using this result in Equation 33.34 gives

Power in an *RLC* circuit

$$P_{av} = \frac{V_{rms}^2 R \omega^2}{R^2 \omega^2 + L^2(\omega^2 - \omega_0^2)^2} \tag{33.35}$$

This expression shows that at resonance, when $\omega = \omega_0$, the *average power is a maximum* and has the value V_{rms}^2 / R. A plot of average power versus frequency is shown in Figure 33.14b for the series *RLC* circuit described in Figure 33.14a, taking $R = 3.5 \ \Omega$ and $R = 10 \ \Omega$. As the resistance is made smaller, the curve becomes sharper in the vicinity of the resonance frequency. The sharpness of the curve is usually described by a dimensionless parameter known as the **quality factor**, denoted by Q_0 (not to be confused with the symbol for charge)[3]:

$$Q_0 = \frac{\omega_0}{\Delta \omega}$$

where $\Delta \omega$ is the width of the curve measured between the two values of ω for which P_{av} has half its maximum value (half-power points, see Fig. 33.14b). It is left as a problem (Problem 87) to show that the width at the half-power points has the value $\Delta \omega = R/L$, so that

$$Q_0 = \frac{\omega_0 L}{R} \tag{33.36}$$

That is, Q_0 is equal to the ratio of the inductive reactance to the resistance evaluated at the resonance frequency, ω_0.

The curves plotted in Figure 33.15 show that a high-Q_0 circuit responds to a very narrow range of frequencies, whereas a low-Q_0 circuit responds to a much

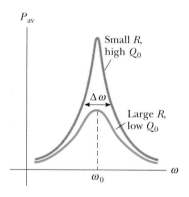

FIGURE 33.15 Plots of the average power versus frequency for a series *RLC* circuit (see Eq. 33.35). The upper, narrow curve is for a small value of *B*, and the lower, broad curve is for a large value of *R*. The width $\Delta \omega$ of each curve is measured between points where the power is half its maximum value. The power is a maximum at the resonance frequency, ω_0.

---

[3] The quality factor is also defined as the ratio $2\pi E/\Delta E$, where E is the energy stored in the oscillating system and ΔE is the energy lost per cycle of oscillation. The quality factor for a mechanical system such as a damped oscillator can also be defined.

broader range of frequencies. Typical values of Q_0 in electronic circuits range from 10 to 100.

The receiving circuit of a radio is an important application of a resonant circuit. The radio is tuned to a particular station (which transmits a specific radio-frequency signal) by varying a capacitor, which changes the resonant frequency of the receiving circuit. When the resonance frequency of the circuit matches that of the incoming radio wave, the current in the receiving circuit increases. This signal is then amplified and fed to a speaker. Since many signals are often present over a range of frequencies, it is important to design a high-Q_0 circuit in order to eliminate unwanted signals. In this manner, stations whose frequencies are near but not at the resonance frequency give negligibly small signals at the receiver relative to the one that matches the resonance frequency.

EXAMPLE 33.8 A Resonating Series *RLC* Circuit

Consider a series *RLC* circuit for which $R = 150\ \Omega$, $L = 20.0$ mH, $V_{rms} = 20.0$ V, and $\omega = 5000\ \text{s}^{-1}$. Determine the value of the capacitance for which the current has its peak value.

Solution The current has its peak value at the resonance frequency ω_0, which should be made to match the "driving" frequency of 5000 s^{-1} in this problem:

$$\omega_0 = 5.00 \times 10^3\ \text{s}^{-1} = \frac{1}{\sqrt{LC}}$$

$$C = \frac{1}{\omega_0^2 L} = \frac{1}{(25.0 \times 10^6\ \text{s}^{-2})(2.00 \times 10^{-3}\ \text{H})} = 2.00\ \mu\text{F}$$

Exercise Calculate the maximum value of the rms current in the circuit.

Answer 0.133 A.

---

*33.8 FILTER CIRCUITS

A filter circuit is used to smooth out or eliminate a time-varying signal. For example, radios are usually powered by a 60-Hz ac voltage, which is converted to dc using a rectifier circuit. After rectification, however, the voltage still contains a small ac component at 60 Hz (sometimes called ripple), which must be filtered. By "filter," we mean that the 60-Hz ripple must be reduced to a value much smaller than the audio signal to be amplified, because without filtering, the resulting audio signal includes an annoying hum at 60 Hz.

First, consider the simple series *RC* circuit shown in Figure 33.16a. The input

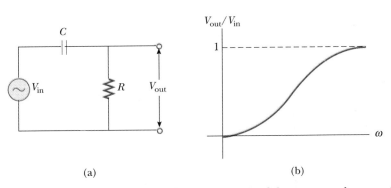

(a) (b)

FIGURE 33.16 (a) A simple *RC* high-pass filter. (b) Ratio of the output voltage to the input voltage for an *RC* high-pass filter.

voltage is across the two elements and is represented by $V_{max} \sin \omega t$. Since we are interested only in maximum values, we can use Equation 33.24, which shows that the maximum input voltage is related to the maximum current by

$$V_{in} = I_{max} Z = I_{max} \sqrt{R^2 + \left(\frac{1}{\omega C}\right)^2}$$

If the voltage across the resistor is considered to be the output voltage, V_{out}, then from Ohm's law the maximum output voltage is

$$V_{out} = I_{max} R$$

Therefore, the ratio of the output voltage to the input voltage is

High-pass filter

$$\frac{V_{out}}{V_{in}} = \frac{R}{\sqrt{R^2 + \left(\frac{1}{\omega C}\right)^2}} \tag{33.37}$$

A plot of Equation 33.37, given in Figure 33.16b, shows that at low frequencies, V_{out} is small compared with V_{in}, whereas at high frequencies the two voltages are equal. Since the circuit preferentially passes signals of higher frequency while low frequencies are filtered (or attenuated), the circuit is called an *RC* high-pass filter. Physically, a high-pass filter is a result of the "blocking action" of a capacitor to direct current or low frequencies.

Now consider the *RC* series circuit shown in Figure 33.17a, where the output voltage is taken across the capacitor. In this case, the maximum voltage equals the voltage across the capacitor. Because the impedance across the capacitor is given by $X_C = 1/\omega C$,

$$V_{out} = I_{max} X_C = \frac{I_{max}}{\omega C}$$

Therefore, the ratio of the output voltage to the input voltage is

Low-pass filter

$$\frac{V_{out}}{V_{in}} = \frac{1/\omega C}{\sqrt{R^2 + \left(\frac{1}{\omega C}\right)^2}} \tag{33.38}$$

This ratio, plotted in Figure 33.17b, shows that in this case the circuit preferentially passes signals of low frequency. Hence, the circuit is called an *RC* low-pass filter. Filters can be designed to block, or pass, a narrow band of frequencies.

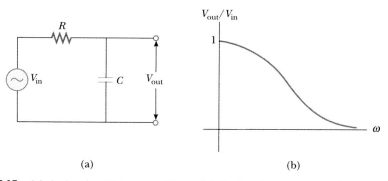

(a)   (b)

FIGURE 33.17   (a) A simple *RC* low-pass filter. (b) Ratio of the output voltage to the input voltage for an *RC* low-pass filter.

*33.9 THE TRANSFORMER AND POWER TRANSMISSION

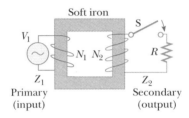

When electrical power is transmitted over large distances, it is economical to use a high voltage and low current to minimize the I^2R heating loss in the transmission lines. For this reason, 350-kV lines are common, and in many areas even higher-voltage (765 kV) lines are under construction. Such high-voltage transmission systems have met with considerable public resistance because of the potential safety and environmental problems they pose. At the receiving end of such lines, the consumer requires power at a low voltage and high current (for safety and efficiency in design) to operate such things as appliances and motor-driven machines. Therefore, a device is required that can increase (or decrease) the ac voltage and current without causing appreciable changes in the power delivered. The ac transformer is the device used for this purpose.

In its simplest form, the ac transformer consists of two coils of wire wound around a core of soft iron as in Figure 33.18. The coil on the left, which is connected to the input ac voltage source and has N_1 turns, is called the primary winding (or primary). The coil on the right, consisting of N_2 turns and connected to a load resistor R, is called the secondary. The purpose of the common iron core is to increase the magnetic flux and to provide a medium in which nearly all the flux through one coil passes through the other coil. Eddy current losses are reduced by using a laminated iron core. Soft iron is used as the core material to reduce hysteresis losses. Joule heat losses caused by the finite resistance of the coil wires are usually quite small. Typical transformers have power efficiencies ranging from 90% to 99%. In what follows, we assume an *ideal transformer,* one in which the energy losses in the windings and core are zero.

First, let us consider what happens in the primary circuit when the switch in the secondary circuit of Figure 33.18 is open. If we assume that the resistance of the primary coil is negligible relative to its inductive reactance, then the primary circuit is equivalent to a simple circuit consisting of an inductor connected to an ac generator (described in Section 33.3). Since the current is 90° out of phase with the voltage, the power factor, $\cos \phi$, is zero, and hence the average power delivered from the generator to the primary circuit is zero. Faraday's law tells us that the voltage V_1 across the primary coil is

$$V_1 = -N_1 \frac{d\Phi_B}{dt} \tag{33.39}$$

where Φ_B is the magnetic flux through each turn. If we assume that no flux leaks out of the iron core, then the flux through each turn of the primary equals the flux through each turn of the secondary. Hence, the voltage across the secondary coil is

$$V_2 = -N_2 \frac{d\Phi_B}{dt} \tag{33.40}$$

Since $d\Phi_B/dt$ is common to Equations 33.39 and 33.40, we find that

$$V_2 = \frac{N_2}{N_1} V_1 \tag{33.41}$$

When $N_2 > N_1$, the output voltage V_2 exceeds the input voltage V_1. This setup is referred to as a step-up transformer. When $N_2 < N_1$, the output voltage is less than the input voltage, and we speak of a step-down transformer.

When the switch in the secondary circuit is closed, a current I_2 is induced in the secondary. If the load in the secondary circuit is a pure resistance, the induced current is in phase with the induced voltage. The power supplied to the secondary

FIGURE 33.18 An ideal transformer consists of two coils wound on the same soft iron core. An ac voltage V_1 is applied to the primary coil, and the output voltage V_2 is across the load resistance R.

Nikola Tesla (1856–1943) was born in Croatia but spent most of his professional life as an inventor in the United States. He was a key figure in the development of alternating-current electricity, high-voltage transformers, and the transport of electrical power using ac transmission lines. Tesla's viewpoint was at odds with the ideas of Edison, who committed himself to the use of direct current in power transmission. Tesla's ac approach won out. *(UPI/Bettmann)*

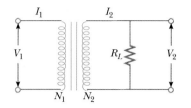

FIGURE 33.19 Conventional circuit diagram for a transformer.

circuit must be provided by the ac generator connected to the primary circuit, as in Figure 33.19. In an ideal transformer, the power supplied by the generator, $I_1 V_1$, is equal to the power in the secondary circuit, $I_2 V_2$. That is,

$$I_1 V_1 = I_2 V_2 \tag{33.42}$$

Clearly, the value of the load resistance R determines the value of the secondary current, since $I_2 = V_2/R$. Furthermore, the current in the primary is $I_1 = V_1/R_{eq}$, where

$$R_{eq} = \left(\frac{N_1}{N_2}\right)^2 R \tag{33.43}$$

is the equivalent resistance of the load resistance when viewed from the primary side. From this analysis, we see that a transformer may be used to match resistances between the primary circuit and the load. In this manner, maximum power transfer can be achieved between a given power source and the load resistance.

We can now understand why transformers are useful for transmitting power over long distances. Because the generator voltage is stepped up, the current in the transmission line is reduced, thereby reducing I^2R losses. In practice, the voltage is stepped up to around 230 000 V at the generating station, then stepped down to around 20 000 V at a distributing station, and finally stepped down to 120–220 V at the customer's utility poles. The power is supplied by a three-wire cable. In the United States, two of these wires are "hot," with voltages of 120 V with respect to a common ground wire. Home appliances operating on 120 V are connected in parallel between one of the hot wires and ground. Larger appliances, such as electric stoves and clothes dryers, require 220 V. This is obtained across the two hot wires, which are 180° out of phase so that the voltage difference between them is 220 V.

There is a practical upper limit to the voltages that can be used in transmission lines. Excessive voltages could ionize the air surrounding the transmission lines, which could result in a conducting path to ground or to other objects in the vicinity. This, of course, would present a serious hazard to any living creatures. For this reason, a long string of insulators is used to keep high-voltage wires away from their supporting metal towers. Other insulators are used to maintain separation between wires.

EXAMPLE 33.9   A Step-Up Transformer

A generator produces 10 A (rms) of current at 400 V. The voltage is stepped up to 4500 V by an ideal transformer and transmitted a long distance through a power line of total resistance 30 Ω. (a) Determine the percentage of power lost when the voltage is stepped up.

Solution   Using Equation 33.42 for an ideal transformer, we find that the current in the transmission line is

$$I_2 = \frac{I_1 V_1}{V_2} = \frac{(10\text{ A})(400\text{ V})}{4500\text{ V}} = 0.89\text{ A}$$

Hence, the power lost in the transmission line is

$$P_{lost} = I_2{}^2 R = (0.89\text{ A})^2(30\ \Omega) = 24\text{ W}$$

Since the output power of the generator is $P = IV = (10\text{ A})(400\text{ V}) = 4000$ W, the percentage of power lost is

$$\% \text{ power lost} = \left(\frac{24}{4000}\right) \times 100 = \boxed{0.60\%}$$

(b) What percentage of the original power would be lost in the transmission line if the voltage were not stepped up?

Solution   If the voltage were not stepped up, the current in the transmission line would be 10 A and the power lost in the line would be $I^2R = (10 \text{ A})^2(30 \text{ }\Omega) = 3000$ W. Hence, the percentage of power lost would be

$$\% \text{ power lost} = \left(\frac{3000}{4000}\right) \times 100 = \boxed{75\%}$$

This example illustrates the advantage of high-voltage transmission lines.

Exercise   If the transmission line is cooled so that the resistance is reduced to 5.0 Ω, how much power will be lost in the line if it carries a current of 0.89 A?

Answer   4.0 W.

SUMMARY

If an ac circuit consists of a generator and a resistor, the current in the circuit is in phase with the voltage. That is, the current and voltage reach their peak values at the same time.

The **rms current** and **rms voltage** in an ac circuit in which the voltages and current vary sinusoidally are given by

$$I_{\text{rms}} = \frac{I_{\text{max}}}{\sqrt{2}} = 0.707 I_{\text{max}} \tag{33.4}$$

$$V_{\text{rms}} = \frac{V_{\text{max}}}{\sqrt{2}} = 0.707 V_{\text{max}} \tag{33.5}$$

where I_{max} and V_{max} are the maximum values.

If an ac circuit consists of a generator and an inductor, the current lags behind the voltage by 90°. That is, the voltage reaches its maximum value one quarter of a period before the current reaches its maximum value.

If an ac circuit consists of a generator and a capacitor, the current leads the voltage by 90°. That is, the current reaches its maximum value one quarter of a period before the voltage reaches its maximum value.

In ac circuits that contain inductors and capacitors, it is useful to define the **inductive reactance** X_L and **capacitive reactance** X_C as

$$X_L = \omega L \tag{33.10}$$

$$X_C = \frac{1}{\omega C} \tag{33.17}$$

where ω is the angular frequency of the ac generator. The SI unit of reactance is the ohm.

The **impedance** Z of an RLC series ac circuit, which also has the unit of ohm, is

$$Z \equiv \sqrt{R^2 + (X_L - X_C)^2} \tag{33.23}$$

The applied voltage and current are out of phase, where the **phase angle** ϕ between the current and voltage is

$$\tan \phi = \frac{X_L - X_C}{R} \tag{33.25}$$

The sign of ϕ can be positive or negative, depending on whether X_L is greater or less than X_C. The phase angle is zero when $X_L = X_C$.

The **average power** delivered by the generator in an RLC ac circuit is

$$P_{\text{av}} = I_{\text{rms}} V_{\text{rms}} \cos \phi \tag{33.29}$$

An equivalent expression for the average power is

$$P_{av} = I_{rms}^2 R \qquad (33.30)$$

The average power delivered by the generator is dissipated as heat in the resistor. There is no power loss in an ideal inductor or capacitor.

The rms current in a series *RLC* circuit is

$$I_{rms} = \frac{V_{rms}}{\sqrt{R^2 + (X_L - X_C)^2}} \qquad (33.32)$$

where V_{rms} is the rms value of the applied voltage.

A series *RLC* circuit is in resonance when the inductive reactance equals the capacitive reactance. When this condition is met, the current given by Equation 33.32 reaches its maximum value. Setting $X_L = X_C$, the **resonance frequency** ω_0 of the circuit has the value

$$\omega_0 = \frac{1}{\sqrt{LC}} \qquad (33.33)$$

The current in a series *RLC* circuit reaches its maximum value when the frequency of the generator equals ω_0, that is, when the "driving" frequency matches the resonance frequency.

QUESTIONS

1. What is meant by the statement "the voltage across an inductor leads the current by 90°"?
2. A night watchman is fired by his boss for being wasteful and keeping all the lights on in the building. The night watchman defends himself by claiming that the building is electrically heated, so his boss's claim is unfounded. Who should win the argument if this were to end up in a court of law?
3. Why does a capacitor act as a short circuit at high frequencies? Why does it act as an open circuit at low frequencies?
4. Explain how the acronym "ELI the ICE man" can be used to recall whether current leads voltage or voltage leads current in *RLC* circuits.
5. Why is the sum of the maximum voltages across each of the elements in a series *RLC* circuit usually greater than the maximum applied voltage? Doesn't this violate Kirchhoff's voltage law?
6. Does the phase angle depend on frequency? What is the phase angle when the inductive reactance equals the capacitive reactance?
7. In a series *RLC* circuit, what is the possible range of values for the phase angle?
8. If the frequency is doubled in a series *RLC* circuit, what happens to the resistance, the inductive reactance, and the capacitive reactance?

9. Energy is delivered to a series *RLC* circuit by a generator. This energy is dissipated as heat in the resistor. What is the source of this energy?
10. Explain why the average power delivered to an *RLC* circuit by the generator depends on the phase between the current and applied voltage.
11. A particular experiment requires a beam of light of very stable intensity. Why would an ac voltage be unsuitable for powering the light source?
12. What is the impedance of an *RLC* circuit at the resonance frequency?
13. Consider a series *RLC* circuit in which *R* is an incandescent lamp, *C* is some fixed capacitor, and *L* is a variable inductance. The source is 120 V ac. Explain why the lamp glows brightly for some values of *L* and does not glow at all for other values.
14. What is the advantage of transmitting power at high voltages?
15. What determines the maximum voltage that can be used on a transmission line?
16. Why do power lines carry electrical energy at several thousand volts potential, but it is always stepped down to 240 V as it enters your home?
17. Will a transformer operate if a battery is used for the input voltage across the primary? Explain.
18. How can the average value of a current be zero and yet

the square root of the average squared current not be zero?

19. What is the time average of a sinusoidal potential with amplitude V_{max}? What is its rms voltage?

20. What is the time average of the "square-wave" potential shown in Figure 33.20? What is its rms voltage?

FIGURE 33.20 (Question 20).

21. Do ac ammeters and voltmeters read maximum, rms, or average values?

22. Is the voltage applied to a circuit always in phase with the current in a resistor in the circuit?

23. Would an inductor and a capacitor used together in an ac circuit dissipate any power?

24. Show that the peak current in an *RLC* circuit occurs when the circuit is in resonance.

25. Explain how the quality factor is related to the response characteristics of a receiver. Which variable most strongly determines the quality factor?

26. List some applications for a filter circuit.

27. The approximate efficiency of an incandescent lamp for converting electrical energy to heat is (a) 30%, (b) 60%, (c) 100%, or (d) 10%.

28. Why are the primary and secondary coils of a transformer wrapped on an iron core that passes through both coils?

29. With reference to Figure 33.21, explain why the capacitor prevents a dc signal from passing between A and B, yet allows an ac signal to pass from A to B. (The circuits are said to be capacitively coupled.)

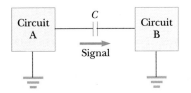

FIGURE 33.21 (Question 29).

30. With reference to Figure 33.22, if *C* is made sufficiently large, an ac signal passes from A to ground rather than from A to B. Hence, the capacitor acts as a filter. Explain.

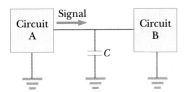

FIGURE 33.22 (Question 30).

PROBLEMS

Review Problem

In the circuit shown below, all parameters except for *C* are given. Find (a) the current as a function of time, (b) the power dissipated in the circuit, (c) the current as a function of time after *only* switch 1 is opened, (d) the capacitance *C* if the current and voltage are in phase after switch 2 is *also* opened, (e) the impedance of the circuit when both switches are open, (f) the maximum energy stored in the capacitor during oscillations, (g) the maximum energy stored in the inductor during oscillations, (h) the phase change between the current and voltage if the frequency of the voltage source is doubled, and (i) the frequency that makes the inductive reactance one-half the capacitive reactance.

Assume all ac voltages and currents are sinusoidal, unless stated otherwise.

Section 33.2   Resistors in an ac Circuit

1. Show that the rms value for the sawtooth voltage shown in Figure P33.1 is $V_{max}/\sqrt{3}$.

2. (a) What is the resistance of a lightbulb that uses an average power of 75 W when connected to a 60-Hz

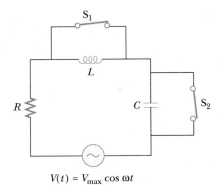

$V(t) = V_{max} \cos \omega t$

□ indicates problems that have full solutions available in the Student Solutions Manual and Study Guide.

FIGURE P33.1

power source having a maximum voltage of 170 V?
(b) What is the resistance of a 100-W bulb?

3. An ac power supply produces a maximum voltage $V_{max} = 100$ V. This power supply is connected to a 24-Ω resistor, and the current and resistor voltage are measured with an ideal ac ammeter and voltmeter, as in Figure P33.3. What does each meter read?

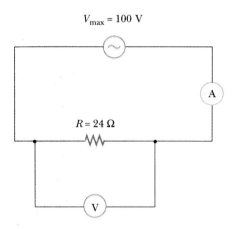

FIGURE P33.3

4. Figure P33.4 shows three lamps connected to a 120-V ac (rms) household supply voltage. Lamps 1 and 2 have 150-W bulbs and lamp 3 has a 100-W bulb. Find the rms current and resistance of each bulb.

4A. Figure P33.4 shows three lamps connected to an ac (rms) voltage V. Lamps 1 and 2 have bulbs that each dissipate power P_1 and lamp 3 has a bulb that dissipates power P_2. Find the rms current and resistance of each bulb.

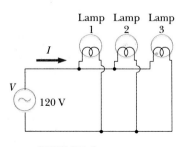

FIGURE P33.4

5. An audio amplifier, represented by the ac source and resistor in Figure P33.5, delivers to the speaker alternating voltage at audio frequencies. If the output voltage has an amplitude of 15.0 V, $R = 8.20\ \Omega$, and the speaker is equivalent to a resistance of 10.4 Ω, what is the time-averaged power input to it?

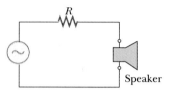

FIGURE P33.5

6. In the simple ac circuit shown in Figure 33.1, $R = 70\ \Omega$, and $v = V_{max} \sin \omega t$. (a) If $V_R = 0.25 V_{max}$ at $t = 0.010$ s, what is the angular frequency of the generator? (b) What is the next value of t for which $V_R = 0.25 V_{max}$?

7. The current in the circuit shown in Figure 33.1 equals 60% of the maximum current at $t = 7.0$ ms, and $v = V_{max} \sin \omega t$. What is the smallest frequency of the generator that gives this current?

Section 33.3   Inductors in an ac Circuit

8. Determine the maximum magnetic flux through an inductor connected to a standard outlet ($V_{rms} = 120$ V, $f = 60$ Hz).

9. In a purely inductive ac circuit, as in Figure 33.4, $V_{max} = 100$ V. (a) If the maximum current is 7.5 A at 50 Hz, calculate the inductance L. (b) At what angular frequency ω is the maximum current 2.5 A?

10. When a particular inductor is connected to a sinusoidal voltage with a 120-V amplitude, a peak current of 3.0 A appears in the inductor. (a) What is the maximum current if the frequency of the applied voltage is doubled? (b) What is the inductive reactance at these two frequencies?

11. An inductor is connected to a 20.0-Hz power supply that produces a 50.0-V rms voltage. What inductance is needed to keep the instantaneous current in the circuit below 80.0 mA?

12. An inductor has a 54.0-Ω reactance at 60.0 Hz. What is the maximum current if this inductor is connected to a 50.0-Hz source that produces a 100-V rms voltage?

13. For the circuit shown in Figure 33.4, $V_{max} = 80.0$ V, $\omega = 65\pi$ rad/s, and $L = 70.0$ mH. Calculate the current in the inductor at $t = 15.5$ ms.

14. (a) If $L = 310$ mH and $V_{max} = 130$ V in Figure 33.4, at what frequency is the inductive reactance 40.0 Ω? (b) Calculate the maximum current at this frequency.

15. A 20.0-mH inductor is connected to a standard outlet (V_{rms} = 120 V, f = 60.0 Hz). Determine the energy stored in the inductor at t = (1/180) s, assuming that this energy is zero at t = 0.

Section 33.4 Capacitors in an ac Circuit

16. A 1.0-mF capacitor is connected to a standard outlet (V_{rms} = 120 V, f = 60.0 Hz). Determine the current in the capacitor at t = (1/180) s, assuming that at t = 0, the energy stored in the capacitor is zero.

17. (a) For what linear frequencies does a 22.0-μF capacitor have a reactance below 175 Ω? (b) Over this same frequency range, what is the reactance of a 44.0-μF capacitor?

18. What maximum current is delivered by a 2.2-μF capacitor when connected across (a) a North American outlet having V_{rms} = 120 V, f = 60 Hz and (b) a European outlet having V_{rms} = 240 V, f = 50 Hz?

19. A 98.0-pF capacitor is connected to a 60.0-Hz power supply that produces a 20.0-V rms voltage. What is the maximum charge that appears on either of the capacitor plates?

19A. A capacitor C is connected to a power supply that operates at a frequency f and produces an rms voltage V. What is the maximum charge that appears on either of the capacitor plates?

20. A sinusoidal voltage $v(t) = V_{max} \cos \omega t$ is applied to a capacitor as in Figure P33.20. (a) Write an expression for the instantaneous charge on the capacitor in terms of V_{max}, C, t, and ω. (b) What is the instantaneous current in the circuit?

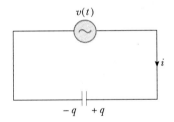

FIGURE P33.20

21. What maximum current is delivered by an ac generator with V_{max} = 48 V and f = 90 Hz when connected across a 3.7-μF capacitor?

22. A variable-frequency ac generator with V_{max} = 18 V is connected across a 9.4×10^{-8}-F capacitor. At what frequency should the generator be operated to provide a maximum current of 5.0 A?

23. The generator in a purely capacitive ac circuit (Fig. 33.6) has an angular frequency of 100π rad/s and V_{max} = 220 V. If C = 20.0 μF, what is the current in the circuit at t = 4.00 ms?

Section 33.5 The *RLC* Series Circuit

24. At what frequency does the inductive reactance of a 57-μH inductor equal the capacitive reactance of a 57-μF capacitor?

25. A series ac circuit contains the following components: R = 150 Ω, L = 250 mH, C = 2.00 μF, and a generator with V_{max} = 210 V operating at 50.0 Hz. Calculate the (a) inductive reactance, (b) capacitive reactance, (c) impedance, (d) maximum current, and (e) phase angle.

26. A sinusoidal voltage $v(t) = (40.0 \text{ V}) \sin(100t)$ is applied to a series *RLC* circuit with L = 160 mH, C = 99.0 μF, and R = 68.0 Ω. (a) What is the impedance of the circuit? (b) What is the maximum current? (c) Determine the numerical values for I_{max}, ω, and ϕ in the equation $i(t) = I_{max} \sin(\omega t - \phi)$.

27. An *RLC* circuit consists of a 150-Ω resistor, a 21-μF capacitor, and a 460-mH inductor, connected in series with a 120-V, 60-Hz power supply. (a) What is the phase angle between the current and the applied voltage? (b) Which reaches its maximum earlier, the current or the voltage?

28. A resistor (R = 900 Ω), a capacitor (C = 0.25 μF), and an inductor (L = 2.5 H) are connected in series across a 240-Hz ac source for which V_{max} = 140 V. Calculate the (a) impedance of the circuit, (b) peak current delivered by the source, and (c) phase angle between the current and voltage. (d) Is the current leading or lagging behind the voltage?

29. A person is working near the secondary of a transformer, as shown in Figure P33.29. The primary voltage is 120 V at 60.0 Hz. The capacitance C_s, which is the capacitance between hand and secondary winding, is 20.0 pF. Assuming the person has a body resistance to ground R_b = 50.0 kΩ, determine the rms voltage across the body. (*Hint:* Redraw the circuit with the secondary of the transformer as a simple ac source.)

29A. A person is working near the secondary of a transformer, as in Figure P33.29. The primary rms voltage

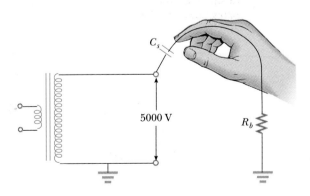

FIGURE P33.29

is V at a frequency f. The stray capacitance between hand and secondary winding is C_s. Assuming the person has a body resistance to ground R_b, determine the rms voltage across the body. (*Hint:* Redraw the circuit with the secondary of the transformer as a simple ac source.)

30. The voltage source in Figure P33.30 has an output $V_{rms} = (100 \text{ V}) \cos(1000t)$. Determine (a) the current in the circuit and (b) the power supplied by the source. (c) Show that the power dissipated in the resistor is equal to the power supplied by the source.

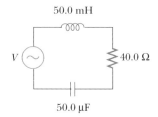

50.0 mH

V 40.0 Ω

50.0 μF

FIGURE P33.30

31. An ac source with $V_{max} = 150$ V and $f = 50.0$ Hz is connected between points a and d in Figure P33.31. Calculate the maximum voltages between points (a) a and b, (b) b and c, (c) c and d, and (d) b and d.

a b c d

40 Ω   185 mH   65 μF

FIGURE P33.31

32. Draw to scale a phasor diagram showing Z, X_L, X_C, and ϕ for an ac series circuit for which $R = 300$ Ω, $C = 11$ μF, $L = 0.20$ H, and $f = 500/\pi$Hz.

33. An inductor ($L = 400$ mH), a capacitor ($C = 4.43$ μF), and a resistor ($R = 500$ Ω) are connected in series. A 50.0-Hz ac generator produces a peak current of 250 mA in the circuit. (a) Calculate the required peak voltage V_{max}. (b) Determine the angle by which the current leads or lags the applied voltage.

34. A series RLC circuit in which $R = 1500$ Ω and $C = 15.0$ nF is connected to an ac generator whose frequency can be varied. When the frequency is adjusted to 50.5 kHz, the rms current in the circuit reaches a maximum at 0.140 A. Determine (a) the inductance and (b) the rms value of the generator voltage.

Section 33.6   Power in an ac Circuit

35. If 100 MW of power at 50.0-kV is to be transmitted over 100 km with only 1.00 percent loss, copper wire

of what diameter should be used? Assume uniform current density in the conductors.

35A. If power P is to be transmitted over a distance d at a voltage V with only 1.00 percent loss, copper wire of what diameter should be used? Assume uniform current density in the conductors.

36. A diode is a device that allows current to pass in only one direction (indicated by the arrowhead). Find, in terms of V and R, the average power dissipated in the diode circuit shown in Figure P33.36.

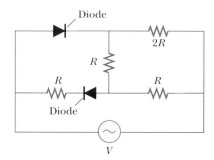

Diode

2R

R

R   R

Diode

V

FIGURE P33.36

37. An ac voltage of the form $v = (100 \text{ V}) \sin(1000t)$ is applied to a series RLC circuit. If $R = 400$ Ω, $C = 5.0$ μF, and $L = 0.50$ H, find the average power dissipated in the circuit.

38. An ac voltage with an amplitude of 100 V is applied to a series combination of a 200-μF capacitor, a 100-mH inductor, and a 20.0-Ω resistor. Calculate the power dissipated and the power factor for a frequency of (a) 60.0 Hz and (b) 50.0 Hz.

39. The rms output voltage of an ac generator is 200 V and the operating frequency is 100 Hz. Write the equation giving the output voltage as a function of time.

40. The average power in a circuit for which the rms current is 5.00 A is 450 W. Calculate the resistance of the circuit.

41. In a certain series RLC circuit, $I_{rms} = 9.0$ A, $V_{rms} = 180$ V, and the current leads the voltage by 37°. (a) What is the total resistance of the circuit? (b) Calculate the magnitude of the reactance of the circuit ($X_L - X_C$).

42. A series RLC circuit has a resistance of 45 Ω and an impedance of 75 Ω. What average power is delivered to this circuit when $V_{rms} = 210$ V?

Section 33.7   Resonance in a Series RLC Circuit

43. Calculate the resonance frequency of a series RLC circuit for which $C = 8.40$ μF and $L = 120$ mH.

44. Show that the Q value in a series RLC circuit is

$$Q_0 = \frac{1}{R}\sqrt{\frac{L}{C}}$$

45. An *RLC* circuit is used in a radio to tune into an FM station broadcasting at 99.7 MHz. The resistance in the circuit is 12.0 Ω, and the inductance is 1.40 μH. What capacitance should be used?

46. The tuning circuit of an AM radio is a parallel *LC* combination that has 1.00-Ω resistance. The inductance is 0.200 mH, and the capacitor is variable, so that the circuit can resonate between 550 kHz and 1650 kHz. Find the range of values for *C*.

47. A coil of resistance 35.0 Ω and inductance 20.5 H is in series with a capacitor and a 200-V (rms), 100-Hz source. The rms current in the circuit is 4.00 A. (a) Calculate the capacitance in the circuit. (b) What is V_{rms} across the coil?

48. A series *RLC* circuit has the following values: $L = 20.0$ mH, $C = 100$ nF, $R = 20.0$ Ω, and $V_{max} = 100$ V, with $v = V_{max} \sin \omega t$. Find (a) the resonant frequency, (b) the amplitude of the current at the resonant frequency, (c) the Q of the circuit, and (d) the amplitude of the voltage across the inductor at resonance.

49. A 10.0-Ω resistor, 10.0-mH inductor, and 100-μF capacitor are connected in series to a 50.0-V (rms) source having variable frequency. Find the heat dissipated in the circuit during one period if the operating frequency is twice the resonance frequency.

49A. A resistor *R*, inductor *L*, and capacitor *C* are connected in series to an ac source of rms voltage *V* and variable frequency. Find the heat dissipated in the circuit during one period if the operating frequency is twice the resonance frequency.

*Section 33.8 Filter Circuits

50. Consider the circuit shown in Figure 33.16, with $R = 800$ Ω and $C = 0.090$ μF. Calculate the ratio V_{out}/V_{in} for (a) $\omega = 300$ s^{-1} and (b) $\omega = 7.0 \times 10^5$ s^{-1}.

51. The *RC* high-pass filter shown in Figure 33.16 has a resistance $R = 0.50$ Ω. (a) What capacitance gives an output signal that has one-half the amplitude of a 300-Hz input signal? (b) What is the gain (V_{out}/V_{in}) for a 600-Hz signal?

52. The *RC* low-pass filter shown in Figure 33.17 has a resistance $R = 90.0$ Ω and a capacitance $C = 8.00$ nF. Calculate the gain (V_{out}/V_{in}) for an input frequency of (a) 600 Hz and (b) 600 kHz.

53. The circuit shown in Figure P33.53 represents a high-pass filter in which the inductor has internal resistance. Determine the source frequency if the output voltage V_2 is one-half the input voltage.

54. (a) For the circuit shown in Figure P33.54, show that the maximum possible value of the ratio V_{out}/V_{in} is unity. (b) At what frequency (expressed in terms of *R*, *L*, and *C*) does this maximum value occur?

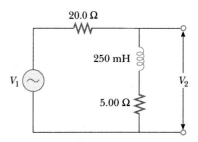

FIGURE P33.53

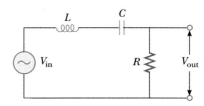

FIGURE P33.54

55. The circuit shown in Figure P33.54 can be used as a filter to pass signals that lie in a certain frequency band. (a) Show that the gain (V_{out}/V_{in}) for an input voltage of frequency ω is

$$\frac{V_{out}}{V_{in}} = \frac{1}{\sqrt{1 + \left[\dfrac{(\omega^2/\omega_0^2) - 1}{\omega RC}\right]^2}}$$

(b) Let $R = 100$ Ω, $C = 0.0500$ μF, and $L = 0.127$ H. Compute the gain of this circuit for input frequencies $f_1 = 1.50$ kHz, $f_2 = 2.00$ kHz, and $f_3 = 2.50$ kHz.

56. Show that two successive high-pass filters having the same values of *R* and *C* give a combined gain

$$\frac{V_{out}}{V_{in}} = \frac{1}{1 + (1/\omega RC)^2}$$

57. Consider a low-pass filter followed by a high-pass filter, as shown in Figure P33.57. If $R = 1000$ Ω and $C = 0.050$ μF, determine V_{out}/V_{in} for a 2.0-kHz input frequency.

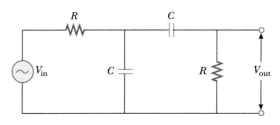

FIGURE P33.57

*Section 33.9   The Transformer and Power Transmission

58. The primary winding of an electric-train transformer has 400 turns, and the secondary has 50. If the input voltage is 120 V (rms), what is the output voltage?

59. A transformer has $N_1 = 350$ turns and $N_2 = 2000$ turns. If the input voltage is $v(t) = (170 \text{ V}) \cos \omega t$, what rms voltage is developed across the secondary coil?

60. In an *LR* circuit, a 120-V (rms), 60-Hz source is in series with a 25-mH inductor and a 20-Ω resistor. What are (a) the rms current and (b) the power factor? (c) What capacitor must be added in series to make the power factor 1?

61. A step-down transformer is used for recharging the batteries of portable devices such as tape players. The turns ratio inside the transformer is 13 : 1 and is used with 120-V (rms) household service. If a particular tape player draws 0.35 A from the house outlet, what are (a) the voltage and (b) the current supplied from the transformer? (c) How much power is delivered?

62. A step-up transformer is designed to have an output voltage of 2200 V (rms) when the primary is connected across a 110-V (rms) source. (a) If there are 80 turns on the primary winding, how many turns are required on the secondary? (b) If a load resistor across the secondary draws a current of 1.5 A, what is the current in the primary, assuming ideal conditions? (c) If the transformer has an efficiency of 95 percent, what is the current in the primary when the secondary current is 1.2 A?

63. In the transformer shown in Figure P33.63, the load resistor is 50.0 Ω. The turn ratio $N_1 : N_2$ is 5 : 2, and the source voltage is 80.0 V (rms). If a voltmeter across the load measures 25.0 V (rms), what is the source resistance R_s?

63A. In the transformer shown in Figure P33.63, the load resistor is R_L and the source resistor is R_s. The turn ratio is $N_1 : N_2$, and the rms source voltage is V_s. If a voltmeter across the load measures an rms voltage V_2, what is the source resistance?

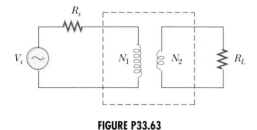

FIGURE P33.63

64. The secondary voltage of an ignition transformer used in a furnace is 10.0 kV. When the primary operates at an rms voltage of 120 V, the primary imped-

ance is 24.0 Ω and the transformer is 90 percent efficient. (a) What turn ratio is required? What are (b) the current and (c) the impedance in the secondary?

ADDITIONAL PROBLEMS

65. A series *RLC* circuit consists of an 8.00-Ω resistor, a 5.00-μF capacitor, and a 50.0-mH inductor. A variable frequency source of amplitude 400 V (rms) is applied across the combination. Determine the power delivered to the circuit when the frequency is equal to one half the resonance frequency.

66. A series *RLC* circuit has $R = 10.0$ Ω, $L = 2.00$ mH, and $C = 4.00$ μF. Determine (a) the impedance at 60.0 Hz, (b) the resonant frequency in hertz, (c) the impedance at resonance, and (d) the impedance at a frequency equal to one-half the resonant frequency.

67. In a series *RLC* ac circuit, $R = 21.0$ Ω, $L = 25.0$ mH, $C = 17.0$ μF, $V_{\max} = 150$ V, and $\omega = (2000/\pi) \text{ s}^{-1}$. (a) Calculate the maximum current in the circuit. (b) Determine the maximum voltage across each element. (c) What is the power factor for the circuit? (d) Show X_L, X_C, R, and ϕ in a phasor diagram.

68. An *RL* series combination consisting of a 1.50-Ω resistor and a 2.50-mH inductor is connected to a 12.5-V (rms), 400-Hz generator. Determine (a) the impedance of the circuit, (b) the rms current, (c) the rms voltage across the resistor, and (d) the rms voltage across the inductor.

69. As a way of determining the inductance of a coil used in a research project, a student first connects the coil to a 12-V battery and measures a current of 0.63 A. The student then connects the coil to a 24-V (rms), 60-Hz generator and measures an rms current of 0.57 A. What is the inductance?

70. In Figure P33.70, find the current delivered by the 45-V (rms) power supply when (a) the frequency is very large and (b) the frequency is very small.

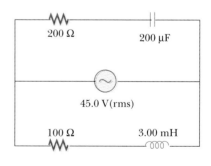

FIGURE P33.70

71. A transmission line that has a resistance per unit length of 4.50×10^{-4} Ω/m is to be used to transmit 5.00 MW over 400 miles (6.44×10^5 m). The output voltage of the generator is 4.50 kV. (a) What is the

line loss if a transformer is used to step up the voltage to 500 kV? (b) What fraction of the input power is lost to the line under these circumstances? (c) What difficulties would be encountered on attempting to transmit the 5.00 MW at the generator voltage of 4.50 kV?

72. A transformer operating from 120 V (rms) supplies a 12-V lighting system for a garden. Eight lights, each rated 40 W, are installed in parallel. (a) Find the equivalent resistance of the system. (b) What is the current in the secondary circuit? (c) What single resistance, connected across the 120-V supply, would consume the same power as when the transformer is used? Show that this resistance equals the answer to part (a) times the square of the turns ratio.

73. *LC* filters are used as both high- and low-pass filters as were the *RC* filters in Section 33.8. However, all real inductors have resistance, as indicated in Figure P33.73, and this resistance must be taken into account. (a) Determine which circuit in Figure P33.73 is the high-pass filter and which is the low-pass filter. (b) Derive the output/input formulas for each circuit following the procedure used for the *RC* filters in Section 33.8.

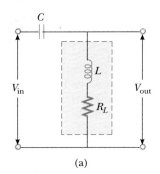

(a)

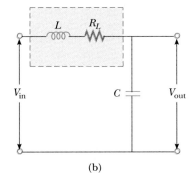

(b)

FIGURE P33.73

74. An 80.0-Ω resistor and a 200-mH inductor are connected in parallel across a 100-V (rms), 60.0-Hz source. (a) What is the rms current in the resistor?

(b) By what angle does the total current lead or lag behind the voltage?

75. A power station sends 1.50 MW to a town 10.0 km from the station. The total resistance in the connecting wires is 1.10 Ω. Find the power lost as heat in the wires if the power is sent at (a) 120 V, (b) 12.0 kV, and (c) 120 kV.

76. The average power delivered to a series *RLC* circuit at frequency ω (Section 33.7) is given by Equation 33.35. (a) Show that the maximum current can be written

$$I_{max} = \omega V_{max}[L^2(\omega_0{}^2 - \omega^2)^2 + (\omega R)^2]^{-1/2}$$

where ω is the operating frequency of the circuit and ω_0 is the resonance frequency. (b) Show that the phase angle can be expressed as

$$\phi = \tan^{-1}\left[\frac{L}{R}\left(\frac{\omega_0{}^2 - \omega^2}{\omega}\right)\right]$$

77. Consider a series *RLC* circuit having the following circuit parameters: $R = 200$ Ω, $L = 663$ mH, and $C = 26.5$ μF. The applied voltage has an amplitude of 50.0 V and a frequency of 60.0 Hz. Find the following amplitudes: (a) The current i, including its phase constant ϕ relative to the applied voltage v; (b) the voltage V_R across the resistor and its phase relative to the current; (c) the voltage V_C across the capacitor and its phase relative to the current; and (d) the voltage V_L across the inductor and its phase relative to the current.

78. A voltage $v = (100$ V$) \sin \omega t$ (in SI units) is applied across a series combination of a 2.00-H inductor, a 10.0-μF capacitor, and a 10.0-Ω resistor. (a) Determine the angular frequency ω_0 at which the power dissipated in the resistor is a maximum. (b) Calculate the power dissipated at that frequency. (c) Determine the two angular frequencies ω_1 and ω_2 at which the power dissipated is one-half the maximum value. [The Q of the circuit is approximately $\omega_0/(\omega_2 - \omega_1)$.]

79. *Impedance matching:* A transformer may be used to provide maximum power transfer between two ac circuits that have different impedances. (a) Show that the ratio of turns N_1/N_2 needed to meet this condition is

$$\frac{N_1}{N_2} = \sqrt{\frac{Z_1}{Z_2}}$$

(b) Suppose you want to use a transformer as an impedance-matching device between an audio amplifier that has an output impedance of 8.00 kΩ and a speaker that has an input impedance of 8.00 Ω. What should your N_1/N_2 ratio be?

80. An ac source has an internal resistance of 3.20 kΩ. In order for the maximum power to be transferred to an 8.00-Ω resistive load R_2, a transformer is used be-

tween the source and the load. Assuming an ideal transformer, (a) find the appropriate turns ratio of the transformer. If the output voltage of the source is 80.0 V (rms), determine (b) the rms voltage across the load resistor and (c) the rms current in the load resistor. (d) Calculate the power dissipated in the load. (e) Verify that the ratio of currents is inversely proportional to the turns ratio.

81. Figure P33.81a shows a parallel *RLC* circuit, and the corresponding phasor diagram is given in Figure P33.81b. The instantaneous voltage (and rms voltage) across each of the three circuit elements is the same, and each is in phase with the current through the resistor. The currents in *C* and *L* lead (or lag behind) the current in the resistor, as shown in Figure P33.81b. (a) Show that the rms current delivered by the source is

$$I_{\text{rms}} = V_{\text{rms}} \left[\frac{1}{R^2} + \left(\omega C - \frac{1}{\omega L} \right)^2 \right]^{1/2}$$

(b) Show that the phase angle ϕ between V_{rms} and I_{rms} is

$$\tan \phi = R \left(\frac{1}{X_C} - \frac{1}{X_L} \right)$$

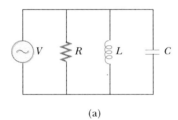

(a)

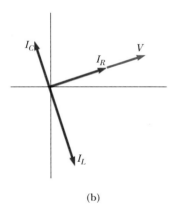

(b)

FIGURE P33.81

82. An 80.0-Ω resistor, a 200-mH inductor, and a 0.150-μF capacitor are connected in parallel across a 120-V (rms) source operating at 374 rad/s. (a) What is the resonant frequency of the circuit? (b) Calculate the rms current in the resistor, inductor, and capacitor.

(c) What is the rms current delivered by the source? (d) Is the current leading or lagging behind the voltage? By what angle?

83. Consider the phase-shifter circuit shown in Figure P33.83. The input voltage is described by the expression $v = (10 \text{ V}) \sin 200t$ (in SI units). Assuming that $L = 500$ mH, find (a) the value of R such that the output voltage v_{out} lags behind the input voltage by 30° and (b) the amplitude of the output voltage.

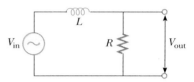

FIGURE P33.83

84. A series *RLC* circuit is operating at 2000 Hz. At this frequency, $X_L = X_C = 1884$ Ω. The resistance of the circuit is 40 Ω. (a) Prepare a table showing the values of X_L, X_C, and Z for $f = 300$, 600, 800, 1000, 1500, 2000, 3000, 4000, 6000, and 10 000 Hz. (b) Plot on the same set of axes X_L, X_C, and Z as a function of ln f.

85. Suppose the high-pass filter shown in Figure 33.16 has $R = 1000$ Ω and $C = 0.050$ μF. (a) At what frequency does $V_{\text{out}}/V_{\text{in}} = \frac{1}{2}$? (b) Plot $\log_{10}(V_{\text{out}}/V_{\text{in}})$ versus $\log_{10}(f)$ over the frequency range from 1 Hz to 1 MHz. (This log–log plot of gain versus frequency is known as a **Bode plot**.)

86. Suppose the low-pass filter shown in Figure 33.17 has $R = 1000$ Ω and $C = 0.050$ μF. (a) At what frequency does $V_{\text{out}}/V_{\text{in}} = \frac{1}{2}$? (b) Plot $\log_{10}(V_{\text{out}}/V_{\text{in}})$ versus $\log_{10}(f)$ over the frequency range from 1 Hz to 1 MHz.

87. A series *RLC* circuit in which $R = 1.00$ Ω, $L = 1.00$ mH, and $C = 1.00$ nF is connected to an ac generator delivering 1.00 V (rms). Make a careful plot of the power delivered to the circuit as a function of the frequency and verify that the half-width of the resonance peak is $R/2\pi L$.

SPREADSHEET PROBLEMS

S1. Spreadsheet 33.1 calculates the impedances (Z, X_L, X_C) and the voltage amplitudes (V_R, V_L, V_C) across each circuit element in an ac series *RLC* circuit as a function of frequency ω. In addition, the resonance frequency ω_0 is calculated. Use $R = 100$ Ω, $L = 0.50$ H, and $C = 1.0$ μF. The amplitude V_{max} of the generator is 5.0 V. (a) Plot the voltage amplitudes versus ω and note their relative magnitudes. (b) At the resonance frequency ω_0, what are the magnitudes of V_L and V_C? (c) For a very low frequency ($\omega \ll \omega_0$), how does V_L compare to V_C and V_R?

(d) Repeat part (c) for a frequency much higher than the resonance frequency. (e) The tuner of your radio is really an *RLC* circuit. Vary *R, L,* and *C* such that a very sharp resonance is obtained at the frequency of your favorite radio station.

S2. Spreadsheet 33.2 calculates the voltages across the resistor, capacitor, and inductor of an ac series *RLC* circuit as functions of time. Input parameters are *R, L, C,* and V_{max} and the generator angular frequency is ω. The spreadsheet also calculates X_L, X_C, Z, ω_0, and the phase angle ϕ. (a) Use $R = 1000\ \Omega$, $L = 0.37$ H, $C = 1.0\ \mu$F, and $V_{max} = 5.0$ V. Initially choose $\omega = 1000$ rad/s. Plot the voltages versus time and note the magnitudes and phase differences of the various voltages. (b) Increase ω to 2200 rad/s in steps of 200 rad/s. Note how the relative phase differences change. (c) Choose $\omega = \omega_0$. What is the phase difference between V_L and V_C? What are their relative magnitudes? What is the sum of V_L and V_C? (d) Choose other values for *R, L,* and *C* and repeat this investigation.

S3. A series *RLC* circuit contains a switch but no battery. The capacitor has an initial charge Q_0 with the switch open, and then the switch is thrown closed at $t = 0$. The current in this *RLC* circuit for $t > 0$ is given by

$$I = -\frac{I_0}{\cos\phi}\sin(\omega_0 t + \phi)\,e^{-Rt/2L}$$

where $I_0 = \omega'Q_0$, $\omega' = \sqrt{(1/LC) - (R/2L)^2}$ and $\tan\phi = R/2L\omega'$.

Construct a spreadsheet to calculate and plot the current versus time for this circuit. Input parameters should be *R, L, C,* and Q_0. Use $R = 10\ \Omega$, $L = 10$ mH, $C = 4.0\ \mu$F, and $Q_0 = 2.0\ \mu$C. Verify that the ratio of successive amplitude peaks is a constant. Why is this the case? Vary *R* from $0\ \Omega$ to $100\ \Omega$ in steps of $10\ \Omega$ and investigate what happens to the damping.

Electromagnetic Waves

Satellite receiver-transmitter dish at night. The photograph was taken at the Land Earth Station at Goonhilly in Cornwall, United Kingdom. This Earth Station serves the INMARSAT (International Maritime Satellite) organization. It provides telephone, telex, data, and facsimile operations to the shipping, aviation, offshore, and land mobile industries. *(Photo Researchers, Inc.)*

The waves described in Chapters 16, 17, and 18 are mechanical waves. By definition, mechanical disturbances, such as sound waves, water waves, and waves on a string, require the presence of a medium. This chapter is concerned with the properties of electromagnetic waves that (unlike mechanical waves) can propagate through empty space.

In Section 31.7 we gave a brief description of Maxwell's equations, which form the theoretical basis of all electromagnetic phenomena.[1] The consequences of Maxwell's equations are far reaching and very dramatic for the history of physics. One of them, the Ampère-Maxwell law, predicts that a time-varying electric field produces a magnetic field just as a time-varying magnetic field produces an electric field (Faraday's law). From this generalization, Maxwell introduced the concept of displacement current, a new source of a magnetic field. Thus, Maxwell's theory provided the final important link between electric and magnetic fields.

Astonishingly, Maxwell's formalism also predicts the existence of electromagnetic waves that propagate through space with the speed of light. This prediction was confirmed experimentally by Heinrich Hertz, who generated and detected

---

[1] The reader should review Section 31.7 as a background for the material in this chapter.

James Clerk Maxwell is generally regarded as the greatest theoretical physicist of the 19th century. Born in Edinburgh to a well-known Scottish family, he entered the University of Edinburgh at age 15, around the time that he discovered an original method for drawing a perfect oval. Maxwell was appointed to his first professorship in 1856 at Aberdeen. This was the beginning of a career during which he would develop the electromagnetic theory of light and explanations of the nature of Saturn's rings, and contribute to the kinetic theory of gases.

Maxwell's development of the electromagnetic theory of light took many years and began with the paper "On Faraday's Lines of Force," in which Maxwell expanded upon Faraday's theory that electric and magnetic effects result from force fields surrounding conductors and magnets. His next publication, "On Physi-

James Clerk Maxwell
| 1 8 3 1 – 1 8 7 9 |

cal Lines of Force," included a series of papers explaining the known effects and the nature of electromagnetism.

Maxwell's other important contributions to theoretical physics were made in the area of the kinetic theory of gases. Here, he furthered the work of Rudolf Clausius, who in 1858 had shown that a gas must consist of molecules in constant motion colliding with one another and with the walls of the container. This resulted in Maxwell's distribution of molecular speeds in addition to important applications of the theory to viscosity, conduction of heat, and diffusion of gases.

Maxwell's successful interpretation of Faraday's concept of the electromagnetic field resulted in the field equation bearing Maxwell's name. Formidable mathematical ability combined with great insight enabled Maxwell to lead the way in the study of the two most important areas of physics at that time. Maxwell died of cancer before he was 50.

(North Wind Picture Archives)

electromagnetic waves. This discovery has led to many practical communication systems, including radio, television, and radar. On a conceptual level, Maxwell unified the subjects of light and electromagnetism by developing the idea that light is a form of electromagnetic radiation.

Electromagnetic waves are generated by oscillating electric charges. The radiated waves consist of oscillating electric and magnetic fields, which are *at right angles to each other* and also *at right angles to the direction of wave propagation*. Thus, electromagnetic waves are transverse in nature. Maxwell's theory shows that the electric and magnetic field amplitudes in an electromagnetic wave are related by $E = cB$. At large distances from the source of the waves, these amplitudes diminish with distance, in proportion to $1/r$. The radiated waves can be detected at great distances from the oscillating charges. Furthermore, electromagnetic waves carry energy and momentum and hence exert pressure on a surface.

Electromagnetic waves cover a wide range of frequencies. For example, radio waves (frequencies of about 10^7 Hz) are electromagnetic waves produced by oscillating currents in a radio tower's transmitting antenna. Light waves are a high-frequency form of electromagnetic radiation (about 10^{14} Hz) produced by electrons within atomic systems.

34.1 MAXWELL'S EQUATIONS AND HERTZ'S DISCOVERIES

In his unified theory of electromagnetism, Maxwell showed that electromagnetic waves are a natural consequence of the fundamental laws expressed in four equations:

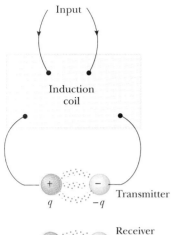

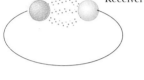

FIGURE 34.1 Schematic diagram of Hertz's apparatus for generating and detecting electromagnetic waves. The transmitter consists of two spherical electrodes connected to an induction coil, which provides short voltage surges to the spheres, setting up oscillations in the discharge. The receiver is a nearby loop containing a second spark gap.

$$\oint \mathbf{E} \cdot d\mathbf{A} = \frac{Q}{\epsilon_0} \tag{34.1}$$

$$\oint \mathbf{B} \cdot d\mathbf{A} = 0 \tag{34.2}$$

$$\oint \mathbf{E} \cdot d\mathbf{s} = -\frac{d\Phi_B}{dt} \tag{34.3}$$

$$\oint \mathbf{B} \cdot d\mathbf{s} = \mu_0 I + \mu_0 \epsilon_0 \frac{d\Phi_E}{dt} \tag{34.4}$$

As we shall see in the next section, Equations 34.3 and 34.4 can be combined to obtain a wave equation for both the electric and the magnetic fields. In empty space ($Q = 0$, $I = 0$), the solution to these two equations shows that the wave speed $(\mu_0 \epsilon_0)^{-1/2}$ equals the measured speed of light. This result led Maxwell to the prediction that light waves are a form of electromagnetic radiation.

Electromagnetic waves were generated and detected by Hertz in 1887, using electrical sources. His experimental apparatus is shown schematically in Figure 34.1. An induction coil is connected to two spherical electrodes having a narrow gap between them (the transmitter). The coil provides short voltage surges to the spheres, making one positive, the other negative. A spark is generated between the spheres when the voltage between them reaches the breakdown voltage for air. As the air in the gap is ionized, it conducts more readily and the discharge between the spheres becomes oscillatory. From an electrical circuit viewpoint, this is equivalent to an *LC* circuit, where the inductance is that of the loop and the capacitance is due to the spherical electrodes.

Since *L* and *C* are quite small, the frequency of oscillation is very high, ≈ 100 MHz. (Recall from Eq. 32.22 that $\omega = 1/\sqrt{LC}$ for an *LC* circuit.) Electromagnetic waves are radiated at this frequency as a result of the oscillation (and hence acceleration) of free charges in the loop. Hertz was able to detect these waves using a single loop of wire with its own spark gap (the receiver). This loop, placed several

Large oscillator (bottom) as well as circular, octagonal, and square resonators used by Heinrich Hertz. *(Photo Deutsches Museum Munich)*

meters from the transmitter, has its own effective inductance, capacitance, and natural frequency of oscillation. Sparks were induced across the gap of the receiving electrodes when the frequency of the receiver was adjusted to match that of the transmitter. Thus, Hertz demonstrated that the oscillating current induced in the receiver was produced by electromagnetic waves radiated by the transmitter. His experiment is analogous to the mechanical phenomenon in which a tuning fork picks up the vibrations from another, identical oscillating tuning fork.

In a series of experiments, Hertz also showed that the radiation generated by his spark-gap device exhibited the wave properties of interference, diffraction, reflection, refraction, and polarization, all of which are properties exhibited by light. Thus, it became evident that the radio-frequency waves had properties similar to light waves and differed only in frequency and wavelength. Perhaps his most convincing experiment was the measurement of the speed of this radiation. Radio-frequency waves of known frequency were reflected from a metal sheet and created an interference pattern whose nodal points (where E was zero) could be detected. The measured distance between the nodal points allowed determination of the wavelength λ. Using the relation $v = \lambda f$, Hertz found that v was close to 3×10^8 m/s, the known speed of visible light.

34.2 PLANE ELECTROMAGNETIC WAVES

The properties of electromagnetic waves can be deduced from Maxwell's equations. One approach to deriving such properties is to solve the second-order differential equation obtained from Maxwell's third and fourth equations. A rigorous mathematical treatment of this sort is beyond the scope of this text. To circumvent this problem, we assume that the electric and magnetic vectors have a specific space-time behavior that is consistent with Maxwell's equations.

First, we assume that the electromagnetic wave is a plane wave, that is, one that travels in one direction. The plane wave we are describing has the following properties. It travels in the x direction (the direction of propagation), the electric field **E** is in the y direction, and the magnetic field **B** is in the z direction, as in Figure 34.2. Waves in which the electric and magnetic fields are restricted to being paral-

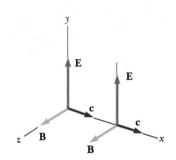

FIGURE 34.2 A plane-polarized electromagnetic wave traveling in the positive x direction. The electric field is along the y direction, and the magnetic field is along the z direction. These fields depend only on x and t.

lel to certain lines in the *yz* plane are said to be **linearly polarized waves.**[2] Furthermore, we assume that *E* and *B* at any point *P* depend only upon *x* and *t* and not upon the *y* or *z* coordinates of *P*.

We can relate *E* and *B* to each other by Equations 34.3 and 34.4. In empty space, where $Q = 0$ and $I = 0$, Equation 34.3 remains unchanged and Equation 34.4 becomes

$$\oint \mathbf{B} \cdot d\mathbf{s} = \epsilon_0 \mu_0 \frac{d\Phi_e}{dt} \tag{34.5}$$

Using Equations 34.3 and 34.5 and the plane wave assumption, the following differential equations relating *E* and *B* are obtained. (We do this more formally later in this section.) For simplicity of notation, we drop the subscripts on the components E_y and B_z:

$$\frac{\partial E}{\partial x} = -\frac{\partial B}{\partial t} \tag{34.6}$$

$$\frac{\partial B}{\partial x} = -\mu_0 \epsilon_0 \frac{\partial E}{\partial t} \tag{34.7}$$

Note that the derivatives here are partial derivatives. For example, when $\partial E/\partial x$ is evaluated, we assume that *t* is constant. Likewise, when evaluating $\partial B/\partial t$, *x* is held constant. Taking the derivative of Equation 34.6 and combining this with Equation 34.7 we get

$$\frac{\partial^2 E}{\partial x^2} = -\frac{\partial}{\partial x}\left(\frac{\partial B}{\partial t}\right) = -\frac{\partial}{\partial t}\left(\frac{\partial B}{\partial x}\right) = -\frac{\partial}{\partial t}\left(-\mu_0 \epsilon_0 \frac{\partial E}{\partial t}\right)$$

Wave equations for electromagnetic waves in free space

$$\frac{\partial^2 E}{\partial x^2} = \mu_0 \epsilon_0 \frac{\partial^2 E}{\partial t^2} \tag{34.8}$$

In the same manner, taking a derivative of Equation 34.7 and combining it with Equation 34.8, we get

$$\frac{\partial^2 B}{\partial x^2} = \mu_0 \epsilon_0 \frac{\partial^2 B}{\partial t^2} \tag{34.9}$$

Equations 34.8 and 34.9 both have the form of the general wave equation,[3] with the wave speed *v* replaced by *c*, where

$$c = \frac{1}{\sqrt{\mu_0 \epsilon_0}} \tag{34.10}$$

---

[2] Waves with other particular patterns of vibrations of **E** and **B** include circularly polarized waves. The most general polarization pattern is elliptical.

[3] The general wave equation is of the form $(\partial^2 f/\partial x^2) = (1/v^2)(\partial^2 f/\partial t^2)$, where *v* is the speed of the wave and *f* is the wave amplitude. The wave equation was first introduced in Chapter 16, and it would be useful for the reader to review this material.

Taking $\mu_0 = 4\pi \times 10^{-7}$ Wb/A·m and $\epsilon_0 = 8.85418 \times 10^{-12}$ C²/N·m² in Equation 34.10, we find that $c = 2.99792 \times 10^8$ m/s. Since this speed is precisely the same as the speed of light in empty space, we are led to believe (correctly) that light is an electromagnetic wave.

The speed of electromagnetic waves

The simplest plane wave solution is a sinusoidal wave, for which the field amplitudes E and B vary with x and t according to the expressions

$$E = E_{max} \cos(kx - \omega t) \tag{34.11}$$

$$B = B_{max} \cos(kx - \omega t) \tag{34.12}$$

Sinusoidal electric and magnetic fields

where E_{max} and B_{max} are the maximum values of the fields. The constant $k = 2\pi/\lambda$, where λ is the wavelength, and the angular frequency $\omega = 2\pi f$, where f is the number of cycles per second. The ratio ω/k equals the speed c, since

$$\frac{\omega}{k} = \frac{2\pi f}{2\pi/\lambda} = \lambda f = c$$

Figure 34.3 is a pictorial representation at one instant of a sinusoidal, linearly polarized plane wave moving in the positive x direction.

Taking partial derivatives of Equations 34.11 and 34.12, we find that

$$\frac{\partial E}{\partial x} = -kE_{max} \sin(kx - \omega t)$$

$$-\frac{\partial B}{\partial t} = -\omega B_{max} \sin(kx - \omega t)$$

Since these must be equal, according to Equation 34.6, we find that at any instant

$$kE_{max} = \omega B_{max}$$

$$\frac{E_{max}}{B_{max}} = \frac{\omega}{k} = c$$

Using these results together with Equations 34.11 and 34.12, we see that

$$\frac{E_{max}}{B_{max}} = \frac{E}{B} = c \tag{34.13}$$

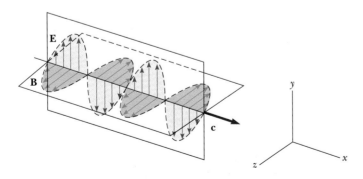

FIGURE 34.3 Representation of a sinusoidal, plane-polarized electromagnetic wave moving in the positive x direction with a speed c. The drawing represents a snapshot, that is, the wave at some instant. Note the sinusoidal variations of E and B with x.

That is, *at every instant the ratio of the electric field to the magnetic field of an electromagnetic wave equals the speed of light.*

Finally, it should be noted that electromagnetic waves obey the superposition principle, because the differential equations involving E and B are linear equations. For example, two waves traveling in opposite directions with the same frequency could be added by simply adding the wave fields algebraically. Furthermore, we now have a theoretical value for c, given by the relationship $c = 1/\sqrt{\mu_0 \epsilon_0}$.

Let us summarize the properties of electromagnetic waves as we have described them:

Properties of electromagnetic waves

- The solutions of Maxwell's third and fourth equations are wavelike, where both E and B satisfy the same wave equation.
- Electromagnetic waves travel through empty space with the speed of light, $c = 1/\sqrt{\epsilon_0 \mu_0}$.
- The electric and magnetic field components of plane electromagnetic waves are perpendicular to each other and also perpendicular to the direction of wave propagation. The latter property can be summarized by saying that electromagnetic waves are transverse waves.
- The relative magnitudes of E and B in empty space are related by $E/B = c$.
- Electromagnetic waves obey the principle of superposition.

EXAMPLE 34.1   An Electromagnetic Wave

A plane electromagnetic sinusoidal wave of frequency 40.0 MHz travels in free space in the x direction, as in Figure 34.4. At some point and at some instant, the electric field has its maximum value of 750 N/C and is along the y axis. (a) Determine the wavelength and period of the wave.

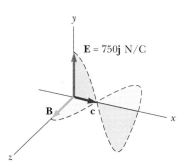

FIGURE 34.4 (Example 34.1) At some instant, a plane electromagnetic wave moving in the x direction has a maximum electric field of 750 N/C in the positive y direction. The corresponding magnetic field at that point has a magnitude E/c and is in the z direction.

Solution Because $c = \lambda f$ and $f = 40.0$ MHz $= 4.00 \times 10^7$ s^{-1}, we get

$$\lambda = \frac{c}{f} = \frac{3.00 \times 10^8 \text{ m/s}}{4.00 \times 10^7 \text{ s}^{-1}} = 7.50 \text{ m}$$

The period of the wave T equals the inverse of the frequency, and so

$$T = \frac{1}{f} = \frac{1}{4.00 \times 10^7 \text{ s}^{-1}} = 2.50 \times 10^{-8} \text{ s}$$

(b) Calculate the magnitude and direction of the magnetic field when $\mathbf{E} = 750\mathbf{j}$ N/C.

Solution From Equation 34.13 we see that

$$B_{\text{max}} = \frac{E_{\text{max}}}{c} = \frac{750 \text{ N/C}}{3.00 \times 10^8 \text{ m/s}} = 2.50 \times 10^{-6} \text{ T}$$

Since **E** and **B** must be perpendicular to each other and both must be perpendicular to the direction of wave propagation (x in this case), we conclude that **B** is in the z direction.

(c) Write expressions for the space-time variation of the electric and magnetic field components for this wave.

Solution We can apply Equations 34.11 and 34.12 directly:

$$E = E_{\text{max}} \cos(kx - \omega t) = (750 \text{ N/C}) \cos(kx - \omega t)$$

$$B = B_{\text{max}} \cos(kx - \omega t) = (2.50 \times 10^{-6} \text{ T}) \cos(kx - \omega t)$$

where

$$\omega = 2\pi f = 2\pi(4.00 \times 10^7 \text{ s}^{-1}) = 8\pi \times 10^7 \text{ rad/s}$$

$$k = \frac{2\pi}{\lambda} = \frac{2\pi}{7.50 \text{ m}} = 0.838 \text{ rad/m}$$

*Derivation of Equations 34.6 and 34.7

In this optional section, we derive Equations 34.6 and 34.7. To derive Equation 34.6, we start with Faraday's law, that is, Equation 34.3:

$$\oint \mathbf{E} \cdot d\mathbf{s} = -\frac{d\Phi_B}{dt}$$

Again, let us assume that the electromagnetic wave is a plane wave traveling in the x direction, with the electric field $\mathbf{E}$ in the positive y direction and the magnetic field $\mathbf{B}$ in the positive z direction.

Consider a thin rectangle of width dx and height ℓ lying in the xy plane, as in Figure 34.5. To apply Equation 34.3, we must first evaluate the line integral of $\mathbf{E} \cdot d\mathbf{s}$ around this rectangle. The contributions from the top and bottom of the rectangle are zero because $\mathbf{E}$ is perpendicular to $d\mathbf{s}$ for these paths. We can express the electric field on the right side of the rectangle as

$$E(x + dx, t) \approx E(x, t) + \frac{dE}{dx}\bigg]_{t \text{ constant}} dx = E(x, t) + \frac{\partial E}{\partial x} dx$$

while the field on the left side is simply $E(x, t)$. Therefore, the line integral over this rectangle becomes approximately[4]

$$\oint \mathbf{E} \cdot d\mathbf{s} = E(x + dx, t) \cdot \ell - E(x, t) \cdot \ell \approx (\partial E/\partial x)\, dx \cdot \ell \qquad (34.14)$$

Because the magnetic field is in the z direction, the magnetic flux through the rectangle of area $\ell\, dx$ is approximately

$$\Phi_B = B\ell\, dx$$

(This assumes that dx is small compared with the wavelength of the wave.) Taking the time derivative of the flux gives

$$\frac{d\Phi_B}{dt} = \ell\, dx \frac{dB}{dt}\bigg]_{x \text{ constant}} = \ell\, dx \frac{\partial B}{\partial t} \qquad (34.15)$$

Substituting Equations 34.14 and 34.15 into Equation 34.3 gives

$$\left(\frac{\partial E}{\partial x}\right) dx \cdot \ell = -\ell\, dx \frac{\partial B}{\partial t}$$

$$\frac{\partial E}{\partial x} = -\frac{\partial B}{\partial t}$$

This expression is equivalent to Equation 34.6.

In a similar manner, we can verify Equation 34.7 by starting with Maxwell's fourth equation in empty space (Eq. 34.5). In this case, we evaluate the line integral of $\mathbf{B} \cdot d\mathbf{s}$ around a rectangle lying in the xz plane and having width dx and length ℓ, as in Figure 34.6. Using the sense of the integration shown and noting that the magnetic field changes from $B(x, t)$ to $B(x + dx, t)$ over the width dx, we get

$$\oint \mathbf{B} \cdot d\mathbf{s} = B(x, t) \cdot \ell - B(x + dx, t) \cdot \ell = -(\partial B/\partial x)\, dx \cdot \ell \qquad (34.16)$$

---

[4] Since dE/dx means the change in E with x at a given instant t, dE/dx is equivalent to the partial derivative $\partial E/\partial x$. Likewise, dB/dt means the change in B with time at a particular position x, and so we can replace dB/dt by $\partial B/\partial t$.

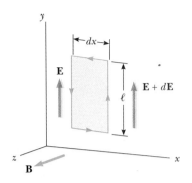

FIGURE 34.5 As a plane wave passes through a rectangular path of width dx lying in the xy plane, the electric field in the y direction varies from $\mathbf{E}$ to $\mathbf{E} + d\mathbf{E}$. This spatial variation in $\mathbf{E}$ gives rise to a time-varying magnetic field along the z direction, according to Equation 34.6.

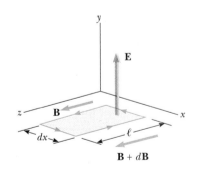

FIGURE 34.6 As a plane wave passes through a rectangular curve of width dx lying in the xz plane, the magnetic field along z varies from $\mathbf{B}$ to $\mathbf{B} + d\mathbf{B}$. This spatial variation in $\mathbf{B}$ gives rise to a time-varying electric field along the y direction, according to Equation 34.7.

The electric flux through the rectangle is

$$\Phi_E = E\ell\,dx$$

which when differentiated with respect to time gives

$$\frac{\partial \Phi_E}{\partial t} = \ell\,dx\,\frac{\partial E}{\partial t} \tag{34.17}$$

Substituting Equations 34.16 and 34.17 into Equation 34.5 gives

$$-(\partial B/\partial x)\,dx\cdot\ell = \mu_0\epsilon_0\ell\,dx(\partial E/\partial t)$$

$$\frac{\partial B}{\partial x} = -\mu_0\epsilon_0\frac{\partial E}{\partial t}$$

which is equivalent to Equation 34.7.

34.3   ENERGY CARRIED BY ELECTROMAGNETIC WAVES

Electromagnetic waves carry energy, and as they propagate through space they can transfer energy to objects placed in their path. The rate of flow of energy in an electromagnetic wave is described by a vector **S**, called the **Poynting vector**, defined by the expression

Poynting vector

$$\mathbf{S} \equiv \frac{1}{\mu_0}\mathbf{E}\times\mathbf{B} \tag{34.18}$$

The magnitude of the Poynting vector represents the rate at which energy flows through a unit surface area perpendicular to the flow and its direction is along the direction of wave propagation (Fig. 34.7). The SI units of the Poynting vector are $J/s\cdot m^2 = W/m^2$. (These are the units **S** must have because it represents the power per unit area, where the unit area is oriented at right angles to the direction of wave propagation.)

As an example, let us evaluate the magnitude of **S** for a plane electromagnetic wave where $|\mathbf{E}\times\mathbf{B}| = EB$. In this case

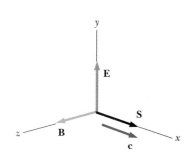

FIGURE 34.7 The Poynting vector **S** for a plane electromagnetic wave is along the direction of propagation.

$$S = \frac{EB}{\mu_0} \tag{34.19}$$

Because $B = E/c$, we can also express this as

$$S = \frac{E^2}{\mu_0 c} = \frac{c}{\mu_0}B^2$$

These equations for S apply at any instant of time.

What is of more interest for a sinusoidal plane electromagnetic wave is the time average of S over one or more cycles, called the wave intensity, I. When this average is taken, we obtain an expression involving the time average of $\cos^2(kx - \omega t)$, which equals $\frac{1}{2}$. Hence, the average value of S (or the intensity of the wave) is

Wave intensity

$$I = S_{av} = \frac{E_{max}B_{max}}{2\mu_0} = \frac{E_{max}^2}{2\mu_0 c} = \frac{c}{2\mu_0}B_{max}^2 \tag{34.20}$$

The constant $\mu_0 c$, called the **impedance of free space,** has the SI unit of ohms and the value

$$\mu_0 c = \sqrt{\frac{\mu_0}{\epsilon_0}} = 120\pi \; \Omega \approx 377 \; \Omega$$

Impedance of free space

Recall that the energy per unit volume u_E, which is the instantaneous energy density associated with an electric field (Section 26.4), is given by Equation 26.12:

$$u_E = \tfrac{1}{2}\epsilon_0 E^2$$

and that the instantaneous energy density u_B associated with a magnetic field (Section 32.3) is given by Equation 32.14:

$$u_B = \frac{B^2}{2\mu_0}$$

Because E and B vary with time for an electromagnetic wave, the energy densities also vary with time. Using the relationships $B = E/c$ and $c = 1/\sqrt{\epsilon_0\mu_0}$, Equation 32.15 becomes

$$u_B = \frac{(E/c)^2}{2\mu_0} = \frac{\epsilon_0\mu_0}{2\mu_0}E^2 = \tfrac{1}{2}\epsilon_0 E^2$$

Comparing this result with the expression for u_E we see that

$$u_B = u_E = \tfrac{1}{2}\epsilon_0 E^2 = \frac{B^2}{2\mu_0}$$

Total energy density

That is, *for an electromagnetic wave, the instantaneous energy density associated with the magnetic field equals the instantaneous energy density associated with the electric field.* Hence, in a given volume the energy is equally shared by the two fields.

The **total instantaneous energy density** u is equal to the sum of the energy densities associated with the electric and magnetic fields:

$$u = u_E + u_B = \epsilon_0 E^2 = \frac{B^2}{\mu_0}$$

When this is averaged over one or more cycles of an electromagnetic wave, we again get a factor of $\tfrac{1}{2}$. Hence, the total average energy per unit volume of an electromagnetic wave is

$$u_{av} = \epsilon_0 (E^2)_{av} = \tfrac{1}{2}\epsilon_0 E_{max}^2 = \frac{B_{max}^2}{2\mu_0} \qquad (34.21)$$

Average energy density of an electromagnetic wave

Comparing this result with Equation 34.20 for the average value of S, we see that

$$I = S_{av} = cu_{av} \qquad (34.22)$$

In other words, *the intensity of an electromagnetic wave equals the average energy density multiplied by the speed of light.*

EXAMPLE 34.2 Fields Due to a Point Source

A point source of electromagnetic radiation has an average power output of 800 W. Calculate the maximum values of the electric and magnetic fields at a point 3.50 m from the source.

Solution Recall from Chapter 17 that the wave intensity, I, a distance r from a point source is

$$I = \frac{P_{av}}{4\pi r^2}$$

where P_{av} is the average power output of the source and $4\pi r^2$ is the area of a sphere of radius r centered on the source. Because the intensity of an electromagnetic wave is also given by Equation 34.20, we have

$$I = \frac{P_{av}}{4\pi r^2} = \frac{E_{max}^2}{2\mu_0 c}$$

Solving for E_{max} gives

$$E_{max} = \sqrt{\frac{\mu_0 c P_{av}}{2\pi r^2}}$$

$$= \sqrt{\frac{(4\pi \times 10^{-7}\,\text{N}/\text{A}^2)(3.00 \times 10^8\,\text{m/s})(800\,\text{W})}{2\pi(3.50\,\text{m})^2}}$$

$$= 62.6\,\text{V/m}$$

We calculate the maximum value of the magnetic field using this result and the relationship $B_{max} = E_{max}/c$ (Eq. 34.13):

$$B_{max} = \frac{E_{max}}{c} = \frac{62.6\,\text{V/m}}{3.00 \times 10^8\,\text{m/s}} = 2.09 \times 10^{-7}\,\text{T}$$

Exercise Calculate the energy density 3.50 m from the point source.

Answer $1.73 \times 10^{-8}\,\text{J/m}^3$.

34.4 MOMENTUM AND RADIATION PRESSURE

Electromagnetic waves transport linear momentum as well as energy. Hence, it follows that pressure is exerted on a surface when an electromagnetic wave impinges on it. In what follows, we assume that the electromagnetic wave transports a total energy U to a surface in a time t. If the surface absorbs all the incident energy U in this time, Maxwell showed that the total momentum **p** delivered to this surface has a magnitude

Momentum delivered to an absorbing surface

$$p = \frac{U}{c} \quad \text{(complete absorption)} \tag{34.23}$$

Furthermore, if the Poynting vector of the wave is **S**, the radiation pressure P (force per unit area) exerted on the perfect absorbing surface is

Radiation pressure exerted on a perfect absorbing surface

$$P = \frac{S}{c} \tag{34.24}$$

A black body is such a perfectly absorbing surface (Chapter 20), for which all of the incident energy is absorbed (none is reflected).

On the other hand, if the surface is a perfect reflector, then the momentum delivered in a time t for normal incidence is twice that given by Equation 34.24. That is, a momentum U/c is delivered first by the incident wave and then again by the reflected wave, in analogy with a ball colliding elastically with a wall. Therefore,

$$p = \frac{2U}{c} \quad \text{(complete reflection)} \tag{34.25}$$

The momentum delivered to a surface having a reflectivity somewhere between these two extremes has a value between U/c and $2U/c$, depending on the properties of the surface. Finally, the radiation pressure exerted on a perfect reflecting

A solar home in Oregon. (*John Neal/Photo Researchers, Inc.*)

surface for normal incidence of the wave is given by[5]

$$P = \frac{2S}{c} \qquad (34.26)$$

Although radiation pressures are very small (about 5×10^{-6} N/m² for direct sunlight), they have been measured using torsion balances such as the one shown in Figure 34.8. Light is allowed to strike either a mirror or a black disk, both of which are suspended from a fine fiber. Light striking the black disk is completely absorbed, and so all of its momentum is transferred to the disk. Light striking the mirror (normal incidence) is totally reflected, hence the momentum transfer is twice as great as that transferred to the disk. The radiation pressure is determined by measuring the angle through which the horizontal connecting rod rotates. The apparatus must be placed in a high vacuum to eliminate the effects of air currents.

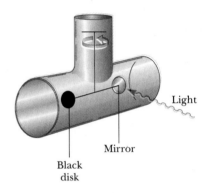

FIGURE 34.8 An apparatus for measuring the pressure exerted by light. In practice, the system is contained in a high vacuum.

EXAMPLE 34.3 Solar Energy

The Sun delivers about 1000 W/m² of electromagnetic flux to the Earth's surface. (a) Calculate the total power incident on a roof of dimensions 8.00 m × 20.0 m.

Solution The Poynting vector has a magnitude $S = 1000$ W/m², which represents the power per unit area, or the light intensity. Assuming the radiation is incident normal to the roof (Sun directly overhead), we get

$$\text{Power} = SA = (1000 \text{ W/m}^2)(8.00 \times 20.0 \text{ m}^2)$$

$$= 1.60 \times 10^5 \text{ W}$$

If this power could all be converted to electrical energy, it would provide more than enough power for the average home. However, solar energy is not easily harnessed, and the prospects for large-scale conversion are not as bright as they may appear from this simple calculation. For example, the conversion efficiency from solar to electrical energy is typically 10% for photovoltaic cells. Roof systems for converting solar energy to thermal energy are approximately 50% efficient; however, there are other practical problems with solar energy that must be considered, such as initial cost, overcast days, geographic location, and energy storage.

(b) Determine the radiation pressure and radiation force on the roof assuming the roof covering is a perfect absorber.

Solution Using Equation 34.24 with $S = 1000$ W/m², we find that the radiation pressure is

$$P = \frac{S}{c} = \frac{1000 \text{ W/m}^2}{3.00 \times 10^8 \text{ m/s}} = 3.33 \times 10^{-6} \text{ N/m}^2$$

Because pressure equals force per unit area, this corresponds to a radiation force of

$$F = PA = (3.33 \times 10^{-6} \text{ N/m}^2)(160 \text{ m}^2) = 5.33 \times 10^{-4} \text{ N}$$

Exercise How much solar energy (in joules) is incident on the roof in 1 h?

Answer 5.76×10^8 J.

---

[5] For oblique incidence, the momentum transferred is $2U \cos \theta / c$ and the pressure is given by $P = 2S \cos \theta / c$, where θ is the angle between the normal to the surface and the direction of propagation.

EXAMPLE 34.4   Poynting Vector for a Wire

A long, straight wire of resistance R, radius a, and length ℓ carries a constant current I as in Figure 34.9. Calculate the Poynting vector for this wire.

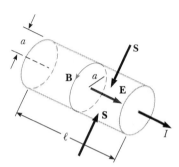

FIGURE 34.9   (Example 34.4) A wire of length ℓ, resistance R, and radius a carrying a current I. The Poynting vector **S** is directed radially inward.

Solution   First, let us find the electric field E along the wire. If V is the potential difference across its ends, then $V = IR$ and

$$E = \frac{V}{\ell} = \frac{IR}{\ell}$$

Recall that the magnetic field at the surface of the wire (Example 30.4) is

$$B = \frac{\mu_0 I}{2 \pi a}$$

The vectors **E** and **B** are mutually perpendicular, as shown in Figure 34.9, and therefore $| \mathbf{E} \times \mathbf{B} | = EB$. Hence, the Poynting vector **S** is directed radially inward and has a magnitude

$$S = \frac{EB}{\mu} = \frac{1}{\mu} \frac{IR}{\ell} \frac{\mu_0 I}{2 \pi a} = \frac{I^2 R}{2 \pi a \ell} = \boxed{\frac{I^2 R}{A}}$$

where $A = 2 \pi a \ell$ is the surface area of the wire, and the total area through which S passes. From this result, we see that

$$SA = I^2 R$$

where SA has units of power (J/s = W). That is, *the rate at which electromagnetic energy flows into the wire, SA, equals the rate of energy (or power) dissipated as joule heat, I^2R.*

Exercise   A heater wire of radius 0.30 mm, length 1.0 m, and resistance 5.0 Ω carries a current of 2.0 A. Determine the magnitude and direction of the Poynting vector for this wire.

Answer 1.1×10^4 W/m² directed radially inward.

*34.5   RADIATION FROM AN INFINITE CURRENT SHEET

In this section, we describe the fields radiated by a conductor carrying a time-varying current. In the symmetric plane geometry we treat, the mathematics is less complex than that required in lower-symmetry situations.

Consider an infinite conducting sheet lying in the yz plane and carrying a surface current per unit length $\mathbf{J}_S$ in the y direction, as in Figure 34.10. Let us assume that J_S varies sinusoidally with time as

$$J_S = J_0 \cos \omega t$$

A similar problem for the case of a steady current was treated in Example 30.6, where we found that the magnetic field outside the sheet is everywhere parallel to the sheet and lies along the z axis. The magnetic field was found to have a magnitude

$$B_z = - \mu_0 \frac{J_S}{2}$$

FIGURE 34.10   An infinite current sheet lying in the yz plane. The current density is sinusoidal and given by $J_s = J_0 \cos \omega t$. The magnetic field is everywhere parallel to the sheet and lies along z.

In the present situation, where J_S varies with time, this equation for B_z is valid only for distances close to the sheet. That is,

$$B_z = - \frac{\mu_0}{2} J_0 \cos \omega t \qquad \text{(for small values of } x\text{)}$$

To obtain the expression for B_z for arbitrary values of x, we can investigate the following solution[6]:

$$B_z = -\frac{\mu_0 J_0}{2} \cos(kx - \omega t) \qquad (34.27)$$

Radiated magnetic field

There are two things to note about this solution, which is unique to the geometry under consideration. First, it agrees with our original solution for small values of x. Second, it satisfies the wave equation as it is expressed in Equation 34.9. Hence, we conclude that the magnetic field lies along the z axis and is characterized by a transverse traveling wave having an angular frequency ω, angular wave number $k = 2\pi/\lambda$, and wave speed c.

We can obtain the radiated electric field that accompanies this varying magnetic field by using Equation 34.13:

$$E_y = cB_z = -\frac{\mu_0 J_0 c}{2} \cos(kx - \omega t) \qquad (34.28)$$

Radiated electric field

That is, the electric field is in the y direction, perpendicular to **B**, and has the same space and time dependencies.

These expressions for B_z and E_y show that the radiation field of an infinite current sheet carrying a sinusoidal current is a plane electromagnetic wave propagating with a speed c along the x axis, as shown in Figure 34.11.

We can calculate the Poynting vector for this wave by using Equation 34.19 together with Equations 34.27 and 34.28:

$$S = \frac{EB}{\mu_0} = \frac{\mu_0 J_0^2 c}{4} \cos^2(kx - \omega t) \qquad (34.29)$$

The intensity of the wave, which equals the average value of S, is

$$S_{av} = \frac{\mu_0 J_0^2 c}{8} \qquad (34.30)$$

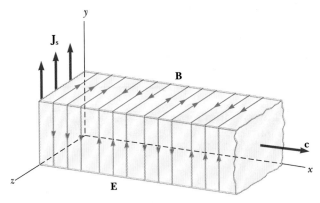

FIGURE 34.11   Representation of the plane electromagnetic wave radiated by an infinite current sheet lying in the yz plane. Note that **B** is in the z direction, **E** is in the y direction, and the direction of wave motion is along x. Both vectors have a $\cos(kx - \omega t)$ behavior.

---

[6] Note that the solution could also be written in the form $\cos(\omega t - kx)$, which is equivalent to $\cos(kx - \omega t)$. That is, $\cos\theta$ is an even function, which means that $\cos(-\theta) = \cos\theta$.

The intensity given by Equation 34.30 represents the average intensity of the outgoing wave on each side of the sheet. The total rate of energy emitted per unit area of the conductor is $2 S_{av} = \mu_0 J_0^2 c / 4$.

EXAMPLE 34.5   An Infinite Sheet Carrying a Sinusoidal Current

An infinite current sheet lying in the yz plane carries a sinusoidal current the density of which has a maximum value of 5.00 A/m. (a) Find the maximum values of the radiated magnetic field and electric field.

Solution   From Equations 34.28 and 34.29, we see that the maximum values of B_z and E_y are

$$B_{max} = \frac{\mu_0 J_0}{2} \quad \text{and} \quad E_{max} = \frac{\mu_0 J_0 c}{2}$$

Using the values $\mu_0 = 4\pi \times 10^{-7}$ Wb/A·m, $J_0 = 5.00$ A/m, and $c = 3.00 \times 10^8$ m/s, we get

$$B_{max} = \frac{(4\pi \times 10^{-7} \text{ Wb/A·m})(5.00 \text{ A/m})}{2}$$

$$= 3.14 \times 10^{-16} \text{ T}$$

$$E_{max} = \frac{(4\pi \times 10^{-7} \text{ Wb/A·m})(5.00 \text{ A/m})(3.00 \times 10^8 \text{ m/s})}{2}$$

$$= 942 \text{ V/m}$$

(b) What is the average power incident on a plane surface that is parallel to the sheet and has an area of 3.00 m²? (The length and width of this surface are both much larger than the wavelength of the light.)

Solution   The power per unit area (the average value of the Poynting vector) radiated in each direction by the current sheet is given by Equation 34.30. Multiplying this by the area of the plane in question gives the incident power:

$$P = \left(\frac{\mu_0 J_0^2 c}{8} \right) A$$

$$= \frac{(4\pi \times 10^{-7} \text{ Wb/A·m})}{8} \frac{(5.00 \text{ A/m})^2 (3.00 \times 10^8 \text{ m/s})}{} (3.00 \text{ m}^2)$$

$$= 3.54 \times 10^3 \text{ W}$$

The result is independent of the distance from the current sheet because we are dealing with a plane wave.

---

*34.6 THE PRODUCTION OF ELECTROMAGNETIC WAVES BY AN ANTENNA

Electromagnetic waves arise as a consequence of two effects:

• A changing magnetic field produces an electric field;
• A changing electric field produces a magnetic field.

Therefore, it is clear that neither stationary charges nor steady currents can produce electromagnetic waves. Whenever the current through a wire changes with time, however, the wire emits electromagnetic radiation.

Accelerating charges produce EM radiation.

The fundamental mechanism responsible for this radiation is the acceleration of a charged particle. Whenever a charged particle accelerates, it must radiate energy.

An alternating voltage applied to the wires of an antenna forces an electric charge in the antenna to oscillate. This is a common technique for accelerating charged particles and is the source of the radio waves emitted by the antenna of a radio station. Figure 34.12 shows how this is done. Two metal rods are connected to an ac generator, which causes charges to oscillate between the two rods. The output voltage of the generator is sinusoidal. At $t = 0$, the upper rod is given a maximum positive charge and the bottom rod an equal negative charge, as in Figure 34.12a. The electric field near the antenna at this instant is also shown in

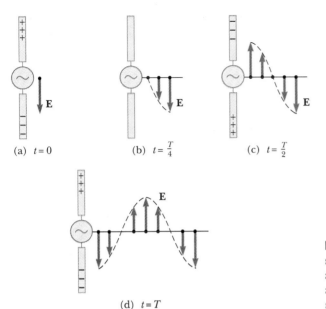

(a) $t = 0$ (b) $t = \frac{T}{4}$ (c) $t = \frac{T}{2}$

(d) $t = T$

FIGURE 34.12   The electric field set up by charges oscillating in an antenna. The field moves away from the antenna with the speed of light.

Figure 34.12a. As the charges oscillate, the rods become less charged, the field near the rods decreases in strength, and the downward-directed maximum electric field produced at $t = 0$ moves away from the rod. When the charges are neutralized, as in Figure 34.12b, the electric field at the rod has dropped to zero. This occurs at a time equal to one quarter of the period of oscillation.

Continuing in this fashion, the upper rod soon obtains a maximum negative charge and the lower rod becomes positive, as in Figure 34.12c, resulting in an electric field near the rod directed upward. This occurs after a time equal to one-half the period of oscillation. The oscillations continue as indicated in Figure 34.12d. (A magnetic field oscillating perpendicular to the plane of the diagram in Figure 34.12 accompanies the oscillating electric field, but it is not shown for clarity.) The electric field near the antenna oscillates in phase with the charge distribution. That is, the field points down when the upper rod is positive and up when the upper rod is negative. Furthermore, the magnitude of the field at any instant depends on the amount of charge on the rods at that instant.

As the charges continue to oscillate (and accelerate) between the rods, the electric field they set up moves away from the antenna at the speed of light. As you can see from Figure 34.12 one cycle of charge oscillation produces one wavelength in the electric field pattern.

Next, consider what happens when two conducting rods are connected to the opposite ends of a battery (Fig. 34.13). Before the switch is closed, the current is zero, and so there are no fields present (Fig. 34.13a). Just after the switch is closed, charge of opposite signs begins to build up on the rods (Fig. 34.13b), which corresponds to a time-varying current. The changing charge causes the electric field to change, which in turn produces a magnetic field around the rods.[7] Finally, when the rods are fully charged, the current is zero and there is no magnetic field (Fig. 34.13c).

---

[7] We have neglected the field caused by the wires leading to the rods. This is a good approximation if the circuit dimensions are small relative to the length of the rods.

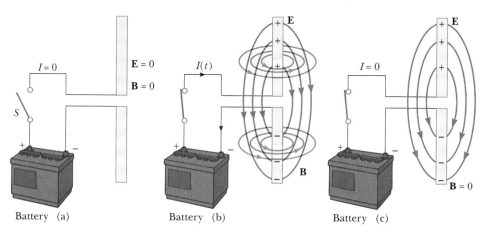

FIGURE 34.13 A pair of metal rods connected to a battery. (a) When the switch is open and there is no current, the electric and magnetic fields are both zero. (b) After the switch is closed and the rods are being charged (so that a current exists), the rods generate changing electric and magnetic fields. (c) When the rods are fully charged, the current is zero, the electric field is a maximum, and the magnetic field is zero.

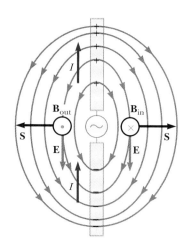

FIGURE 34.14 A half-wave (dipole) antenna consists of two metal rods connected to an alternating voltage source. The diagram shows **E** and **B** at an instant when the current is upward. Note that the electric field lines resemble those of a dipole.

Now let us consider the production of electromagnetic waves by a half-wave antenna. In this arrangement, two conducting rods, each one quarter of a wavelength long, are connected to a source of alternating emf (such as an *LC* oscillator), as in Figure 34.14. The oscillator forces charges to accelerate back and forth between the two rods. Figure 34.14 shows the field configuration at some instant when the current is upward. The electric field lines resemble those of an electric dipole, that is, two equal and opposite charges. Since these charges are continuously oscillating between the two rods, the antenna can be approximated by an oscillating electric dipole. The magnetic field lines form concentric circles around the antenna and are perpendicular to the electric field lines at all points. The magnetic field is zero at all points along the axis of the antenna. Furthermore, **E** and **B** are 90° out of phase in time, that is, **E** at some point reaches its maximum value when **B** is zero and vice versa. This is because when the charges at the ends of the rods are at a maximum, the current is zero.

At the two points where the magnetic field is shown in Figure 34.14, the Poynting vector **S** is radially outward. This indicates that energy is flowing away from the antenna at this instant. At later times, the fields and the Poynting vector change direction as the current alternates. Since **E** and **B** are 90° out of phase at points near the dipole, the net energy flow is zero. From this, we might conclude (incorrectly) that no energy is radiated by the dipole.

Since the dipole fields fall off as $1/r^3$ (as in the case of a static dipole discussed in Chapter 23), they are not important at large distances from the antenna. However, at these large distances, another effect produces the radiation field. The source of this radiation is the continuous induction of an electric field by a time-varying magnetic field and the induction of a magnetic field by a time-varying electric field, predicted by Equations 34.3 and 34.4. The electric and magnetic fields produced in this manner are in phase with each other and vary as $1/r$. The result is an outward flow of energy at all times.

The electric field lines produced by an oscillating dipole at some instant are shown in Figure 34.15. Note that the intensity (and the power radiated) is a maximum in a plane that is perpendicular to the antenna and passing through its midpoint. Furthermore, the power radiated is zero along the antenna's axis. A

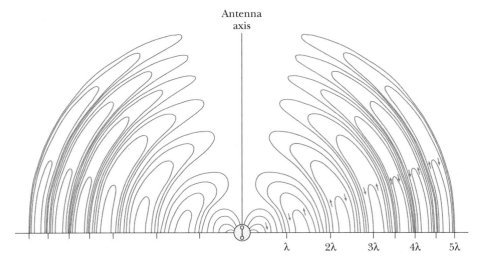

FIGURE 34.15   Electric field lines surrounding an oscillating dipole at a given instant. The radiation fields propagate outward from the dipole with a speed *c*.

mathematical solution to Maxwell's equations for the oscillating dipole shows that the intensity of the radiation field varies as $\sin^2 \theta / r^2$, where θ is measured from the axis of the antenna. The angular dependence of the radiation intensity (power per unit area) is sketched in Figure 34.16.

Electromagnetic waves can also induce currents in a receiving antenna. The response of a dipole-receiving antenna at a given position is a maximum when the antenna axis is parallel to the electric field at that point and zero when the axis is perpendicular to the electric field.

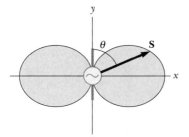

FIGURE 34.16   Angular dependence of the intensity of radiation produced by an oscillating electric dipole.

34.7   THE SPECTRUM OF ELECTROMAGNETIC WAVES

Since all electromagnetic waves travel through vacuum with a speed *c*, their frequency *f* and wavelength λ are related by the important expression

$$c = f\lambda \tag{34.31}$$

For instance, a radio wave of frequency 5.00 MHz (a typical value) has a wavelength

$$\lambda = \frac{c}{f} = \frac{3.00 \times 10^8 \text{ m/s}}{5.00 \times 10^6 \text{ s}^{-1}} = 60.0 \text{ m}$$

The various types of electromagnetic waves are listed in Figure 34.17. Note the wide range of frequencies and wavelengths. There is no sharp dividing point between one kind of wave and the next. It should be noted that all forms of radiation are produced (classically) by accelerating charges.

Radio waves, as we just saw, are the result of charges accelerating through conducting wires. They are generated by such electronic devices as *LC* oscillators and are used in radio and television communication systems.

Microwaves have wavelengths ranging between approximately 1 mm and 30 cm and are also generated by electronic devices. Because of their short wavelength, they are well suited for the radar systems used in aircraft navigation and for study-

Most widely used in rural locations, satellite-dish television antennas receive television-station signals from satellites in orbit around the Earth. *(© Hank Delespinasse/The IMAGE Bank)*

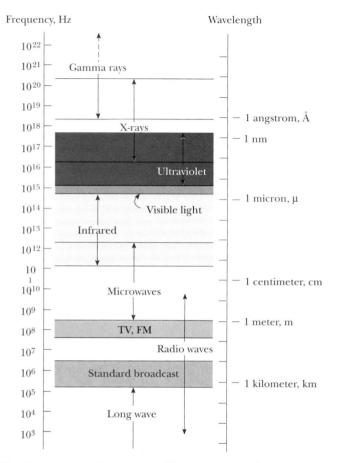

FIGURE 34.17   The electromagnetic spectrum. Note the overlap between adjacent wave types.

ing the atomic and molecular properties of matter. Microwave ovens represent an interesting domestic application of these waves. It has been suggested that solar energy could be harnessed by beaming microwaves down to Earth from a solar collector in space.[8]

Infrared waves (sometimes called heat waves) have wavelengths ranging from approximately 1 mm to the longest wavelength of visible light, 7×10^{-7} m. These waves, produced by hot bodies and molecules, are readily absorbed by most materials. The infrared energy absorbed by a substance appears as heat because the energy agitates the atoms of the body, increasing their vibrational and rotational motion, which results in a temperature rise. Infrared radiation has many practical and scientific applications, including physical therapy, infrared photography, and vibrational spectroscopy.

Visible light, the most familiar form of electromagnetic waves, is that part of the electromagnetic spectrum that the human eye can detect. Light is produced by the rearrangement of electrons in atoms and molecules. The various wavelengths of visible light are classified with colors ranging from violet ($\lambda \approx 4 \times 10^{-7}$ m) to red ($\lambda \approx 7 \times 10^{-7}$ m). The eye's sensitivity is a function of wavelength, the sensitivity being a maximum at a wavelength of about 5.6×10^{-7} m (yellow-green).

Ultraviolet light covers wavelengths ranging from approximately 3.8×10^{-7} m (380 nm) down to 6×10^{-10} m (0.6 nm). The Sun is an important source of ultravi-

Infrared waves

Visible waves

Ultraviolet waves

---

[8] P. Glaser, "Solar Power from Satellites," *Physics Today*, February, 1977, p. 30.

olet light, which is the main cause of suntans. Most of the ultraviolet light from the Sun is absorbed by atoms in the upper atmosphere, or stratosphere. This is fortunate since uv light in large quantities produces harmful effects on humans. One important constituent of the stratosphere is ozone (O_3), which results from reactions of oxygen with ultraviolet radiation. This ozone shield converts lethal high-energy ultraviolet radiation to heat, which in turn warms the stratosphere. Recently, there has been a great deal of controversy concerning the possible depletion of the protective ozone layer as a result of the use of the freons used in aerosol spray cans and as refrigerants.

X-rays are electromagnetic waves with wavelengths in the range of approximately 10^{-8} m (10 nm) down to 10^{-13} m (10^{-4} nm). The most common source of x-rays is the deceleration of high-energy electrons bombarding a metal target. X-rays are used as a diagnostic tool in medicine and as a treatment for certain forms of cancer. Since x-rays damage or destroy living tissues and organisms, care must be taken to avoid unnecessary exposure or overexposure. X-rays are also used in the study of crystal structure, since x-ray wavelengths are comparable to the atomic separation distances (≈ 0.1 nm) in solids.

X-rays

Gamma rays are electromagnetic waves emitted by radioactive nuclei (such as ^{60}Co and ^{137}Cs) and during certain nuclear reactions. They have wavelengths ranging from approximately 10^{-10} m to less than 10^{-14} m. They are highly penetrating and produce serious damage when absorbed by living tissues. Consequently, those working near such dangerous radiation must be protected with heavily absorbing materials, such as thick layers of lead.

Gamma rays

SUMMARY

Electromagnetic waves, which are predicted by Maxwell's equations, have the following properties:

- The electric and magnetic fields satisfy the following wave equations, which can be obtained from Maxwell's third and fourth equations:

$$\frac{\partial^2 E}{\partial x^2} = \mu_0 \epsilon_0 \frac{\partial^2 E}{\partial t^2} \tag{34.8}$$

$$\frac{\partial^2 B}{\partial x^2} = \mu_0 \epsilon_0 \frac{\partial^2 B}{\partial t^2} \tag{34.9}$$

- Electromagnetic waves travel through a vacuum with the speed of light c, where

$$c = \frac{1}{\sqrt{\mu_0 \epsilon_0}} = 3.00 \times 10^8 \text{ m/s} \tag{34.10}$$

- The electric and magnetic fields of an electromagnetic wave are perpendicular to each other and perpendicular to the direction of wave propagation. (Hence, electromagnetic waves are transverse waves.)
- The instantaneous magnitudes of $|\mathbf{E}|$ and $|\mathbf{B}|$ in an electromagnetic wave are related by the expression

$$\frac{E}{B} = c \tag{34.13}$$

- Electromagnetic waves carry energy. The rate of flow of energy crossing a unit area is described by the Poynting vector **S**, where

$$\mathbf{S} \equiv \frac{1}{\mu_0}\,\mathbf{E} \times \mathbf{B} \qquad (34.18)$$

- Electromagnetic waves carry momentum and hence can exert pressure on surfaces. If an electromagnetic wave whose Poynting vector is **S** is completely absorbed by a surface upon which it is normally incident, the radiation pressure on that surface is

$$P = \frac{S}{c} \qquad \text{(complete absorption)} \qquad (34.24)$$

If the surface totally reflects a normally incident wave, the pressure is doubled.

The electric and magnetic fields of a sinusoidal plane electromagnetic wave propagating in the positive *x* direction can be written

$$E = E_{max}\cos(kx - \omega t) \qquad (34.11)$$

$$B = B_{max}\cos(kx - \omega t) \qquad (34.12)$$

where ω is the angular frequency of the wave and k is the angular wave number. These equations represent special solutions to the wave equations for E and B. Since $\omega = 2\pi f$ and $k = 2\pi/\lambda$, where f and λ are the frequency and wavelength, respectively, it is found that

$$\frac{\omega}{k} = \lambda f = c$$

The average value of the Poynting vector for a plane electromagnetic wave has a magnitude

$$S_{av} = \frac{E_{max}B_{max}}{2\mu_0} = \frac{E_{max}^2}{2\mu_0 c} = \frac{c}{2\mu_0}B_{max}^2 \qquad (34.20)$$

The intensity of a sinusoidal plane electromagnetic wave equals the average value of the Poynting vector taken over one or more cycles.

The electromagnetic spectrum includes waves covering a broad range of frequencies and wavelengths. The frequency f and wavelength λ of a given wave are related by

$$c = f\lambda \qquad (34.31)$$

QUESTIONS

1. For a given incident energy of an electromagnetic wave, why is the radiation pressure on a perfect reflecting surface twice as large as that on a perfect absorbing surface?
2. Describe the physical significance of the Poynting vector.
3. Do all current-carrying conductors emit electromagnetic waves? Explain.
4. What is the fundamental source of electromagnetic radiation?
5. Electrical engineers often speak of the radiation resistance of an antenna. What do you suppose they mean by this phrase?

6. If a high-frequency current is passed through a solenoid containing a metallic core, the core heats up by induction. Explain why the materials heat up in these situations.
7. Certain orientations of the receiving antenna on a television set give better reception than others. Furthermore, the best orientation varies from station to station. Explain.
8. Does a wire connected to a battery emit an electromagnetic wave? Explain.
9. If you charge a comb by running it through your hair and

then hold the comb next to a bar magnet, do the electric and magnetic fields produced constitute an electromagnetic wave?

10. An empty plastic or glass dish removed from a microwave oven is cool to the touch right after it is removed from the oven. How can this be possible? (You can assume that your electric bill has been paid.)

11. Often when you touch the indoor antenna on a radio or television receiver, the reception instantly improves. Why?

12. Explain how the (dipole) VHF antenna of a television set works.

13. Explain how the UHF (loop) antenna of a television set works.

14. Explain why the voltage induced in a UHF (loop) antenna depends on the frequency of the signal, while the voltage in a VHF (dipole) antenna does not.

15. List as many similarities and differences as you can between sound waves and light waves.

16. What does a radio wave do to the charges in the receiving antenna to provide a signal for your car radio?

17. What determines the height of an AM radio station's broadcast antenna?

18. Some radio transmitters use a "phased array" of antennas. What is their purpose?

19. What happens to the radio reception in an airplane as it flies over the (vertical) dipole antenna of the control tower?

20. When light (or other electromagnetic radiation) travels across a given region, what is it that moves?

21. Why should an infrared photograph of a person look different from a photograph taken with visible light?

PROBLEMS

Section 34.2   Plane Electromagnetic Waves

1. If the North Star, Polaris, were to burn out today, in what year would it disappear from our vision? The distance from the Earth to Polaris is approximately 6.44×10^{18} m.

2. An electromagnetic wave in vacuum has an electric field amplitude of 220 V/m. Calculate the amplitude of the corresponding magnetic field.

3. (a) Use the relationship $B = \mu_0 H$ (Eq. 30.37) for free space where $\mu_m = \mu_0$ together with the properties of E and B described in Section 34.2 to show that $E/H = \sqrt{\mu_0/\epsilon_0}$. Recall that H is the magnetic intensity. (b) Calculate the numerical value of this ratio and show that it has SI units of ohms. (Because $E/H = \sqrt{\mu_0/\epsilon_0} = \mu_0 c$, we see that ratio E/H is equal to the impedance of free space discussed in Section 34.3.)

4. Show that $E = f(x - ct) + g(x + ct)$ satisfies Equation 34.8, where f and g are any functions.

5. The magnetic field amplitude of an electromagnetic wave is 5.4×10^{-7} T. Calculate the electric field amplitude if the wave is traveling (a) in free space and (b) in a medium in which the speed of the wave is $0.8c$.

6. The speed of an electromagnetic wave traveling in a transparent substance is $v = 1/\sqrt{\kappa \mu_0 \epsilon_0}$, where κ is the dielectric constant of the substance. Determine the speed of light in water, which has a dielectric constant at optical frequencies of 1.78.

7. Calculate the maximum value of the magnetic field in a medium where the speed of light is two-thirds that of the speed of light in vacuum and the electric field amplitude is 7.6 mV/m.

8. Write down expressions for the electric and magnetic fields of a sinusoidal plane electromagnetic wave having a frequency of 3.00 GHz and traveling in the positive x direction. The amplitude of the electric field is 300 V/m.

9. Figure 34.3 shows a plane electromagnetic sinusoidal wave propagating in the x direction. The wavelength is 50.0 m, and the electric field vibrates in the xy plane with an amplitude of 22.0 V/m. Calculate (a) the sinusoidal frequency and (b) the magnitude and direction of B when the electric field has its maximum value in the negative y direction. (c) Write an expression for B in the form

$$B = B_{max} \cos(kx - \omega t)$$

with numerical values for B_{max}, k, and ω.

10. Verify that the following equations are solutions to Equations 34.8 and 34.9, respectively:

$$E = E_{max} \cos(kx - \omega t) \qquad B = B_{max} \cos(kx - \omega t)$$

11. In SI units, the electric field in an electromagnetic wave is described by

$$E_y = 100 \sin(1.00 \times 10^7 x - \omega t)$$

Find (a) the amplitude of the corresponding magnetic wave, (b) the wavelength λ, and (c) the frequency f.

Section 34.3   Energy Carried by Electromagnetic Waves

12. How much electromagnetic energy is contained per cubic meter near the Earth's surface if the intensity of sunlight under clear skies is 1000 W/m²?

☐ indicates problems that have full solutions available in the Student Solutions Manual and Study Guide.

13. At what distance from a 100-W electromagnetic wave point source does $E_{max} = 15$ V/m?

14. A 10-mW laser has a beam diameter of 1.6 mm. (a) What is the intensity of the light, assuming it is uniform across the circular beam? (b) What is the average energy density of the beam?

15. What is the average magnitude of the Poynting vector 5.0 miles from a radio transmitter broadcasting isotropically with an average power of 250 kW?

16. The Sun radiates electromagnetic energy at the rate of $P_{Sun} = 3.85 \times 10^{26}$ W. (a) At what distance from the Sun does the intensity of its radiation fall to 1000 W/m²? (Compare this distance to the radius of the Earth's orbit.) (b) At the distance you just found, what is the average energy density of the Sun's radiation?

17. The amplitude of the electric field is 0.20 V/m 10 km from a radio transmitter. What is the total power emitted by the transmitter?

18. In a region of free space the electric field intensity at an instant of time is E = (80i + 32j − 64k) N/C and the magnetic field intensity is B = (0.20i + 0.080j + 0.29k) μT. (a) Show that the two fields are perpendicular to each other. (b) Determine the Poynting vector for these fields.

19. The filament of an incandescent lamp has a 150-Ω resistance and carries a direct current of 1.0 A. The filament is 8.0 cm long and 0.90 mm in radius. (a) Calculate the Poynting vector at the surface of the filament. (b) Find the magnitude of the electric and magnetic fields at the surface of the filament.

20. A monochromatic light source emits 100 W of electromagnetic power uniformly in all directions. (a) Calculate the average electric-field energy density 1 m from the source. (b) Calculate the average magnetic-field energy density at the same distance from the source. (c) Find the wave intensity at this location.

21. A helium-neon laser intended for instructional use operates at 5.0 mW. (a) Determine the maximum value of the electric field at a point where the cross-sectional area of the beam is 4.0 mm². (b) Calculate the electromagnetic energy in a 1.0-m length of the beam.

22. A lightbulb's filament has a resistance of 110 Ω. The bulb is plugged into a standard 110-V (rms) outlet and emits 1.0% of the joule heat as electromagnetic radiation of frequency f. Assuming that the bulb is covered with a filter, absorbing all other frequencies, find the amplitude of the magnetic field 1.0 m from the bulb.

23. At one location on the Earth, the rms value of the magnetic field caused by solar radiation is 1.8 μT. From this value, calculate (a) the average electric field due to solar radiation, (b) the average energy density of the solar component of electromagnetic radiation at this location, and (c) the magnitude of the Poynting vector (S_{av}) for the Sun's radiation. (d) Compare the value found in part (c) to the value of the solar flux given in Example 34.3.

24. High-power lasers in factories are used to cut through cloth and metal. One such laser has a beam diameter of 1.00 mm and generates an electric field at the target having an amplitude 0.70 MV/m. Find (a) the amplitude of the magnetic field produced, (b) the intensity of the laser, and (c) the power dissipated.

Section 34.4 Momentum and Radiation Pressure

25. A radio wave transmits 25 W/m² of power per unit area. A flat surface of area A is perpendicular to the direction of propagation of the wave. Calculate the radiation pressure on it if the surface is a perfect absorber.

26. A 100-mW laser beam is reflected back upon itself by a mirror. Calculate the force on the mirror.

27. A 15-mW helium-neon laser ($\lambda = 632.8$ nm) emits a beam of circular cross-section whose diameter is 2.0 mm. (a) Find the maximum electric field in the beam. (b) What total energy is contained in a 1.0-m length of the beam? (c) Find the momentum carried by a 1.0-m length of the beam.

28. Given that the solar radiation incident on the upper atmosphere of the Earth is 1340 W/m², determine (a) the solar radiation incident on Mars, (b) the total power incident on Mars, and (c) the total force acting on Mars. (d) Compare this force with the gravitational attraction between Mars and the Sun. (See Table 14.2.)

29. A plane electromagnetic wave has an energy flux of 750 W/m². A flat, rectangular surface of dimensions 50 cm × 100 cm is placed perpendicularly to the direction of the wave. If the surface absorbs half of the energy and reflects half, calculate (a) the total energy absorbed by the surface in 1.0 min and (b) the momentum absorbed in this time.

30. Lasers have been used to suspend spherical glass beads in the Earth's gravitational field. (a) If a bead has a mass of 1.00 μg and a density of 0.20 g/cm³, determine the radiation intensity needed to support the bead. (b) If the beam has a radius of 0.20 cm, what is the power required for this laser?

30A. Lasers have been used to suspend spherical glass beads in the Earth's gravitational field. (a) If a bead has a mass m and a density ρ, determine the radiation intensity needed to support the bead. (b) If the beam has a radius r, what is the power required for this laser?

*Section 34.5 Radiation from an Infinite Current Sheet

31. A rectangular surface of dimensions 120 cm × 40 cm is parallel to and 4.4 m from a much larger

conducting sheet in which there is a sinusoidally varying surface current that has a maximum value of 10 A/m. (a) Calculate the average power incident on the smaller sheet. (b) What power per unit area is radiated by the larger sheet?

32. A large current-carrying sheet is expected to radiate in each direction (normal to the plane of the sheet) at a rate equal to 570 W/m². What maximum value of sinusoidal current density is required?

*Section 34.6 The Production of Electromagnetic Waves by an Antenna

33. What is the length of a half-wave antenna designed to broadcast 20-MHz radio waves?

34. An AM radio station broadcasts isotropically with an average power of 4.0 kW. A dipole-receiving antenna 65 cm long is located 4.0 miles from the transmitter. Compute the emf induced by this signal between the ends of the receiving antenna.

35. A television set uses a dipole-receiving antenna for VHF channels and a loop antenna for UHF channels. The UHF antenna produces a voltage from the changing magnetic flux through the loop. (a) Using Faraday's law, derive an expression for the amplitude of the voltage that appears in a single-turn circular loop antenna with a radius r. The TV station broadcasts a signal with a frequency f, and the signal has an electric field amplitude E_{max} and magnetic field amplitude B_{max} at the receiving antenna's location. (b) If the electric field in the signal points vertically, what should be the orientation of the loop for best reception?

36. Figure 34.14 shows a Hertz antenna (also known as a half-wave antenna, since its length is $\lambda/2$). The antenna is located far enough from the ground that reflections do not significantly affect its radiation pattern. Most AM radio stations, however, use a Marconi antenna, which consists of the top half of a Hertz antenna. The lower end of this (quarter-wave) antenna is connected to Earth ground, and the ground itself serves as the missing lower half. What is the antenna length for a radio station broadcasting at (a) 560 kHz and (b) 1600 kHz?

37. Accelerating charges can radiate electromagnetic waves. Calculate the wavelength of radiation produced by a proton in a cyclotron of radius 0.50 m and magnetic field strength 0.35 T.

37A. Accelerating charges can radiate electromagnetic waves. Calculate the wavelength of radiation produced by a proton in a cyclotron of radius R and magnetic field strength B.

38. Two radio-transmitting antennas are separated by half the broadcast wavelength and are driven in phase with each other. In which directions are (a) the strongest and (b) the weakest signals radiated?

Section 34.7 The Spectrum of Electromagnetic Waves

39. What is the wavelength of an electromagnetic wave in free space that has a frequency of (a) 5.00×10^{19} Hz and (b) 4.00×10^{9} Hz?

40. Suppose you are located 180 m from a radio transmitter. How many wavelengths are you from the transmitter if the station calls itself (a) 1150 AM (the AM band frequencies are in kilohertz) and (b) 98.1 FM (the FM band frequencies are in megahertz)?

41. An important news announcement is transmitted by radio waves to people who are 100 km from the station, listening to their radio, and by sound waves to people sitting across the newsroom, 3.0 m from the newscaster. Who receives the news first? Explain. Take the speed of sound in air to be 343 m/s.

42. What are the wavelength ranges in (a) the AM radio band (540–1600 kHz) and (b) the FM radio band (88–108 MHz)?

43. There are 12 VHF television channels (Channels 2–13) that lie in a frequency range from 54 MHz to 216 MHz. Each channel has a width of 6 MHz, with the two ranges 72–76 MHz and 88–174 MHz reserved for non-TV purposes. (Channel 2, for example, lies between 54 and 60 MHz.) Calculate the wavelength range for (a) Channel 4, (b) Channel 6, and (c) Channel 8.

ADDITIONAL PROBLEMS

44. Assume that the solar radiation incident on the Earth is 1340 W/m². (a) Calculate the total power radiated by the Sun, taking the average Earth-Sun separation to be 1.49×10^{11} m. (b) Determine the maximum values of the electric and magnetic fields at the Earth's surface due to solar radiation.

45. A community plans to build a facility to convert solar radiation to electrical power. They require 1.00 MW of power, and the system to be installed has an efficiency of 30% (that is, 30% of the solar energy incident on the surface is converted to electrical energy). What must be the effective area of a perfectly absorbing surface used in such an installation, assuming a constant energy flux of 1000 W/m²?

46. A microwave source produces pulses of 20-GHz radiation, with each pulse lasting 1.0 ns. A parabolic reflector ($R = 6.0$ cm) is used to focus these into a parallel beam of radiation, as in Figure P34.46. The average power during each pulse is 25 kW. (a) What is the wavelength of these microwaves? (b) What is the total energy contained in each pulse? (c) Com-

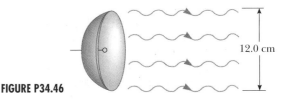

FIGURE P34.46

12.0 cm

pute the average energy density inside each pulse. (d) Determine the amplitude of the electric and magnetic fields in these microwaves. (e) If this pulsed beam strikes an absorbing surface, compute the force exerted on the surface during the 1.0-ns duration of each pulse.

47. A dish antenna having a diameter of 20 m receives (at normal incidence) a radio signal from a distant source, as shown in Figure P34.47. The radio signal is a continuous sinusoidal wave with amplitude $E_{max} = 0.20 \ \mu V/m$. Assume the antenna absorbs all the radiation that falls on the dish. (a) What is the amplitude of the magnetic field in this wave? (b) What is the intensity of the radiation received by this antenna? (c) What is the power received by the antenna? (d) What force is exerted on the antenna by the radio waves?

FIGURE P34.47

48. The electromagnetic power radiated by a nonrelativistic moving point charge q having an acceleration a is

$$P = \frac{q^2 a^2}{6\pi\epsilon_0 c^3}$$

where ϵ_0 is the permittivity of vacuum and c is the speed of light in vacuum. (a) Show that the right side of this equation is in watts. (b) If an electron is placed in a constant electric field of 100 N/C, determine its acceleration and the electromagnetic power it radiates. (c) If a proton is placed in a cyclotron of radius 0.50 m and magnetic field of magnitude 0.35 T, what is the electromagnetic power radiated by this proton?

49. A thin tungsten filament of length 1.0 m radiates 60 W of power in the form of electromagnetic waves. A perfectly absorbing surface in the form of a hollow cylinder of radius 5.0 cm and length 1.0 m is placed concentrically with the filament. Calculate the radiation pressure acting on the cylinder. (Assume that the radiation is emitted in the radial direction, and neglect end effects.)

50. A group of astronauts plans to propel a spaceship by using a "sail" to reflect solar radiation. The sail is totally reflecting, oriented with its plane perpendicular to the direction of the Sun, and 1.00 km × 1.50 km in size. What is the maximum acceleration that can be expected for a spaceship of 4.00 metric tons (4000 kg)? (Use the solar radiation data from Problem 44 and neglect gravitational forces.)

51. In 1965, Penzias and Wilson discovered the cosmic microwave radiation left over from the Big Bang expansion of the Universe. The energy density of this radiation is $4.0 \times 10^{-14} \ J/m^3$. Determine the corresponding electric field amplitude.

52. A possible means of space flight is to place a perfectly reflecting aluminized sheet into Earth's orbit and use the light from the Sun to push this solar sail. Suppose a sail of area $6.00 \times 10^4 \ m^2$ and mass 6000 kg is placed in orbit facing the Sun. (a) What force is exerted on the sail? (b) What is the sail's acceleration? (c) How long does it take the sail to reach the Moon, $3.84 \times 10^8 \ m$ away? Ignore all gravitational effects, assume that the acceleration calculated in part (b) remains constant, and assume a solar intensity of 1380 W/m². (*Hint:* The radiation pressure exerted by a reflected wave is given as twice the average power per area divided by the speed of light.)

53. An astronaut in a spacecraft moving with constant velocity wishes to increase the speed of the craft by using a laser beam attached to the spaceship. The laser beam emits 100 J of electromagnetic energy per pulse, and the laser is pulsed at the rate of 0.2 pulse/s. If the mass of the spaceship plus its contents is 5000 kg, for how long a time must the beam be on in order to increase the speed of the vehicle by 1 m/s in the direction of its initial motion? In what direction should the beam be pointed to achieve this?

54. Consider a small, spherical particle of radius r located in space a distance R from the Sun. (a) Show that the ratio $F_{rad}/F_{grav} \propto 1/r$, where F_{rad} = the force exerted by solar radiation and F_{grav} = the force of gravitational attraction. (b) The result of part (a) means that, for a sufficiently small value of r, the force exerted on the particle by solar radiation exceeds the force of gravitational attraction. Calculate the value of r for which the particle is in equilibrium under the two forces. (Assume that the particle has a perfectly absorbing surface and a mass density of 1.50 g/cm³. Let the particle be located 3.75×10^{11} m from the Sun and use 214 W/m² as the value of the solar flux at that point.)

55. The torsion balance shown in Figure 34.8 is used in an experiment to measure radiation pressure. The torque constant (elastic restoring torque) of the suspension fiber is 1.0×10^{-11} N·m/deg, and the length of the horizontal rod is 6.0 cm. The beam from a 3.0-mW helium-neon laser is incident on the black disk, and the mirror disk is completely

shielded. Calculate the angle between the equilibrium positions of the horizontal bar when the beam is switched from "off" to "on."

56. The Earth reflects approximately 38% of the incident sunlight by reflection from its clouds and oceans. (a) Given that the intensity of solar radiation is 1340 W/m², find the radiation pressure at the location on Earth where the Sun is straight overhead. (b) Compare this to normal atmospheric pressure, which is 1.01×10^5 N/m² at the Earth's surface.

57. A linearly polarized microwave of wavelength 1.50 cm is directed along the positive x axis. The electric field vector has a maximum value of 175 V/m and vibrates in the xy plane. (a) Assume that the magnetic field component of the wave can be written in the form $B = B_{\max} \sin(kx - \omega t)$ and give values for $B_{\max}$, k, and ω. Also, determine in which plane the magnetic field vector vibrates. (b) Calculate the magnitude of the Poynting vector for this wave. (c) What maximum radiation pressure would this wave exert if directed at normal incidence onto a perfectly reflecting sheet? (d) What maximum acceleration would be imparted to a 500-g sheet (perfectly reflecting and at normal incidence) of dimensions 1.0 m × 0.75 m?

58. A police radar unit transmits at 10.525 GHz, better known as the X-band. (a) Show that when this radar wave is reflected from the front of a moving car, the reflected wave is shifted in frequency by the amount $\Delta f \cong 2fv/c$, where v is the speed of the car. (*Hint:* Treat the reflection of a wave as two separate processes: First, the motion of the car produces a "moving-observer" Doppler shift in the frequency of the waves striking the car, and then these Doppler-shifted waves are re-emitted by a moving source. Also, automobile speeds are low enough that you can use the binomial expansion $(1 + x)^n \cong 1 + nx$ in the acoustic Doppler formulas derived in Chapter 17.) (b) The unit is usually calibrated before and after an arrest for speeds of 35 mph and 80 mph. Calculate the frequency shift produced by these two speeds.

59. An astronaut, stranded in space "at rest" 10 m from his spacecraft, has a mass (including equipment) of 110 kg. Having a 100-W light source that forms a directed beam, he decides to use the beam as a photon rocket to propel himself continuously toward the spacecraft. (a) Calculate how long it takes him to reach the spacecraft by this method. (b) Suppose, instead, he decides to throw the light source away in a direction opposite the spacecraft. If the mass of the light source is 3.0 kg and, after being thrown, moves at 12 m/s *relative to the recoiling astronaut,* how long does he take to reach the spacecraft?

60. A "laser cannon" on a spacecraft has a beam of cross-sectional area A. The maximum electric field in the beam is E. At what rate a will an asteroid acceler-

ate away from the spacecraft if the laser beam strikes the asteroid perpendicularly to its surface, and the surface is nonreflecting? The mass of the asteroid is m. Neglect the acceleration of the spacecraft.

61. (a) For a parallel-plate capacitor having a small plate separation compared with the length or width of a plate, show that the displacement current is

$$I_d = C\frac{dV}{dt}$$

(b) Calculate the value of dV/dt required to produce a displacement current of 1.00 A in a 1.00-μF capacitor.

62. Consider the situation shown in Figure P34.62. An electric field of 300 V/m is confined to a circular area 10 cm in diameter and directed outward from the plane of the figure. If the field is increasing at a rate of 20 V/m·s, what are the direction and magnitude of the magnetic field at the point P, 15 cm from the center of the circle?

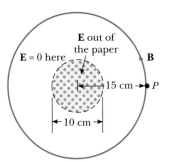

FIGURE P34.62

63. A plane electromagnetic wave varies sinusoidally at 90.0 MHz as it travels along the $+x$ direction. The peak value of the electric field is 2.00 mV/m, and it is directed along the $\pm y$ direction. (a) Find the wavelength, the period, and the maximum value of the magnetic field. (b) Write expressions in SI units for the space and time variations of the electric field and of the magnetic field. Include numerical values as well as subscripts to indicate coordinate directions. (c) Find the average power per unit area that this wave propagates through space. (d) Find the average energy density in the radiation (in joules per cubic meter). (e) What radiation pressure would this wave exert upon a perfectly reflecting surface at normal incidence?

64. A 1.00-m diameter mirror focuses the Sun's rays onto an absorbing plate 2.00 cm in radius, which holds a can containing 1.00 liter of water at 20°C. (a) If the solar intensity is 1.00 kW/m², what is the intensity on the absorbing plate? (b) What are the maximum **E** and **B** field intensities? (c) If 40% of the energy is absorbed, how long would it take to bring the water to its boiling point?

APPENDICES

TABLE A.1   Conversion Factors

Length

	m	cm	km	in.	ft	mi
1 meter	1	10^2	10^{-3}	39.37	3.281	6.214×10^{-4}
1 centimeter	10^{-2}	1	10^{-5}	0.3937	3.281×10^{-2}	6.214×10^{-6}
1 kilometer	10^3	10^5	1	3.937×10^4	3.281×10^3	0.6214
1 inch	2.540×10^{-2}	2.540	2.540×10^{-5}	1	8.333×10^{-2}	1.578×10^{-5}
1 foot	0.3048	30.48	3.048×10^{-4}	12	1	1.894×10^{-4}
1 mile	1609	1.609×10^5	1.609	6.336×10^4	5280	1

Mass

	kg	g	slug	u
1 kilogram	1	10^3	6.852×10^{-2}	6.024×10^{26}
1 gram	10^{-3}	1	6.852×10^{-5}	6.024×10^{23}
1 slug	14.59	1.459×10^4	1	8.789×10^{27}
1 atomic mass unit	1.660×10^{-27}	1.660×10^{-24}	1.137×10^{-28}	1

Time

	s	min	h	day	year
1 second	1	1.667×10^{-2}	2.778×10^{-4}	1.157×10^{-5}	3.169×10^{-8}
1 minute	60	1	1.667×10^{-2}	6.994×10^{-4}	1.901×10^{-6}
1 hour	3600	60	1	4.167×10^{-2}	1.141×10^{-4}
1 day	8.640×10^4	1440	24	1	2.738×10^{-3}
1 year	3.156×10^7	5.259×10^5	8.766×10^3	365.2	1

Speed

	m/s	cm/s	ft/s	mi/h
1 meter/second	1	10^2	3.281	2.237
1 centimeter/second	10^{-2}	1	3.281×10^{-2}	2.237×10^{-2}
1 foot/second	0.3048	30.48	1	0.6818
1 mile/hour	0.4470	44.70	1.467	1

Note: 1 mi/min = 60 mi/h = 88 ft/s.

Force

	N	dyn	lb
1 newton	1	10^5	0.2248
1 dyne	10^{-5}	1	2.248×10^{-6}
1 pound	4.448	4.448×10^5	1

TABLE A.1 *Continued*

Work, Energy, Heat

	J	erg	ft·lb
1 joule	1	10^7	0.7376
1 erg	10^{-7}	1	7.376×10^{-8}
1 ft·lb	1.356	1.356×10^7	1
1 eV	1.602×10^{-19}	1.602×10^{-12}	1.182×10^{-19}
1 cal	4.186	4.186×10^7	3.087
1 Btu	1.055×10^3	1.055×10^{10}	7.779×10^2
1 kWh	3.600×10^6	3.600×10^{13}	2.655×10^6

	eV	cal	Btu	kWh
1 joule	6.242×10^{18}	0.2389	9.481×10^{-4}	2.778×10^{-7}
1 erg	6.242×10^{11}	2.389×10^{-8}	9.481×10^{-11}	2.778×10^{-14}
1 ft·lb	8.464×10^{18}	0.3239	1.285×10^{-3}	3.766×10^{-7}
1 eV	1	3.827×10^{-20}	1.519×10^{-22}	4.450×10^{-26}
1 cal	2.613×10^{19}	1	3.968×10^{-3}	1.163×10^{-6}
1 Btu	6.585×10^{21}	2.520×10^2	1	2.930×10^{-4}
1 kWh	2.247×10^{25}	8.601×10^5	3.413×10^2	1

Pressure

	Pa	dyn/cm²	atm
1 pascal	1	10	9.869×10^{-6}
1 dyne/centimeter²	10^{-1}	1	9.869×10^{-7}
1 atmosphere	1.013×10^5	1.013×10^6	1
1 centimeter mercury*	1.333×10^3	1.333×10^4	1.316×10^{-2}
1 pound/inch²	6.895×10^3	6.895×10^4	6.805×10^{-2}
1 pound/foot²	47.88	4.788×10^2	4.725×10^{-4}

	cm Hg	lb/in.²	lb/ft²
1 newton/meter²	7.501×10^{-4}	1.450×10^{-4}	2.089×10^{-2}
1 dyne/centimeter²	7.501×10^{-5}	1.450×10^{-5}	2.089×10^{-3}
1 atmosphere	76	14.70	2.116×10^3
1 centimeter mercury*	1	0.1943	27.85
1 pound/inch²	5.171	1	144
1 pound/foot²	3.591×10^{-2}	6.944×10^{-3}	1

* At 0°C and at a location where the acceleration due to gravity has its "standard" value, 9.80665 m/s².

TABLE A.2 Symbols, Dimensions, and Units of Physical Quantities

Quantity	Common Symbol	Unit*	Dimensions†	Unit in Terms of Base SI Units
Acceleration	**a**	m/s^2	L/T^2	m/s^2
Amount of substance	n	mole		mol
Angle	θ, ϕ	radian (rad)	1	
Angular acceleration	$\boldsymbol{\alpha}$	rad/s^2	T^{-2}	s^{-2}
Angular frequency	ω	rad/s	T^{-1}	s^{-1}
Angular momentum	**L**	$kg \cdot m^2/s$	ML^2/T	$kg \cdot m^2/s$
Angular velocity	$\boldsymbol{\omega}$	rad/s	T^{-1}	s^{-1}
Area	A	m^2	L^2	m^2
Atomic number	Z			
Capacitance	C	farad (F) $(= Q/V)$	Q^2T^2/ML^2	$A^2 \cdot s^4/kg \cdot m^2$
Charge	q, Q, e	coulomb (C)	Q	$A \cdot s$
Charge density				
Line	λ	C/m	Q/L	$A \cdot s/m$
Surface	σ	C/m^2	Q/L^2	$A \cdot s/m^2$
Volume	ρ	C/m^3	Q/L^3	$A \cdot s/m^3$
Conductivity	σ	$1/\Omega \cdot m$	Q^2T/ML^3	$A^2 \cdot s^3/kg \cdot m^3$
Current	I	AMPERE	Q/T	A
Current density	J	A/m^2	Q/T^2	A/m^2
Density	ρ	kg/m^3	M/L^3	kg/m^3
Dielectric constant	κ			
Displacement	s	METER	L	m
Distance	d, h			
Length	ℓ, L			
Electric dipole moment	**p**	$C \cdot m$	QL	$A \cdot s \cdot m$
Electric field	**E**	V/m	ML/QT^2	$kg \cdot m/A \cdot s^3$
Electric flux	Φ	$V \cdot m$	ML^3/QT^2	$kg \cdot m^3/A \cdot s^3$
Electromotive force	$\mathcal{E}$	volt (V)	ML^2/QT^2	$kg \cdot m^2/A \cdot s^3$
Energy	E, U, K	joule (J)	ML^2/T^2	$kg \cdot m^2/s^2$
Entropy	S	J/K	$ML^2/T^2 \cdot K$	$kg \cdot m^2/s^2 \cdot K$
Force	**F**	newton (N)	ML/T^2	$kg \cdot m/s^2$
Frequency	f, ν	hertz (Hz)	T^{-1}	s^{-1}
Heat	Q	joule (J)	ML^2/T^2	$kg \cdot m^2/s^2$
Inductance	L	henry (H)	ML^2/Q^2	$kg \cdot m^2/A^2 \cdot s^2$
Magnetic dipole moment	$\boldsymbol{\mu}$	$N \cdot m/T$	QL^2/T	$A \cdot m^2$
Magnetic field	**B**	tesla (T) $(= Wb/m^2)$	M/QT	$kg/A \cdot s^2$
Magnetic flux	Φ_m	weber (Wb)	ML^2/QT	$kg \cdot m^2/A \cdot s^2$
Mass	m, M	KILOGRAM	M	kg
Molar specific heat	C	$J/mol \cdot K$		$kg \cdot m^2/s^2 \cdot mol \cdot K$
Moment of inertia	I	$kg \cdot m^2$	ML^2	$kg \cdot m^2$
Momentum	**p**	$kg \cdot m/s$	ML/T	$kg \cdot m/s$
Period	T	s	T	s
Permeability of space	μ_0	N/A^2 $(= H/m)$	ML/Q^2T	$kg \cdot m/A^2 \cdot s^2$
Permittivity of space	ϵ_0	$C^2/N \cdot m^2$ $(= F/m)$	Q^2T^2/ML^3	$A^2 \cdot s^4/kg \cdot m^3$
Potential (voltage)	V	volt (V) $(= J/C)$	ML^2/QT^2	$kg \cdot m^2/A \cdot s^3$
Power	P	watt (W) $(= J/s)$	ML^2/T^3	$kg \cdot m^2/s^3$

continued

TABLE A.2   *Continued*

Quantity	Common Symbol	Unit*	Dimensions†	Unit in Terms of Base SI Units
Pressure	P, p	pascal (Pa) = (N/m²)	M/LT^2	$kg/m \cdot s^2$
Resistance	R	ohm $(\Omega)(=V/A)$	ML^2/Q^2T	$kg \cdot m^2/A^2 \cdot s^3$
Specific heat	c	J/kg·K	$L^2/T^2 \cdot K$	$m^2/s^2 \cdot K$
Temperature	T	KELVIN	K	K
Time	t	SECOND	T	s
Torque	τ	N·m	ML^2/T^2	$kg \cdot m^2/s^2$
Speed	v	m/s	L/T	m/s
Volume	V	m³	L^3	m³
Wavelength	λ	m	L	m
Work	W	joule (J)(= N·m)	ML^2/T^2	$kg \cdot m^2/s^2$

* The base SI units are given in upper case letters.

† The symbols M, L, T, and Q denote mass, length, time, and charge, respectively.

TABLE A.3   **Table of Atomic Masses**[a]

Z	Element	Symbol	Chemical Atomic Mass (u)	Mass Number (* Indicates Radioactive) A	Atomic Mass (u)	Percent Abundance	Half-Life (if Radioactive) $T_{1/2}$
0	(Neutron)	n		1*	1.008 665		10.4 m
1	Hydrogen	H	1.0079	1	1.007 825	99.985	
	Deuterium	D		2	2.014 102	0.015	
	Tritium	T		3*	3.016 049		12.33 y
2	Helium	He	4.00260	3	3.016 029	0.00014	
				4	4.002 602	99.99986	
				6*	6.018 886		0.81 s
3	Lithium	Li	6.941	6	6.015 121	7.5	
				7	7.016 003	92.5	
				8*	8.022 486		0.84 s
4	Beryllium	Be	9.0122	7*	7.016 928		53.3 d
				9	9.012 174	100	
				10*	10.013 534		1.5×10^6 y
5	Boron	B	10.81	10	10.012 936	19.9	
				11	11.009 305	80.1	
				12*	12.014 352		0.0202 s
6	Carbon	C	12.011	10*	10.016 854		19.3 s
				11*	11.011 433		20.4 m
				12	12.000 000	98.90	
				13	13.003 355	1.10	
				14*	14.003 242		5730 y
				15*	15.010 599		2.45 s
7	Nitrogen	N	14.0067	12*	12.018 613		0.0110 s
				13*	13.005 738		9.96 m
				14	14.003 074	99.63	
				15	15.000 108	0.37	
				16*	16.006 100		7.13 s
				17*	17.008 450		4.17 s

TABLE A.3 *Continued*

Z	Element	Symbol	Chemical Atomic Mass (u)	Mass Number (* Indicates Radioactive) A	Atomic Mass (u)	Percent Abundance	Half-Life (if Radioactive) $T_{1/2}$
8	Oxygen	O	15.9994	14*	14.008 595		70.6 s
				15*	15.003 065		122
				16	15.994 915	99.761	
				17	16.999 132	0.039	
				18	17.999 160	0.20	
				19*	19.003 577		26.9 s
9	Fluorine	F	18.99840	17*	17.002 094		64.5 s
				18*	18.000 937		109.8 m
				19	18.998 404	100	
				20*	19.999 982		11.0 s
				21*	20.999.950		4.2 s
10	Neon	Ne	20.180	18*	18.005 710		1.67 s
				19*	19.001 880		17.2 s
				20	19.992 435	90.48	
(10)	(Neon)			21	20.993 841	0.27	
				22	21.991 383	9.25	
				23*	22.994 465		37.2 s
11	Sodium	Na	22.98987	21*	20.997 650		22.5 s
				22*	21.994 434		2.61 y
				24*	23.990 961		14.96 h
12	Magnesium	Mg	24.305	23*	22.994 124		11.3 s
				24	23.985 042	78.99	
				25	24.985 838	10.00	
				26	25.982 594	11.01	
				27*	26.984 341		9.46 m
13	Aluminum	Al	26.98154	26*	25.986 892		7.4×10^5 y
				27	26.981 538	100	
				28*	27.981 910		2.24 m
14	Silicon	Si	28.086	28	27.976 927	92.23	
				29	28.976 495	4.67	
				30	29.973 770	3.10	
				31*	30.975 362		2.62 h
				32*	31.974 148		172 y
15	Phosphorus	P	30.97376	30*	29.978 307		2.50 m
				31	30.973 762	100	
				32*	31.973 908		14.26 d
				33*	32.971 725		25.3 d
16	Sulfur	S	32.066	32	31.972 071	95.02	
				33	32.971 459	0.75	
				34	33.967 867	4.21	
				35*	34.969 033		87.5 d
				36	35.967 081	0.02	
17	Chlorine	Cl	35.453	35	34.968 853	75.77	
				36*	35.968 307		3.0×10^5 y
				37	36.965 903	24.23	

continued

TABLE A.3   *Continued*

Z	Element	Symbol	Chemical Atomic Mass (u)	Mass Number (* Indicates Radioactive) A	Atomic Mass (u)	Percent Abundance	Half-Life (if Radioactive) $T_{1/2}$
18	Argon	Ar	39.948	36	35.967 547	0.337	
				37*	36.966 776		35.04 d
				38	37.962 732	0.063	
				39*	38.964 314		269 y
				40	39.962 384	99.600	
				42*	41.963 049		33 y
19	Potassium	K	39.0983	39	38.963 708	93.2581	
				40*	39.964 000	0.0117	1.28×10^9 y
				41	40.961 827	6.7302	
20	Calcium	Ca	40.08	40	39.962 591	96.941	
				41*	40.962 279		1.0×10^5 y
				42	41.958 618	0.647	
				43	42.958 767	0.135	
				44	43.955 481	2.086	
				46	45.953 687	0.004	
				48	47.952 534	0.187	
21	Scandium	Sc	44.9559	41*	40.969 250		0.596 s
				45	44.955 911	100	
22	Titanium	Ti	47.88	44*	43.959 691		49 y
				46	45.952 630	8.0	
				47	46.951 765	7.3	
				48	47.947 947	73.8	
(22)	(Titanium)			49	48.947 871	5.5	
				50	49.944 792	5.4	
23	Vanadium	V	50.9415	48*	47.952 255		15.97 d
				50*	49.947 161	0.25	1.5×10^{17} y
				51	50.943 962	99.75	
24	Chromium	Cr	51.996	48*	47.954 033		21.6 h
				50	49.946 047	4.345	
				52	51.940 511	83.79	
				53	52.940 652	9.50	
				54	53.938 883	2.365	
25	Manganese	Mn	54.93805	54*	53.940 361		312.1 d
				55	54.938 048	100	
26	Iron	Fe	55.847	54	53.939 613	5.9	
				55*	54.938 297		2.7 y
				56	55.934 940	91.72	
				57	56.935 396	2.1	
				58	57.933 278	0.28	
				60*	59.934 078		1.5×10^6 y
27	Cobalt	Co	58.93320	59	58.933 198	100	
				60*	59.933 820		5.27 y
28	Nickel	Ni	58.693	58	57.935 346	68.077	
				59*	58.934 350		7.5×10^4 y
				60	59.930 789	26.223	
				61	60.931 058	1.140	
				62	61.928 346	3.634	
				63*	62.929 670		100 y
				64	63.927 967	0.926	

TABLE A.3 *Continued*

Z	Element	Symbol	Chemical Atomic Mass (u)	Mass Number (* Indicates Radioactive) A	Atomic Mass (u)	Percent Abundance	Half-Life (if Radioactive) $T_{1/2}$
29	Copper	Cu	63.54	63	62.929 599	69.17	
				65	64.927 791	30.83	
30	Zinc	Zn	65.39	64	63.929 144	48.6	
				66	65.926 035	27.9	
				67	66.927 129	4.1	
				68	67.924 845	18.8	
				70	69.925 323	0.6	
31	Gallium	Ga	69.723	69	68.925 580	60.108	
				71	70.924 703	39.892	
32	Germanium	Ge	72.61	70	69.924 250	21.23	
				72	71.922 079	27.66	
				73	72.923 462	7.73	
				74	73.921 177	35.94	
				76	75.921 402	7.44	
33	Arsenic	As	74.9216	75	74.921 594	100	
34	Selenium	Se	78.96	74	73.922 474	0.89	
				76	75.919 212	9.36	
				77	76.919 913	7.63	
				78	77.917 307	23.78	
				79*	78.918 497		$\leq 6.5 \times 10^4$ y
				80	79.916 519	49.61	
				82*	81.916 697	8.73	1.4×10^{20} y
35	Bromine	Br	79.904	79	78.918 336	50.69	
				81	80.916 287	49.31	
36	Krypton	Kr	83.80	78	77.920 400	0.35	
				80	79.916 377	2.25	
				81*	80.916 589		2.1×10^5 y
(36)	(Krypton)			82	81.913 481	11.6	
				83	82.914 136	11.5	
				84	83.911 508	57.0	
				85*	84.912 531		10.76 y
				86	85.910 615	17.3	
37	Rubidium	Rb	85.468	85	84.911 793	72.17	
				87*	86.909 186	27.83	4.75×10^{10} y
38	Strontium	Sr	87.62	84	83.913 428	0.56	
				86	85.909 266	9.86	
				87	86.908 883	7.00	
				88	87.905 618	82.58	
				90*	89.907 737		29.1 y
39	Yttrium	Y	88.9058	89	88.905 847	100	
40	Zirconium	Zr	91.224	90	89.904 702	51.45	
				91	90.905 643	11.22	
				92	91.905 038	17.15	
				93*	92.906 473		1.5×10^6 y
				94	93.906 314	17.38	
				96	95.908 274	2.80	

continued

TABLE A.3 *Continued*

Z	Element	Symbol	Chemical Atomic Mass (u)	Mass Number (* Indicates Radioactive) A	Atomic Mass (u)	Percent Abundance	Half-Life (if Radioactive) $T_{1/2}$
41	Niobium	Nb	92.9064	91*	90.906 988		6.8×10^2 y
				92*	91.907 191		3.5×10^7 y
				93	92.906 376	100	
				94*	93.907 280		2×10^4 y
42	Molybdenum	Mo	95.94	92	91.906 807	14.84	
				93*	92.906 811		3.5×10^3 y
				94	93.905 085	9.25	
				95	94.905 841	15.92	
				96	95.904 678	16.68	
				97	96.906 020	9.55	
				98	97.905 407	24.13	
				100	99.907 476	9.63	
43	Technetium	Tc		97*	96.906 363		2.6×10^6 y
				98*	97.907 215		4.2×10^6 y
				99*	98.906 254		2.1×10^5 y
44	Ruthenium	Ru	101.07	96	95.907 597	5.54	
				98	97.905 287	1.86	
				99	98.905 939	12.7	
				100	99.904 219	12.6	
				101	100.905 558	17.1	
				102	101.904 348	31.6	
				104	103.905 428	18.6	
45	Rhodium	Rh	102.9055	103	102.905 502	100	
46	Palladium	Pd	106.42	102	101.905 616	1.02	
				104	103.904 033	11.14	
				105	104.905 082	22.33	
				106	105.903 481	27.33	
				107*	106.905 126		6.5×10^6 y
				108	107.903 893	26.46	
				110	109.905 158	11.72	
47	Silver	Ag	107.868	107	106.905 091	51.84	
				109	108.904 754	48.16	
48	Cadmium	Cd	112.41	106	105.906 457	1.25	
				108	107.904 183	0.89	
				109*	108.904 984		462 d
(48)	(Cadmium)			110	109.903 004	12.49	
				111	110.904 182	12.80	
				112	111.902 760	24.13	
				113*	112.904 401	12.22	9.3×10^{15} y
				114	113.903 359	28.73	
				116	115.904 755	7.49	
49	Indium	In	114.82	113	112.904 060	4.3	
				115*	114.903 876	95.7	4.4×10^{14} y
50	Tin	Sn	118.71	112	111.904 822	0.97	
				114	113.902 780	0.65	
				115	114.903 345	0.36	
				116	115.901 743	14.53	
				117	116.902 953	7.68	

TABLE A.3 *Continued*

Z	Element	Symbol	Chemical Atomic Mass (u)	Mass Number (* Indicates Radioactive) A	Atomic Mass (u)	Percent Abundance	Half-Life (if Radioactive) $T_{1/2}$
				118	117.901 605	24.22	
				119	118.903 308	8.58	
				120	119.902 197	32.59	
				121*	120.904 237		55 y
				122	121.903 439	4.63	
				124	123.905 274	5.79	
51	Antimony	Sb	121.76	121	120.903 820	57.36	
				123	122.904 215	42.64	
				125*	124.905 251		2.7 y
52	Tellurium	Te	127.60	120	119.904 040	0.095	
				122	121.903 052	2.59	
				123*	122.904 271	0.905	1.3×10^{13} y
				124	123.902 817	4.79	
				125	124.904 429	7.12	
				126	125.903 309	18.93	
				128*	127.904 463	31.70	$> 8 \times 10^{24}$ y
				130*	129.906 228	33.87	$\leq 1.25 \times 10^{21}$ y
53	Iodine	I	126.9045	127	126.904 474	100	
				129*	128.904 984		1.6×10^{7} y
54	Xenon	Xe	131.29	124	123.905 894	0.10	
				126	125.904 268	0.09	
				128	127.903 531	1.91	
				129	128.904 779	26.4	
				130	129.903 509	4.1	
				131	130.905 069	21.2	
				132	131.904 141	26.9	
				134	133.905 394	10.4	
				136*	135.907 215	8.9	$\geq 2.36 \times 10^{21}$ y
55	Cesium	Cs	132.9054	133	132.905 436	100	
				134*	133.906 703		2.1 y
				135*	134.905 891		2×10^{6} y
				137*	136.907 078		30 y
56	Barium	Ba	137.33	130	129.906 289	0.106	
				132	131.905 048	0.101	
				133*	132.905 990		10.5 y
				134	133.904 492	2.42	
				135	134.905 671	6.593	
				136	135.904 559	7.85	
				137	136.905 816	11.23	
				138	137.905 236	71.70	
57	Lanthanum	La	138.905	137*	136.906 462		6×10^{4} y
(57)	(Lanthanum)			138*	137.907 105	0.0902	1.05×10^{11} y
				139	138.906 346	99.9098	
58	Cerium	Ce	140.12	136	135.907 139	0.19	
				138	137.905 986	0.25	
				140	139.905 434	88.43	
				142*	141.909 241	11.13	$> 5 \times 10^{16}$ y
59	Praseodymium	Pr	140.9076	141	140.907 647	100	

continued

TABLE A.3 *Continued*

Z	Element	Symbol	Chemical Atomic Mass (u)	Mass Number (* Indicates Radioactive) A	Atomic Mass (u)	Percent Abundance	Half-Life (if Radioactive) $T_{1/2}$
60	Neodymium	Nd	144.24	142	141.907 718	27.13	
				143	142.909 809	12.18	
				144*	143.910 082	23.80	2.3×10^{15} y
				145	144.912 568	8.30	
				146	145.913 113	17.19	
				148	147.916 888	5.76	
				150*	149.920 887	5.64	$> 1 \times 10^{18}$ y
61	Promethium	Pm		143*	142.910 928		265 d
				145*	144.912 745		17.7 y
				146*	145.914 698		5.5 y
				147*	146.915 134		2.623 y
62	Samarium	Sm	150.36	144	143.911 996	3.1	
				146*	145.913 043		1.0×10^{8} y
				147*	146.914 894	15.0	1.06×10^{11} y
				148*	147.914 819	11.3	7×10^{15} y
				149*	148.917 180	13.8	$> 2 \times 10^{15}$ y
				150	149.917 273	7.4	
				151*	150.919 928		90 y
				152	151.919 728	26.7	
				154	153.922 206	22.7	
63	Europium	Eu	151.96	151	150.919 846	47.8	
				152*	151.921 740		13.5 y
				153	152.921 226	52.2	
				154*	153.922 975		8.59 y
				155*	154.922 888		4.7 y
64	Gadolinium	Gd	157.25	148*	147.918 112		75 y
				150*	149.918 657		1.8×10^{6} y
				152*	151.919 787	0.20	1.1×10^{14} y
				154	153.920 862	2.18	
				155	154.922 618	14.80	
				156	155.922 119	20.47	
				157	156.923 957	15.65	
				158	157.924 099	24.84	
				160	159.927 050	21.86	
65	Terbium	Tb	158.9253	159	158.925 345	100	
66	Dysprosium	Dy	162.50	156	155.924 277	0.06	
				158	157.924 403	0.10	
				160	159.925 193	2.34	
				161	160.926 930	18.9	
				162	161.926 796	25.5	
				163	162.928 729	24.9	
				164	163.929 172	28.2	
67	Holmium	Ho	164.9303	165	164.930 316	100	
				166*	165.932 282		1.2×10^{3} y
68	Erbium	Er	167.26	162	161.928 775	0.14	
				164	163.929 198	1.61	
				166	165.930 292	33.6	

TABLE A.3 *Continued*

Z	Element	Symbol	Chemical Atomic Mass (u)	Mass Number (* Indicates Radioactive) A	Atomic Mass (u)	Percent Abundance	Half-Life (if Radioactive) $T_{1/2}$
(68)	(Erbium)			167	166.932 047	22.95	
				168	167.932 369	27.8	
				170	169.935 462	14.9	
69	Thulium	Tm	168.9342	169	168.934 213	100	
				171*	170.936 428		1.92 y
70	Ytterbium	Yb	173.04	168	167.933 897	0.13	
				170	169.934 761	3.05	
				171	170.936 324	14.3	
				172	171.936 380	21.9	
				173	172.938 209	16.12	
				174	173.938 861	31.8	
				176	175.942 564	12.7	
71	Lutecium	Lu	174.967	173*	172.938 930		1.37 y
				175	174.940 772	97.41	
				176*	175.942 679	2.59	3.78×10^{10} y
72	Hafnium	Hf	178.49	174*	173.940 042	0.162	2.0×10^{15} y
				176	175.941 404	5.206	
				177	176.943 218	18.606	
				178	177.943 697	27.297	
				179	178.945 813	13.629	
				180	179.946 547	35.100	
73	Tantalum	Ta	180.9479	180	179.947 542	0.012	
				181	180.947 993	99.988	
74	Tungsten (Wolfram)	W	183.85	180	179.946 702	0.12	
				182	181.948 202	26.3	
				183	182.950 221	14.28	
				184	183.950 929	30.7	
				186	185.954 358	28.6	
75	Rhenium	Re	186.207	185	184.952 951	37.40	
				187*	186.955 746	62.60	4.4×10^{10} y
76	Osmium	Os	190.2	184	183.952 486	0.02	
				186*	185.953 834	1.58	2.0×10^{15} y
				187	186.955 744	1.6	
				188	187.955 832	13.3	
				189	188.958 139	16.1	
				190	189.958 439	26.4	
				192	191.961 468	41.0	
				194*	193.965 172		6.0 y
77	Iridium	Ir	192.2	191	190.960 585	37.3	
				193	192.962 916	62.7	
78	Platinum	Pt	195.08	190*	189.959 926	0.01	6.5×10^{11} y
				192	191.961 027	0.79	
				194	193.962 655	32.9	
				195	194.964 765	33.8	
				196	195.964 926	25.3	
				198	197.967 867	7.2	
79	Gold	Au	196.9665	197	196.966 543	100	

continued

TABLE A.3   *Continued*

Z	Element	Symbol	Chemical Atomic Mass (u)	Mass Number (* Indicates Radioactive) A	Atomic Mass (u)	Percent Abundance	Half-Life (if Radioactive) $T_{1/2}$
80	Mercury	Hg	200.59	196	195.965 806	0.15	
				198	197.966 743	9.97	
				199	198.968 253	16.87	
				200	199.968 299	23.10	
				201	200.970 276	13.10	
				202	201.970 617	29.86	
				204	203.973 466	6.87	
81	Thallium	Tl	204.383	203	202.972 320	29.524	
				204*	203.973 839		3.78 y
				205	204.974 400	70.476	
		(Ra E″)		206*	205.976 084		4.2 m
		(Ac C″)		207*	206.977 403		4.77 m
		(Th C″)		208*	207.981 992		3.053 m
		(Ra C″)		210*	209.990 057		1.30 m
82	Lead	Pb	207.2	202*	201.972 134		5×10^4 y
				204*	203.973 020	1.4	$\geq 1.4 \times 10^{17}$ y
				205*	204.974 457		1.5×10^7 y
				206	205.974 440	24.1	
				207	206.975 871	22.1	
				208	207.976 627	52.4	
		(Ra D)		210*	209.984 163		22.3 y
		(Ac B)		211*	210.988 734		36.1 m
		(Th B)		212*	211.991 872		10.64 h
		(Ra B)		214*	213.999 798		26.8 m
83	Bismuth	Bi	208.9803	207*	206.978 444		32.2 y
				208*	207.979 717		3.7×10^5 y
				209	208.980 374	100	
		(Ra E)		210*	209.984 096		5.01 d
		(Th C)		211*	210.987 254		2.14 m
				212*	211.991 259		60.6 m
		(Ra C)		214*	213.998 692		19.9 m
				215*	215.001 836		7.4 m
84	Polonium	Po		209*	208.982 405		102 y
		(Ra F)		210*	209.982 848		138.38 d
		(Ac C′)		211*	210.986 627		0.52 s
		(Th C′)		212*	211.988 842		0.30 μs
		(Ra C′)		214*	213.995 177		164 μs
		(Ac A)		215*	214.999 418		0.0018 s
		(Th A)		216*	216.001 889		0.145 s
		(Ra A)		218*	218.008 965		3.10 m
85	Astatine	At		215*	214.998 638		$\approx 100\ \mu$s
				218*	218.008 685		1.6 s
				219*	219.011 294		0.9 m
86	Radon	Rn					
		(An)		219*	219.009 477		3.96 s
		(Tn)		220*	220.011 369		55.6 s
		(Rn)		222*	222.017 571		3.823 d
87	Francium	Fr					
		(Ac K)		223*	223.019 733		22 m

TABLE A.3 *Continued*

Z	Element	Symbol	Chemical Atomic Mass (u)	Mass Number (* Indicates Radioactive) A	Atomic Mass (u)	Percent Abundance	Half-Life (if Radioactive) $T_{1/2}$
88	Radium	Ra					
		(Ac X)		223*	223.018 499		11.43 d
		(Th X)		224*	224.020 187		3.66 d
		(Ra)		226*	226.025 402		1600 y
		(Ms Th$_1$)		228*	228.031 064		5.75 y
89	Actinium	Ac		227*	227.027 749		21.77 y
		(Ms Th$_2$)		228*	228.031 015		6.15 h
90	Thorium	Th	232.0381				
		(Rd Ac)		227*	227.027 701		18.72 d
		(Rd Th)		228*	228.028 716		1.913 y
				229*	229.031 757		7300 y
		(Io)		230*	230.033 127		75.000 y
(90)	(Thorium)	(UY)		231*	231.036 299		25.52 h
		(Th)		232*	232.038 051	100	1.40×10^{10} y
		(UX$_1$)		234*	234.043 593		24.1 d
91	Protactinium	Pa		231*	231.035 880		32.760 y
		(Uz)		234*	234.043 300		6.7 h
92	Uranium	U	238.0289	232*	232.037 131		69 y
				233*	233.039 630		1.59×10^5 y
				234*	234.040 946	0.0055	2.45×10^5 y
		(Ac U)		235*	235.043 924	0.720	7.04×10^8 y
				236*	236.045 562		2.34×10^7 y
		(UI)		238*	238.050 784	99.2745	4.47×10^9 y
93	Neptunium	Np		235*	235.044 057		396 d
				236*	236.046 560		115,000 y
				237*	237.048 168		2.14×10^6 y
94	Plutonium	Pu		236*	236.046 033		2.87 y
				238*	238.049 555		87.7 y
				239*	239.052 157		24,120 y
				240*	240.053 808		6560 y
				241*	241.056 846		14.4 y
				242*	242.058 737		3.73×10^5 y
				244*	244.064 200		8.1×10^7 y

[a] The masses in the sixth column are atomic masses, which include the mass of Z electrons. Data are from the National Nuclear Data Center, Brookhaven National Laboratory, prepared by Jagdish K. Tuli, July 1990. The data are based on experimental results reported in *Nuclear Data Sheets* and *Nuclear Physics* and also from *Chart of the Nuclides,* 14th ed. Atomic masses are based on those by A. H. Wapstra, G. Audi, and R. Hoekstra. Isotopic abundances are based on those by N. E. Holden.

Mathematics Review

These appendices in mathematics are intended as a brief review of operations and methods. Early in this course, you should be totally familiar with basic algebraic techniques, analytic geometry, and trigonometry. The appendices on differential and integral calculus are more detailed and are intended for those students who have difficulty applying calculus concepts to physical situations.

B.1 SCIENTIFIC NOTATION

Many quantities that scientists deal with often have very large or very small values. For example, the speed of light is about 300 000 000 m/s and the ink required to make the dot over an i in this textbook has a mass of about 0.000 000 001 kg. Obviously, it is very cumbersome to read, write, and keep track of numbers such as these. We avoid this problem by using a method dealing with powers of the number 10:

$$10^0 = 1$$

$$10^1 = 10$$

$$10^2 = 10 \times 10 = 100$$

$$10^3 = 10 \times 10 \times 10 = 1000$$

$$10^4 = 10 \times 10 \times 10 \times 10 = 10\ 000$$

$$10^5 = 10 \times 10 \times 10 \times 10 \times 10 = 100\ 000$$

and so on. The number of zeros corresponds to the power to which 10 is raised, called the **exponent** of 10. For example, the speed of light, 300 000 000 m/s, can be expressed as 3×10^8 m/s.

In this method, some representative numbers smaller than unity are

$$10^{-1} = \frac{1}{10} = 0.1$$

$$10^{-2} = \frac{1}{10 \times 10} = 0.01$$

$$10^{-3} = \frac{1}{10 \times 10 \times 10} = 0.001$$

$$10^{-4} = \frac{1}{10 \times 10 \times 10 \times 10} = 0.0001$$

$$10^{-5} = \frac{1}{10 \times 10 \times 10 \times 10 \times 10} = 0.00001$$

In these cases, the number of places the decimal point is to the left of the digit 1 equals the value of the (negative) exponent. Numbers expressed as some power of 10 multiplied by another number between 1 and 10 are said to be in **scientific notation.** For example, the scientific notation for 5 943 000 000 is 5.943×10^9 and that for 0.0000832 is 8.32×10^{-5}.

When numbers expressed in scientific notation are being multiplied, the following general rule is very useful:

$$10^n \times 10^m = 10^{n+m} \qquad \text{(B.1)}$$

where n and m can be *any* numbers (not necessarily integers). For example, $10^2 \times 10^5 = 10^7$. The rule also applies if one of the exponents is negative: $10^3 \times 10^{-8} = 10^{-5}$.

When dividing numbers expressed in scientific notation, note that

$$\frac{10^n}{10^m} = 10^n \times 10^{-m} = 10^{n-m} \qquad \text{(B.2)}$$

EXERCISES

With help from the above rules, verify the answers to the following:

1. $86\ 400 = 8.64 \times 10^4$
2. $9\ 816,762.5 = 9.8167625 \times 10^6$
3. $0.0000000398 = 3.98 \times 10^{-8}$
4. $(4 \times 10^8)(9 \times 10^9) = 3.6 \times 10^{18}$
5. $(3 \times 10^7)(6 \times 10^{-12}) = 1.8 \times 10^{-4}$
6. $\dfrac{75 \times 10^{-11}}{5 \times 10^{-3}} = 1.5 \times 10^{-7}$
7. $\dfrac{(3 \times 10^6)(8 \times 10^{-2})}{(2 \times 10^{17})(6 \times 10^5)} = 2 \times 10^{-18}$

B.2 ALGEBRA

Some Basic Rules

When algebraic operations are performed, the laws of arithmetic apply. Symbols such as x, y, and z are usually used to represent quantities that are not specified, what are called the **unknowns.**

First, consider the equation

$$8x = 32$$

If we wish to solve for x, we can divide (or multiply) each side of the equation by the same factor without destroying the equality. In this case, if we divide both sides by 8, we have

$$\frac{8x}{8} = \frac{32}{8}$$

$$x = 4$$

Next consider the equation

$$x + 2 = 8$$

In this type of expression, we can add or subtract the same quantity from each side. If we subtract 2 from each side, we get

$$x + 2 - 2 = 8 - 2$$

$$x = 6$$

In general, if $x + a = b$, then $x = b - a$.

Now consider the equation

$$\frac{x}{5} = 9$$

If we multiply each side by 5, we are left with x on the left by itself and 45 on the right:

$$\left(\frac{x}{5}\right)(5) = 9 \times 5$$

$$x = 45$$

In all cases, *whatever operation is performed on the left side of the equality must also be performed on the right side.*

The following rules for multiplying, dividing, adding, and subtracting fractions should be recalled, where a, b, and c are three numbers:

	Rule	**Example**
Multiplying	$\left(\dfrac{a}{b}\right)\left(\dfrac{c}{d}\right) = \dfrac{ac}{bd}$	$\left(\dfrac{2}{3}\right)\left(\dfrac{4}{5}\right) = \dfrac{8}{15}$
Dividing	$\dfrac{(a/b)}{(c/d)} = \dfrac{ad}{bc}$	$\dfrac{2/3}{4/5} = \dfrac{(2)(5)}{(4)(3)} = \dfrac{10}{12}$
Adding	$\dfrac{a}{b} \pm \dfrac{c}{d} = \dfrac{ad \pm bc}{bd}$	$\dfrac{2}{3} - \dfrac{4}{5} = \dfrac{(2)(5) - (4)(3)}{(3)(5)} = -\dfrac{2}{15}$

EXERCISES

In the following exercises, solve for x:

Answers

1. $a = \dfrac{1}{1 + x}$ $x = \dfrac{1 - a}{a}$

2. $3x - 5 = 13$ $x = 6$

3. $ax - 5 = bx + 2$ $x = \dfrac{7}{a - b}$

4. $\dfrac{5}{2x + 6} = \dfrac{3}{4x + 8}$ $x = -\dfrac{11}{7}$

Powers

When powers of a given quantity x are multiplied, the following rule applies:

$$x^n x^m = x^{n+m} \tag{B.3}$$

For example, $x^2 x^4 = x^{2+4} = x^6$.

When dividing the powers of a given quantity, the rule is

$$\frac{x^n}{x^m} = x^{n-m} \qquad \text{(B.4)}$$

For example, $x^8/x^2 = x^{8-2} = x^6$.

A power that is a fraction, such as $\frac{1}{3}$, corresponds to a root as follows:

$$x^{1/n} = \sqrt[n]{x} \qquad \text{(B.5)}$$

For example, $4^{1/3} = \sqrt[3]{4} = 1.5874$. (A scientific calculator is useful for such calculations.)

Finally, any quantity x^n raised to the mth power is

$$(x^n)^m = x^{nm} \qquad \text{(B.6)}$$

Table B.1 summarizes the rules of exponents.

TABLE B.1 Rules of Exponents

$$x^0 = 1$$
$$x^1 = x$$
$$x^n x^m = x^{n+m}$$
$$x^n/x^m = x^{n-m}$$
$$x^{1/n} = \sqrt[n]{x}$$
$$(x^n)^m = x^{nm}$$

EXERCISES

Verify the following:

1. $3^2 \times 3^3 = 243$
2. $x^5 x^{-8} = x^{-3}$
3. $x^{10}/x^{-5} = x^{15}$
4. $5^{1/3} = 1.709975$ (Use your calculator.)
5. $60^{1/4} = 2.783158$ (Use your calculator.)
6. $(x^4)^3 = x^{12}$

Factoring

Some useful formulas for factoring an equation are

$$ax + ay + az = a(x + y + x) \qquad \text{common factor}$$
$$a^2 + 2ab + b^2 = (a + b)^2 \qquad \text{perfect square}$$
$$a^2 - b^2 = (a + b)(a - b) \qquad \text{differences of squares}$$

Quadratic Equations

The general form of a quadratic equation is

$$ax^2 + bx + c = 0 \qquad \text{(B.7)}$$

where x is the unknown quantity and a, b, and c are numerical factors referred to as **coefficients** of the equation. This equation has two roots, given by

$$x = \frac{-b \pm \sqrt{b^2 - 4ac}}{2a} \qquad \text{(B.8)}$$

If $b^2 \geq 4ac$, the roots are real.

EXAMPLE 1

The equation $x^2 + 5x + 4 = 0$ has the following roots corresponding to the two signs of the square-root term:

$$x = \frac{-5 \pm \sqrt{5^2 - (4)(1)(4)}}{2(1)} = \frac{-5 \pm \sqrt{9}}{2} = \frac{-5 \pm 3}{2}$$

$$x_+ = \frac{-5 + 3}{2} = -1 \qquad x_- = \frac{-5 - 3}{2} = -4$$

where x_+ refers to the root corresponding to the positive sign and x_- refers to the root corresponding to the negative sign.

EXERCISES

Solve the following quadratic equations:

Answers

1. $x^2 + 2x - 3 = 0$ $x_+ = 1$ $x_- = -3$
2. $2x^2 - 5x + 2 = 0$ $x_+ = 2$ $x_- = \frac{1}{2}$
3. $2x^2 - 4x - 9 = 0$ $x_+ = 1 + \sqrt{22}/2$ $x_- = 1 - \sqrt{22}/2$

Linear Equations

A linear equation has the general form

$$y = mx + b \tag{B.9}$$

where m and b are constants. This equation is referred to as being linear because the graph of y versus x is a straight line, as shown in Figure B.1. The constant b, called the **y-intercept**, represents the value of y at which the straight line intersects the y axis. The constant m is equal to the **slope** of the straight line and is also equal to the tangent of the angle that the line makes with the x axis. If any two points on the straight line are specified by the coordinates (x_1, y_1) and (x_2, y_2), as in Figure B.1, then the **slope** of the straight line can be expressed as

$$\text{Slope} = \frac{y_2 - y_1}{x_2 - x_1} = \frac{\Delta y}{\Delta x} = \tan \theta \tag{B.10}$$

Note that m and b can have either positive or negative values. If $m > 0$, the straight line has a *positive* slope, as in Figure B.1. If $m < 0$, the straight line has a *negative* slope. In Figure B.1, both m and b are positive. Three other possible situations are shown in Figure B.2.

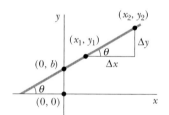

FIGURE B.1

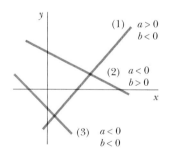

FIGURE B.2

EXERCISES

1. Draw graphs of the following straight lines:
(a) $y = 5x + 3$ (b) $y = -2x + 4$ (c) $y = -3x - 6$
2. Find the slopes of the straight lines described in Exercise 1.

Answers (a) 5   (b) -2 (c) -3

3. Find the slopes of the straight lines that pass through the following sets of points:

(a) $(0, -4)$ and $(4, 2)$, (b) $(0, 0)$ and $(2, -5)$, and (c) $(-5, 2)$ and $(4, -2)$

Answers (a) $3/2$ (b) $-5/2$ (c) $-4/9$

Solving Simultaneous Linear Equations

Consider the equation $3x + 5y = 15$, which has two unknowns, x and y. Such an equation does not have a unique solution. Instead, $(x = 0, y = 3)$, $(x = 5, y = 0)$, and $(x = 2, y = 9/5)$ are all solutions to this equation.

    If a problem has two unknowns, a unique solution is possible only if we have *two* equations. In general, if a problem has n unknowns, its solution requires n equations. In order to solve two simultaneous equations involving two unknowns, x and y, we solve one of the equations for x in terms of y and substitute this expression into the other equation.

EXAMPLE 2

Solve the following two simultaneous equations:

$$(1) \quad 5x + y = -8$$
$$(2) \quad 2x - 2y = 4$$

Solution From (2), $x = y + 2$. Substitution of this into (1) gives

$$5(y + 2) + y = -8$$
$$6y = -18$$
$$y = -3$$
$$x = y + 2 = \boxed{-1}$$

Alternate Solution Multiply each term in (1) by the factor 2 and add the result to (2):

$$10x + 2y = -16$$
$$\underline{2x - 2y = 4}$$
$$12x = -12$$
$$x = -1$$
$$y = x - 2 = \boxed{-3}$$

    Two linear equations containing two unknowns can also be solved by a graphical method. If the straight lines corresponding to the two equations are plotted in a conventional coordinate system, the intersection of the two lines represents the solution. For example, consider the two equations

$$x - y = 2$$
$$x - 2y = -1$$

These are plotted in Figure B.3. The intersection of the two lines has the coordinates $x = 5$, $y = 3$. This represents the solution to the equations. You should check this solution by the analytical technique discussed above.

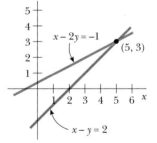

FIGURE B.3

EXERCISES

Solve the following pairs of simultaneous equations involving two unknowns:

		Answers
1.	$x + y = 8$ $x - y = 2$	$x = 5, y = 3$
2.	$98 - T = 10a$ $T - 49 = 5a$	$T = 65, a = 3.27$
3.	$6x + 2y = 6$ $8x - 4y = 28$	$x = 2, y = -3$

Logarithms

Suppose that a quantity x is expressed as a power of some quantity a:

$$x = a^y \tag{B.11}$$

The number a is called the **base** number. The **logarithm** of x with respect to the base a is equal to the exponent to which the base must be raised in order to satisfy the expression $x = a^y$:

$$y = \log_a x \tag{B.12}$$

Conversely, the **antilogarithm** of y is the number x:

$$x = \text{antilog}_a y \tag{B.13}$$

In practice, the two bases most often used are base 10, called the *common* logarithm base, and base $e = 2.718 \ldots$, called the *natural* logarithm base. When common logarithms are used,

$$y = \log_{10} x \qquad (\text{or } x = 10^y) \tag{B.14}$$

When natural logarithms are used,

$$y = \ln_e x \qquad (\text{or } x = e^y) \tag{B.15}$$

For example, $\log_{10} 52 = 1.716$, so that $\text{antilog}_{10} 1.716 = 10^{1.716} = 52$. Likewise, $\ln_e 52 = 3.951$, so $\text{antiln}_e 3.951 = e^{3.951} = 52$.

In general, note that you can convert between base 10 and base e with the equality

$$\ln_e x = (2.302585) \log_{10} x \tag{B.16}$$

Finally, some useful properties of logarithms are

$$\log(ab) = \log a + \log b$$
$$\log(a/b) = \log a - \log b$$
$$\log(a^n) = n \log a$$
$$\ln e = 1$$
$$\ln e^a = a$$
$$\ln\left(\frac{1}{a}\right) = -\ln a$$

B.3 GEOMETRY

The **distance** d between two points having coordinates (x_1, y_1) and (x_2, y_2) is

$$d = \sqrt{(x_2 - x_1)^2 + (y_2 - y_1)^2} \tag{B.17}$$

Radian measure: The arc length s of a circular arc (Fig. B.4) is proportional to the radius r for a fixed value of θ (in radians):

$$s = r\theta$$

$$\theta = \frac{s}{r}$$

(B.18)

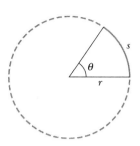

FIGURE B.4

Table B.2 gives the areas and volumes for several geometric shapes used throughout this text:

TABLE B.2   Useful Information for Geometry

Shape	Area or Volume	Shape	Area or Volume
Rectangle	Area $= \ell w$	Sphere	Surface area $= 4\pi r^2$ Volume $= \dfrac{4\pi r^3}{3}$
Circle	Area $= \pi r^2$ (Circumference $= 2\pi r$)	Cylinder	Volume $= \pi r^2 \ell$
Triangle	Area $= \frac{1}{2} bh$	Rectangular box	Area $=$ $2(\ell h + \ell w + hw)$ Volume $= \ell wh$

The equation of a **straight line** (Fig. B.5) is

$$y = mx + b$$

(B.19)

where b is the y-intercept and m is the slope of the line.

The equation of a **circle** or radius R centered at the origin is

$$x^2 + y^2 = R^2$$

(B.20)

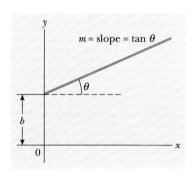

FIGURE B.5

The equation of an **ellipse** having the origin at its center (Fig. B.6) is

$$\frac{x^2}{a^2} + \frac{y^2}{b^2} = 1$$

(B.21)

where a is the length of the semi-major axis (the longer one) and b is the length of the semi-minor axis (the shorter one).

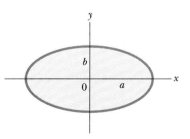

FIGURE B.6

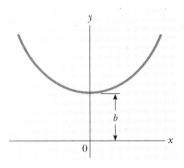

FIGURE B.7

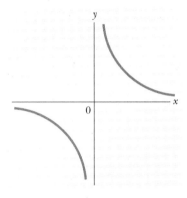

FIGURE B.8

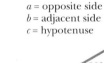
a = opposite side
b = adjacent side
c = hypotenuse

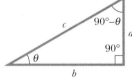

FIGURE B.9

The equation of a **parabola** the vertex of which is at $y = b$ (Fig. B.7) is

$$y = ax^2 + b \tag{B.22}$$

The equation of a **rectangular hyperbola** (Fig. B.8) is

$$xy = \text{constant} \tag{B.23}$$

B.4 TRIGONOMETRY

That portion of mathematics based on the special properties of the right triangle is called trigonometry. By definition, a right triangle is one containing at 90° angle. Consider the right triangle shown in Figure B.9, where side a is opposite the angle θ, side b is adjacent to the angle θ, and side c is the hypotenuse of the triangle. The three basic trigonometric functions defined by such a triangle are the sine (sin), cosine (cos), and tangent (tan) functions. In terms of the angle θ, these functions are defined by

$$\sin \theta \equiv \frac{\text{side opposite } \theta}{\text{hypotenuse}} = \frac{a}{c} \tag{B.24}$$

$$\cos \theta \equiv \frac{\text{side adjacent to } \theta}{\text{hypotenuse}} = \frac{b}{c} \tag{B.25}$$

$$\tan \theta \equiv \frac{\text{side opposite } \theta}{\text{side adjacent to } \theta} = \frac{a}{b} \tag{B.26}$$

The Pythagorean theorem provides the following relationship between the sides of a right triangle:

$$c^2 = a^2 + b^2 \tag{B.27}$$

From the above definitions and the Pythagorean theorem, it follows that

$$\sin^2 \theta + \cos^2 \theta = 1$$

$$\tan \theta = \frac{\sin \theta}{\cos \theta}$$

The cosecant, secant, and cotangent functions are defined by

$$\csc \theta \equiv \frac{1}{\sin \theta} \qquad \sec \theta \equiv \frac{1}{\cos \theta} \qquad \cot \theta \equiv \frac{1}{\tan \theta}$$

The relationship below follow directly from the right triangle shown in Figure B.9:

$$\sin \theta = \cos(90° - \theta)$$

$$\cos \theta = \sin(90° - \theta)$$

$$\cot \theta = \tan(90° - \theta)$$

Some properties of trigonometric functions are

$$\sin(-\theta) = -\sin \theta$$

$$\cos(-\theta) = \cos \theta$$

$$\tan(-\theta) = -\tan \theta$$

The following relationships apply to *any* triangle, as shown in Figure B.10:

$$\alpha + \beta + \gamma = 180°$$

Law of cosines
$$a^2 = b^2 + c^2 - 2bc \cos \alpha$$
$$b^2 = a^2 + c^2 - 2ac \cos \beta$$
$$c^2 = a^2 + b^2 - 2ab \cos \gamma$$

Law of sines
$$\frac{a}{\sin \alpha} = \frac{b}{\sin \beta} = \frac{c}{\sin \gamma}$$

Table B.3 lists a number of useful trigonometric identities.

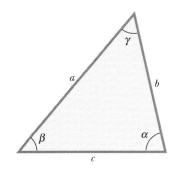

FIGURE B.10

TABLE B.3 Some Trigonometric Identities

$$\sin^2 \theta + \cos^2 \theta = 1 \qquad\qquad \csc^2 \theta = 1 + \cot^2 \theta$$

$$\sec^2 \theta = 1 + \tan^2 \theta \qquad\qquad \sin^2 \frac{\theta}{2} = \frac{1}{2}(1 - \cos \theta)$$

$$\sin 2\theta = 2 \sin \theta \cos \theta \qquad\qquad \cos^2 \frac{\theta}{2} = \frac{1}{2}(1 + \cos \theta)$$

$$\cos 2\theta = \cos^2 \theta - \sin^2 \theta \qquad\qquad 1 - \cos \theta = 2 \sin^2 \frac{\theta}{2}$$

$$\tan 2\theta = \frac{2 \tan \theta}{1 - \tan^2 \theta} \qquad\qquad \tan \frac{\theta}{2} = \sqrt{\frac{1 - \cos \theta}{1 + \cos \theta}}$$

$$\sin(A \pm B) = \sin A \cos B \pm \cos A \sin B$$
$$\cos(A \pm B) = \cos A \cos B \mp \sin A \sin B$$
$$\sin A \pm \sin B = 2 \sin[\tfrac{1}{2}(A \pm B)]\cos[\tfrac{1}{2}(A \mp B)]$$
$$\cos A + \cos B = 2 \cos[\tfrac{1}{2}(A + B)]\cos[\tfrac{1}{2}(A - B)]$$
$$\cos A - \cos B = 2 \sin[\tfrac{1}{2}(A + B)]\sin[\tfrac{1}{2}(B - A)]$$

EXAMPLE 3

Consider the right triangle in Figure B.11, in which $a = 2$, $b = 5$, and c is unknown. From the Pythagorean theorem, we have

$$c^2 = a^2 + b^2 = 2^2 + 5^2 = 4 + 25 = 29$$

$$c = \sqrt{29} = \boxed{5.39}$$

To find the angle θ, note that

$$\tan \theta = \frac{a}{b} = \frac{2}{5} = 0.400$$

From a table of functions or from a calculator, we have

$$\theta = \tan^{-1}(0.400) = \boxed{21.8°}$$

where $\tan^{-1}(0.400)$ is the notation for "angle whose tangent is 0.400," sometimes written as arctan(0.400).

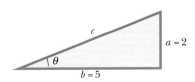

FIGURE B.11

EXERCISES

1. In Figure B.12, identify (a) the side opposite θ and (b) the side adjacent to ϕ and then find (c) $\cos \theta$, (d) $\sin \phi$, and (e) $\tan \phi$.

Answers (a) 3, (b) 3, (c) $\frac{4}{5}$, (d) $\frac{4}{5}$, and (e) $\frac{4}{3}$

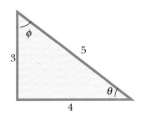

FIGURE B.12

2. In a certain right triangle, the two sides that are perpendicular to each other are 5 m and 7 m long. What is the length of the third side?

Answer 8.60 m

3. A right triangle has a hypotenuse of length 3 m, and one of its angles is 30°. What is the length of (a) the side opposite the 30° angle and (b) the side adjacent to the 30° angle?

Answers (a) 1.5 m, (b) 2.60 m

B.5 SERIES EXPANSIONS

$$(a + b)^n = a^n + \frac{n}{1!} a^{n-1}b + \frac{n(n-1)}{2!} a^{n-2}b^2 + \cdots$$

$$(1 + x)^n = 1 + nx + \frac{n(n-1)}{2!} x^2 + \cdots$$

$$e^x = 1 + x + \frac{x^2}{2!} + \frac{x^3}{3!} + \cdots$$

$$\ln(1 \pm x) = \pm x - \tfrac{1}{2}x^2 \pm \tfrac{1}{3}x^3 - \cdots$$

$$\sin x = x - \frac{x^3}{3!} + \frac{x^5}{5!} - \cdots$$

$$\cos x = 1 - \frac{x^2}{2!} + \frac{x^4}{4!} - \cdots \qquad \Bigg\rbrace \; x \text{ in radians}$$

$$\tan x = x + \frac{x^3}{3} + \frac{2x^5}{15} + \cdots \qquad |x| < \pi/2$$

For $x \ll 1$, the following approximations can be used:

$$(1 + x)^n \approx 1 + nx \qquad \sin x \approx x$$

$$e^x \approx 1 + x \qquad \cos x \approx 1$$

$$\ln(1 \pm x) \approx \pm x \qquad \tan x \approx x$$

B.6 DIFFERENTIAL CALCULUS

In various branches of science, it is sometimes necessary to use the basic tools of calculus, invented by Newton, to describe physical phenomena. The use of calculus is fundamental in the treatment of various problems in newtonian mechanics, electricity, and magnetism. In this section, we simply state some basic properties and "rules of thumb" that should be a useful review to the student.

First, a **function** must be specified that relates one variable to another (such as a coordinate as a function of time). Suppose one of the variables is called y (the dependent variable), the other x (the independent variable). We might have a function relationship such as

$$y(x) = ax^3 + bx^2 + cx + d$$

If a, b, c, and d are specified constants, then y can be calculated for any value of x. We usually deal with continuous functions, that is, those for which y varies "smoothly" with x.

The **derivative** of y with respect to x is defined as the limit, as Δx approaches zero, of the slopes of chords drawn between two points on the y versus x curve. Mathematically, we write this definition as

$$\frac{dy}{dx} = \lim_{\Delta x \to 0} \frac{\Delta y}{\Delta x} = \lim_{\Delta x \to 0} \frac{y(x + \Delta x) - y(x)}{\Delta x} \qquad \text{(B.28)}$$

where Δy and Δx are defined as $\Delta x = x_2 - x_1$ and $\Delta y = y_2 - y_1$ (Fig. B.13). It is important to note that dy/dx *does not* mean dy divided by dx, but is simply a notation of the limiting process of the derivative as defined by Equation B.28.

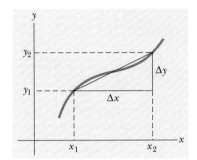

FIGURE B.13

A useful expression to remember when $y(x) = ax^n$, where a is a *constant* and n is *any* positive or negative number (integer or fraction), is

$$\frac{dy}{dx} = nax^{n-1} \qquad \text{(B.29)}$$

If $y(x)$ is a polynomial or algebraic function of x, we apply Equation B.29 to *each* term in the polynomial and take $da/dx = 0$. In Examples 4 through 7, we evaluate the derivatives of several functions.

EXAMPLE 4

Suppose $y(x)$ (that is, y as a function of x) is given by

$$y(x) = ax^3 + bx + c$$

where a and b are constants. Then it follows that

$$y(x + \Delta x) = a(x + \Delta x)^3$$
$$+ b(x + \Delta x) + c$$

$$y(x + \Delta x) = a(x^3 + 3x^2\,\Delta x + 3x\,\Delta x^2 + \Delta x^3)$$
$$+ b(x + \Delta x) + c$$

so

$$\Delta y = y(x + \Delta x) - y(x) = a(3x^2\,\Delta x + 3x\,\Delta x^2 + \Delta x^3)$$
$$+ b\,\Delta x$$

Substituting this into Equation B.28 gives

$$\frac{dy}{dx} = \lim_{\Delta x \to 0} \frac{\Delta y}{\Delta x} = \lim_{\Delta x \to 0} [3ax^2 + 3x\,\Delta x + \Delta x^2] + b$$

$$\frac{dy}{dx} = \boxed{3ax^2 + b}$$

EXAMPLE 5

$$y(x) = 8x^5 + 4x^3 + 2x + 7$$

Solution Applying Equation B.29 to each term independently, and remembering that d/dx (constant) $= 0$, we have

$$\frac{dy}{dx} = 8(5)x^4 + 4(3)x^2 + 2(1)x^0 + 0$$

$$\frac{dy}{dx} = 40x^4 + 12x^2 + 2$$

Special Properties of the Derivative

A. **Derivative of the product of two functions** If a function $f(x)$ is given by the product of two functions, say, $g(x)$ and $h(x)$, then the derivative of $f(x)$ is defined as

$$\frac{d}{dx}f(x) = \frac{d}{dx}[g(x)h(x)] = g\frac{dh}{dx} + h\frac{dg}{dx} \tag{B.30}$$

B. **Derivative of the sum of two functions** If a function $f(x)$ is equal to the sum of two functions, then the derivative of the sum is equal to the sum of the derivatives:

$$\frac{d}{dx}f(x) = \frac{d}{dx}[g(x) + h(x)] = \frac{dg}{dx} + \frac{dh}{dx} \tag{B.31}$$

C. **Chain rule of differential calculus** If $y = f(x)$ and $x = f(z)$, then dy/dx can be written as the product of two derivatives:

$$\frac{dy}{dx} = \frac{dy}{dz}\frac{dz}{dx} \tag{B.32}$$

D. **The second derivative** The second derivative of y with respect to x is defined as the derivative of the function dy/dx (the derivative of the derivative). It is usually written

$$\frac{d^2y}{dx^2} = \frac{d}{dx}\left(\frac{dy}{dx}\right) \tag{B.33}$$

EXAMPLE 6

Find the derivative of $y(x) = x^3/(x + 1)^2$ with respect to x.

Solution We can rewrite this function as $y(x) = x^3(x + 1)^{-2}$ and apply Equation B.30:

$$\frac{dy}{dx} = (x + 1)^{-2}\frac{d}{dx}(x^3) + x^3\frac{d}{dx}(x + 1)^{-2}$$

$$= (x + 1)^{-2}3x^2 + x^3(-2)(x + 1)^{-3}$$

$$\frac{dy}{dx} = \frac{3x^2}{(x + 1)^2} - \frac{2x^3}{(x + 1)^3}$$

EXAMPLE 7

A useful formula that follows from Equation B.30 is the derivative of the quotient of two functions. Show that

$$\frac{d}{dx}\left[\frac{g(x)}{h(x)}\right] = \frac{h\dfrac{dg}{dx} - g\dfrac{dh}{dx}}{h^2}$$

Solution   We can write the quotient as gh^{-1} and then apply Equations B.29 and B.30:

$$\frac{d}{dx}\left(\frac{g}{h}\right) = \frac{d}{dx}(gh^{-1}) = g\frac{d}{dx}(h^{-1}) + h^{-1}\frac{d}{dx}(g)$$

$$= -gh^{-2}\frac{dh}{dx} + h^{-1}\frac{dg}{dx}$$

$$= \frac{h\dfrac{dg}{dx} - g\dfrac{dh}{dx}}{h^2}$$

Some of the more commonly used derivatives of functions are listed in Table B.4.

B.7   INTEGRAL CALCULUS

We think of integration as the inverse of differentiation. As an example, consider the expression

$$f(x) = \frac{dy}{dx} = 3ax^2 + b \tag{B.34}$$

which was the result of differentiating the function

$$y(x) = ax^3 + bx + c$$

in Example 4. We can write Equation B.34 as $dy = f(x)\, dx = (3ax^2 + b)\, dx$ and obtain $y(x)$ by "summing" over all values of x. Mathematically, we write this inverse operation

$$y(x) = \int f(x)\, dx$$

For the function $f(x)$ given by Equation B.34, we have

$$y(x) = \int (3ax^2 + b)\, dx = ax^3 + bx + c$$

where c is a constant of the integration. This type of integral is called an *indefinite integral* because its value depends on the choice of c.

A general **indefinite integral** $I(x)$ is defined as

$$I(x) = \int f(x)\, dx \tag{B.35}$$

where $f(x)$ is called the *integrand* and $f(x) = \dfrac{dI(x)}{dx}$.

For a *general continuous* function $f(x)$, the integral can be described as the area under the curve bounded by $f(x)$ and the x axis, between two specified values of x, say, x_1 and x_2, as in Figure B.14.

The area of the blue element is approximately $f_i\, \Delta x_i$. If we sum all these area elements from x_1 to x_2 and take the limit of this sum as $\Delta x_i \to 0$, we obtain the *true* area under the curve bounded by $f(x)$ and x, between the limits x_1 and x_2:

$$\text{Area} = \lim_{\Delta x_i \to 0} \sum_i f(x_i)\, \Delta x_i = \int_{x_1}^{x_2} f(x)\, dx \tag{B.36}$$

Integrals of the type defined by Equation B.36 are called **definite integrals**.

TABLE B.4   Derivatives for Several Functions

$$\frac{d}{dx}(a) = 0$$

$$\frac{d}{dx}(ax^n) = nax^{n-1}$$

$$\frac{d}{dx}(e^{ax}) = ae^{ax}$$

$$\frac{d}{dx}(\sin ax) = a\cos ax$$

$$\frac{d}{dx}(\cos ax) = -a\sin ax$$

$$\frac{d}{dx}(\tan ax) = a\sec^2 ax$$

$$\frac{d}{dx}(\cot ax) = -a\csc^2 ax$$

$$\frac{d}{dx}(\sec x) = \tan x\sec x$$

$$\frac{d}{dx}(\csc x) = -\cot x\csc x$$

$$\frac{d}{dx}(\ln ax) = \frac{1}{x}$$

Note: The letters a and n are constants.

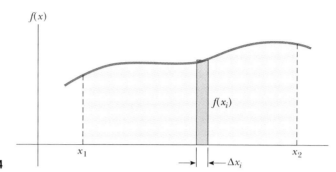

FIGURE B.14

One common integral that arises in practical situations has the form

$$\int x^n \, dx = \frac{x^{n+1}}{n+1} + c \qquad (n \neq -1) \tag{B.37}$$

This result is obvious, being that differentiation of the right-hand side with respect to x gives $f(x) = x^n$ directly. If the limits of the integration are known, this integral becomes a *definite integral* and is written

$$\int_{x_1}^{x_2} x^n \, dx = \frac{x_2^{n+1} - x_1^{n+1}}{n+1} \qquad (n \neq -1) \tag{B.38}$$

EXAMPLES

1. $\displaystyle\int_0^a x^2 \, dx = \frac{x^3}{3}\bigg]_0^a = \frac{a^3}{3}$

2. $\displaystyle\int_0^b x^{3/2} \, dx = \frac{x^{5/2}}{5/2}\bigg]_0^b = \frac{2}{5} b^{5/2}$

3. $\displaystyle\int_3^5 x \, dx = \frac{x^2}{2}\bigg]_3^5 = \frac{5^2 - 3^2}{2} = 8$

Partial Integration

Sometimes it is useful to apply the method of *partial integration* (also called "integrating by parts") to evaluate certain integrals. The method uses the property that

$$\int u \, dv = uv - \int v \, du \tag{B.39}$$

where u and v are *carefully* chosen so as to reduce a complex integral to a simpler one. In many cases, several reductions have to be made. Consider the function

$$I(x) = \int x^2 e^x \, dx$$

This can be evaluated by integrating by parts twice. First, if we choose $u = x^2$, $v = e^x$, we get

$$\int x^2 e^x \, dx = \int x^2 \, d(e^x) = x^2 e^x - 2 \int e^x x \, dx + c_1$$

Now, in the second term, choose $u = x$, $v = e^x$, which gives

$$\int x^2 e^x \, dx = x^2 e^x - 2xe^x + 2 \int e^x \, dx + c_1$$

or

$$\int x^2 e^x \, dx = x^2 e^x - 2xe^x + 2e^x + c_2$$

The Perfect Differential

Another useful method to remember is the use of the *perfect differential,* in which we look for a change of variable such that the differential of the function is the differential of the independent variable appearing in the integrand. For example, consider the integral

$$I(x) = \int \cos^2 x \sin x \, dx$$

This becomes easy to evaluate if we rewrite the differential as $d(\cos x) = -\sin x \, dx$. The integral then becomes

$$\int \cos^2 x \sin x \, dx = -\int \cos^2 x \, d(\cos x)$$

If we now change variables, letting $y = \cos x$, we get

$$\int \cos^2 x \sin x \, dx = -\int y^2 dy = -\frac{y^3}{3} + c = -\frac{\cos^3 x}{3} + c$$

Table B.5 lists some useful indefinite integrals. Table B.6 gives Gauss's probability integral and other definite integrals. A more complete list can be found in various handbooks, such as *The Handbook of Chemistry and Physics,* CRC Press.

TABLE B.5 Some Indefinite Integrals (an arbitrary constant should be added to each of these integrals)

$$\int x^n \, dx = \frac{x^{n+1}}{n+1} \qquad \text{(provided } n \neq -1\text{)}$$

$$\int \frac{dx}{x} = \int x^{-1} \, dx = \ln x$$

$$\int \frac{dx}{a+bx} = \frac{1}{b} \ln(a+bx)$$

$$\int \frac{dx}{(a+bx)^2} = -\frac{1}{b(a+bx)}$$

$$\int \frac{dx}{a^2+x^2} = \frac{1}{a} \tan^{-1} \frac{x}{a}$$

$$\int \frac{dx}{a^2-x^2} = \frac{1}{2a} \ln \frac{a+x}{a-x} \qquad (a^2 - x^2 > 0)$$

$$\int \frac{dx}{x^2-a^2} = \frac{1}{2a} \ln \frac{x-a}{x+a} \qquad (x^2 - a^2 > 0)$$

$$\int \frac{x \, dx}{a^2 \pm x^2} = \pm \frac{1}{2} \ln(a^2 \pm x^2)$$

$$\int \frac{dx}{\sqrt{a^2-x^2}} = \sin^{-1} \frac{x}{a} = -\cos^{-1} \frac{x}{a} \qquad (a^2 - x^2 > 0)$$

$$\int \frac{dx}{\sqrt{x^2 \pm a^2}} = \ln(x + \sqrt{x^2 \pm a^2})$$

$$\int \frac{x \, dx}{\sqrt{a^2-x^2}} = -\sqrt{a^2-x^2}$$

$$\int \frac{x \, dx}{\sqrt{x^2 \pm a^2}} = \sqrt{x^2 \pm a^2}$$

$$\int \sqrt{a^2-x^2} \, dx = \frac{1}{2}\left(x\sqrt{a^2-x^2} + a^2 \sin^{-1} \frac{x}{a} \right)$$

$$\int x\sqrt{a^2-x^2} \, dx = -\frac{1}{3}(a^2-x^2)^{3/2}$$

$$\int \sqrt{x^2 \pm a^2} \, dx = \frac{1}{2}[x\sqrt{x^2 \pm a^2} \pm a^2 \ln(x + \sqrt{x^2 \pm a^2})]$$

$$\int x(\sqrt{x^2 \pm a^2}) \, dx = \frac{1}{3}(x^2 \pm a^2)^{3/2}$$

$$\int e^{ax} \, dx = \frac{1}{a} e^{ax}$$

$$\int \ln ax \, dx = (x \ln ax) - x$$

$$\int xe^{ax} \, dx = \frac{e^{ax}}{a^2}(ax - 1)$$

$$\int \frac{dx}{a+be^{cx}} = \frac{x}{a} - \frac{1}{ac} \ln(a + be^{cx})$$

$$\int \sin ax \, dx = -\frac{1}{a} \cos ax$$

$$\int \cos ax \, dx = \frac{1}{a} \sin ax$$

$$\int \tan ax \, dx = -\frac{1}{a} \ln(\cos ax) = \frac{1}{a} \ln(\sec ax)$$

$$\int \cot ax \, dx = \frac{1}{a} \ln(\sin ax)$$

$$\int \sec ax \, dx = \frac{1}{a} \ln(\sec ax + \tan ax) = \frac{1}{a} \ln\left[\tan\left(\frac{ax}{2} + \frac{\pi}{4} \right) \right]$$

$$\int \csc ax \, dx = \frac{1}{a} \ln(\csc ax - \cot ax) = \frac{1}{a} \ln\left(\tan \frac{ax}{2} \right)$$

$$\int \sin^2 ax \, dx = \frac{x}{2} - \frac{\sin 2ax}{4a}$$

$$\int \cos^2 ax \, dx = \frac{x}{2} + \frac{\sin 2ax}{4a}$$

$$\int \frac{dx}{\sin^2 ax} = -\frac{1}{a} \cot ax$$

$$\int \frac{dx}{\cos^2 ax} = \frac{1}{a} \tan ax$$

$$\int \tan^2 ax \, dx = \frac{1}{a}(\tan ax) - x$$

$$\int \cot^2 ax \, dx = -\frac{1}{a}(\cot ax) - x$$

$$\int \sin^{-1} ax \, dx = x(\sin^{-1} ax) + \frac{\sqrt{1 - a^2 x^2}}{a}$$

$$\int \cos^{-1} ax \, dx = x(\cos^{-1} ax) - \frac{\sqrt{1 - a^2 x^2}}{a}$$

$$\int \frac{dx}{(x^2 + a^2)^{3/2}} = \frac{x}{a^2 \sqrt{x^2 + a^2}}$$

$$\int \frac{x \, dx}{(x^2 + a^2)^{3/2}} = -\frac{1}{\sqrt{x^2 + a^2}}$$

TABLE B.6   Gauss's Probability Integral and Related Integrals

$$I_0 = \int_0^\infty e^{-\alpha x^2}\, dx = \frac{1}{2}\sqrt{\frac{\pi}{\alpha}} \qquad \text{(Gauss's probability integral)}$$

$$I_1 = \int_0^\infty x e^{-\alpha x^2}\, dx = \frac{1}{2\alpha}$$

$$I_2 = \int_0^\infty x^2 e^{-\alpha x^2}\, dx = -\frac{dI_0}{d\alpha} = \frac{1}{4}\sqrt{\frac{\pi}{\alpha^3}}$$

$$I_3 = \int_0^\infty x^3 e^{-\alpha x^2}\, dx = -\frac{dI_1}{d\alpha} = \frac{1}{2\alpha^2}$$

$$I_4 = \int_0^\infty x^4 e^{-\alpha x^2}\, dx = \frac{d^2 I_0}{d\alpha^2} = \frac{3}{8}\sqrt{\frac{\pi}{\alpha^5}}$$

$$I_5 = \int_0^\infty x^5 e^{-\alpha x^2}\, dx = \frac{d^2 I_1}{d\alpha^2} = \frac{1}{\alpha^3}$$

$$\vdots$$

$$I_{2n} = (-1)^n \frac{d^n}{d\alpha^n} I_0$$

$$I_{2n+1} = (-1)^n \frac{d^n}{d\alpha^n} I_1$$

Periodic Table of the Elements*

Group I	Group II	Transition elements						
H 1								
1.0080								
$1s^1$								
Li 3	**Be** 4							
6.94	9.012							
$2s^1$	$2s^2$							
Na 11	**Mg** 12							
22.99	24.31							
$3s^1$	$3s^2$							
K 19	**Ca** 20	**Sc** 21	**Ti** 22	**V** 23	**Cr** 24	**Mn** 25	**Fe** 26	**Co** 27
39.102	40.08	44.96	47.90	50.94	51.996	54.94	55.85	58.93
$4s^1$	$4s^2$	$3d^14s^2$	$3d^24s^2$	$3d^34s^2$	$3d^54s^1$	$3d^54s^2$	$3d^64s^2$	$3d^74s^2$
Rb 37	**Sr** 38	**Y** 39	**Zr** 40	**Nb** 41	**Mo** 42	**Tc** 43	**Ru** 44	**Rh** 45
85.47	87.62	88.906	91.22	92.91	95.94	(99)	101.1	102.91
$5s^1$	$5s^2$	$4d^15s^2$	$4d^25s^2$	$4d^45s^1$	$4d^55s^1$	$4d^55s^2$	$4d^75s^1$	$4d^85s^1$
Cs 55	**Ba** 56	57-71*	**Hf** 72	**Ta** 73	**W** 74	**Re** 75	**Os** 76	**Ir** 77
132.91	137.34		178.49	180.95	183.85	186.2	190.2	192.2
$6s^1$	$6s^2$		$5d^26s^2$	$5d^36s^2$	$5d^46s^2$	$5d^56s^2$	$5d^66s^2$	$5d^76s^2$
Fr 87	**Ra** 88	89-103**	**Unq** 104	**Unp** 105	**Unh** 106	**Uns** 107	**Uno** 108	**Une** 109
(223)	(226)		(261)	(262)	(263)	(262)	(265)	(266)
$7s^1$	$7s^2$		$6d^27s^2$	$6d^37s^2$				

Symbol — **Ca** 20 — Atomic number
Atomic mass † — 40.08
$4s^2$ — Electron configuration

*Lanthanide series

La 57	**Ce** 58	**Pr** 59	**Nd** 60	**Pm** 61	**Sm** 62
138.91	140.12	140.91	144.24	(147)	150.4
$5d^16s^2$	$5d^14f^16s^2$	$4f^36s^2$	$4f^46s^2$	$4f^56s^2$	$4f^66s^2$

**Actinide series

Ac 89	**Th** 90	**Pa** 91	**U** 92	**Np** 93	**Pu** 94
(227)	(232)	(231)	(238)	(239)	(239)
$6d^17s^2$	$6d^27s^2$	$5f^26d^17s^2$	$5f^36d^17s^2$	$5f^46d^17s^2$	$5f^66d^07s^2$

◻ Atomic mass values given are averaged over isotopes in the percentages in which they exist in nature.
† For an unstable element, mass number of the most stable known isotope is given in parentheses.

		Group III	Group IV	Group V	Group VI	Group VII	Group 0
						H 1 1.0080 $1s^1$	**He** 2 4.0026 $1s^2$
		B 5 10.81 $2p^1$	**C** 6 12.011 $2p^2$	**N** 7 14.007 $2p^3$	**O** 8 15.999 $2p^4$	**F** 9 18.998 $2p^5$	**Ne** 10 20.18 $2p^6$
		Al 13 26.98 $3p^1$	**Si** 14 28.09 $3p^2$	**P** 15 30.97 $3p^3$	**S** 16 32.06 $3p^4$	**Cl** 17 35.453 $3p^5$	**Ar** 18 39.948 $3p^6$

Ni 28 58.71 $3d^84s^2$	**Cu** 29 63.54 $3d^{10}4s^2$	**Zn** 30 65.37 $3d^{10}4s^2$	**Ga** 31 69.72 $4p^1$	**Ge** 32 72.59 $4p^2$	**As** 33 74.92 $4p^3$	**Se** 34 78.96 $4p^4$	**Br** 35 79.91 $4p^5$	**Kr** 36 83.80 $4p^6$
Pd 46 106.4 $4d^{10}$	**Ag** 47 107.87 $4d^{10}5s^1$	**Cd** 48 112.40 $4d^{10}5s^2$	**In** 49 114.82 $5p^1$	**Sn** 50 118.69 $5p^2$	**Sb** 51 121.75 $5p^3$	**Te** 52 127.60 $5p^4$	**I** 53 126.90 $5p^5$	**Xe** 54 131.30 $5p^6$
Pt 78 195.09 $5d^96s^1$	**Au** 79 196.97 $5d^{10}6s^1$	**Hg** 80 200.59 $5d^{10}6s^2$	**Tl** 81 204.37 $6p^1$	**Pb** 82 207.2 $6p^2$	**Bi** 83 208.98 $6p^3$	**Po** 84 (210) $6p^4$	**At** 85 (218) $6p^5$	**Rn** 86 (222) $6p^6$

Eu 63 152.0 $4f^76s^2$	**Gd** 64 157.25 $5d^14f^76s^2$	**Tb** 65 158.92 $5d^14f^86s^2$	**Dy** 66 162.50 $4f^{10}6s^2$	**Ho** 67 164.93 $4f^{11}6s^2$	**Er** 68 167.26 $4f^{12}6s^2$	**Tm** 69 168.93 $4f^{13}6s^2$	**Yb** 70 173.04 $4f^{14}6s^2$	**Lu** 71 174.97 $5d^14f^{14}6s^2$
Am 95 (243) $5f^76d^07s^2$	**Cm** 96 (245) $5f^76d^17s^2$	**Bk** 97 (247) $5f^86d^17s^2$	**Cf** 98 (249) $5f^{10}6d^07s^2$	**Es** 99 (254) $5f^{11}6d^07s^2$	**Fm** 100 (253) $5f^{12}6d^07s^2$	**Md** 101 (255) $5f^{13}6d^07s^2$	**No** 102 (255) $6d^07s^2$	**Lr** 103 (257) $6d^17s^2$

SI Units

TABLE D.1 SI Base Units

	SI Base Unit	
Base Quantity	Name	Symbol
Length	Meter	m
Mass	Kilogram	kg
Time	Second	s
Electric current	Ampere	A
Temperature	Kelvin	K
Amount of substance	Mole	mol
Luminous intensity	Candela	cd

TABLE D.2 Some Derived SI Units

Quantity	Name	Symbol	Expression in Terms of Base Units	Expression in Terms of Other SI Units
Plane angle	Radian	rad	m/m	
Frequency	Hertz	Hz	s^{-1}	
Force	Newton	N	$kg \cdot m/s^2$	J/m
Pressure	Pascal	Pa	$kg/m \cdot s^2$	N/m^2
Energy: work	Joule	J	$kg \cdot m^2/s^2$	$N \cdot m$
Power	Watt	W	$kg \cdot m^2/s^3$	J/s
Electric charge	Coulomb	C	$A \cdot s$	
Electric potential (emf)	Volt	V	$kg \cdot m^2/A \cdot s^3$	W/A
Capacitance	Farad	F	$A^2 \cdot s^4/kg \cdot m^2$	C/V
Electric resistance	Ohm	Ω	$kg \cdot m^2/A^2 \cdot s^3$	V/A
Magnetic flux	Weber	Wb	$kg \cdot m^2/A \cdot s^2$	$V \cdot s$
Magnetic field intensity	Tesla	T	$kg/A \cdot s^2$	Wb/m^2
Inductance	Henry	H	$kg \cdot m^2/A^2 \cdot s^2$	Wb/A

Nobel Prizes

All Nobel Prizes in physics are listed (and marked with a P), as well as relevant Nobel Prizes in Chemistry (C). The key dates for some of the scientific work are supplied; they often antedate the prize considerably.

1901 (P) *Wilhelm Roentgen* for discovering x-rays (1895).

1902 (P) *Hendrik A. Lorentz* for predicting the Zeeman effect and *Pieter Zeeman* for discovering the Zeeman effect, the splitting of spectral lines in magnetic fields.

1903 (P) *Antoine-Henri Becquerel* for discovering radioactivity (1896) and *Pierre* and *Marie Curie* for studying radioactivity.

1904 (P) *Lord Rayleigh* for studying the density of gases and discovering argon.
(C) *William Ramsay* for discovering the inert gas elements helium, neon, xenon, and krypton, and placing them in the periodic table.

1905 (P) *Philipp Lenard* for studying cathode rays, electrons (1898–1899).

1906 (P) *J. J. Thomson* for studying electrical discharge through gases and discovering the electron (1897).

1907 (P) *Albert A. Michelson* for inventing optical instruments and measuring the speed of light (1880s).

1908 (P) *Gabriel Lippmann* for making the first color photographic plate, using interference methods (1891).
(C) *Ernest Rutherford* for discovering that atoms can be broken apart by alpha rays and for studying radioactivity.

1909 (P) *Guglielmo Marconi* and *Carl Ferdinand Braun* for developing wireless telegraphy.

1910 (P) *Johannes D. van der Waals* for studying the equation of state for gases and liquids (1881).

1911 (P) *Wilhelm Wien* for discovering Wien's law giving the peak of a blackbody spectrum (1893).
(C) *Marie Curie* for discovering radium and polonium (1898) and isolating radium.

1912 (P) *Nils Dalén* for inventing automatic gas regulators for lighthouses.

1913 (P) *Heike Kamerlingh Onnes* for the discovery of superconductivity and liquefying helium (1908).

1914 (P) *Max T. F. von Laue* for studying x-rays from their diffraction by crystals, showing that x-rays are electromagnetic waves (1912).
(C) *Theodore W. Richards* for determining the atomic weights of sixty elements, indicating the existence of isotopes.

1915 (P) *William Henry Bragg* and *William Lawrence Bragg*, his son, for studying the diffraction of x-rays in crystals.

1917 (P) *Charles Barkla* for studying atoms by x-ray scattering (1906).

1918 (P) *Max Planck* for discovering energy quanta (1900).

1919 (P) *Johannes Stark,* for discovering the Stark effect, the splitting of spectral lines in electric fields (1913).

1920   (P) *Charles-Édouard Guillaume* for discovering invar, a nickel-steel alloy with low coefficient of expansion.

(C) *Walther Nernst* for studying heat changes in chemical reactions and formulating the third law of thermodynamics (1918).

1921   (P) *Albert Einstein* for explaining the photoelectric effect and for his services to theoretical physics (1905).

(C) *Frederick Soddy* for studying the chemistry of radioactive substances and discovering isotopes (1912).

1922   (P) *Niels Bohr* for his model of the atom and its radiation (1913).

(C) *Francis W. Aston* for using the mass spectrograph to study atomic weights, thus discovering 212 of the 287 naturally occurring isotopes.

1923   (P) *Robert A. Millikan* for measuring the charge on an electron (1911) and for studying the photoelectric effect experimentally (1914).

1924   (P) *Karl M. G. Siegbahn* for his work in x-ray spectroscopy.

1925   (P) *James Franck* and *Gustav Hertz* for discovering the Franck-Hertz effect in electron-atom collisions.

1926   (P) *Jean-Baptiste Perrin* for studying Brownian motion to validate the discontinuous structure of matter and measure the size of atoms.

1927   (P) *Arthur Holly Compton* for discovering the Compton effect on x-rays, their change in wavelength when they collide with matter (1922), and *Charles T. R. Wilson* for inventing the cloud chamber, used to study charged particles (1906).

1928   (P) *Owen W. Richardson* for studying the thermionic effect and electrons emitted by hot metals (1911).

1929   (P) *Louis Victor de Broglie* for discovering the wave nature of electrons (1923).

1930   (P) *Chandrasekhara Venkata Raman* for studying Raman scattering, the scattering of light by atoms and molecules with a change in wavelength (1928).

1932   (P) *Werner Heisenberg* for creating quantum mechanics (1925).

1933   (P) *Erwin Schrödinger* and *Paul A. M. Dirac* for developing wave mechanics (1925) and relativistic quantum mechanics (1927).

(C) *Harold Urey* for discovering heavy hydrogen, deuterium (1931).

1935   (P) *James Chadwick* for discovering the neutron (1932).

(C) *Irène* and *Frédéric Joliot-Curie* for synthesizing new radioactive elements.

1936   (P) *Carl D. Anderson* for discovering the positron in particular and antimatter in general (1932) and *Victor F. Hess* for discovering cosmic rays.

(C) *Peter J. W. Debye* for studying dipole moments and diffraction of x-rays and electrons in gases.

1937   (P) *Clinton Davisson* and *George Thomson* for discovering the diffraction of electrons by crystals, confirming de Broglie's hypothesis (1927).

1938   (P) *Enrico Fermi* for producing the transuranic radioactive elements by neutron irradiation (1934–1937).

1939   (P) *Ernest O. Lawrence* for inventing the cyclotron.

1943   (P) *Otto Stern* for developing molecular-beam studies (1923), and using them to discover the magnetic moment of the proton (1933).

1944   (P) *Isidor I. Rabi* for discovering nuclear magnetic resonance in atomic and molecular beams.

(C) *Otto Hahn* for discovering nuclear fission (1938).

1945   (P) *Wolfgang Pauli* for discovering the exclusion principle (1924).

1946   (P) *Percy W. Bridgman* for studying physics at high pressures.

1947   (P) *Edward V. Appleton* for studying the ionosphere.

1948   (P) *Patrick M. S. Blackett* for studying nuclear physics with cloud-chamber photographs of cosmic-ray interactions.

1949   (P) *Hideki Yukawa* for predicting the existence of mesons (1935).

1950   (P) *Cecil F. Powell* for developing the method of studying cosmic rays with photographic emulsions and discovering new mesons.

1951   (P) *John D. Cockcroft* and *Ernest T. S. Walton* for transmuting nuclei in an accelerator (1932).

        (C) *Edwin M. McMillan* for producing neptunium (1940) and *Glenn T. Seaborg* for producing plutonium (1941) and further transuranic elements.

1952   (P) *Felix Bloch* and *Edward Mills Purcell* for discovering nuclear magnetic resonance in liquids and gases (1946).

1953   (P) *Frits Zernike* for inventing the phase-contrast microscope, which uses interference to provide high contrast.

1954   (P) *Max Born* for interpreting the wave function as a probability (1926) and other quantum-mechanical discoveries and *Walther Bothe* for developing the coincidence method to study subatomic particles (1930–1931), producing, in particular, the particle interpreted by Chadwick as the neutron.

1955   (P) *Willis E. Lamb, Jr.,* for discovering the Lamb shift in the hydrogen spectrum (1947) and *Polykarp Kusch* for determining the magnetic moment of the electron (1947).

1956   (P) *John Bardeen, Walter H. Brattain,* and *William Shockley* for inventing the transistor (1956).

1957   (P) *T.-D. Lee* and *C.-N. Yang* for predicting that parity is not conserved in beta decay (1956).

1958   (P) *Pavel A. Čerenkov* for discovering Čerenkov radiation (1935) and *Ilya M. Frank* and *Igor Tamm* for interpreting it (1937).

1959   (P) *Emilio G. Segrè* and *Owen Chamberlain* for discovering the antiproton (1955).

1960   (P) *Donald A. Glaser* for inventing the bubble chamber to study elementary particles (1952).

        (C) *Willard Libby* for developing radiocarbon dating (1947).

1961   (P) *Robert Hofstadter* for discovering internal structure in protons and neutrons and *Rudolf L. Mössbauer* for discovering the Mössbauer effect of recoilless gamma-ray emission (1957).

1962   (P) *Lev Davidovich Landau* for studying liquid helium and other condensed matter theoretically.

1963   (P) *Eugene P. Wigner* for applying symmetry principles to elementary-particle theory and *Maria Goeppert Mayer* and *J. Hans D. Jensen* for studying the shell model of nuclei (1947).

1964   (P) *Charles H. Townes, Nikolai G. Basov,* and *Alexandr M. Prokhorov* for developing masers (1951–1952) and lasers.

1965   (P) *Sin-itiro Tomonaga, Julian S. Schwinger,* and *Richard P. Feynman* for developing quantum electrodynamics (1948).

1966   (P) *Alfred Kastler* for his optical methods of studying atomic energy levels

1967   (P) *Hans Albrecht Bethe* for discovering the routes of energy production in stars (1939).

1968   (P) *Luis W. Alvarez* for discovering resonance states of elementary particles.

1969   (P) *Murray Gell-Mann* for classifying elementary particles (1963).

1970   (P) *Hannes Alfvén* for developing magnetohydrodynamic theory and *Louis Eugène Félix Néel* for discovering antiferromagnetism and ferrimagnetism (1930s).

1971   (P) *Dennis Gabor* for developing holography (1947).

      (C) *Gerhard Herzberg* for studying the structure of molecules spectroscopically.

1972   (P) *John Bardeen, Leon N. Cooper,* and *John Robert Schrieffer* for explaining superconductivity (1957).

1973   (P) *Leo Esaki* for discovering tunneling in semiconductors, *Ivar Giaever* for discovering tunneling in superconductors, and *Brian D. Josephson* for predicting the Josephson effect, which involves tunneling of paired electrons (1958–1962).

1974   (P) *Anthony Hewish* for discovering pulsars and *Martin Ryle* for developing radio interferometry.

1975   (P) *Aage N. Bohr, Ben R. Mottelson,* and *James Rainwater* for discovering why some nuclei take asymmetric shapes.

1976   (P) *Burton Richter* and *Samuel C. C. Ting* for discovering the J/psi particle, the first charmed particle (1974).

1977   (P) *John H. Van Vleck, Nevill F. Mott,* and *Philip W. Anderson* for studying solids quantum-mechanically.

      (C) *Ilya Prigogine* for extending thermodynamics to show how life could arise in the face of the second law.

1978   (P) *Arno A. Penzias* and *Robert W. Wilson* for discovering the cosmic background radiation (1965) and *Pyotr Kapitsa* for his studies of liquid helium.

1979   (P) *Sheldon L. Glashow, Abdus Salam,* and *Steven Weinberg* for developing the theory that unified the weak and electromagnetic forces (1958–1971).

1980   (P) *Val Fitch* and *James W. Cronin* for discovering CP (charge-parity) violation (1964), which possibly explains the cosmological dominance of matter over antimatter.

1981   (P) *Nicolaas Bloembergen* and *Arthur L. Schawlow* for developing laser spectroscopy and *Kai M. Siegbahn* for developing high-resolution electron spectroscopy (1958).

1982   (P) *Kenneth G. Wilson* for developing a method of constructing theories of phase transitions to analyze critical phenomena.

1983   (P) *William A. Fowler* for theoretical studies of astrophysical nucleosynthesis and *Subramanyan Chandrasekhar* for studying physical processes of importance to stellar structure and evolution, including the prediction of white dwarf stars (1930).

1984   (P) *Carlo Rubbia* for discovering the W and Z particles, verifying the electroweak unification, and *Simon van der Meer,* for developing the method of stochastic cooling of the CERN beam that allowed the discovery (1982–1983).

1985   (P) *Klaus von Klitzing* for the quantized Hall effect, relating to conductivity in the presence of a magnetic field (1980).

1986   (P) *Ernst Ruska* for inventing the electron microscope (1931), and *Gerd Binnig* and *Heinrich Rohrer* for inventing the scanning-tunneling electron microscope (1981).

1987   (P) *J. Georg Bednorz* and *Karl Alex Müller* for the discovery of high temperature superconductivity (1986).

1988   (P) *Leon M. Lederman, Melvin Schwartz,* and *Jack Steinberger* for a collaborative experiment that led to the development of a new tool for studying the weak nuclear force, which affects the radioactive decay of atoms.

1989   (P) *Norman Ramsay* (U.S.) for various techniques in atomic physics; and

Hans Dehmelt (U.S.) and *Wolfgang Paul* (Germany) for the development of techniques for trapping single charge particles.

1990   (P) *Jerome Friedman, Henry Kendall* (both U.S.), and *Richard Taylor* (Canada) for experiments important to the development of the quark model.

1991   (P) *Pierre-Gilles de Gennes* for discovering that methods developed for studying order phenomena in simple systems can be generalized to more complex forms of matter, in particular to liquid crystals and polymers.

1992   (P) *George Charpak* for developing detectors that trace the paths of evanescent subatomic particles produced in particle accelerators.

1993   (P) *Russell Hulse* and *Joseph Taylor* for discovering evidence of gravitational waves.

1994   (P) *Bertram N. Brockhouse* and *Clifford G. Shull* for pioneering work in neutron scattering.

Spreadsheet Problems

OVERVIEW

Students come to introductory physics courses with a wide variety of computing experience. Many are already accomplished programmers in one or more programming languages (BASIC, Pascal, FORTRAN, and so forth). Others have never even turned on a computer. To further complicate matters, a wide variety of hardware environments exists, although most can be classified as IBM/compatible (MS-DOS) or Macintosh environments. We have designed the end-of-chapter spreadsheet problems and the text ancillary, *Spreadsheet Investigations in Physics,* to be usable by and useful to students in all these diverse situations. Our goal is to enable students to investigate a range of physical phenomena and obtain a feel for the physics. Merely "getting the right answer" by plugging numbers into a formula and comparing the result to the answer in the back of the book is discouraged.

Spreadsheets are particularly valuable in exploratory investigations. Once you have constructed a spreadsheet, you can simply vary the parameters and see instantly how things change. Even more important is the ease with which you can construct accurate graphs of relations between physical variables. When you change a parameter, you can view the effects of the change upon the graphs simply by pressing a key. "What if" questions can be easily addressed and depicted graphically.

HOW TO USE THE TEMPLATES

The computer spreadsheet problems are arranged by level of difficulty. The least difficult problems are coded in black. For most of these problems, spreadsheets are provided on disk, and only the input parameters need to be changed. Problems of moderate difficulty, coded in blue, require additional analysis, and the provided spreadsheets must be modified to solve them. The most challenging problems are coded in magenta. For most of these, you must develop your own spreadsheets. The emphasis should be on understanding what the results mean rather than just getting an answer. For example, one spreadsheet problem explores how the distance of the horizon varies with height above the ground. You can explore why you can see farther distances when you're on top of a tall building than when you are on the ground. Why were lookouts on sailing ships placed in the crow's nest at the top of the mast?

SOFTWARE REQUIREMENTS

The spreadsheet templates are provided on a high-density (1.44 Megabyte) MS-DOS diskette using the Lotus 1-2-3 WK1 format. This format was introduced with versions 2.x of the Lotus 1-2-3 program and can be read by all subsequent versions. It can also be read directly by all the other major spreadsheet programs, including the latest Windows versions of Lotus 1-2-3, Microsoft Excel, Microsoft Works, and Novell/Wordperfect Quattro Pro as well as Microsoft Excel for the Macintosh. The program f(g) Scholar can import WK1 spreadsheets; however, some minor format changes of the templates are needed.

The Lotus WK1 format was chosen so that the templates will be usable in the widest possible variety of computing environments. Even though most spreadsheet programs operate in basically the same way, many of the latest spreadsheet programs have very powerful formatting and graphing capabilities along with many other useful features. The user of these powerful programs can exploit these capabilities to improve the appearance of their spreadsheets.

HARDWARE REQUIREMENTS

You will need a microcomputer that can run one of the spreadsheet programs in one of their many versions. Your computer should be connected to a printer that can print text and graphics. Older versions of the software will run on a 8086/8088 MS-DOS system with just a single floppy disk drive or on a 512K Macintosh with two floppy drives. Newer versions require a more powerful computer to run effectively. For example, to run Excel for Windows, Version 5.0, you must have a hard disk with about 15 megabytes of disk memory available and four to eight megabytes of RAM. Your software manuals will tell you exactly what you need to run the particular version of your spreadsheet program. However, all problems require only a minimal computer system.

There are many different software versions and many different computer configurations. You might have one floppy drive, two floppy drives, a hard disk, a local area network, and so on. The combinations are almost endless. Our best suggestion is to read your software manual and ask your instructor or computer laboratory personnel how to start your spreadsheet program.

SPREADSHEET TUTORIAL

Some students will have the required computer and spreadsheet skills to start working with the templates immediately. Other students, who have not had experience with a spreadsheet program, will need some instruction. We have written an ancillary entitled *Spreadsheet Investigations in Physics* for both these groups of students. The first part of this ancillary contains a spreadsheet tutorial that the novice student can use *independently* to gain the required spreadsheet skills. A two- or three-hour initial session with the tutorial and the computer is all that most students need to get started. Once the students have mastered the basic operations of the spreadsheet program, they should try one or two of the easier problems.

Because very few introductory physics students have studied numerical methods, we have also included a brief introduction to numerical methods in this ancillary. This section covers numerical interpolation, differentiation, integration, and the solution of simple differential equations. The student should not try to master all of this material at one time; only study the sections that are needed to solve the currently assigned problems.

The templates supplied on the distribution diskettes with *Spreadsheet Investigations in Physics* constitute an outline. You must enter the appropriate data and parameters. The parameters must be adjusted to fit the needs of your problem. Feel free to change any parameters, to expand or decrease the number of rows of output, and to change the size of increments (for example, in time or distance).

Most templates have graphs associated with them. You may have to adjust the ranges of variables plotted and the scales for the axes. See the tutorials for how to adjust the appearance of your graphs.

COPY YOUR DISTRIBUTION DISKETTES

Since you will be modifying the spreadsheets on the distribution diskettes, copy the distribution diskettes and place the originals in a safe place.

Answers to Odd-Numbered Problems

Chapter 1

1. $2.80\ \text{g}/\text{cm}^3$
3. $184\ \text{g}$
3A. $m = \frac{4}{3}\pi\rho(r_2^{\ 3} - r_1^{\ 3})$
5. (a) $4\ \text{u} = 6.64 \times 10^{-27}\ \text{kg}$
    (b) $56\ \text{u} = 9.30 \times 10^{-26}\ \text{kg}$
    (c) $207\ \text{u} = 3.44 \times 10^{-25}\ \text{kg}$
7. (a) $72.58\ \text{kg}$ (b) 7.82×10^{26} atoms
9. It is.
11. It is.
13. (b) only
15. L^3/T^3, L^3T
17. The units of G are $\text{m}^3/(\text{kg}\cdot\text{s}^2)$.
19. $1.39 \times 10^3\ \text{m}^2$
21. $8.32 \times 10^{-4}\ \text{m}/\text{s}$
23. $11.4 \times 10^3\ \text{kg}/\text{m}^3$
25. (a) $6.31 \times 10^4\ \text{AU}$ (b) $1.33 \times 10^{11}\ \text{AU}$
27. (a) $127\ \text{y}$ (b) $15\,500$ times
29. (a) $1\ \text{mi}/\text{h} = 1.609\ \text{km}/\text{h}$ (b) $88.5\ \text{km}/\text{h}$
    (c) $16.1\ \text{km}/\text{h}$
31. $1.51 \times 10^{-4}\ \text{m}$
33. $1.00 \times 10^{10}\ \text{lb}$
35. $5\ \text{m}$
37. $5.95 \times 10^{24}\ \text{kg}$
39. $2.86\ \text{cm}$
41. $\approx 10^6$
43. $1.79 \times 10^{-9}\ \text{m}$
45. $3.84 \times 10^8\ \text{m}$
47. $34.1\ \text{m}$
49. $\approx 10^2$
51. (a) $(346 \pm 13)\ \text{m}^2$ (b) $(66.0 \pm 1.3)\ \text{m}$
53. $195.8\ \text{cm}^2 \pm 0.7\%$
55. $3, 4, 3, 2$
57. $5.2\ \text{m}^3 \pm 3\%$
59. It is not.
61. 0.449%
63. (a) $1000\ \text{kg}$ (b) $5 \times 10^{-16}\ \text{kg}, 300\ \text{g}, 0.01\ \text{g}$
65. (a) 10^6 (b) 10^7 (c) 10^3
S1. (a) Jud's horizon is $5.060\ \text{m}$ and Spud's horizon is $4.382\ \text{m}$. It makes no difference whether you use d, s, or l. (b) On the Moon, Jud's horizon is $2.638\ \text{m}$ and Spud's horizon is $2.285\ \text{m}$.
S3. (a) A plot of log T versus log L for the given data shows an approximate linear relationship. Applying the least-squares method to the data yields $1.017\,647$ for the slope and $0.890\,686$ for the intercept of the straight line that best fits the data. The data points and the best-fit line, log $T = 1.017\,647$ log $m + 0.890\,686$ are shown in the figure. Paying attention to significant figures, a reasonable interpretation of this result is that $n = 1.1$. In terms of T and m, our best-fit equation is $T = Cm^n$, where $C = 10^{1.1} = 12.6$.

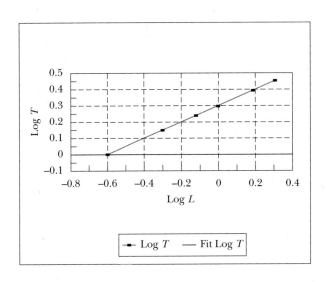

Chapter 2

1. (a) $2.3\ \text{m}/\text{s}$ (b) $16.1\ \text{m}/\text{s}$ (c) $11.5\ \text{m}/\text{s}$
3. (a) $5.0\ \text{m}/\text{s}$ (b) $1.2\ \text{m}/\text{s}$ (c) $-2.5\ \text{m}/\text{s}$
    (d) $-3.3\ \text{m}/\text{s}$ (e) 0
5. (a) $3.75\ \text{m}/\text{s}$ (b) 0
7. $50.0\ \text{km}/\text{h}$
9. (a) $-2.5\ \text{m}/\text{s}$ (b) $-3.4\ \text{m}/\text{s}$ (c) $4.2\ \text{s}$
11. (b) $1.60\ \text{m}/\text{s}$
13. (a) $5.0\ \text{m}/\text{s}$ (b) $-2.5\ \text{m}/\text{s}$ (c) 0
    (d) $5.0\ \text{m}/\text{s}$
15. $-4.00\ \text{m}/\text{s}^2$
17. $20.0\ \text{m}/\text{s}; 6.00\ \text{m}/\text{s}^2$
19. (a) $20.0\ \text{m}/\text{s}, 5.00\ \text{m}/\text{s}$ (b) $262\ \text{m}$
21. (a) $2.00\ \text{m}$ (b) $-3.00\ \text{m}/\text{s}$ (c) $-2.00\ \text{m}/\text{s}^2$
23. (a) $1.3\ \text{m}/\text{s}^2$ (b) $2.2\ \text{m}/\text{s}^2$ at $3.0\ \text{s}$
    (c) At $t = 6.2\ \text{s}$ and for the interval $10\ \text{s} < t < 12\ \text{s}$
    (d) $-2.0\ \text{m}/\text{s}^2$ at $8.2\ \text{s}$

25. -16.0 cm/s^2
27. 160 ft
29. (a) 12.7 m/s   (b) -2.30 m/s
31. (a) 20.0 s   (b) no
33. (a) 8.94 s   (b) 89.4 m/s
35. (a) 0.444 m/s^2 (b) 1.33 m/s   (c) 2.12 s
     (d) 0.943 m/s
37. (a) 45.7 s   (b) 574 m   (c) 12.6 m/s   (d) 765 s
39. (a) $x = 30t - t^2$, $v = 30 - 2t$ (b) 225 m
41. 11.4 s, 212 m
43. (a) -662 ft/s^2 (b) 649 ft
45. (a) 96 ft/s   (b) 3.08×10^3 ft/s^2
     (c) 3.12×10^{-2} s
47. (a) 10.0 m/s   (b) -4.68 m/s
49. (a) 1.53 s   (b) 11.5 m
     (c) -4.60 m/s, -9.80 m/s^2
51. (a) 29.4 m/s   (b) 44.1 m
53. 7.96 s
55. (a) 7.82 m   (b) 0.782 s
57. (a) 7.00 m/s   (b) -5.35 m/s   (c) -9.8 m/s^2
59. $a(t) = a_0 + Jt$, $v(t) = v_0 + a_0t + \frac{1}{2}Jt^2$,
     $x(t) = x_0 + v_0t + \frac{1}{2}a_0t^2 + \frac{1}{6}Jt^3$
61. 0.509 s
63. (a) 3.00 s   (b) -15.3 m/s
     (c) -31.4 m/s, -34.8 m/s
65. (a) -6.26 m/s   (b) 6.02 m/s   (c) 1.25 s
67. 4.63 m
69. (a) 5.45 s   (b) 73.0 m
     (c) $v_{\text{STAN}} = 22.6$ m/s, $v_{\text{KATHY}} = 26.7$ m/s
71. (a) 12.5 s   (b) -2.29 m/s^2 (c) 13.1 s
73. (a) 5.28 m/s   (b) 4.83×10^{-4} m/s^2
75. $t_{AB} = t_{CD} = 2.00$ min, $t_{BC} = 1.00$ min
77. (a) 5.43 m/s^2, 3.83 m/s^2 (b) 10.9 m/s, 11.5 m/s
     (c) Maggie, 2.62 m
79. 155 s; 129 s
81. $0.577v$
S4. (a) At approximately $t = 37.0$ s after the police car
     starts, or 42.0 s after the first policeman sees the
     speeder.   (b) 74.0 m/s   (c) 1370 m

Chapter 3

1. (a) 8.60 m   (b) 4.47 m at 297°; 4.24 m at 135°
3. $(-2.75$ m, -4.76 m$)$
5. $(2.24$ m, $26.6°)$
7. $(2.05$ m, 1.43 m$)$
9. 70.0 m
11. 310 km at 57° south of west
13. (a) 10.0 m   (b) 15.7 m   (c) 0
15. (a) 5.20 m at 60.0°   (b) 3.00 m at 330°
     (c) 3.00 m at 150°   (d) 5.20 m at 300°
17. 421 ft at $-2.63°$
19. 86.6 m, -50.0 m
21. 5.83 m at 59.0° to the right of first direction
23. 47.2 units at 122°

25. (b) $5\mathbf{i} + 4\mathbf{j} = 6.40$ at 38.7°;
     $-\mathbf{i} + 8\mathbf{j} = 8.06$ at 97.2°
27. 7.21 m at 56.3°
29. (a) $2\mathbf{i} - 6\mathbf{j}$ (b) $4\mathbf{i} + 2\mathbf{j}$ (c) 6.32   (d) 4.47
     (e) 288°; 26.6°
31. (a) $(-11.1$ m$)\mathbf{i} + (6.40$ m$)\mathbf{j}$
     (b) $(1.65$ cm$)\mathbf{i} + (2.86$ cm$)\mathbf{j}$
     (c) $(-18.0$ in.$)\mathbf{i} - (12.6$ in.$)\mathbf{j}$
33. 9.48 m at 166°
35. 390 mph at 7.37° north of east
37. $(2.60$ m$)\mathbf{i} + (4.50$ m$)\mathbf{j}$
39. (a) $8\mathbf{i} + 12\mathbf{j} - 4\mathbf{k}$ (b) $2\mathbf{i} + 3\mathbf{j} - \mathbf{k}$
     (c) $-24\mathbf{i} - 36\mathbf{j} + 12\mathbf{k}$
41. (a) 5.92   (b) 19.0
43. (a) $-3\mathbf{i} + 2\mathbf{j}$ (b) 3.61 at 146°   (c) $3\mathbf{i} - 6\mathbf{j}$
47. (a) 49.5, 27.1   (b) 56.4 at 28.7°
49. 240 m at 237°
51. $(10.0$ m, 20.0 m$)$

Chapter 4

1. $(8a + 2b)\mathbf{i} + 2c\mathbf{j}$
3. (a) 4.87 km at 209° from east   (b) 23.3 m/s
     (c) 13.5 m/s at 209°
5. (a) $(2\mathbf{i} + 3\mathbf{j})$ m/s^2
     (b) $(3t + t^2)\mathbf{i} + (-2t + 1.5t^2)\mathbf{j}$
7. (a) $(0.8\mathbf{i} - 0.3\mathbf{j})$ m/s^2 (b) at 339°
     (c) $(360\mathbf{i} - 72.8\mathbf{j})$ m; at 345°
9. (a) $\mathbf{v} = (-5\mathbf{i} + 0\mathbf{j})$ m/s, $\mathbf{a} = (0\mathbf{i} - 5\mathbf{j})$ m/s^2
     (b) $\mathbf{r} = -5\mathbf{i}\sin t + 4\mathbf{j} - 5\mathbf{j}\cos t$
     $\mathbf{v} = -5\mathbf{i}\cos t + 5\mathbf{j}\sin t$
     $\mathbf{a} = 5\mathbf{i}\sin t + 5\mathbf{j}\cos t$
     (c) a circle of radius 5 m centered at $(0, 4$ m$)$
11. (a) 3.34 m/s at 0°   (b) 309°
13. (a) 2.67 s   (b) 29.9 m/s   (c) $v_x = 29.9$ m/s;
     $v_y = -26.2$ m/s
15. 9.91 m/s
17. (a) clears by 0.89 m   (b) while falling 13.3 m/s
19. (a) 1.69 km/s   (b) 6490 s
21. (a) 277 km   (b) 284 s
23. 53.1°
25. 22.4° or 89.4°
27. (a) 7.90 km/s   (b) 5070 s
29. 377 m/s^2
31. (a) 1.02 km/s   (b) 2.72 mm/s^2
33. 54.4 m/s^2
35. (a) 13.0 m/s^2 (b) 5.70 m/s   (c) 7.50 m/s^2
37. 1.48 m/s^2
39. (a) $-30.8\mathbf{j}$ m/s^2 (b) $70.4\mathbf{j}$ m/s^2
41. (a) 26.9 m/s   (b) 67.3 m   (c) $(2\mathbf{i} - 5\mathbf{j})$ m/s^2
43. 2.02×10^3 s; 21.0% longer
45. 2.50 m/s
47. 153 km/h at 11.3° north of west
49. (a) 57.7 km/h at 210°   (b) 28.9 km/h down
51. (a) 10.1 m/s^2 south at 75.7° below horizontal
     (b) 9.80 m/s^2 down
53. (a) $4.00\mathbf{i}$ m/s   (b) $(4.00$ m, 6.00 m$)$

55. (a) 20.0 m/s, 5.00 s   (b) 31.4 m/s at 301°
    (c) 6.53 s   (d) 24.5 m away
57. 3.14 m
59. 20.0 m
61. (a) 0.60 m   (b) 0.40 m
    (c) 1.87 m/s² toward center   (d) 9.80 m/s² down
63. 4.12 m
65. (a) $\sqrt{gR}$ (b) $(\sqrt{2} - 1)R$
67. 10.8 m
69. (a) 6.80 km   (b) directly above explosion
    (c) 66.2°
71. (a) $(-7.05 \text{ cm})\mathbf{j}$ (b) $(7.61 \text{ cm})\mathbf{i} - (6.48 \text{ cm})\mathbf{j}$
    (c) $(10.0 \text{ cm})\mathbf{i} - (7.05 \text{ cm})\mathbf{j}$
73. (a) 22.2° or 67.8°   (b) 235 m   (c) 235 m
75. (a) 407 km/h at 10.6° N of E   (b) 10.8° S of E
77. (a) 5.15 s   (b) 4.85 m/s at 74.5° N of W
    (c) 19.4 m
79. (a) 43.2 m   (b) $(9.66 \text{ m/s})\mathbf{i} - (25.6 \text{ m/s})\mathbf{j}$
81. (18.8 m, −17.4 m)
83. (a) 46.5 m/s   (b) −77.6°   (c) 6.34 s
85. 2.98 km/s forward and 1.96° inward
S1. There are an infinite number of solutions to the problem; however, there is one practical limitation. We can estimate that the maximum speed that the punter can give the ball is about 20 to 30 m/s. Use a speed in this range.
S3. There are an infinite number of solutions. For example if $v_0 = 22.32$ m/s at 45°, then the ball clears the crossbar in 3.01 s. Or if $v_0 = 24.60$ m/s at 30°, then the ball clears the crossbar in 2.23 s. The time it takes the ball to clear the crossbar is immaterial, since in all likelihood time will run out before the clock is stopped.

Chapter 5

1. (a) 1/3   (b) 0.750 m/s²
3. (a) 3.00 s   (b) 20.1 m   (c) $(18.0\mathbf{i} - 9.0\mathbf{j})$ m
5. 312 N
7. $(6\mathbf{i} + 15\mathbf{j})$ N, 16.2 N
9. (a) 556 N   (b) 56.7 kg
11. (a) 4.47×10^{15} m/s² outward
    (b) 2.09×10^{-10} N inward
13. 1.72 kg, 6.97 m/s²
15. (c) Forces of brick on spring and spring on brick; of spring on table and table on spring; of table on Earth and Earth on table; of brick on Earth and of Earth on brick; of spring on Earth and of Earth on spring.
17. (a) 5.10 kN   (b) 2.65×10^3 kg
19. (a) 2.0 m/s²   (b) 170 N   (c) 2.93 m/s²
21. (a) $(2.50 \text{ N})\mathbf{i} + (5.00 \text{ N})\mathbf{j}$ (b) 5.59 N
23. 1.24 ft/s²
25. 640 N for $0 \leq t \leq 1.0$ s, 627 N at $t = 1.3$ s, 589 N at $t = 2.0$ s
27. $(14.7 \text{ N})\mathbf{i} - (2.5 \text{ N})\mathbf{j}$, 14.9 N
29. 613 N
31. (b) $T_1 = 513.5$ N, $T_2 = 557.4$ N, $T_3 = 325.0$ N
33. (a) 33.9 N   (b) 39.0 N
35. (a) $g \tan \theta$ (b) 4.16 m/s²

37. (a) $F_x > 19.6$ N   (b) $F_x \leq -78.4$ N
39. survival chance better with force on larger mass
41. (a) 4.90 m/s²   (b) 3.13 m/s   (c) 1.35 m
    (d) 1.14 s   (e) no
43. (a) 706 N   (b) 814 N   (c) 706 N   (d) 648 N
45. 21.8 m/s
47. 36.9 N
49. 81.0 m/s
51. $\mu = 0.0773$
53. (a) 0.161   (b) 1.01 m/s²
55. (b) 27.2 N, 1.286 m/s²
57. (a) 1.78 m/s²   (b) 0.368   (c) 9.37 N
    (d) 2.67 m/s
59. (a) $a_1 = 2.31$ m/s² down, $a_2 = 2.31$ m/s² left,
    $a_3 = 2.31$ m/s² up,
    (b) $T_{\text{Left}} = 30.0$ N, $T_{\text{Right}} = 24.2$ N
61. 0.293
63. 182.5 m
65. (a) $Mg/2, Mg/2, Mg/2, 3Mg/2, Mg$ (b) $Mg/2$
67. (a) $\mu_s = \dfrac{h}{\sqrt{L^2 - h^2}}$ (b) $a = \dfrac{2L}{t^2}$
    (c) $\sin \theta = h/L$ (d) $\mu_k = \dfrac{h - \dfrac{2L^2}{gt^2}}{\sqrt{L^2 - h^2}}$
69. (a) 0.232 m/s²   (b) 9.68 N
71. (a) F forward   (b) $3F/2Mg$
    (c) $F/(M + m_1 + m_2 + m_3)$
    (d) $m_1F/(M + m_1 + m_2 + m_3)$,
    $(m_1 + m_2)F/(M + m_1 + m_2 + m_3)$,
    $(m_1 + m_2 + m_3)F/(M + m_1 + m_2 + m_3)$
    (e) $m_2F/(M + m_1 + m_2 + m_3)$
73. (a) friction between the two blocks   (b) 34.7 N
    (c) 0.306
75. (a) 0.408 m/s²   (b) 83.3 N
77. (a) 4.00 m   (b) 3.72 m/s
81. (a) $(-45\mathbf{i} + 15\mathbf{j})$ m/s   (b) at 162°
    (c) $(-225\mathbf{i} + 75\mathbf{j})$ m   (d) $(-227$ m, 79 m)
83. $(M + m_1 + m_2) m_2 g / m_1$
85. $T_1 = 74.5$ N, $T_2 = 34.7$ N, $\mu_k = 0.572$
87. (a) 2.20 m/s²   (b) 27.37 N
89. (a) 30.7°   (b) 0.843 N
91. 6.00 cm

Chapter 6

1. (a) 8.0 m/s   (b) 3.02 N
3. (a) 5.40 kN down   (b) 1.60 kN down
    (c) seatbelt tension plus gravity
5. $0 < v < 8.08$ m/s
7. (a) 1.52 m/s²   (b) 1.66 km/s   (c) 6820 s
9. $v \leq 14.3$ m/s
11. (a) 9.80 N   (b) 9.80 N   (c) 6.26 m/s
13. (a) static friction   (b) 0.085
15. 3.13 m/s

17. (a)4.81 m/s   (b) 700 N up
19. (a)$(-0.163 \text{ m/s}^2)\mathbf{i} + (0.233 \text{ m/s}^2)\mathbf{j}$
    (b)6.53 m/s   (c) $(-0.181 \text{ m/s}^2)\mathbf{i} + (0.181 \text{ m/s}^2)\mathbf{j}$
21. no
23. (a)0.822 m/s²   (b) 37.0 N   (e) 0.0839
25. (a)17.0°   (b) 5.12 N
27. (a)491 N   (b) 50.1 kg   (c) 2.00 m/s
31. (a)3.47×10^{-2} s⁻¹   (b) 2.50 m/s   (c) $a = -cv$
33. (a)1.47 N·s/m   (b) 2.04×10^{-3} s
    (c)2.94×10^{-2} N
35. (a)8.32×10^{-8} N   (b) 9.13×10^{22} m/s²
    (c)6.61×10^{15} rev/s
37. (a)$\mathbf{T} = (68.6 \text{ N})\mathbf{i} + (784 \text{ N})\mathbf{j}$ (b) 0.857 m/s²
39. (a)The true weight is greater than the apparent weight.
    (b)$w = w' = 735$ N at the poles; $w' = 732.4$ N at the
    equator
41. 780 N
43. 12.8 N
45. (a)967 lb   (b) 647 lb up
47. (a)6.67 kN   (b) 20.3 m/s

47A. (a) $mg - \dfrac{mv^2}{R}$ (b) $\sqrt{gR}$

49. (b) 2.54 s, 23.6 rev/min
51. (a)1.58 m/s²   (b) 455 N   (c) 329 N
    (d)397 N upward and 9.15° inward
53. (a)0.0132 m/s   (b) 1.03 m/s   (c) 6.87 m/s
S1. Spreadsheet 6.1 typifies the solution of second-order dif-
    ferential equations. In this spreadsheet, we want to solve
    $a = dv/dt$, where $v = dx/dt$. To find v as a function of t,
    we assume that a is constant over the time interval dt.
    Hence, we can use Euler's method to integrate $dv/dt =$
    a. Therefore, $v_{i+1} = v_i + a_i \Delta t$. In the Lotus 1-2-3
    Spreadsheet 6.1, cells F35 and down implement this
    equation. To find x as a function of t, we know that v
    varies over the time interval, so we use Euler's modified
    method to integrate $dx/dt = v$. Or, $x_{i+1} = x_i +$
    $1/2(v_{i+1} + v_i) \Delta t$. Cells F35 and down implement this
    equation.
S2. All objects fall faster when there is no air resistance than
    when there is air resistance. As the mass of the objects
    increases, the difference between their positions at the
    same time with and without air resistance becomes
    smaller.
S4. $F_{min} \cong 252$ N at 31°.
S5. Try large positive speeds, that is $v_0 > 100$ m/s. You may
    need to increase Δt.
S7. If the terminal speeds are to be equal, then the rela-
    tionship between b_1 (for $n = 1$) and b_2 (for $n = 2$) is $b_1 =$
    $b_2 mg$.

Chapter 7

1. 30.6 m
3. (a) 31.9 J   (b) 0   (c) 0   (d) 31.9 J
5. 5.88 kJ

7. (a) 900 J   (b) −900 J   (c) 0.383
9. (a) 137 W   (b) −137 W
11. (a) 79.4 N   (b) 1.49 kJ   (c) −1.49 kJ
11A. (a) $\mu_k mg/(\cos\theta + \mu_k\sin\theta)$
    (b) $\mu_k mg\, d\cos\theta/(\cos\theta + \mu_k\sin\theta)$
    (c) $-\mu_k mg\, d\cos\theta/(\cos\theta + \mu_k\sin\theta)$
13. 14.0
13A. $r_1 r_2 \cos(\theta_1 - \theta_2)$
17. (a) 16.0 J   (b) 36.9°
19. $\mathbf{s} = 2\mathbf{i} + 23.5\mathbf{j}$ or $22\mathbf{i} + 8.5\mathbf{j}$
21. (a) 11.3°   (b) 156°   (c) 82.3°
23. (a) 7.50 J   (b) 15.0 J   (c) 7.50 J   (d) 30.0 J
25. (a) 575 N/m   (b) 46.0 J
25A. (a) F/d (b) $\frac{1}{2}Fd$
27. 0.299 m/s
29. (b) mgR
31. 12.0 J
31A. $3W$
33. (a) 4.10×10^{-18} J
    (b) 1.14×10^{-17} N   (c) 1.25×10^{13} m/s²
    (d) 240 ns
35. (a) 2.00 m/s   (b) 200 N
35A. (a) $v = \sqrt{2W/m}$ (b) $\overline{F} = W/d$
37. (a) 650 J   (b) −588 J   (c) 62.0 J
    (d) 1.76 m/s
39. 6.34 kN
41. (a) $\sqrt{\dfrac{2\,mgh}{m + M/4}}$ (b) $\sqrt{\dfrac{2\,mgh - \mu_k Mgh}{m + M/4}}$
43. 1.25 m/s
45. 2.04 m
47. (a) −168 J   (b) 184 J   (c) 500 J   (d) 148 J
    (e) 5.65 m/s
49. (a) 4.51 m   (b) no, since $f > mg\sin\theta$
51. (a) 63.9 J   (b) −35.4 J   (c) −9.51 J
    (d) 19.0 J
53. 875 W
55. (a) 7.92 hp   (b) 14.9 hp
57. (a) 7.5×10^4 J   (b) 2.50×10^4 W (33.5 hp)
    (c) 3.33×10^4 W (44.7 hp)
57A. (a) $\dfrac{1}{2}mv^2$ (b) $\dfrac{mv^2}{2t}$ (c) $\dfrac{mv^2 t_1}{t^2}$
59. 220 ft·lb/s
61. 685
63. 80.0 hp
65. (a) 1.35×10^{-2} gal   (b) 73.8   (c) 8.08 kW
67. 5.90 km/liter
69. (a) 5.37×10^{-11} J   (b) 1.33×10^{-9} J
71. 3.70 m/s
75. (a) $(2 + 24t^2 + 72t^4)$ J   (b) $a = 12t$ m/s²; $F = 48t$ N
    (c) $(48t + 288t^3)$ W   (d) 1.25×10^3 J
77. 878 kN
79. (a) 4.12 m   (b) 3.35 m
81. (a) −5.60 J   (b) 0.152   (c) 2.29 rev
83. (a) $W = mgh$ (b) $\Delta K = mgh$
    (c) $K_f = mgh + mv_0^2/2$

85. 1.94 kJ
87. (b)8.49 × 10⁵ kg/s   (c) 7.34 × 10⁷ m³
    (d)1.53 km
89. 1.68 m/s
S1. (a)A plot of F as the independent variable and L as the dependent variable shows that the last four points tend to vary the most from a straight line. However, because the first point has the largest percentage deviation from a straight line, we probably are not justified in throwing any of the data points out. The slope of the best straight line obtained from the least-squares fit is 8.654 545 5 mm/N or $k = 0.116$ N/mm = 116 N/m. (b) The least-squares fit we used was of the form $L = aF + b$; solving for F gives $F = L/a - b/a = 0.116L - 0.561$. Hence, for $L = 105$ mm, $F = 12.7$ mm.

Chapter 8

1. (a) -196 J   (b) -196 J   (c) -196 J
    The force is conservative.
3. (b) conservative 62.7 J, nonconservative 20.7 J
    (c) $\mu = 0.330$
5. (a) 125 J   (b) 50.0 J   (c) 66.7 J
    (d) nonconservative, since W is path-dependent
7. (a) 40.0 J   (b) -40.0 J   (c) 62.5 J
9. (a) -9.00 J; No. A constant force is conservative.
    (b) 3.39 m/s   (c) 9.00 J
11. $v_A = \sqrt{3gR}$; 0.098 N downward
13. (a) $v = (gh + v_0^2)^{1/2}$ (b) $v_x = 0.6v_0$;
    $v_y = -(0.64v_0^2 + gh)^{1/2}$
15. (a) 18.5 km, 51.0 km   (b) 10.0 MJ
17. (a) 4.43 m/s   (b) 5.00 m
17A. (a) $\sqrt{2(m_1 - m_2)gh/(m_1 + m_2)}$
    (b) $2m_1 h/(m_1 + m_2)$
19. (a) -160 J   (b) 73.5 J   (c) 28.8 N
    (d) 0.679
21. 489 kJ
23. (a) -4.1 MJ   (b) 9.97 m/s   (c) 50.8 m
    (d) It is better to keep the engine with the train.
25. 3.74 m/s
29. 914 N/m
31. (a) -28.0 J   (b) 0.446 m
33. 10.2 m
33A. $(kd^2/2mg) - d$
35. 0.327
37. (a) $F_r = A/r^2$
39. $\mathbf{F} = (7 - 9x^2y)\mathbf{i} - 3x^3\mathbf{j}$
41. (b) $x = 0$ (c) $v = \sqrt{0.80\ \text{J}/m}$
43. (a) $v_B = 5.94$ m/s; $v_C = 7.67$ m/s   (b) 147 J
45. (a) 1.50×10^{-10} J   (b) 1.07×10^{-9} J
    (c) 9.15×10^{-10} J
47. (a) 0.225 J   (b) 0.363 J
    (c) No. The normal force varies with position, and so the frictional force also varies.

49. $\dfrac{h}{5}(4\sin^2\theta + 1)$
51. (a) 349 J, 676 J, 741 J   (b) 174 N, 338 N, 370 N
    (c) yes
53. (a) $\Delta U = -\dfrac{ax^2}{2} - \dfrac{bx^3}{3}$ (b) $\Delta U = \dfrac{A}{\alpha}(1 - e^{\alpha x})$
55. 0.115
59. 1.24 m/s
61. (b) 7.42 m/s
63. (a) 3.19 m   (b) 2.93 m/s
65. (a) 0.400 m   (b) 4.10 m/s
    (c) It reaches the top.
67. 3.92 kJ
67A. $m_1 gd(m_2 - \mu_k m_1 \cos\theta - m_1 \sin\theta)/(m_1 + m_2)$
69. (a) 0.378 m   (b) 2.30 m/s   (c) 1.08 m
S1. If the particle has an initial energy less than 2471 J, it will be trapped in the potential well; for example, if $E_T = 1000$ J, it will be confined approximately to -3.15 m $\le x \le 4.58$ m.
S2. $x = 0$ is a point of stable equilibrium; $x = 8.33$ m is a point of unstable equilibrium.

Chapter 9

1. $(9.00\mathbf{i} - 12.0\mathbf{j})$ kg·m/s, 15.0 kg·m/s
3. 1.60 kN
5. (a) 12.0 kg·m/s   (b) 6.00 m/s   (c) 4.00 m/s
7. (a) 13.5 kg·m/s   (b) 9.00×10^3 N
    (c) 18.0×10^3 N
9. 87.5 N
11. (a) 7.50 kg·m/s   (b) 375 N
13. (a) 13.5 kg·m/s toward the pitcher
    (b) 6.75×10^3 N toward the pitcher
15. 260 N toward the left in the diagram
15A. $\dfrac{-2mv\sin\theta}{t}\mathbf{i}$
17. (a) 0.125 m/s   (b) 8 times
19. 120 m
21. (a) 1.15 m/s   (b) -0.346 m/s
23. 4.01×10^{-20} m/s
25. 301 m/s
27. (a) 20.9 m/s east   (b) 8.74 kJ into thermal energy
29. (a) 0.284, or 28.4%   (b) $K_n = 1.15 \times 10^{-13}$ J,
    $K_c = 4.54 \times 10^{-14}$ J
31. 3.75 kN; no
33. (a) 0.571 m/s   (b) 28.6 J   (c) 0.003 97
35. 91.2 m/s
37. 0.556 m
39. 497 m/s
41. $\mathbf{v} = (3.00\mathbf{i} - 1.20\mathbf{j})$ m/s
43. (a) $v_x = -9.33 \times 10^6$ m/s, $v_y = -8.33 \times 10^6$ m/s
    (b) 4.39×10^{-13} J
45. 3.01 m/s, 3.99 m/s
47. 2.50 m/s at $-60.0°$

51. -0.429 m
53. CM = 454 km, well within the Sun
55. (2.54 m, 4.75 m)
57. 70/6 cm, 80/6 cm
59. (a) $(1.40\mathbf{i} + 2.40\mathbf{j})$m/s   (b) $(7.00\mathbf{i} + 12.0\mathbf{j})$kg·m/s
61. (a) 2.10 m/s, 0.900 m/s   (b) 6.30×10^{-3} kg·m/s, -6.30×10^{-3} kg·m/s
61A. (a) $m_2 v_1/(m_1 + m_2)$ and $m_1 v_1/(m_1 + m_2)$
(b) $m_1 m_2 v_1/(m_1 + m_2)$ toward the CM
63. 200 kN
65. 2150 kg
67. 0.595 m³/s
67A. $F/\rho v$
69. 291 N
71. (a) 1.80 m/s to the left   (b) 257 N to the left
(c) larger than part b
73. (a) 4160 N   (b) 4.17 m/s
75. 32.0 kN; 7.13 MW
77. (a) 6.81 m/s   (b) 1.00 m
79. 240 s
81. $(3Mgx/L)\mathbf{j}$
83. (a) As the child walks to the right, the boat moves to the left, but the center of mass remains fixed.
(b) 5.55 m from the pier   (c) Since the turtle is 7 m from the pier, the boy will not be able to reach the turtle, even with a 1 m reach.
85. (a) 100 m/s   (b) 374 J
85A. (a) $v_0 - d\sqrt{\dfrac{kM}{m^2}}$ (b) $v_0\, d\sqrt{kM} - \dfrac{1}{2}\, kd^2\left(1 + \dfrac{M}{m}\right)$
87. $2v_0$ and 0
89. (a) 3.8 kg·m/s²   (b) 3.8 N   (c) 3.8 N
(d) 2.8 J   (e) 1.4 J
(f) Friction between sand and belt converts half of the input work into thermal energy.
S1. (a) The maximum acceleration is 100 m/s². It occurs at the end of the burn time of 80 s, when the rocket has its smallest mass. The maximum speed that the rocket reaches is 3.22 km/s. (b) The speed reaches half its maximum after 55.3 s; if the acceleration were constant, it would reach half its maximum speed at 40 s (half the burn time), but the acceleration is always increasing during the burn time.
S3. (b) The disadvantages are that the ship has to withstand twice the acceleration and that it has only traveled half as far when the fuel burns out. The advantage is that it takes half as long to reach its final speed; hence, it travels farther in 100 s.

Chapter 10

1. (a) 4.00 rad/s²   (b) 18.0 rad
3. (a) 1.99×10^{-7} rad/s   (b) 2.66×10^{-6} rad/s
5. (a) 5.24 s   (b) 27.4 rad
7. 13.7 rad/s²
9. (a) 0.18 rad/s   (b) 8.10 m/s² toward the center of the track

9A. (a) v/R (b) v^2/R toward center
11. (a) 8.00 rad/s   (b) 8.00 m/s, $a_r = -64.0$ m/s²,
$a_t = 4.00$ m/s²   (c) 9.00 rad
13. (a) 126 rad/s   (b) 3.77 m/s   (c) 1.26 km/s²
(d) 20.1 m
15. 29.4 m/s², 9.80 m/s²
15A. $-2g\dfrac{(h - R)}{R}\mathbf{i} - g\mathbf{j}$
17. (a) 143 kg·m²   (b) 2.57×10^3 J
19. (a) 92.0 kg·m², 184 J   (b) 6.00 m/s, 4.00 m/s, 8.00 m/s, 184 J
23. (a) $(3/2)MR^2$ (b) $(7/5)MR^2$
25. -3.55 N·m
27. 2.79%
29. (a) 0.309 m/s²   (b) $T_1 = 7.67$ N, $T_2 = 9.22$ N
29A. (a) $\dfrac{(m_2 \sin\theta - \mu_k)(m_1 + m_2 \cos\theta)}{m_1 + M/2 + m_2}\, g$
(b) $T_1 = \mu_k mg + m_1 a$, $T_2 = T_1 + \frac{1}{2}Ma$
31. (a) 56.3 J   (b) 8.38 rad/s   (c) 2.35 m/s
(d) 0.4% greater
33. (a) $2(Rg/3)^{1/2}$ (b) $4(Rg/3)^{1/2}$ (c) $(Rg)^{1/2}$
35. (a) 11.4 N, 7.57 m/s², 9.53 m/s down   (b) 9.53 m/s
37. (a) 1.03 s   (b) 10.3 rev
39. 168 N·m (clockwise)
41. (a) 4.00 J   (b) 1.60 s   (c) yes
43. (a) $\omega = \sqrt{3g/L}$ (b) $\alpha = 3g/2L$
(c) $-\frac{3}{2}g\mathbf{i} - \frac{3}{4}g\mathbf{j}$ (d) $-\frac{3}{2}Mg\mathbf{i} + \frac{1}{4}Mg\mathbf{j}$
45. (a) $0.707R$ (b) $0.289L$ (c) $0.632R$
47. 149 rad/s
49. (a) 2.60×10^{29} J   (b) -1.65×10^{17} J/day
51. (a) 118 N, 156 N   (b) 1.19 kg·m²
51A. (a) $T_1 = m_1(a + g\sin\theta)$, $T_2 = m_2(g - a)$
(b) $m_2 R^2 g/a - m_1 R^2 - m_2 R^2 - m_1 R^2(g/a)\sin\theta$
53. (a) -0.176 rad/s²   (b) 1.29 rev   (c) 9.26 rev
S1. The answer is not unique because the torque $\tau = FR$.
S3. Replace X^2 with $(X - H)^2$ in line 110.

Chapter 11

1. (a) 500 J   (b) 250 J   (c) 750 J
3. (a) $a_{CM} = \frac{2}{3}g\sin\theta$ (disk), $a_{CM} = \frac{1}{2}g\sin\theta$ (hoop)
(b) $\frac{1}{3}\tan\theta$
5. 44.8 J
5A. $0.7Mv^2$
7. (a) $-17\mathbf{k}$ (b) 70.5°
9. (a) negative z direction   (b) positive z direction
11. 45.0°
13. $|\mathbf{F}_3| = |\mathbf{F}_1| + |\mathbf{F}_2|$, no
15. $(17.5$ kg·m²/s$)\mathbf{k}$
15A. $\frac{1}{2}(m_1 + m_2)vd$
17. $(60$ kg·m²/s$)\mathbf{k}$
19. $mvR\left[\cos\left(\dfrac{vt}{R}\right) + 1\right]\mathbf{k}$
21. $-mg\ell t\cos\theta\,\mathbf{k}$

23. (a) zero   (b) $[-mv_0^3 \sin^2\theta \cos\theta/2g]\mathbf{k}$
    (c) $[-2mv_0^3 \sin^2\theta \cos\theta/g]\mathbf{k}$ (d) The downward force of gravity exerts a torque in the $-z$ direction.

25. (a) 0.433 kg·m²/s   (b) 1.73 kg·m²/s

27. (a) $\omega = \omega_0 I_1/(I_1 + I_2)$ (b) $I_1/(I_1 + I_2)$

29. (a) 0.360 rad/s in the counterclockwise direction
    (b) 99.9 J

31. (a) 6.05 rad/s   (b) 113 J

33. (a) $mv\ell$ down   (b) $M/(M+m)$

35. (a) 2.19×10^6 m/s   (b) 2.18×10^{-18} J
    (c) 4.13×10^{16} rad/s

37. 0.91 km/s

41. (a) The net torque around this axis is zero.
    (b) Since $\tau = 0$, $L =$ const. But initially, $L = 0$, hence it remains zero throughout the motion. Consequently, the monkey and bananas move upward with the same speed at any instant. The distance between the monkey and bananas stays constant. Hence, the monkey will not reach the bananas.

47. 30.3 rev/s

49. (a) $v_0 r_0/r$ (b) $T = (mv_0^2 r_0^2)r^{-3}$

    (c) $\frac{1}{2}mv_0^2\left(\dfrac{r_0^2}{r^2} - 1\right)$ (d) 4.50 m/s, 10.1 N, 0.450 J

51. (a) $F_y = \dfrac{W}{L}\left(d - \dfrac{ah}{g}\right)$ (b) 0.306 m

    (c) $(-306\mathbf{i} + 553\mathbf{j})$ N

53. (a) 3.75×10^3 kg·m²/s   (b) 1.875 kJ
    (c) 3.75×10^3 kg·m²/s   (d) 10.0 m/s
    (e) 7.50 kJ   (f) 5.625 kJ

53A. (a) Mvd (b) Mv^2 (c) Mvd (d) $2v$
    (e) $4Mv^2$ (f) $3Mv^2$

55. $\frac{1}{3}L$

57. (c) $(8Fd/3M)^{1/2}$

61. $v_0 = [ag(16/3)(\sqrt{2}-1)]^{1/2}$

63. F_1 clockwise torque, F_2 zero torque, F_3 and F_4 counterclockwise torque

65. (a) 0.800 m/s², 0.400 m/s²
    (b) 0.600 N (top), 0.200 N (bottom)

Chapter 12

1. 10.0 N up; 6.00 N·m counterclockwise

3. $[(w_1 + w)d + w_1\ell/2]/W_2$

5. $F_W = 480$ N, $F_v = 1200$ N

5A. $\left(\dfrac{w_1}{2} + \dfrac{w_2 x}{L}\right)\left(\dfrac{d}{\sqrt{L^2 - d^2}}\right);\ w_1 + w_2$

9. -1.50 m, -1.50 m

11. (a) 859 N   (b) 1040 N, left and upward at $36.9°$

13. 0.789

15. $F_f = 4410$ N, $F_r = 2940$ N

17. $2R/5$

19. $\frac{1}{3}$ by the left string, $\frac{2}{3}$ by the right string

21. $x = \frac{3}{4}L$

23. 4.90 mm

25. (a) 73.6 kN   (b) 2.50 mm

---

27. 29.2 μm

27A. $\dfrac{8m_1 m_2 gL}{\pi d^2 Y(m_1 + m_2)}$

29. (a) 3.14×10^4 N   (b) 62.8 kN

31. 1800 atm

33. $N_A = 5.98 \times 10^5$ N, $N_B = 4.80 \times 10^5$ N

35. (b) 69.8 N   (c) 0.877ℓ

37. (a) 160 N right   (b) 13.2 N right   (c) 292 N up
    (d) 192 N

39. (a) $T = w(\ell + d)/\sin\theta(2\ell + d)$ and
    (b) $R_x = w(\ell + d)\cot\theta/(2\ell + d)$; $R_y = w\ell/(2\ell + d)$

41. (a) $F_x = 268$ N, $F_y = 1300$ N   (b) 0.324

41A. (a) $\dfrac{m_1 g}{2\tan\theta} + \dfrac{m_2 gx}{L\tan\theta}$; $(m_1 + m_2)g$

    (b) $\dfrac{m_1/2 + m_2 d/L}{(m_1 + m_2)\tan\theta}$

43. 5.08 kN, $R_x = 4.77$ kN, $R_y = 8.26$ kN

45. $T = 2.71$ kN, $R_x = 2.65$ kN, $R_y = -12.0$ N

47. (a) 20.1 cm to the left of the front edge, $\mu = 0.571$
    (b) 0.501 m

47A. (a) $\dfrac{F\cos\theta}{mg - F\sin\theta}$; $\dfrac{mgw/2 - Fh\cos\theta}{(mg - F\sin\theta)}$ (b) $\dfrac{mgw}{2F\cos\theta}$

49. (a) $W = \dfrac{w}{2}\left(\dfrac{2\mu_s\sin\theta - \cos\theta}{\cos\theta - \mu_s\sin\theta}\right)$
    (b) $R = (w + W)\sqrt{1 + \mu_s^2}$, $F = \sqrt{W^2 + \mu_s^2(w + W)^2}$

51. (a) 133 N   (b) $N_A = 429$ N, $N_B = 257$ N
    (c) $R_x = 133$ N, $R_y = -257$ N

53. 66.7 N

55. $F = \frac{3}{8}w$

57. (a) 1.67 N, 3.33 N, 1.67 N   (b) 2.36 N

59. (a) 4500 N   (b) 4.50×10^6 N/m²
    (c) This is more than sufficient to break the board.

61. $y_{cg} = 16.7$ cm

Chapter 13

1. (a) 1.50 Hz, 0.667 s   (b) 4.00 m   (c) π rad
    (d) 2.83 m

3. (b) 1.81 s   (c) no

5. (a) 13.9 cm/s, 16.0 cm/s²   (b) 16.0 cm/s, 0.262 s
    (c) 32.0 cm/s², 1.05 s

7. (b) 6π cm/s, 0.333 s   (c) $18\pi^2$ cm/s², 0.500 s
    (d) 12.0 cm

9. (a) 0.542 kg   (b) 1.81 s   (c) 1.20 m/s²

11. 40.9 N/m

13. (a) 2.40 s   (b) 0.417 Hz   (c) 2.62 rad/s

15. (a) 0.400 m/s, 1.60 m/s²
    (b) ± 0.320 m/s, -0.960 m/s²   (c) 0.232 s

17. (a) 0.750 m   (b) $x = -(0.75\text{ m})\sin(2.0t)$

17A. (a) v/ω (b) $(v/\omega)\cos(\omega t + \pi/2)$

19. 2.23 m/s

21. (a) quadrupled   (b) doubled
    (c) doubled   (d) no change

23. ± 2.60 cm

25. (a) 1.55 m   (b) 6.06 s
27. (a) 3.65 s   (b) 6.41 s   (c) 4.24 s
27A. (a) $2\pi\sqrt{L/(g+a)}$ (b) $2\pi\sqrt{L/(g-a)}$
(c) $2\pi L^{1/2}(g^2 + a^2)^{-1/4}$
29. (a) 0.817 m/s   (b) 2.57 rad/s²   (c) 0.634 N
31. increases by 1.78×10^{-3} s
33. 0.944 kg·m²
35. (a) 5.00×10^{-7} kg·m²
(b) 3.16×10^{-4} N·m/rad
39. 1.00×10^{-3} s⁻¹
41. (a) 1.42 Hz   (b) 0.407 Hz
43. 318 N

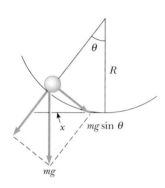

45. 1.57 s
47. (a) $E = \frac{1}{2}mv^2 + mgL(1 - \cos\theta)$ (b) $U = \frac{1}{2}m\omega^2 s^2$
49. Referring to the sketch, we have $F = -mg\sin\theta$ and $\tan\theta = x/R$. For small displacements, $\tan\theta \approx \sin\theta$ and $F = -(mg/R)x = -kx$ and $\omega = (k/m)^{1/2} = (g/R)^{1/2}$.

51. (a) $2Mg$, $T_P = Mg\left(1 + \dfrac{y}{L}\right)$

(b) $\dfrac{4\pi}{3}\sqrt{\dfrac{2L}{g}} = 2.68$ s

55. $f = \dfrac{1}{2\pi}\sqrt{\dfrac{MgL + kh^2}{ML^2}}$

57. 0.0662 m

57A. $\dfrac{\mu_s g}{4\pi^2 f^2}$

59. (a) 3.00 s   (b) 14.3 J   (c) 0.441 rad
61. 9.19×10^{13} Hz
63. (a) 15.8 rad/s   (b) 5.23 cm   (c) 1.31 cm, π
67. (a) $k = 1.74$ N/m ± 6%   (b) $k = 1.82$ N/m ± 3%;
the values of k agree   (c) $m_s = 8$ g ± 12%, in
agreement with 7.4 g
S2. Since $E_{tot} = K(t) + U(t) = \frac{1}{2}kA^2[\cos^2(\omega t + \delta) + \sin^2(\omega t + \delta)] = \frac{1}{2}kA^2$, the total energy is independent of ω and δ. It depends only on k and A.
S3. The periods increase as ϕ_0 increases. These periods are always greater than those calculated using $T_0 = 2\pi\sqrt{L/g}$. For example, if $\phi_0 = 45° = \pi/4$ rad, and $L = 1$ m, then $T_0 = 2.00\ 709$ s, but the actual period is 2.08 s. (*Note:* Due to numerical errors in the integration of the differential equations, the amplitudes may tend to increase. If this occurs, try smaller time steps.)

Chapter 14

1. (a) 3.46×10^8 m   (b) 3.34×10^{-3} m/s²
3. (1.00 m − 61.3 nm)

5. $\dfrac{GM}{\ell^2}\left(\dfrac{2\sqrt{2} + 1}{2}\right)$ toward the opposite corner

7. 35.0 N toward the Moon
9. 3.73 m/s²
11. 12.6×10^{31} kg

11A. $\dfrac{2v^3 T}{\pi G}$

13. (a) 4.39×10^{20} N   (b) 1.99×10^{20} N
(c) 3.55×10^{22} N
15. 1.90×10^{27} kg
17. Y has completed 1.30 revolutions
19. 8.98×10^7 m
21. $2GMr/(r^2 + a^2)^{3/2}$, to the left
23. 3.84×10^4 km from the Moon's center
25. 2.82×10^9 J
27. (a) 1.84×10^9 kg/m³   (b) 3.27×10^6 m/s²
(c) -2.08×10^{13} J
29. 1.66×10^4 m/s
31. 11.8 km/s
35. 1.58×10^{10} J

35A. $\dfrac{mGM_E(R_E + 2h)}{2R_E(R_E + h)} - \frac{1}{2}mv^2$

37. (a) 42.1 km/s relative to the Sun   (b) 2.20×10^{11} m
39. (a) 1.31×10^{14} N/kg   (b) 2.62×10^{12} N/kg

39A. (a) $\dfrac{GM}{(d + \ell/2)^2}$ (b) $\dfrac{GM\ell(2d + \ell)}{d^2(d + \ell)^2}$

41. (a) 7.41×10^{-10} N   (b) 1.04×10^{-8} N
(c) 5.21×10^{-9} N
43. 2.26×10^{-7}
45. 0.0572 rad/s = 32.7 rev/h
45A. $\omega = \sqrt{2g/d}$
47. 7.41×10^{-10} N

49. (a) $k = \dfrac{GmM_E}{R_E^3}$, $A = \dfrac{L}{2}$

(b) $\dfrac{L}{2}\left(\dfrac{GM_E}{R_E}\right)^{1/2}$, at the middle of the tunnel

(c) 1.55×10^3 m/s

51. $\dfrac{2\sqrt{2}\,Gm}{a^2}(-\mathbf{i})$

53. 2.99×10^3 rev/min

55. (a) $v_1 = m_2\left[\dfrac{2G}{d(m_1 + m_2)}\right]^{1/2}$

$v_2 = m_1\left[\dfrac{2G}{d(m_1 + m_2)}\right]^{1/2}$

$v_{rel} = \left[\dfrac{2G(m_1 + m_2)}{d}\right]^{1/2}$

(b) $K_1 = 1.07 \times 10^{32}$ J, $K_2 = 2.67 \times 10^{31}$ J

57. (a) 7.34×10^{22} kg   (b) 1.63×10^3 m/s
    (c) 1.32×10^{10} J
59. 119 km
61. (a) 5300 s   (b) 7.79 km/s   (c) 6.45×10^9 J
61A. (a) $2\pi(GM_E)^{1/2}(R_E + h)^{3/2}$

   (b) $\sqrt{GM_E/(R_E + h)}$ (c) $\dfrac{mGM_E(R_E + 2h)}{2R_E(R_E + h)}$

63. (a) $M/\pi R^4$ (b) $-GmM/r^2$
    (c) $-(GmM/R^4)r^2$
65. 1.48×10^{22} kg
67. (b) 981 kg/m^3
69. (b) $GMm/2R$
S5. The kinetic energy is

$$K = \tfrac{1}{2}mv^2 = \tfrac{1}{2}m(v_x^2 + v_y^2)$$

   The potential energy is

$$U = \frac{GM_E m}{R_E} - \frac{GM_E m}{r}$$

   where G is the universal gravitation constant, M_E is the mass of the Earth, R_E is the radius of the Earth, m is the mass of the satellite, and r is the distance from the center of the Earth to the satellite. The total energy, $K + U$, is constant. There may be a small change in the numerical value of the total energy, because of numerical errors during the integration of the differential equations.
S6. According to Kepler's laws of planetary motion the angular momentum, L, is a constant. There may be a small change in the numerical value of L, because of numerical errors during the integration of the differential equations.

Chapter 15

1. 0.111 kg
3. 3.99×10^{17} kg/m^3. Matter is mostly free space.
5. 6.24×10^6 Pa
7. 4.77×10^{17} kg/m^3

9. $P_{\text{ATM}} + \rho\sqrt{g^2 + a^2}\,(L/\sqrt{2})\cos\left(45° - \arctan\dfrac{a}{g}\right)$

11. 1.62 m
13. 77.4 cm^2
15. 0.722 mm
17. 9.12 MPa
19. 12.6 cm
21. 10.5 m; no, a little alcohol and water evaporate
23. 1.08 cm
25. 1470 N down
27. (a) 7.00 cm   (b) 2.80 kg
29. $\rho_{\text{oil}} = 1250$ kg/m^3; $\rho_{\text{sphere}} = 500$ kg/m^3
31. 0.611 kg
33. 1.07 m^2

33A. $\dfrac{m}{h(\rho_w - \rho_s)}$

35. 1430 m^3
37. (a) 17.7 m/s   (b) 1.73 mm
37A. (a) $\sqrt{2gh}$ (b) $(R/\pi)^{1/2}(8/gh)^{1/4}$
39. 0.0128 m^3/s
41. 31.6 m/s
43. (a) 28.0 m/s   (b) 392 kPa
45. Av/a
47. 103 m/s
49. $2[h(h_0 - h)]^{1/2}$
51. 5 kW at 20°C
53. (b) $\tfrac{1}{2}\rho Av^3$ if the mill could make the air stop; the same
55. 0.258 N
57. 1.91 m
59. 455 kPa
63. 8 cm/s
65. 2.01×10^6 N
69. 90.04% Zn
71. 5.02 GW
73. 4.43 m/s
75. (a) 1.25 cm   (b) 13.8 m/s
77. (a) 18.3 mm   (b) 14.3 mm   (c) 8.56 mm

Chapter 16

1. $y = \dfrac{6}{(x - 4.5t)^2 + 3}$
3. (a) longitudinal   (b) 666 s
5.

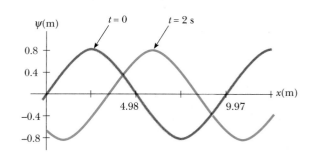

7. (a) 5.00 rad   (b) 0.858 cm
9. (a) Wave 1 travels in the $+x$ direction; wave 2 travels in the $-x$ direction.   (b) 0.75 s   (c) $x = 1.00$ m
11. 520 m/s
13. 13.5 N
15. 586 m/s
17. 0.329 s
19. (b) 0.125 s
21. 0.319 m
23. (b) $k = 18.0$ rad/m, $T = 0.0833$ s, $\omega = 75.4$ rad/s, $v = 4.20$ m/s
    (c) $y(x, t) = (0.20\text{ m})\sin(18.0x + 75.4t - 0.151)$
25. $y_1 + y_2 = 11.2\sin(2.0x - 10t + 63.4°)$
27. (a) $y = (0.0800\text{ m})\sin(7.85x + 6\pi t)$
    (b) $y = (0.0800\text{ m})\sin(7.85x + 6\pi t - 0.785)$

29. (a) 2.15 cm   (b) 0.379 rad   (c) 541 cm/s
   (d) $y(x, t) = (2.15 \text{ cm})\cos(80\pi t + 8\pi x/3 + 0.379)$
31. $A = 2.0$ cm; $k = 2.11$ rad/m; $\lambda = 2.98$ m;
   $\omega = 3.62$ rad/s; $f = 0.576$ Hz; $v = 1.72$ m/s
33. (a) $y = (0.200 \text{ mm}) \sin[16.0x - 3140t]$
   (b) $T = 158$ N
35. 1.07 kW
35A. $2\pi^2 M v^3 A^2 / L\lambda^2$
37. (a) remains constant   (b) remains constant
   (c) remains constant   (d) p is quadrupled
39. (a) 62.5 m/s   (b) 7.85 m   (c) 7.96 Hz
   (d) 21.1 W
43. (b) $f(x + vt) = \frac{1}{2}(x + vt)^2$ and $g(x-vt) = \frac{1}{2}(x-vt)^2$
45. (a) 3.33 m/s in the positive x direction
   (b) -5.48 cm   (c) 0.667 m, 5.00 Hz
   (d) 11.0 m/s
47. (a) 179 m/s   (b) 17.7 kW
49. (a) 39.2 N   (b) 89.2 cm   (c) 83.6 m/s
49A. (a) $2Mg$ (b) $L_0 + 2Mg/k$
   (c) $(2MgL_0/m + 4M^2g^2/km)^{1/2}$
51. (a) 5.00 m/s + x (b) 5.00 m/s − x
   (c) 7.5 m/s − x (d) 24.0 m/s + x
55. 3.86×10^{-4} (at 5.93°C)
57. $(2L/g)^{1/2}$, $L/4$

59. (a) $\dfrac{\mu\omega^3}{2k} A_0^2 e^{-2bx}$ (b) $\dfrac{\mu\omega^3}{2k} A_0^2$ (c) e^{-2bx}

Chapter 17

1. 5.56 km
3. 1430 m/s
5. 332 m/s
7. 1.988 km
9. (a) 27.2 s   (b) 25.7 s   It is shorter by 5.30%.
11. 1.55×10^{-10} m
13. 5.81 m
15. (a) 2.00 μm, 0.400 m, 54.6 m/s   (b) -0.433 μm
   (c) 1.72 mm/s
17. $(0.200 \text{ Pa}) \sin(62.8x - 2.16 \times 10^4 t)$
19. 66.0 dB
23. 100.0 m and 10.0 m
25. (a) 65.0 dB   (b) 67.8 dB   (c) 69.6 dB
27. 241 W
29. (a) 30.0 m   (b) 9.49×10^5 m
31. 50.0 km
33. 46.4°
35. 56.4°
37. 26.4 m/s
39. (a) 338 Hz   (b) 483 Hz
41. 2.82×10^8 m/s
43. (a) 56.3 s
   (b) (56.6 km)$\mathbf{i}$ + (20.0 km)$\mathbf{j}$ from the observer
45. 130 m/s, 1.73 km
47. 80.0°
49. 1204 Hz
51. (a) 0.948°   (b) 4.40°

53. 1.34×10^4 N
55. 95.5 s

55A. $\dfrac{0.3E}{4\pi d^2 I_0} 10^{-\beta/10}$

57. (a) 55.8 m/s   (b) 2500 Hz
59. (a) 6.45   (b) 0
61. 1.60
63. The measured wavelengths depend on your monitor. However, the wavelengths should be proportional to those given here. For $u/v = 0.0$, $\lambda_0 = 0.75$ cm. For $u/v = 0.5$, $\lambda_{\text{front}} = 0.37$ cm and $\lambda_{\text{back}} = 1.13$ cm. Therefore,

$$\left| \frac{\Delta\lambda_{\text{front}}}{\lambda_0} \right| = \frac{0.37 \text{ cm} - 0.75 \text{ cm}}{0.75 \text{ cm}} = 0.5$$

and

$$\left| \frac{\Delta\lambda_{\text{back}}}{\lambda_0} \right| = \frac{1.13 \text{ cm} - 0.75 \text{ cm}}{0.75 \text{ cm}} = 0.5$$

We see that $\dfrac{\Delta\lambda}{\lambda_0} = \dfrac{u}{v}$.

Chapter 18

1. (a) 9.24 m   (b) 600 Hz
3. 0.500 s
5. (a) The path difference to A is $\lambda/2$.
   (b) $9x^2 - 16y^2 = 144$
7. at 0.0891 m, 0.303 m, 0.518 m, 0.732 m, 0.947 m, and 1.16 m
9. (a) 4.24 cm   (b) 6.00 cm   (c) 6.00 cm
   (d) $x = 0.5$ cm, 1.5 cm, 2.5 cm
11. 25.1 m, 60.0 Hz
13. (a) 2.00 cm   (b) 2.40 cm
15. (a) $0, \pm 2\pi/3k, \pm 4\pi/3k, \ldots$
   (b) $(\pm \pi - 2\omega t)/k$, $(\pm 3\pi - 2\omega t)/k$, $(\pm 5\pi - 2\omega t)/k$
17. (a) 60.0 cm   (b) 30.0 Hz
19. $L/4$, $L/2$
21. 0.786 Hz, 1.57 Hz, 2.36 Hz, 3.14 Hz
23. 2.80 g

23A. $m = \dfrac{Mg}{4Lf_1^2 \tan \theta}$

25. (a) $T = 163$ N   (b) 660 Hz
27. 19.976 kHz
29. 338 N
31. 20.5 kg

31A. $m_w = \rho_w A \left(L - \dfrac{v_s}{4f} \right)$

33. 50.4 cm, 84.0 cm
35. 35.8 cm, 71.7 cm
37. 349 m/s
39. (a) 531 Hz   (b) 4.25 cm
41. 328 m/s
43. (a) 350 m/s   (b) 114 cm

45. $n(206$ Hz$)$ and $n(84.5$ Hz$)$, where $n = 1, 2, 3, \ldots$
47. 1.88 kHz
49. (a) 1.59 kHz　　(b) odd　　(c) 1.11 kHz
51. It is.
53. (a) 1.99 Hz　　(b) 3.38 m/s
55. (a) 3.33 rad　　(b) 283 Hz
57. 85.7 Hz
59. $f = 50.0$ Hz; $L = 1.70$ m
61. (a) 78.9 N　　(b) 211 Hz
63. $\lambda = 4.86$ m
65. 3.87 m/s *away* from the station *or* 3.78 m/s *toward* the
station
67. (a) 59.9 Hz　　(b) 20 cm
69. (a) 0.5　　(b) $\dfrac{n^2 F}{(n + 1)^2}$　　(c) $\dfrac{F'}{F} = \dfrac{9}{16}$

S4. The following steps can be used to modify the spreadsheet.

　1. MOVE the entire Y_T column — one column to the right.
　2. COPY the Y_2 column — one column to the right.
　　EDIT the heading label to Y_3.
　3. COPY the second wave input data block to the right
　　and EDIT the labels to reflect the third wave.
　4. EDIT the Y_3 column to reflect the third wave data
　　block addresses.
　5. EDIT the Y_T column to include Y_1, Y_2, and Y_3 in
　　the sum.

S6. Plot $Y(t)$ versus ωt. You may want to start with three
terms in the series and then add additional terms and
watch how $Y(t)$ changes.

Chapter 19

1. (a) $-273.5°C$　　(b) 1.27 atm, 1.74 atm
3. (a) 30.4 mm Hg　　(b) 18.0 K
5. 139 K, $-134°C$　　(b) 6.56 kPa
7. (a) $-320°F$　　(b) 77.3 K
9. $-297°F$
11. (a) 810°F　　(b) 450 K
13. (a) 90.0°C　　(b) 90.0 K
15. $-40.0°C$
17. 3.27 cm
19. 1.32 cm
21. 0.548 gal
23. 217 kN
25. 1.20 cm
27. (a) 437°C　　(b) 2100°C. No; they melt first.
29. (a) 99.4 cm³　　(b) 0.943 cm
31. 1.08 L
33. (a) 0.176 mm　　(b) 8.78 μm　　(c) 93.0 mm³
35. 7.95 m³
37. 4.39 kg
39. 472 K
41. 2.28 kg
41A. $\dfrac{M P_0 V}{R T_1}\left(1 - \dfrac{T_1}{T_2}\right)$

43. 1.61 MPa = 16.1 atm
45. 594 kPa
47. 400 kPa, 448 kPa
49. 1.13
51. (a) $A = 1.85 \times 10^{-3}$ (1/°C), $R_0 = 50.0\ \Omega$
　　(b) 421 °C
53. $\alpha \Delta T \ll 1$
55. 3.55 cm
55A. $\Delta h = \dfrac{V}{A} \beta\, \Delta T$
57. (a) 94.97 cm　　(b) 95.03 cm
59. (b) 1.33 kg/m³
63. 2.74 m
63A. $y = \frac{1}{2}\sqrt{(L + \Delta L)^2 - L^2}$, where $\Delta L = \alpha L\, \Delta T$
65. 30.4°C
67. (a) 18.0 m　　(b) 277 kPa
69. (a) 7.06 mm　　(b) 297 K
71. (a) 0.0374 mol　　(b) 0.732 atm
73. (a) 6.17×10^{-3} kg/m　　(b) 632 N
　　(c) 580 N; 192 Hz
75. (a) $(\alpha_2 - \alpha_1)\, L\, \Delta T/(r_2 - r_1)$
　　(c) It bends the other way.
S1. From the figure below, note that

$$h = \frac{L}{20}(1 - \cos\theta)$$

and

$$\frac{L}{L_0} = (1 + \alpha\, \Delta T) = \frac{\theta}{\sin\theta} = 1.000\ 055$$

Solving this transcendental equation, $\theta = 0.018\ 165$ rad
and $h = 4.54$ m.

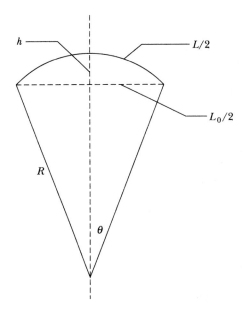

Chapter 20

1. 0.105°C
3. 10.117°C
5. 0.234 kJ/kg·°C
7. 85.3°C
9. 29.6°C
11. 34.7°C
13. 19.5 kJ
15. 50.7 ks
17. 720 cal
19. 47.1°C
21. (a) 0°C   (b) 115 g
23. 2.99 mg
25. (a) 25.760°C   (b) no
27. 0.258 g if the bullet is at 0°C
29. 810 J, 506 J, 203 J
31. 466 J
31A. $nR\,\Delta T$
33. 1.18 MJ
35. (a) 7.65 L   (b) 305 K
37. (a) − 567 J   (b) 167 J
37A. (a) $W = P\,\Delta V$ (b) $\Delta U = Q - W$
39. (a) 12.0 kJ   (b) − 12.0 kJ
41. (a) 23.1 kJ   (b) 23.1 kJ
43. 0.0962 g
45. (a) 7.50 kJ   (b) 900 K
47. 2.47 L
47A. $V_i = V_f e^{-W/nRT_0}$, where $W = M_w c_w (T_h - T_c)$
49. (a) 48.6 mJ   (b) 16.2 kJ   (c) 16.2 kJ
51. (a) 10.0 L·atm   (b) 0.0100 atm   (c) 7.00 kJ
53. 1.34 kW
55. 51.0°C
57. 138 MJ
59. 0.0222 W/m·°C
59A. $k = \dfrac{Pt}{A\,\Delta T}$
61. (a) 61.1 kWh   (b) $3.67
63. (a) 0.89 ft²·°F·h/BTU
    (b) 1.85 ft²·°F·h/BTU   (c) 2.08
65. 781 kg
67. 1.87 kJ
69. (a) 16.8 L   (b) 0.351 L/s
71. The bullet will partially melt.
73. 44.5°C
75. 5.26°C
79. 9.32 kW
81. 5.31 h
83. 800 J/kg·°C
S1. By varying h until $T = 45\ °C$ at $t = 180\ s$, one finds $h =$
    0.010 855 cal/s·cm²·°C. Examine the associated graph
    for each choice of h.
S2. (b) $\Delta U = 4669\ J$

Chapter 21

1. 2.43×10^5 m²/s²
3. 2.30 kmol

5. 3.32 mol
7. 8.76×10^{-21} J
9. (a) 40.1 K   (b) 6.01 km/s
11. 477 m/s
13. 109 kPa
15. 75.0 J
17. (a) 316 K   (b) 200 J
17A. (a) $dT = \dfrac{Q}{C_V} - \dfrac{Q}{C_p}$ (b) $\dfrac{QR}{C_p}$
19. (a) 3.46 kJ   (b) 2.45 kJ   (c) 1.01 kJ
21. 24.0 kJ; 68.7 kJ
23. (a) 118 kJ   (b) 6.03×10^3 kg
25. (a) 1.39 atm   (b) 366 K, 254 K
27. (a) 2.06×10^{-4} m³   (b) 560 K   (c) 8.72 K
29. (a) 0.118, so the compression ratio $V_i/V_f = 8.50$
    (b) 2.35
31. 227 K
33. 91.2 J
33A. $9\,P_0 V_0$
35. 1.51×10^{-20} J
37. 2.33×10^{-21} J
39. (a) 7.27×10^{-20} J/molecule   (b) 2.21 km/s
    (c) 3510 K
41. (a) 5.63×10^{18} m, 1.00×10^9 y
    (b) 5.63×10^{12} m, 1.00×10^3 y
43. (a) 1.028   (b) ^{35}Cl
45. (a) 2.01×10^4 K   (b) 902 K
47. (a) 3.21×10^{12} molecules
    (b) 778 km   (c) 6.42×10^{-4} s^{-1}
49. 193
51. 4.65×10^{-8} cm
55. (a) 3.65 v (b) 3.99 v (c) 3.00 v
    (d) 106 mv^2/V (e) 7.98 mv^2
57. zero, 2.70×10^{20}
59. 0.625
63. (c) 2.0×10^3
65. (b) 5.47 km
67. (a) 10^{82} (b) 10^{12} m   (c) 10^{58} moles
69. (a) 0.510 m/s   (b) 20 ms
S1. (a) At $T = 100$ K, $f(1000)\ dv = 0.0896$ and
        $f(3000)\ dv = 0.000\ 05$.
    (b) At $T = 273$ K, $f(1000)\ dv = 0.0428$ and
        $f(3000)\ dv = 0.011\ 09$.
    (c) At $T = 1000$ K, $f(1000)\ dv = 0.0084$ and
        $f(3000)\ dv = 0.028\ 77$.

Chapter 22

1. (a) 6.94%   (b) 335 J
3. (a) 0.333   (b) 0.667
5. (a) 1.00 kJ   (b) 0
7. (a) 0.375   (b) 600 J   (c) 2.00 kW
9. 0.330
11. (a) 5.12%   (b) 5.27 TJ
13. (a) 0.672   (b) 58.8 kW

15. 0.478°C
17. (a) 0.268   (b) 0.423
19. 453 K
21. 146 kW, 70.8 kW
23. 192 J
25. (a) 24.0 J   (b) 144 J
27. 72.2 J

27A. $W = \dfrac{\Delta T}{T_c} Q$

29. $\Delta S = -90.2$ J/K
31. 195 J/K
33. 717 J/K
35. 3.27 J/K
37. 5.76 J/K, no temperature change
39. 18.4 J/K
41. (a) 154.5 J/K   (b) 54.2 kJ
43. (a) 5.00 kW   (b) 763 W
45. (a) 4.10 kJ   (b) 14.2 kJ
    (c) 10.1 kJ   (d) 28.8%
47. (a) $2nRT_0 \ln 2$ (b) 0.273
49. (a) $10.5nRT_0$ (b) $8.5nRT_0$ (c) 0.190
    (d) 0.833
51. $nC_p \ln 3$
53. 5.97×10^4 kg/s

53A. $\dfrac{dm}{dt} = \dfrac{P}{c_w \Delta T}\left(\dfrac{T_h}{T_h - T_c}\right)$

57. (a) 96.9 W   (b) 1.19°C/h

59. $e = \dfrac{2(T_2 - T_1) \ln (V_2/V_1)}{3(T_2 - T_1) + 2T_2 \ln (V_2/V_1)}$

61. (b) 12.0 kJ   (c) -12.0 kJ
63. -8.26×10^5 J

Chapter 23

1. 5.14×10^3 N
3. (a) 1.59 nN away   (b) 1.24×10^{36} times larger
   (c) 8.61×10^{-11} C/kg
5. (a) 57.1 TC   (b) 3.48×10^6 N/C
7. 0.873 N at 330°
9. 40.9 N at 263°
11. 2.51×10^{-10}
13. 3.60 MN down on the top and up on the bottom of the cloud
15. (a) $(-5.58 \times 10^{-11}$ N/C$)\,$j
    (b) $(1.02 \times 10^{-7}$ N/C$)\,$j
17. (a) 18.8 nC   (b) 1.17×10^{11} electrons
19. (a) $(1.29 \times 10^4$ N/C$)\,$j   (b) $(-3.87 \times 10^{-2}$ N$)\,$j
21. (a) $k_e qx\,(R^2 + x^2)^{-3/2}$
23. (a) at the center   (b) $\left(\dfrac{\sqrt{3}\,kg}{a^2}\right)\mathbf{j}$
25. (a) $5.91 k_e\,q/a^2$ at 58.8°   (b) $5.91 k_e\,q^2/a^2$ at 58.8°
27. $-\pi^2 k_e\,q\mathbf{i}/6a^2$
29. $-\left(\dfrac{k_e \lambda_0}{x_0}\right)\mathbf{i}$

31. (a) $(6.65 \times 10^6$ N/C$)\,$i   (b) $(2.42 \times 10^7$ N/C$)\,$i
    (c) $(6.40 \times 10^6$ N/C$)\,$i   (d) $(6.65 \times 10^5$ N/C$)\,$i

33. (a) $\dfrac{k_e Q\mathbf{i}}{h}\,[(d^2 + R^2)^{-1/2} - ((d + h)^2 + R^2)^{-1/2}]$

    (b) $\dfrac{2k_e Q\mathbf{i}}{R^2 h}\,[h + (d^2 + R^2)^{1/2} - ((d + h)^2 + R^2)^{1/2}]$

35. (a) 9.35×10^7 N/C away from the center; 1.039×10^8 N/C is 10.0% larger
    (b) 515.1 kN/C away from the center; 519.3 kN/C is 0.8% larger
37. 7.20×10^7 N/C away from the center; 1.00×10^8 N/C axially away
39. $(-21.6$ MN/C$)\,$i

41.

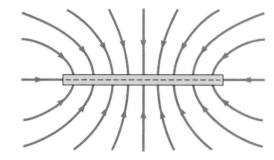

43. (a) $\dfrac{q_1}{q_2} = -1/3$ (b) q_1 is negative and q_2 is positive
45. (a) 6.14×10^{10} m/s²   (b) 19.5 μs
    (c) 11.7 m   (d) 1.20 fJ
47. 1.00×10^3 N/C in the direction of the beam
47A. K/ed parallel to $\mathbf{v}$
49. (a) $(-5.75 \times 10^{13}$ m/s²$)\,$i   (b) 2.84×10^6 m/s
    (c) 49.4 ns
51. (a) 111 ns   (b) 5.67 mm
    (c) $(450$ km/s$)\,$i $+ (102$ km/s$)\,$j
53. (a) 36.9°, 53.1°   (b) 167 ns, 221 ns
55. (a) 10.9 nC   (b) 5.43×10^{-3} N
55A. (a) $\dfrac{mg}{E_x \cot \theta + E_y}$ (b) $\dfrac{mg\,E_x}{E_x \cos \theta + E_y \sin \theta}$
57. (a) $\theta_1 = \theta_2$
59. 204 nC
63. (a) $-\left(\dfrac{4k_e q}{3a^2}\right)\mathbf{j}$ (b) $(0, 2.00$ m$)$
65. (a) 307 ms   (b) Yes; neglecting gravity causes a 2.28% error.
65A. (a) $2\pi\left(\dfrac{L}{g + qE/m}\right)^{1/2}$ (b) Yes. If qE is small compared to mg, then gravity determines its period.
67. 5.27×10^{17} m/s²; 0.854 mm
71. (a) $F = \dfrac{k_e q^2}{s^2}\,(1.90)\,(\mathbf{i} + \mathbf{j} + \mathbf{k})$

    (b) $F = 3.29\,\dfrac{k_e q^2}{s^2}$ in a direction away from the vertex diagonally opposite to it

S4. (a) at $d < 0.005$ m ($Y/L = 0.1$); (b) at $d > 0.124$ m ($Y/L = 2.48$); (c) same as parts (a) and (b); (d) at $d < 0.010$ m ($Y/L = 0.1$) and at $d > 0.248$ m ($Y/L = 2.48$); (e) In terms of Y/L, the answers do not change.

S5. The dipole approximation of the electric field $E = 2k_e p/x^3$ is within 20 percent of the actual value when $x > 6.2$ cm. It is within 5 percent when $x > 12.6$ cm.

Chapter 24

1. 0
3. (a) aA   (b) bA   (c) 0
5. 4.14×10^6 N/C
5A. $4\Phi/\pi d^2$
7. EhR
9. 1.87×10^3 Nm²/C
11. (a) $q/2\epsilon_0$ (b) $q/2\epsilon_0$
    (c) Plane and square look the same to the charge.
13. (a) 1.36×10^6 Nm²/C   (b) 6.78×10^5 Nm²/C
    (c) No, the same field lines go through spheres of all sizes.
13A. (a) Q/ϵ_0 (b) $Q/2\epsilon_0$
    (c) No. As the radius increases, the area increases but the field decreases to compensate.
15. -6.89×10^6 Nm²/C. The number of lines entering exceeds the number leaving by 2.91 times or more.
17. 0 if $R < d$; $2\lambda(R^2 - d^2)^{1/2}/\epsilon_0$ if $R > d$
19. 28.3 N·m²/C
21. (a) 761 nC   (b) It may have any distribution. Any and all point and smeared-out charges, positive and negative, must add algebraically to $+$ 761 nC.
    (c) Total charge is $-$ 761 nC.
23. (a) $\dfrac{Q}{2\epsilon_0}$ (out of the volume enclosed)

    (b) $-\dfrac{Q}{2\epsilon_0}$ (into it)
25. (a) 0   (b) 7.20×10^6 N/C away from the center
27. (a) 0.713 μC   (b) 5.7 μC
29. (a) 0   (b) $(3.66 \times 10^5$ N/C$)\hat{r}$
    (c) $(1.46 \times 10^6$ N/C$)\hat{r}$ (d) $(6.50 \times 10^5$ N/C$)\hat{r}$
31. $E = (a/2\epsilon_0)\hat{r}$
33. (a) 5.14×10^4 N/C outward   (b) 646 Nm²/C
35. $E = (\rho r/2\epsilon_0)\hat{r}$
37. 5.08×10^5 N/C up.
39. (a) 0   (b) 5.40×10^3 N/C
    (c) 540 N/C, both radially outward
41. (a) 80.0 nC/m² on each face
    (b) $(9.04 \times 10^3$ N/C$)$k
    (c) $(-9.04 \times 10^3$ N/C$)$k
43. (a) -99.5 μC/m²   (b) $+382$ μC/m²
43A. (a) $-q/4\pi a^2$ (b) $(Q + q)/4\pi b^2$
45. (a) 0   (b) $(8.00 \times 10^7$ N/C$)\hat{r}$ (c) 0
    (d) $(7.35 \times 10^6$ N/C$)\hat{r}$
47. (a) $-\lambda$, $+3\lambda$ (b) $\left(\dfrac{3\lambda}{2\pi\epsilon_0 r}\right)\hat{r}$
49. (b) $\dfrac{Q}{2\epsilon_0}$ (c) $\dfrac{Q}{\epsilon_0}$

51. (a) $E = \left(\dfrac{\rho r}{3\epsilon_0}\right)\hat{r}$ for $r < a$; $E = \left(\dfrac{k_e Q}{r^2}\right)\hat{r}$ for $a < r < b$;

    $E = 0$ for $b < r < c$; $E = \left(\dfrac{k_e Q}{r^2}\right)\hat{r}$ for $r > c$

    (b) $\sigma_1 = -\dfrac{Q}{4\pi b^2}$ inner; $\sigma_2 = +\dfrac{Q}{4\pi c^2}$ outer
53. (c) $f = \dfrac{1}{2\pi}\sqrt{\dfrac{k_e e^2}{mR^3}}$ (d) 102 pm

57. $g = \left(\dfrac{GM_e r}{R_e^3}\right)\hat{r}$
59. (a) σ/ϵ_0 to the left   (b) zero
    (c) σ/ϵ_e to the right
63. $E = \dfrac{\rho a}{3\epsilon_0}$ j

Chapter 25

1. 1.80 kV
3. (a) 152 km/s   (b) 6.50×10^6 m/s
5. (a) 2.7 keV   (b) 509 km/s
7. 6.41×10^{-19} C
9. 2.10×10^6 m/s
11. 1.35 MJ
13. 432 V; 432 eV
15. -38.9 V; the origin
17. (a) 20.0 keV, 83.8 Mm/s   (b) 7.64×10^{-23} kg·m/s
19. (a) 0.400 m/s   (b) The same
19A. (a) $\sqrt{2E\lambda d/\mu}$ (b) The same
21. 2.00 m
23. 119 nC, 2.67 m
25. 4.00 nC at $(-1, 0)$ and -5.01 nC at $(0, 2)$
27. -11.0 MV
29. (a) -386 nJ. Positive binding energy would have to be put in to separate them.   (b) 103 V
31. (a) -27.3 eV   (b) -6.81 eV   (c) 0
35. 1.74 m/s
35A. $((1 + \sqrt{2}/4)\, k_e q^2/Lm)^{1/2}$
37. (a) 1.00 kV $- (1.41$ kV/m$)x + (1.44$ kV$)$ ln $\left(\dfrac{3\,\text{m}}{3\,\text{m} - x}\right)$

    (b) $+$ 633 nJ
37A. (a) $V_0 - \dfrac{\sigma x}{2\epsilon_0} + \dfrac{\lambda}{2\pi\epsilon_0}$ ln $\left(\dfrac{d}{d - x}\right)$

    (b) $qV_0 - \dfrac{q\sigma d}{8\epsilon_0} + \dfrac{q\lambda}{2\pi\epsilon_0}$ ln $(4/3)$
39. $E_x = -5 + 6xy$ $E_y = 3x^2 - 2z^2$ $E_z = -4yz$
    7.07 N/C
41. (a) 10.0 V, -11.0 V, -32.0 V   (b) $(7.00$ N/C$)$i
43. $E_x = \dfrac{3\,E_0 a^3 xz}{(x^2 + y^2 + z^2)^{5/2}}$ $E_y = \dfrac{3E_0 a^3 yz}{(x^2 + y^2 + z^2)^{5/2}}$

    $E_z = E_0 + \dfrac{E_0 a^3\,(2z^2 - x^2 - y^2)}{(x^2 + y^2 + z^2)^{5/2}}$ outside the sphere, and

    $E = 0$ inside.
45. $-(0.553)k_e Q/R$

47. (a) C/m²   (b) $k_e \alpha \left[L - d \ln \dfrac{d + L}{d} \right]$

49. $(\sigma/2\epsilon_0) (\sqrt{x^2 + b^2} - \sqrt{x^2 + a^2})$

51. 1.56×10^{12} electrons removed

53. (a) 0, 1.67 MV
    (b) 5.85×10^6 N/C away, 1.17 MV
    (c) 1.19×10^7 N/C away, 1.67 MV

55. (a) 4.50×10^7 N/C outward, 30.0 MN/C outward
    (b) 1.80 MV

57. (a) 450 kV   (b) 7.50 μC

59. 5.00 μC

61. (a) 6.00 m   (b) − 2.00 μC

63. (a) 13.3 μC   (b) 20.0 cm

65. (a) 180 kV   (b) 127 kV

67. (a) $2 k_e Q d^2 (3x^2 - d^2)(x^3 - xd^2)^{-2} \mathbf{i}$
    (b) $(609 \text{ MN/C}) \mathbf{i}$

69.

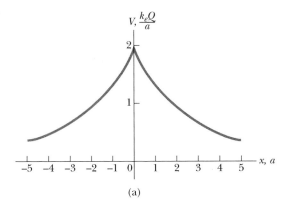

(a)

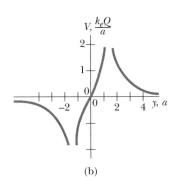

(b)

71. (a) $1.26 \sigma_0$ (b) $1.26 E_0$ (c) $1.59 V_0$

73. $k_e \dfrac{Q^2}{2R}$

75. $V_2 - V_1 = -\dfrac{\lambda}{2\pi\epsilon_0} \ln \left(\dfrac{r_2}{r_1} \right)$

79. $E_y = k_e \dfrac{Q}{\ell y} \left[1 - \dfrac{y^2}{\ell^2 + y^2 + \ell\sqrt{\ell^2 + y^2}} \right]$

81. (a) $E_r = \dfrac{2 k_e p \cos \theta}{r^3}$; $E_\theta = \dfrac{k_e p \sin \theta}{r^3}$; yes; no

    (b) $\mathbf{E} = \dfrac{3 k_e p x y \mathbf{i}}{(x^2 + y^2)^{5/2}} + \dfrac{k_e p (2 y^2 - x^2) \mathbf{j}}{(x^2 + y^2)^{5/2}}$

83. $\dfrac{3}{5} \left(\dfrac{k_e Q^2}{R} \right)$

85. $x = 0.57735$ m and $x = 0.24859$ m

Chapter 26

1. 13.3 kV

3. (a) 1.00 μF   (b) 100 V

5. 684 μC

7. (a) 1.33 μC/m²   (b) 13.3 pF

9. (a) 423 fF   (b) 0.652

9A. (a) $4\pi\epsilon_0 (R_1 + R_2)$ (b) R_1/R_2

11. 1.52 mm

13. 4.42 μm

15. (a) 1.11×10^4 N/C toward the negative plate
    (b) 98.3 nC/m²   (c) 3.74 pF   (d) 74.8 pC

17. $(69.1 \text{ pF}) (\pi - \theta)$

17A. $\epsilon_0 N R^2 (\pi - \theta)/d$

19. 2.13×10^{16} m³

19A. $7 C^3 / 384 \pi^2 \epsilon_0^3$

21. (a) 2.68 nF   (b) 3.02 kV

23. (a) 15.6 pF   (b) 256 kV

25. 66.7 nC

27. 18.0 μF

29. (a) 4.00 μF   (b) 8.00 V, 4.00 V, 12.0 V, 24.0 μC, 24.0 μC, 24.0 μC

31. (a) 5.96 μF   (b) 89.2 μC, 63.1 μC, 26.4 μC, 26.4 μC

33. 120 μC; 80.0 μC and 40.0 μC

35. $60R/37k_e$

37. 10

39. 83.6 μC

41. 12.9 μF

43. $\dfrac{\epsilon_0 A}{(s - d)}$

45. 90.0 mJ

47. (a) 55.9 μC   (b) 4.65 V

49. 800 pJ, 5.79 mJ/m³

55. (a) 369 pC   (b) 118 pF, 3.12 V   (c) − 45.5 nJ

55A. (a) $\epsilon_0 AV/d$ (b) $C_f = \kappa\epsilon_0 A/d$, $V_f = V/\kappa$
     (c) $- \epsilon_0 AV^2(\kappa - 1)/2d\kappa$

57. 16.7 pF, 1.62 kV

59. 1.04 m

61. $\kappa = 8.00$

63. 22.5 V

63A. 1.5 V

65. 416 pF

67. 1.00 μF and 3.00 μF

69. (b) $4\pi\epsilon_0/(a^{-1} + b^{-1})$

71. 2.33

71A. $1 + q/q_0$

73. (a) 243 μJ   (b) 2.30 mJ

75. 4.29 μF

75A. $CV/(V_0 - V)$

77. 480 V

79. 0.188 m²

81. 3.00 μF

83. (b) $Q/Q_0 = \kappa$
85. 2/3
89. 19.0 kV
91. 3.00 μF

Chapter 27

1. (b) 1.05 mA
3. 400 nA
3A. $q\omega/2\pi$
5. 0.265 C
7. (a) 221 nm   (b) No
9. (a) 1.50×10^5 A   (b) 5.40×10^8 C
11. 13.3 μA/m^2
13. 1.32×10^{11} A/m^2
15. 1.59 Ω
17. 1.98 A
19. 1.33 Ω
19A. $R/9$
21. $1.56R$
23. (a) 1.82 m   (b) 280 μm
25. 6.43 A
27. (a) 3.75 kΩ (b) 536 m
29. (a) 3.15×10^{-8} $\Omega \cdot$m   (b) 6.35×10^6 A/m^2
    (c) 49.9 mA   (d) 6.59×10^{-4} m/s (assume 1 conduction electron per atom)   (e) 0.400 V
31. 0.125
33. 20.8 Ω
35. 67.6°C
37. 26.2°C
39. 3.03×10^7 A/m^2
41. 21.2 nm
43. 0.833 W
45. 36.1%
47. (a) 0.660 kW·h   (b) 3.96¢
49. (a) 133 Ω (b) 9.42 m
51. 28.9 Ω
51A. $V^2 t/mc\,(T_2 - T_1)$
53. 26.9 cents/day
55. (a) 184 W   (b) 461°C
57. 2020°C
59. (a) 667 A   (b) 50.0 km
63. (a) $R = \dfrac{\rho L}{\pi(r_b^2 - r_a^2)}$ (b) 37.4 MΩ

    (c) $R = \dfrac{\rho}{2\pi L} \ln\left(\dfrac{r_b}{r_a}\right)$ (d) 1.22 MΩ

69. Average $\rho = 1.47$ $\mu\Omega \cdot$m; they agree.
S1. (a) The savings are \$254.92.

Chapter 28

1. (a) 7.67 Ω (b) 1.76 W
3. (a) 1.79 A   (b) 10.4 V
5. 12.0 Ω
7. (a) 6.73 Ω (b) 1.98 Ω

9. (a) 4.59 Ω (b) 8.16%
11. 0.923 $\Omega \leq R \leq 9.0$ Ω
13. 1.00 kΩ
15. 55.0 Ω
17. 1.41 Ω
17A. $\sqrt{2}\,R$
19. 14.3 W, 28.5 W, 1.33 W, 4.00 W
21. (a) 0.227 A   (b) 5.68 V
23. 470 Ω; 220 Ω
23A. $\frac{1}{2}R_s + (R_s^2/4 - R_s R_p)^{1/2}$ and $\frac{1}{2}R_s - (R_s^2/4 - R_s R_p)^{1/2}$
25. (a) -10.4 V   (b) 141 mA, 915 mA, 774 mA
27. $\frac{11}{13}$ A, $\frac{6}{13}$ A, $\frac{17}{13}$ A
29. Starter: 171 A   Battery: 0.283 A
31. 3.50 A, 2.50 A, 1.00 A
33. (a) $I_1 = \dfrac{5}{13}$ mA; $I_2 = \dfrac{40}{13}$ mA; $I_3 = \dfrac{35}{13}$ mA
    (b) 69.2 V; c
35. (a) 12.4 V   (b) 9.65 V
37. (a) 909 mA   (b) -1.82 V
39. 800 W, 450 W, 25.0 W, 25.0 W
41. 3.00 J
41A. $U_0/4$
43. (a) 1.50 s   (b) 1.00 s
    (c) 200 μA + (100 μA)$e^{-t/(1.00\,s)}$
45. (a) 12.0 s   (b) $i(t) = (3.00\ \mu A)e^{-t/12}$
    $q(t) = (36.0\ \mu C)[1 - e^{-t/12}]$
47. (a) 6.00 V   (b) 8.29 μs
49. 425 mA
51. 1.60 MΩ
51A. $t/C \ln 2$
53. 16.6 kΩ
55. 0.302 Ω
57. 49.9 kΩ
59. (b) 0.0501 Ω, 0.451 Ω
61. 0.588 A
63. 60.0
65. (a) 12.5 A, 6.25 A, 8.33 A
    (b) 27.1 A; No, it would not be sufficient since the current drawn is greater than 25 A.
67. (a) 0.101 W   (b) 10.1 W
69. (a) 16.7A   (b) 33.3 A
    (c) The 120-V heater requires four times as much mass.
71. 6.00 Ω; 3.00 Ω
71A. $P_s/2I^2 + (P_s^2/4I^4 - P_s P_p/I^4)^{1/2}$ and
    $P_s/2I^2 - (P_s^2/4I^4 - P_s P_p/I^4)^{1/2}$
73. (a) 72.0 W   (b) 72.0 W
75. (a) 40W   (b) 80 V, 40 V, 40 V
77. (a) $R \leq 1050$ Ω (b) $R \geq 10.0$ Ω
79. (a) $R \to \infty$ (b) $R \to 0$ (c) $R \to r$
81. (a) 9.93 μC   (b) 3.37×10^{-8} A
    (c) 3.34×10^{-7} W   (d) 3.37×10^{-7} W
83. T = $(R_A + 2R_B)C \ln 2$
85. $R = 0.521$ Ω, 0.260 Ω, 0.260 Ω, assuming resistors are in series with the galvanometer
87. (a) 1/3 mA for R_1, R_2 (b) 50 μC
    (c) (0.278 mA)$e^{-t/0.18s}$ (d) 0.290 s

89. (a) 1.96 μC (b) 53.3 Ω

91. (a) $\ln \dfrac{\mathcal{E}}{V} = (0.0118 \text{ s}^{-1})t + 0.0882$

(b) 85 s $\pm$ 6%; 8.5 μF $\pm$ 6%

93. 48.0 W

93A. 1.50P

S1. Kirchhoff's equations for this circuit can be written as

$$\mathcal{E}_1 - I_1 R_1 - I_4 R_4 = 0$$
$$\mathcal{E}_2 - I_2 R_2 - I_4 R_4 = 0$$
$$\mathcal{E}_3 - I_3 R_3 - I_4 R_4 = 0$$

and

$$I_1 + I_2 + I_3 = I_4$$

In matrix form, they are

$$\begin{bmatrix} R_1 & 0 & 0 & R_4 \\ 0 & R_2 & 0 & R_4 \\ 0 & 0 & R_3 & R_4 \\ 1 & 1 & 1 & -1 \end{bmatrix} \begin{bmatrix} I_1 \\ I_2 \\ I_3 \\ I_4 \end{bmatrix} = \begin{bmatrix} \mathcal{E}_1 \\ \mathcal{E}_2 \\ \mathcal{E}_3 \\ 0 \end{bmatrix}$$

In Lotus 1-2-3 use the */DataMatrixInvert* and */DataMatrixMultiply* commands and in Excel use the array formulas $=MINVERSE(array)$ and $=MMULTI(array1, array2)$ to carry out the calculations. Using the data given in the problem, we find

$$I_1 = -1.26 \text{ A}, I_2 = 0.87 \text{ A}, I_3 = 1.08 \text{ A}, \text{ and } I_4 = 0.69 \text{ A}.$$

Chapter 29

1. (a) West
   (b) zero deflection (c) up (d) down
3. B_x is indeterminate; $B_y = -2.62$ mT; $B_z = 0$
5. 48.8° or 131°
7. 26.0 pN west
9. 2.34×10^{-18} N
11. zero
13. $(-2.88 \text{ N})\mathbf{j}$
15. 0.245 T east
17. (a) 4.73 N (b) 5.46 N (c) 4.73 N
19. 196 A east if $\mathbf{B} = 50.0 \ \mu$T north
21. $F = 2\pi r I B \sin\theta$, up
23. 9.98 N·m, clockwise as seen looking in the negative y-direction
23A. $NBabI \cos\theta$, clockwise as seen looking down
25. (a) 376 μA (b) 1.67 μA
27. (a) 3.97° (b) 3.39 mN·m
27A. (a) $\tan^{-1}(IBL/2mg)$ (b) $\frac{1}{4} IBLd \cos\theta$
29. 1.98 cm
31. 65.6 mT
33. $r_\alpha = r_d = \sqrt{2} r_p$
35. 7.88 pT
37. 2.99 u; $^3_1$H$^+$ or $^3_2$He$^+$
39. 5.93×10^5 N/C
41. $mg = 8.93 \times 10^{-30}$ N down, $qE = 1.60 \times 10^{-17}$ N up, $qvB = 4.74 \times 10^{-17}$ N down
43. 0.278 m

45. 31.2 cm
47. (a) 4.31×10^7 rad/s (b) 5.17×10^7 m/s
49. 70.1 mT
51. 3.70×10^{-9} m³/C
53. 4.32×10^{-5} T
55. 7.37×10^{28} electrons/m³
57. 128 mT north at 78.7° below the horizon
59. (a) $(3.52\mathbf{i} - 1.60\mathbf{j}) \times 10^{-18}$ N (b) 24.4°
61. 0.588 T
65. 4.38×10^5 Hz
67. 3.82×10^{-25} kg
69. 3.70×10^{-24} N·m
71. (a) $(-8.00 \times 10^{-21}$ kg·m/s$)\mathbf{j}$ (b) 8.91°
S1. The figure below shows a plot of the data and the best straight-line fit to the data. The slope is 1.58 μA/rad. The torsion constant κ is given by $\kappa = NAB \times$ slope $= 4.74 \times 10^{-10}$ N·m/rad $= 8.28 \times 10^{-12}$ N·m/deg.

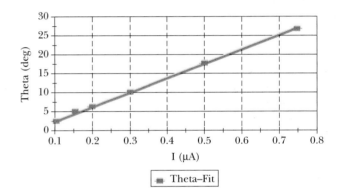

S2. This problem is somewhat similar to Problem 14.4, which dealt with gravitation and orbits, except that here the acceleration is velocity dependent. The equation of motion is

$$\mathbf{F} = q\mathbf{E} + q(\mathbf{v} \times \mathbf{B}) = m\mathbf{a} = q(E_x - v_z B_y)\mathbf{i} + q v_x B_y \mathbf{k}$$

The acceleration in the y direction is zero, so the y component of the velocity of the electron is constant.

Chapter 30

1. 200 nT
3. 31.4 cm
5. (a) 28.3 μT (b) 24.7 μT into the page
7. 54.0 mm
9. $\dfrac{\mu_0 I}{4\pi x}$ into the plane of the page
11. 26.2 μT into the plane of the page
11A. $\mu_0 I/8R$ into the plane of the page
13. $\dfrac{\mu_0 I (a^2 + d^2 - d\sqrt{a^2 + d^2})}{2\pi a d \sqrt{a^2 + d^2}}$ into the page
15. 80.0 μN/m
17. 2000 N/m; attractive

19. $(-27.0 \ \mu N)\mathbf{i}$

21. 13.0 μT directed downward

21A. $\dfrac{\mu_0}{2\pi \text{ m}} (400 \ I_1^2 + 69.4 \ I_2^2)^{1/2}$ at $\tan^{-1}\left(\dfrac{18.5 \ I_1 + 3.21 \ I_2}{7.69 \ I_2 - 7.69 \ I_1}\right)$ below the x-axis

23. (a) 3.98 kA   (b) ≈ 0

25. 5.03 T

27. (a) 3.60 T   (b) 1.94 T

29. Assuming constant current, make the wire long and thin. The solenoid radius does not affect the magnetic field.

31. (a) 6.34×10^{-3} N/m, inward
    (b) **F** is greatest at the outer surface.

33. 464 mT

33A. $\mu_0 \mathcal{E} \pi r / 2\rho L$

35. 4.74 mT

37. (a) 3.13 mWb   (b) zero

39. (a) $BL^2/2$ (b) $BL^2/2$

41. (a) $(8.00 \ \mu A)e^{-t/4}$ (b) 2.94 μA

43. (a) 11.3×10^9 V·m/s   (b) 100 mA

45. 1.0001

47. 191 mT

49. 277 mA

51. 150 μWb

53. M/H

55. 1.27×10^3 turns

57. 2.02

59. (a) 9.39×10^{45} (b) 4.36×10^{20} kg

61. 675 A down

63. 81.7 A

63A. $2\pi d\mu g/\mu_0 I_A$

65. $\mathbf{B} = \dfrac{\mu_0 I}{2\pi\omega} \ln\left(\dfrac{b+w}{b}\right) \mathbf{k}$

67. 594 A east

69. 1.43×10^{-10} T directed away from the center

69A. $\dfrac{\mu_0 \omega q}{8\sqrt{2}\pi R}$

73. (a) $B = \frac{1}{3} \mu_0 b r_1^2$ (b) $B = \dfrac{\mu_0 b R^3}{3 r_2}$

75. (a) 2.46 N   (b) 107.3 m/s^2

77. (a) 12.0 kA-turns/m   (b) 2.07×10^{-5} T·m/A

79. 933 μN to the right perpendicular to the straight segments

79A. $\dfrac{\mu_0 I_1 I_2 L}{\pi R}$ to the right perpendicular to the straight segments

83. $\dfrac{\mu_0 I}{4\pi}(1 - e^{-2\pi})$ perpendicularly out of the paper

85. 20.0 μT toward the top of the page

87. $\dfrac{4}{3} \rho\mu_0\omega R^2$

89. $\dfrac{4}{15} \pi\rho\omega R^5$

S3. When integrating $F(r/R)$ when $r = R$, there is a singularity in the integrand at $\theta = \pi/2$ rad. The magnetic field at the wire is infinite, which we would expect even for a straight wire. We suggest you calculate the integral at $r/R = 0.0, 0.2, 0.4, 0.6, 0.8,$ and 0.9.

Chapter 31

1. 500 mV

3. 160 A

5. + 121 mA

7. 61.8 mV

9. $(200 \ \mu V)e^{-t/7}$

11. $Nn\pi R^2\mu_0 I_0\alpha e^{-\alpha t} = (68.2 \text{ mV})e^{-1.6t}$ counterclockwise

11A. $Nn\pi R^2 \mu_0 I_0\alpha e^{-\alpha t}$ counterclockwise

13. 272 m

15. -6.28 V

15A. $-2\pi R^2 B/t$

17. 763 mV, with the left-hand wingtip positive

19. (a) 3.00 N to the right   (b) 6.00 W

21. 2.00 mV; the west end is positive in the northern hemisphere

23. 2.83 mV

25. 145 μA

25A. $Bd = \left(\dfrac{v_2 R_3 - v_3 R_2}{R_1 R_2 + R_1 R_3 + R_2 R_3}\right)$

27. (a) to the right   (b) to the right   (c) to the right
    (d) into the plane of the paper

29. 0.742 T

31. 114 μV clockwise

31A. $N\mu_0 (I_1 - I_2)\pi r^2/\ell \ \Delta t$ clockwise

33. 1.80×10^{-3} N/C counterclockwise

35. (a) $(9.87 \times 10^{-3}$ V/m$)\cos(100\pi t)$ (b) clockwise

37. (a) 1.60 A counterclockwise
    (b) 20.1 μT   (c) up

37A. (a) $\dfrac{n\mu_0\pi r_2^2}{2R} \dfrac{\Delta I}{\Delta t}$ counterclockwise   (b) $\dfrac{n\mu_0^2\pi r_2^2}{4Rr_1} \dfrac{\Delta I}{\Delta t}$
    (c) up

39. 12.6 mV

41. (a) 7.54 kV   (b) **B** is parallel to the plane of the loop.

43. $(28.6 \text{ mV})\sin(4\pi t)$

45. (a) 0.640 N·m   (b) 241 W

47. 0.513 T

49. (a) $F = \dfrac{N^2 B^2 w^2 v}{R}$ to the left   (b) 0
    (c) $F = \dfrac{N^2 B^2 w^2 v}{R}$ to the left

51. $(-2.87\mathbf{j} + 5.75\mathbf{k}) \times 10^9$ m/s^2

53. It is, with the top end in the picture positive.

57. (a) 36.0 V   (b) 600 mWb/s   (c) 35.9 V
    (d) 4.32 N·m

59. (a) 97.4 nV   (b) clockwise

61. Moving east; 458 μV

63. It is, with the left end in the picture positive

65. 1.20 μC

65A. Ba^2/R

67. 6.00 A

67A. b^2/aR if $t \geq b/3a$

69. (a) 900 mA   (b) 108 mN   (c) b   (d) No

71. (a) Counterclockwise   (b) $\dfrac{K\pi r^2}{R}$

73. (a) $\dfrac{\mu_0 IL}{2\pi}\ln\!\left(\dfrac{h+w}{h}\right)$ (b) $-4.80\ \mu$V

Chapter 32

1. 100 V
3. 1.36 μH
5. $\mathcal{E}_0/k^2L$
7. (a) 188 μT   (b) 33.3 nWb   (c) 375 μH
   (d) field and flux
9. 21.0 μWb
11. $(18.8\text{ V})\cos(377t)$
13. $\frac{1}{2}$
15. (a) 15.8 μH   (b) 12.6 mH
17. $(500\text{ mA})\,(1-e^{-10t/s})$, $1.50\text{ A}-(0.25\text{ A})e^{-10t/s}$
19. 1.92 Ω
21. (a) 1.00 kΩ (b) 3.00 ms
21A. (a) $\sqrt{L/C}$ (b) $\sqrt{LC}$
23. (a) 139 ms   (b) 461 ms
25. (a) 5.66 ms   (b) 1.22 A   (c) 58.1 ms
27. (a) 113 mA   (b) 600 mA
29. (a) 0.800   (b) 0
31. (a) 1.00 A   (b) 12.0 V, 1.20 kV, 1.21 kV
    (c) 7.62 ms
33. 2.44 μJ
35. (a) 20.0 W   (b) 20.0 W   (c) 0   (d) 20.0 J
37. (a) $8.06\times10^6\text{ J/m}^3$ (b) 6.32 kJ
39. 44.3 nJ/m^3 in the **E** field; 995 μJ/m^3 in the **B** field
41. 30.7 μJ and 72.2 μJ
43. (a) 668 mW   (b) 34.3 mW   (c) 702 mW
45. 1.73 mH
47. 80.0 mH
49. 553 μH
51. (a) 18.0 mH   (b) 34.3 mH   (c) -9.00 mV
53. 400 mA
55. (a) -20.0 mV   (b) $-(10.0\text{ MV/s}^2)\,t^2$
    (c) 63.2 μs
55A. (a) $-LK$ (b) $-Kt^2/2C$ (c) $2\sqrt{LC}$
57. 608 pF
59. (a) 36.0 μF   (b) 8.00 ms
61. (a) 6.03 J   (b) 0.529 J   (c) 6.56 J
63. (a) 2.51 kHz   (b) 69.9 Ω
65. (a) 4.47 krad/s   (b) 4.36 krad/s   (c) 2.53%
69. 979 mH
71. (a) 20.0 ms   (b) -37.9 V   (c) 3.03 mV
    (d) 104 mA
73. 95.6 mH
79. (a) 72.0 V; b   (c) 75.2 μs
81. $\dfrac{\mu_0}{\pi}\ln\!\left(\dfrac{d-a}{a}\right)$
83. 300 Ω
85. 45.6 mH
85A. $9t^2/\pi^2 C$
S1. (a) $\tau=0.35$ ms, (b) $t_{50\%}=0.24$ ms $=0.686\tau$, and
    (c) $t_{90\%}=0.80$ ms $=2.29\tau$; $t_{99\%}=1.6$ ms $=4.57\tau$.

Chapter 33

3. 2.95 A, 70.7 V
5. 3.38 W
7. 14.6 Hz
9. (a) 42.4 mH   (b) 942 rad/s
11. 7.03 H
13. 5.58 A
15. 3.80 J
17. (a) $f>41.3$ Hz   (b) $X_C<87.5\ \Omega$
19. 2.77 nC
19A. $\sqrt{2}\ CV$
21. 100 mA
23. 0.427 A
25. (a) 78.5 Ω (b) 1.59 kΩ (c) 1.52 kΩ
    (d) 138 mA   (e) $-84.3°$
27. (a) 17.4°   (b) voltage leads the current
29. 1.88 V
29A. $R_b V_2/\sqrt{R_b^2+1/4\ \pi^2 f^2 C_s^2}$ where V_2 is the transformer secondary voltage
31. (a) 146 V   (b) 213 V   (c) 179 V   (d) 33.4 V
33. (a) 194 V   (b) current leads by 49.9°
35. 132 mm
35A. $\sqrt{800\ P\rho d/\pi V^2}$ where ρ is the material's resistivity.
37. 8.00 W
39. $v(t)=(283\text{ V})\sin(628t)$
41. (a) 16.0 Ω (b) $-12.0\ \Omega$
43. 159 Hz
45. 1.82 pF
47. (a) 124 nF   (b) 51.5 kV
49. 242 mJ
49A. $\dfrac{4\pi RCV^2\sqrt{LC}}{9L+4CR^2}$
51. (a) 613 μF   (b) 0.756
53. 8.42 Hz
55. (a) True, if $\omega_0=(LC)^{-1/2}$ (b) 0.107, 0.999, 0.137
57. 0.317
59. 687 V
61. (a) 9.23 V   (b) 4.55 A   (c) 42.0 W
63. 87.5 Ω
63A. $R_s=\dfrac{R_L N_1\,(N_2 V_s-N_1 V_2)}{V_2 N_2^{\,2}}$
65. 56.7 W
67. (a) 1.89 A
    (b) $V_R=39.7$ V, $V_L=30.1$ V, $V_C=175$ V
    (c) $\cos\phi=0.265$
    (d)

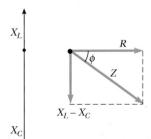

69. 99.6 mH
71. (a) 2.90 kW   (b) 5.80×10^{-3}
    (c) If the generator is limited to 4500 V, no more than
    17.5 kW could be delivered to the load, never 5000 kW.
73. (a) Circuit (a) is a high-pass filter, (b) is a low-pass filter.
    (b) $\dfrac{V_{\text{out}}}{V_{\text{in}}} = \dfrac{\sqrt{R_L{}^2 + X_L{}^2}}{\sqrt{R_L{}^2 + (X_L - X_C)^2}}$ for circuit (a);

    $\dfrac{V_{\text{out}}}{V_{\text{in}}} = \dfrac{X_C}{\sqrt{R_L{}^2 + (X_L - X_C)^2}}$ for circuit (b)
75. (a) 172 MW   (b) 17.2 kW   (c) 172 W
77. (a) 200 mA; voltage leads by 36.8°   (b) 40.0 V;
    $\phi = 0°$ (c) 20.0 V; $\phi = -90°$
    (d) 50.0 V; $\phi = +90°$
83. (a) 173 Ω   (b) 8.66 V
85. (a) 1.838 kHz

87.

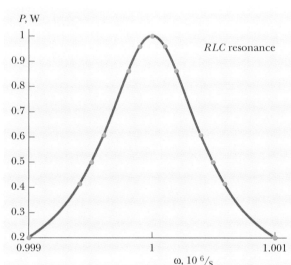

S1. (a)

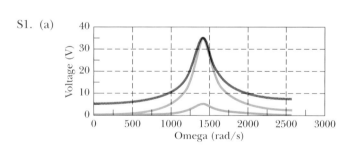

$\boxed{-V_R - V_C - V_L}$

(b) $|V_L| = |V_C|$; (c) for $\omega < \omega_0$, $V_C > V_L$; (d) for $\omega > \omega_0$, $V_L > V_C$

Chapter 34

1. 2.68×10^3 AD
5. (a) 162 N/C   (b) 130 N/C

7. 38.0 pT
9. (a) 6.00 MHz   (b) $(73.3 \text{ nT})(-\mathbf{k})$
   (c) $\mathbf{B} = (73.3 \text{ nT}) \cos(0.126x - 3.77 \times 10^7 t)(-\mathbf{k})$
11. (a) $B = 333$ nT   (b) $\lambda = 628$ nm
    (c) $f = 4.77 \times 10^{14}$ Hz
13. 5.16 m
15. 307 μW/m²
17. 66.7 kW
19. (a) 332 kW/m²   (b) 1.88 kV/m, 222 μT
21. (a) 971 V/m   (b) 16.7 pJ
23. (a) 540 N/C   (b) 2.58 μJ/m³   (c) 774 W/m²
    (d) This is 77.4% of the flux mentioned in Example 34.3
    and 57.8% of the 1340 W/m² intensity above the atmo-
    sphere. It may be cloudy at this location, or the sun may
    be setting.
25. 83.3 nPa
27. (a) 1.90 kV/m   (b) 50.0 pJ
    (c) 1.67×10^{-19} kg·m/s
29. (a) 11.3 kJ   (b) 5.65×10^{-5} kg·m/s
31. (a) 2.26 kW   (b) 4.71 kW/m²
33. 7.50 m
35. (a) $\mathcal{E}_m = 2\pi^2 r^2 f B_m \cos\theta$, where θ is the angle between
    the magnetic field and the normal to the loop. (b) Verti-
    cal, with its plane pointing toward the broadcast antenna
37. 56.2 m
37A. $2\pi cm/qB$
39. (a) 6.00 pm   (b) 7.50 cm
41. The radio audience hears it 8.41 ms sooner.
43. (a) 4.17 m to 4.55 m   (b) 3.41 to 3.66 m
    (c) 1.61 m to 1.67 m
45. 3.33×10^3 m²
47. (a) 6.67×10^{-16} T   (b) 5.31×10^{-17} W/m²
    (c) 1.67×10^{-14} W   (d) 5.56×10^{-23} N
49. 6.37×10^{-7} Pa
51. 95.1 mV/m
53. 7.50×10^{10} s = 2370 y; out the back
55. 3.00×10^{-2} degrees
57. (a) $B_0 = 583$ nT, $k = 419$ rad/m,
    $\omega = 1.26 \times 10^{11}$ rad/s; xz
    (b) 40.6 W/m² in average value   (c) 271 nPa
    (d) 406 nm/s²
59. (a) 22.6 h   (b) 30.5 s
61. (b) 1.00 MV/s
63. (a) 3.33 m; 11.1 ns; 6.67 pT
    (b) $\mathbf{E} = (2.00 \text{ mV/m}) \cos 2\pi \left(\dfrac{x}{3.33 \text{ m}} - \dfrac{t}{11.1 \text{ ns}} \right) \mathbf{j}$
    $\mathbf{B} = (6.67 \text{ pT}) \cos 2\pi \left(\dfrac{x}{3.33 \text{ m}} - \dfrac{t}{11.1 \text{ ns}} \right) \mathbf{k}$
    (c) 5.31×10^{-9} W/m²   (d) 1.77×10^{-14} J/m³
    (e) 3.54×10^{-14} Pa

Chapter 35

1. 299.5 Mm/s
3. (b) 294 Mm/s
5. 114 rad/s

7. 198 Gm

9. (a) 4.74×10^{14} Hz   (b) 422 nm
   (c) 2.00×10^8 m/s

11. 70.5° from the vertical

13. 61.3°

15. 19.5°, 19.5°, 30.0°.

17. (a) 327 nm   (b) 287 nm

19. 59.83°, 59.78°, 0.0422°

21. 30.0°, 19.5° at entry; 40.5°, 77.1° at exit

23. 0.171°

23A. $\sin^{-1}\left(\dfrac{\sin\theta}{n_{700}}\right) - \sin^{-1}\left(\dfrac{\sin\theta}{n_{400}}\right)$

27. 18.4°

29. 86.8°

31. 4.61°

33. 62.4°

35. (a) 24.4°   (b) 37.0°   (c) 49.8°

37. 1.00008

39. $\theta < 48.2°$

41. 53.6°

43. 2.27 m

45. 2.37 cm

49. 90°, 30°, No

51. 62.2%

53. $\sin^{-1}[(n^2 - 1)^{1/2}\sin\phi - \cos\phi]$ If $n\sin\phi \leq 1$, $\theta = 0$

55. 82

57. 27.5°

59. 7.91°

59A. $\phi = \sin^{-1}\left[n\sin\left(90° - 2\theta + \sin^{-1}\left(\dfrac{\sin\theta}{n}\right)\right)\right]$

61. (a) 1.20   (b) 3.40 ns

S1. Using Snell's Law and plane geometry, the following relationships can be derived:

$$\sin\theta_1 = n\sin\rho_1$$
$$\rho_2 = A - \rho_1$$
$$n\sin\rho_2 = \sin\theta_2$$
$$\theta = \theta_1 + \theta_2 - A$$

These equations are used to find ρ_1, ρ_2, θ_2, and θ in the spreadsheet. IF statements are used in the calculation of θ_2 and θ so that error messages are not printed when ρ_2 exceeds the critical angle for total internal reflection.

Chapter 36

3. 2'11"

3A. $h/2$

5. 30 cm

7. (a) $q = 45.0$ cm, $M = -\frac{1}{2}$
   (b) $q = -60.0$ cm, $M = 3.00$
   (c) Similar to Figures 36.8 and 36.12b

9. (a) 15.0 cm   (b) 60.0 cm

9A. (a) $d/2$ (b) $2d$

11. concave with radius 40.0 cm

13. (a) 2.08 m (concave)
   (b) 1.25 m in front of the object

15. (a) $q = -12.0$ cm, $M = 0.400$
   (b) $q = -15.0$ cm, $M = 0.250$
   (c) The images are erect

17. 11.8 cm above the floor

19. 1.50 cm/s

19A. v/n

21. 8.57 cm

23. 3.88 mm

25. 2

27. (a) 16.4 cm   (b) 16.4 cm

29. 25.0 cm; -0.250

31. (a) 13.3 cm
   (b) A trapezoid

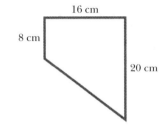

   (c) 224 cm²

33. (a) -12.3 cm, to left of lens   (b) $+0.615$
   (c)

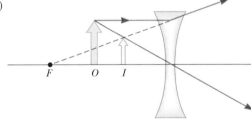

35. (a) 39.0 mm   (b) 39.5 mm

37. 2.84 cm

39. $\dfrac{f}{1.41}$

41. -4 diopters, a diverging lens

43. 0.558 cm

45. 20.0 m

45A. $vf\,\Delta t/\Delta f$

47. 3.5

49. -800, image is inverted

51. -18.8

53. 2.14 cm

55. (a) 1.99   (b) 10.0 cm to the left of the lens, -2.50
   (c) inverted since the overall magnification is negative.

57. (a) 20.0 cm to the right of the second lens, -6.00
   (b) inverted   (c) 6.67 cm to the right of the second lens, -2.00, inverted

59. 10.7 cm beyond the curved surface

61. 20.0 cm

61A. f

63. (a) 44.6 diopters   (b) 3.03 diopters

65. $d = 8$ cm

67. 21.3 cm

67A. $h_1 \cot \left(\sin^{-1} \dfrac{nh_1}{R} - \sin^{-1} \dfrac{h_1}{R} \right) + \sqrt{R^2 - h_1^2}$

     $- h_2 \cot \left(\sin^{-1} \dfrac{nh_2}{R} - \sin^{-1} \dfrac{h_2}{R} \right) - \sqrt{R^2 - h_2^2}$

69. (a) 52.5 cm   (b) 1.50 cm

71. $q' = 1.5$ m, $h' = -13.1$ mm

73. (a) -0.400 cm   (b) $q' = -3.94$ mm, $h' = 535$ μm

75. (a) 30.0 cm and 120 cm   (b) 24.0 cm

     (c) real, inverted, diminished

77. real, inverted, actual size

S1. See Figure 36.1. Applying the law of sines to triangle *PAC*, one finds $r \sin \theta_1 = (r + p) \sin \alpha$. Snell's Law gives $n_1 \sin \theta_1 = n_2 \sin \theta_2$. Using plane geometry gives $\gamma = \theta_1 - \alpha - \theta_2$. Applying the law of sines to triangle *ACP'* gives $q' - r = r \sin \theta_2 / \sin \gamma$. These equations are used to calculate θ_1, θ_2, γ, and q in the spreadsheet. (a) The maximum angle α for which the error in the image distance is 3 percent or less is 2.35°. (b) 2.25° (d) No. (For a plot of the percent error versus α, just call up the associated graph.)

Chapter 37

1. (a) 2.62×10^{-3} m   (b) 2.62×10^{-3} m
3. 515 nm
5. (a) 36.2°   (b) 5.08 cm   (c) 508 THz
7. 11.3 m
9. 2.50 m
9A. $c/2f$
13. 4.80×10^{-5} m
15. 423.5 nm
17. 343 nm
17A. $\lambda/2(n - 1)$
19. 641
21. (a) 2.63 rad   (b) 246 nm
23. (a) 7.95 rad   (b) 0.453
27. $10 \sin(100\pi t + 0.93)$
29. $\pi/2$
31. $360°/N$
33. No reflection maxima in the visible spectrum
35. 512 nm
37. 85.4 nm, or 256 nm, or 427 nm . . .
39. (a) Green   (b) Purple
41. 167 nm
43. 4.35 μm
45. 3.96×10^{-5} m
47. 654 dark fringes
49. (a) 5.99 m   (b) 2.99 m
49A. (a) $2\sqrt{4h^2 + d^2} - 2d$ (b) $\sqrt{4h^2 + d^2} - d$
51. 3.58°
53. 421 nm
55. 2.52 cm
57. 1.54 mm
59. 3.6×10^{-5} m

61. $x_{\text{bright}} = \dfrac{\lambda \ell (m + \frac{1}{2})}{2hn}$, $x_{\text{dark}} = \dfrac{\lambda \ell \, m}{2hn}$
63. (b) 115 nm
65. 1.73 cm
69. (b) 266 nm
S1. (a) 9 : 1   (b) 1 : 9

Chapter 38

1. 632.8 nm
3. 560 nm
5. $\cong 10^{-3}$ rad
7. 0.230 mm
9. $\phi = \beta/2 = 1.392$ rad

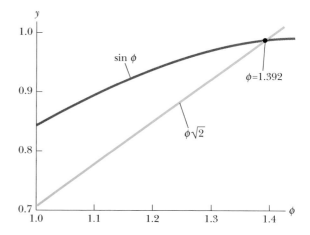

11. 1.62×10^{-2}
13. 3.09 m
15. 51.2 cm
17. 20 cm
17A. (0.8 μm) (vt/nd)
19. 15.7 km
21. 13 m
23. 105 m
27. (a) 5.7; 5 orders is the maximum
     (b) 10; 10 orders to be in the short-wavelength region.
29. 0.0683°
31. (a) 2800   (b) 4.72 μm
33. 2
35. 7.35°
37. 14.7°
39. 31.9°
41. (a) 0°, 19.9°, 42.9°   (b) 8.33 cm, 135 cm
43. (a) 0.281 nm   (b) 0.18%
45. 14.4°
47. 1.11
49. 31.2°
51. (a) 18.4°   (b) 45.0°   (c) 71.6°
53. (a) 54.7°   (b) 63.4°   (c) 71.6°
55. 60.5°

57. 2.2
59. 5.9°
61. 0.244 rad ≈ 14.0°
63. 545 nm
65. (a) 12 000, 24 000, 36 000   (b) 0.0111 nm
67. (a) 3.53×10^3 lines/cm
    (b) Eleven maxima can be observed.
69. $\frac{1}{8}$
71. (a) 6   (b) 7.50°
73. (a) 41.8°   (b) 0.593   (c) 0.262 m
S1. (a) 9:1   (b) 1:9

Chapter 39

5. (a) 60 m/s   (b) 20 m/s   (c) 44.7 m/s
5A. (a) $v_b + v$ (b) $v - v_b$ (c) $\sqrt{v^2 + v_b^2}$
7. (a) 39.2 μs   (b) Accurate to one digit. More precisely, he aged 1.78 μs less on each orbit.
9. $0.800c$
9A. $v = cL_p / \sqrt{L_p^2 + c^2 t^2}$
11. $0.436L_0$
13. $0.789c$
15. $0.696c$
17. $0.960c$
19. 42 g/cm^3
19A. $\dfrac{m}{V(1 - v^2/c^2)}$
21. 1625 MeV/c
25. (a) 939.4 MeV   (b) 3.008×10^3 MeV
    (c) 2.069×10^3 MeV
27. $0.864c$
29. (a) 0.582 MeV   (b) 2.45 MeV
31. (a) 3.91×10^4 (b) $0.9999999997c$ (c) 7.66 cm
33. 4 MeV and 29 MeV
35. (a) 3.29 MeV   (b) 2.77 MeV
37. 4.2×10^9 kg/s
39. (a) $0.800c$ (b) $0.929c$
39A. (a) $\dfrac{2v}{1 + v^2/c^2}$ (b) $\dfrac{3v + v^3/c^2}{1 + 3v^2/c^2}$

41. 0.7%
43. (a) 6.67 ks   (b) 4.00 ks
43A. (a) $\dfrac{2d}{v + c}$ (b) $\dfrac{2d\sqrt{1 - v^2/c^2}}{v + c}$
47. (a) 76.0 min   (b) 52.1 min
47A. (a) $\dfrac{t_{\text{II}}}{\sqrt{1 - \left(\dfrac{(v_{\text{I}} + v_{\text{II}})\,c}{c^2 + v_{\text{I}}v_{\text{II}}}\right)^2}}$ (b) $\dfrac{t_{\text{II}}}{\sqrt{1 - v_{\text{II}}^2/c^2}}$
49. 15.0 h in the spacecraft frame, 10.0 h less than in the Earth frame.
51. (a) $0.554c, 0.866c$ (b) 0.833 m
51A. (a) $u = \dfrac{v - u'}{1 - vu'/c^2}$ where $u' = c\sqrt{1 - L'^2/L_p^2}$
    (b) $L_p\sqrt{1 - u^2/c^2}$
53. (a) 83.3 m and 62.5 m   (b) 27.0 m and 20.3 m
    (c) 6.00 ks   (d) 5.33 ks   (e) 7.10 ks
    (f) Rocket one is destroyed with crew aboard − they were going too fast.
55. (b) For $v \ll c$, $a = qE/m$ as in the classical description. As $v \to c$, $a \to 0$, describing how the particle can never reach the speed of light.
    (c) Perform $\displaystyle\int_0^v \left(1 - \frac{v^2}{c^2}\right)^{-3/2} dv = \int_0^t \frac{qE}{m} dt$ to obtain $v = \dfrac{qEct}{\sqrt{m^2c^2 + q^2E^2t^2}}$ and then
    $\displaystyle\int_0^x dx = \int_0^t \frac{qEtc}{\sqrt{m^2c^2 + q^2E^2t^2}}\, dt$

S1. (a)

Z	0.2	0.5	1.0	2.0
v/c	0.180	0.385	0.600	0.800

(b) For $Z = 3.8$, $v/c = 0.870$.

S3. For $Z = 0.2$, $r = 2710$ Mly; $Z = 0.5$, $r = 5770$ Mly; $Z = 1.2$, $r = 9860$ Mly; and $Z = 3.8$, $r = 13\ 800$ Mly.

Index

Page numbers in *italics* indicate illustrations; page numbers followed by an "n" indicate footnotes, page numbers followed by "t" indicate tables.

Standard Abbreviations and Symbols of Units

Abbreviation	Unit	Abbreviation	Unit
A	ampere	in.	inch
Å	angstrom	J	joule
u	atomic mass unit	K	kelvin
atm	atmosphere	kcal	kilocalorie
Btu	British thermal unit	kg	kilogram
C	coulomb	kmol	kilomole
°C	degree Celsius	lb	pound
cal	calorie	m	meter
deg	degree (angle)	min	minute
eV	electron volt	N	newton
°F	degree Fahrenheit	Pa	pascal
F	farad	rev	revolution
ft	foot	s	second
G	gauss	T	tesla
g	gram	V	volt
H	henry	W	watt
h	hour	Wb	weber
hp	horsepower	μm	micrometer
Hz	hertz	Ω	ohm

Mathematical Symbols Used in the Text and Their Meaning

Symbol	Meaning
$=$	is equal to
$\equiv$	is defined as
$\neq$	is not equal to
$\propto$	is proportional to
$>$	is greater than
$<$	is less than
$\gg (\ll)$	is much greater (less) than
$\approx$	is approximately equal to
Δx	the change in x
$\sum_{i=1}^{N} x_i$	the sum of all quantities x_i from $i = 1$ to $i = N$
$\lvert x \rvert$	the magnitude of x (always a nonnegative quantity)
$\Delta x \rightarrow 0$	Δx approaches zero
$\dfrac{dx}{dt}$	the derivative of x with respect to t
$\dfrac{\partial x}{\partial t}$	the partial derivative of x with respect to t
$\displaystyle\int$	integral